Man's Physical Universe

Man's Physical Universe

5th edition

Arthur Talbot Bawden
Emeritus Professor of Chemistry and Physical Science
San Joaquin Delta College

Keith Kearney Fredericks
Assistant Professor of Physical Science
Kearney State College

Illustrated by Domitilo De La Torre

The Macmillan Company, New York
Collier-Macmillan Limited, London

Library of Congress catalog card number: 66–10693

The Macmillan Company, New York
Collier-Macmillan Canada, Ltd., Toronto, Ontario

Printed in the United States of America

Preface to the Teacher

MOTIF

If civilization is to be worth what it has cost in effort and struggle, if the vast accumulation of knowledge and power which our age has come to possess is to be directed toward ends of general human advance, there must be a great and rapid increase in the number of persons who possess the spirit and attitudes of liberal and cultural education.

Adapted from Everett Dean Martin by
BENJAMIN F. SHAMBAUGH

THIS FIFTH EDITION of MAN'S PHYSICAL UNIVERSE represents a complete revision, but it, in common with the previous editions, is intended for use in a program of liberal or general education. General education seeks to push forward the development of a good life. The educational experience which it provides is rich to the extent that it deals with the problems of life today. This text is designed to bring from the archives of physical science the most important facts, generalizations and applications which have a bearing on these problems.

Man's Physical Universe represents the culmination of many years' experience by the authors with college classes in physical science. It was written for the kinds of students who have been enrolled in their classes. Less than one fourth of these students had a course in Physics, and less than one half had a course in Chemistry. As a rule, most of these students had a very weak background in mathematics, not many having gone beyond Elementary Algebra. Such students are typical of many of the students who are enrolled in junior colleges and many four-year liberal arts colleges and teachers' colleges. For such students, mathematical formulas and chemical symbols, formulas and equations, so dear to both authors, would be stumbling blocks. For this reason, they have been omitted from this text. Teachers may want to introduce such formulas in classes where the background of the students will permit. In addition to the students with weak backgrounds in mathematics, chemistry, and physics, more than half of the students in the authors' classes in physical science have been preparing to be elementary school teachers.

This text was specially designed in terms of the following objectives:

1. To meet the needs of students who have a weak background in mathematics, chemistry, and physics, as mentioned above.

2. To meet the needs of students who plan to be elementary school teachers.

Part I of this text is designed to cover all of the physical science topics included in the usual science curricula of elementary schools. For such students the text will prove to be a useful reference handbook in their future teaching. Part II will prove to be a valuable source of information concerning modern applications of physical science.

3. To meet the needs of both one-semester and two-semester courses in physical science. Many colleges and universities find that the portion of the student's time available for general education is not sufficient to include a five or six-unit course in physical science, and, therefore, offer a three-unit course having three lecture periods per week, or in some cases, offer a four-unit course having three lecture periods and one laboratory period per week for one semester. For a three or four-unit course, having three lecture periods per week, Part I of this text presents a complete, integrated course in the fundamentals of physical science. For a one-semester course, Part II will serve as a source of supplementary reading dealing with applications studied in Part I.

The entire text will serve to meet the needs of a five-unit one-semester course or a two-semester course of six to ten units, depending upon whether or not laboratory work is provided for on an individual basis in one or two laboratory periods per week. Part II covers some of the principles in greater depth than is possible in Part I, but for the most part it deals with the role of physical science in modern living. The applications of physical science to modern living thus make a very desirable addition to the fundamental principles found in Part I if time permits, but for a short course the fundamentals must have preference.

We have decided not to include a glossary because we prefer to define each new term where it is first used. However, the pages where definitions are given are indicated in the Index by bold-face type.

We have not attempted to include references because they cannot be kept up-to-date. Teachers generally prefer to prepare their own lists of books and current magazine articles in terms of the resources of their libraries. One of the authors will be happy to send a suggested list of references to any teacher requesting it. Interested teachers should address their requests to Keith Fredericks, Kearney State College, Kearney, Nebraska. However, we have suggested selected references to supplement the chapter on the scientific attitude and method.

We highly recommend individual laboratory work if time will permit an additional unit or two per semester. Many excellent ideas for experiments for such a laboratory course may be found in the following books:

Freeman, *Invitation to Experiment,* New York: E. P. Dutton and Company, 1940

Haun, *A Laboratory Manual for the Physical Science Course,* Dubuque, Iowa: Wm. C. Brown Company, 1950

Hone, Joseph, Victor, *A Sourcebook for Elementary Science,* New York: Harcourt, Brace and World, 1962

Joseph, Brandwein, Morholt, Pollack, Castka, *A Sourcebook for the Physical Sciences,* New York: Harcourt, Brace and World, 1961

Lynde, *Science Experiments with Home Equipment,* New York: D. Van Nostrand Company, 1937

Lynde, *Science Experiments with Inexpensive Equipment,* New York: D. Van Nostrand Company, 1939

Lynde, *Science Experiments with Ten-Cent Store Equipment,* New York: D. Van Nostrand Company, 1950

Maurer and Krauskopf, *Experiments and Exercises in Physical Science,* New York: McGraw-Hill Book Company, 1959

Parker, *Science Experiences, Elementary School,* White Plains, New York: Row, Peterson and Company, 1952

This text is divided into units and chapters for pedagogical reasons. Each chapter is intended to be used as the assignment for one lesson, and constitutes a complete topic in itself. Each chapter has been kept short, thus enabling the average student to study it within a reasonable time. If one chapter is assigned for each day, with the exception of a few days reserved for an introductory lecture and one-hour examinations, it will be found that a course which meets three times a week for a semester will be able to cover the material presented in Part I. It is suggested that examinations be given at the end of each triad. Each triad would thus include two units.

We acknowledge the valuable contribution of Elizabeth C. Bawden in typing the manuscript, and checking for errors.

We welcome criticisms and suggestions.

Arthur Talbot Bawden
Keith Kearney Fredericks

Preface to the Student

PART I OF THIS TEXT presents the fundamentals of physical science and some of their most important applications to modern life, but it leaves most of the applications for Part II, to be studied in the second semester of a one-year course in Physical Science, or to be explored by the student in connection with related sections in Part I.

One could obtain a basic knowledge of the physical sciences by taking an introductory course in each of the fields, but such a plan would involve too much time in the program of the non-science major. Furthermore, such highly special-ized courses are not designed to meet the needs of non-science majors. An integrated approach, such as is used in this text, not only eliminates the time spent on technical matter of no future value to the non-science major, but it also eliminates the duplication and overlapping usually encountered in the introductory courses in the different fields of physical science. It results in more efficient learning because the many facts and generalizations are part of an integrated whole.

It is important that a chemistry student learn how to use an analytical balance and to balance equations, but such skills are of little value to the majority of students, whose future careers will not require them. These students usually know that this is true and they react accordingly.

Students in chemistry and physics courses must learn to solve specialized mathematical problems which the non-science major knows he will never be called upon to solve in the future. These courses emphasize specialized skills to the extent that there is little time left to meet the needs of non-science majors. To a certain extent, they even fail to meet some of the general education needs of science majors, because there is not enough time available to stress the relation-ships between the different physical sciences, the generalizations and applications to daily life, and the social implications which should be a part of the back-ground of modern man.

For the reasons listed above, Physical Science courses have been developed to meet the needs of non-science majors. Many colleges and universities maintain rigorous entrance requirements in mathematics and laboratory physical sciences. In such schools, the physical science course may employ mathematical formulas and chemical symbols, formulas, and equations, if it is considered that they are essential to the desired outcomes of the course. In many schools, the non-science majors do not have adequate backgrounds for such rigorous courses. This text is designed for such students and, therefore, omits mathematical formulas and chemical symbols, formulas, and equations.

BREADTH AND DEPTH

Some authors prefer to treat a few selected topics in depth, but this text is biased toward breadth. Critics might call this a shallow approach. However, it is easy for beginners to drown in water which is over their heads in depth. We want our students to learn how to swim rather than drown. Nevertheless, while it is desirable to see the forest, once we are in it, a few trees may be worth studying. Perhaps your teacher will assign special triad or term papers which will require the study of several topics in depth.

VOCABULARY GROWTH

One objective of a physical science course is to provide a minimum vocabulary, which will later enable you to keep up with scientific developments, which may have a bearing on your job, or perhaps determine your success with investments in common stocks.

New technical terms in each chapter are printed in bold-face type, and their definitions are printed in italics. The first question in the Study Questions for each chapter lists the new terms defined therein. Try to memorize and understand these definitions from day to day. In Science, the terms used have precise meanings. Hazy ideas concerning the meaning of technical words, as they are used later in the text, can only result in hazy understandings of the basic principles. To aid you in finding the page on which a term is defined, the page is listed in the Index by bold-face type.

THE SCIENTIFIC METHOD AND ATTITUDE IN SCIENCE COURSES

One or more courses in physics or chemistry have been required for entrance to many colleges and universities, because such courses are laboratory courses, and as such, "teach the scientific method and attitude." However, there is often very little relationship between such a goal and what actually takes place in the laboratory. As a rule, the experiments are not designed to teach the scientific method, and the laboratory record books bear out this conclusion. Frequently the notes consist of filling out blanks, which in many cases could be filled out without carrying out the experiment. Furthermore, the instructor seldom has time enough to carefully check the notebook soon enough to stimulate growth in the use of the scientific method.

The scientific method and attitude are usually listed as one of the important objectives in any program of general education, and a course in physical science should be designed to contribute to the attainment of this desirable outcome. Some teachers believe that a historical approach will cause the student to acquire the scientific attitude, and result in his use of the scientific method. The authors of this text believe that a historical approach may serve to provide an appreciation of the scientist, his attitude, and his work, and for this reason they employ a historical approach insofar as space permits. However, they do not believe that such an approach will result in an increased use of the scientific method by the student in solving his everyday problems, which constitutes its chief value to the student.

THE SCIENTIFIC METHOD IS DEVELOPED BY USING IT TO SOLVE REAL PROBLEMS

The scientific approach to the solution of problems is not learned quickly or easily. It is a lifetime goal, never fully attained, but gradually approached by daily use. You will not become a scientist as a result of taking a physical science course. However, if you make a start in this course, it could lead to a lifelong habit which would be very rewarding. It is suggested that you select problems that are of genuine concern to you, and that you try to apply the scientific method discussed in Chapter 2 to the solution of these problems with the help of your instructor. To provide time for work on such problems, the daily assignments have been kept short.

You should start with relatively simple problems, such as the selection of a new or used automobile, or the selection of a dentifrice. Later, you may want to attempt to solve such problems as the selection of a vocation, or the selection of a dentist or a physician. You may already have begun to work on the problem of the selection of a lifemate, a problem in which you have only about a fifty-fifty chance of success if you follow the usual methods.

THE SCIENTIFIC ATTITUDE

The scientific attitude, like other attitudes, is caught rather than taught. One of the best ways of catching this attitude is association with someone who has it. One is not likely to acquire a health attitude from a physician who does not pay attention to his own health. Since most attitudes are developed during the formative years, it is very important that elementary teachers exhibit the scientific attitude in their classes. Since many of the students taking this course in physical science plan to be elementary school teachers, this objective should be a matter of concern to them. It may be that you will catch this attitude from your physical science teacher. Another approach is to read about the lives and work of great scientists. A list of biographies and autobiographies of great scientists is given at the close of this preface. Your library may have additional books of this type. A book such as *The Life of Pasteur*, by Vallery-Radot, should prove to be a very rewarding supplement to this text.

SCIENCE AND RELIGION

For many students, there will be an apparent conflict between Science and Religion. It is true that some religious teachings do not appear to be in harmony with the scientific facts presented in this text. For students who are rightly disturbed by such apparent conflicts, the authors have provided a selected list of references which may be helpful in resolving their problems. The student may have to give up certain religious dogmas which vary from one religious group to another. Both of the authors of this text are active church members, and they have not found any conflict between their scientific knowledge and their religious faith. They would not want any student to forsake his religion because of a course in physical science. It may be desirable to throw out the bath water containing some of the troublesome religious dogmas, but do not throw out the baby (your religious faith) with it. Keep in mind that many of our greatest scientists have been devoutly religious men and women.

The Authors

References

1. SCIENCE AND RELIGION

Fendrich, J. I., *Science Discovers God*. New York: Dodd, Mead and Company, 1949.

Lindsay, A. D., *Religion, Science, and Society in the Modern World*. New Haven, Conn.: Yale University Press, 1949.

Long, E. L., *Science and Christian Faith*. New York: Association Press, 1949.

McLaughlin, P. J., *Modern Science and God*. Philosophical Library, 1951.

Miller, C. W., *Scientist's Approach to Religion*. New York: The Macmillan Company, 1952.

Raven, C. E., *Science and the Christian Man*. New York: The Macmillan Company, 1952.

2. THE SCIENTIFIC ATTITUDE

Cameron, F., *Cottrell: Samaritan of Science*. New York: Doubleday and Company, Inc., 1950.

Dubos, R. J., *Louis Pasteur: Free Lance of Science*. Boston, Mass.: Little, Brown and Company, 1950.

Marquardt, M., *Paul Ehrlich*. Henry Schuman, Inc., 1951.

Millikan, R. A., *Autobiography of Robert A. Millikan*. New York: Appleton-Century-Crofts, Inc., 1950.

Schuck, H., *et al.*, *Nobel, The Man and His Prizes*. Norman, Oklahoma: University of Oklahoma Press, 1951.

Sidgwick, J. B., *William Herschel: Explorer of the Heavens*. New York: The Macmillan Company, 1955.

Sootin, H., *Isaac Newton*. New York: Julian Messner, Inc., 1955.

Sootin, H., *Michael Faraday*. New York: Julian Messner, Inc., 1954.

Vallery-Radot, *The Life of Pasteur*. New York: Dover Publications, 1962.

Waddington, C. H., *The Scientific Attitude*. Baltimore, Maryland: Penquin Books, Inc., 1942.

Westcott, E., *Roger Bacon in Life and Legend*. New York: Philosophical Library, 1954.

Wheeler, L. P., *Josiah Willard Gibbs*, New Haven, Conn.: Yale University Press, 1951.

Wiener, N., *Ex-Prodigy*. New York: Simon and Schuster, Inc., 1953.

Yost, E., *American Women of Science*. Frederick A. Stokes, 1943.

3. THE SCIENTIFIC METHOD

Baker, J. R., *The Scientific Life*. New York: The Macmillan Company, 1943.

Barry, F., *The Scientific Habit of Thought*. New York: Columbia University Press, 1930.

Beveridge, W., *The Art of Scientific Investigation*. New York: W. W. Norton and Company, 1950.

Castetter, L. L., *What Is Thinking?* Boston, Mass.: Bruce Humphreys, Inc., 1937.

Conant, J. B., *Science and Common Sense*. New York: New American Library, 1951.

duNouy, L., *The Road to Reason*. New York: Longmans, Green and Company, Inc., 1949.

George, W. H., *The Scientist in Action*. New York: Emerson Books, Inc., 1945.

Gregory, R. A., Sir, *Discovery*. New York: The Macmillan Company, 1931.

Hesse, M. B., *Science and the Human Imagination*. New York: Philosophical Library, 1955.

Hill, D. W., *Impact and Value of Science*. New York: Hutchinson and Company, 1947.

Horkheimer, M., *Studies in Prejudice*. New York: Harper & Brothers, 1950.

Huff, D., *How to Lie with Statistics*. New York: Norton Publishing Company, 1954.

Keyes, K. S., *How to Develop Your Thinking Ability*. New York: McGraw-Hill Book Company, 1950.

Keyser, C. J., *The Human Worth of Rigorous Thinking*. New York: Scripta Mathematica, 1940.

Kogan, Z., *Essentials in Problem Solving*. Zuce Kogan, 1951.

Lee, A. M., *How to Understand Propaganda*. New York: Rinehart and Company, 1952.

Polya, G., *How to Solve It*. Princeton, New Jersey: Princeton University Press, 1948.

Somerville, J., *The Way of Science: Its Growth and Method*. Henry Schuman, Inc., 1953.

Synge, J. L., *Science: Sense and Nonsense*. New York: W. W. Norton and Company, Inc., 1951.

Taylor, F. S., *Concerning Science*. New York: The Macmillan Company, 1949.

Thouless, R. H., *How to Think Straight*. New York: Simon and Schuster, Inc., 1939.

Contents

Introduction

Indulge your passion for science, says nature, but let your science be human, and such as may have a direct reference to action and society. . . . Be a philosopher; but, amidst all your philosophy, be still a man.

HUME

THE GOAL OF HUMANITY

Although some people have no goal and others seem to be working at cross-purposes, there are many who agree that satisfaction is the goal of humanity.

Satisfaction is not the same as pleasure or happiness, though ordinarily these things go together. Satisfaction is not mere sluggish contentment. It is something we have to work for, and our efforts must have some measure of success to be satisfying. Some successful adventures yield more satisfaction than others, and usually the best things cost the most effort. So it is important to regulate our wants judicially, to use intelligent foresight in selecting the things for which we work the hardest, and to get all of the help that we can in pushing on toward the chosen goal. In the advancement of this program natural forces have been harnessed in the service of man, and social institutions have been organized for more efficient teamwork.

Successful use of natural resources and of social opportunities depends on knowledge about these things and either some measure of control over them or else intelligent adjustment of the individual to them. The acquisition of knowledge and active adjustment broaden experience and make life richer. This more abundant life brings wider and higher satisfactions.

As society is now organized, nobody can live by and for himself alone because his own welfare is bound up with that of the community in which he lives. Accordingly, our finest satisfactions arise within the social adjustments, and the greatest happiness comes from maintaining right relations with our fellowmen; the right relations are those which are mutually beneficial.

Insofar as man devotes his life to the betterment of mankind to the best of his ability, he is fulfilling his purpose in life. Thus, today, more than ever before, man values preparation for life, and young people are going to colleges and universities in ever increasing numbers to obtain this preparation. While good intentions to serve humanity are absolutely essential, they will not take us far without the knowledge of how to carry them out. This is where Science comes in. Science has been frequently defined as organized knowledge and the method by which it is obtained. Knowledge of mankind, knowledge of one's self, knowledge of one's physical environment—every kind of knowledge is essential to the progress of individual and social goals, and knowledge is most effective when it is organized. The method by which new knowledge is obtained is the chief characteristic of Science. This method will be discussed in Chapter 2.

Progress in the discovery and utilization of knowledge requires a more general acceptance of the scientific attitude and a more widespread use of the scientific method. Such progress is essential to the attainment of the goal of humanity. Unfortunately the spirit and method of science have not appreciably influenced the average man.

THE ROLE OF SCIENCE IN SOLVING PROBLEMS

The outstanding characteristic of Science is its success in solving problems. No other method of solving problems gives satisfactory results, although many methods, such as magic, palm-reading, astrology, and quackery are tried by many people.

You are living in a period of cultural transition which results in the development of new problems almost faster than we can keep up with them. The greatly improved modern methods of transportation and communication have increased contacts between cultures which often result in struggles between conflicting interests and social strains. Not only are new social problems arising but modern young people are faced with problems which the youth of previous generations never dreamed of. There are indications that we have reached a very critical point in our cultural change, in which pressing individual and social problems must be solved to avoid a cultural upheaval. Indeed, problem-solving ability is coming to be recognized as one of the most important aims of education in a democracy. One of the reasons why you are now enrolled in a course in physical science is because of its possible contribution to your ability to solve problems.

UNSOLVED PROBLEMS LEAD TO FRUSTRATION

Almost everything that we do is done about a problem. We eat and sleep to satisfy basic needs, but improper food or sleep may fail to meet these needs satisfactorily. We marry to satisfy human needs, but a large number of people find that their marriages have been failures and frustration is the result. Wrong solutions to problems lead to failure. Right solutions lead to success.

Adaptation is conformity to a need. The ability to quickly adapt one's self to a changed situation requires problem solving. There are many different kinds of problems, and, therefore, there are many different kinds of problem-solving abilities. The intelligent person selects problems which his abilities will enable him to solve with success. One person becomes a physician and another becomes a mechanic. In each case the measure of his particular kind of intelligence is his ability to solve problems.

Problem solving does not have much influence upon subsequent behavior unless one's experience fits into an existing pattern in such a way as to make the next step toward the goal more definite. Goals constitute one of the best integrating factors available to give meaning to experience.

Mental growth results from one's own act of integrating and organizing knowledge. This text has been designed to help you develop a pattern for the organization of knowledge concerning the physical universe.

THE GOALS OF THIS TEXT

1. To impart an understanding and appreciation of the nature of the Universe and man's relation to it, thus helping you to develop a wholesome philosophy of life.

2. To provide a background of facts and principles in the realm of physical science which will enable you to live intelligently in this modern world.

A photograph of large molecules of deoxyribonucleic acid (DNA) taken with an electron microscope. (Courtesy, Julius Marmur and Paul Doty)

Part **I**

The Fundamentals of Physical Science

The Aurora Borealis. (Courtesy, National Bureau of Standards)

An Introduction to Physical Science — The Science of Matter and Energy

Science moves but slowly, slowly, creeping on from point to point.

ALFRED TENNYSON

*T*HIS UNIT is an introduction to physical science, which has revolutionized our way of life and provided more and more of what is called the "good life." This good life is a healthier life, a longer life, a fuller and richer life, with shorter working days and more leisure time.

Physical science is one of the sciences which make up Science as a whole, so we must first introduce the head of the family—Science. It is the attitude and method of Science which has been responsible for its success in any realm in which it has been applied. It is this attitude and method which has made Physical science so successful in providing us with the good life. The attitude and method of Science is of comparatively recent origin, so our first task is to place it in its historical perspective, and show that the present age is indeed the age of physical science.

The introduction to the attitude and method of Science is then followed by an introduction to matter and energy.

The growth of Science has been likened to a light source. The brighter and larger it is, the farther one can see, and yet the more extensive the darkness becomes. Regardless of the field of Science one soon reaches the frontiers where more knowledge must be obtained if further progress toward truth is to be made. At the very center of the light we start with an ultimate reality—energy. So Science proceeds from an unknown, ultimate reality and soon reaches the frontiers of knowledge where it again is confronted by the unknown.

Again, the growth of Science has been compared to a rolling snowball. As it is rolled along the ground it picks up ever increasing amounts of snow, and its growth rapidly accelerates. Soon the snowball becomes so large that one man cannot push it any farther, and it becomes necessary for many men to pool their knowledge and resources to keep the "ball rolling." But, at the core of the snowball, there is a great unknown, ultimate reality—matter.

Again, the growth of Science has been likened to a developing spiral, reaching up into space—another ultimate reality. At the base, providing a sure foundation is an ultimate reality—matter. Matter takes form through its interaction with the ultimate reality—energy. As it reaches into space, there is no limit to its growth, for space is endless and timeless. Matter and energy are likewise endless, and timeless. For matter, energy, and space there appears to be no beginning and no end. They are ultimate realities, or perhaps manifestations of *an* Ultimate Reality.

This unit introduces these ultimate realities. Little is known concerning space, but much is known concerning the properties of matter and energy.

As we progress with this study of matter and energy, whether we are studying a galaxy in the heavens or a proton at the heart of an atom, we are impressed with the orderliness and the simplicity of Nature.

> "Nature is pleased with simplicity"
> —Isaac Newton

Finally, we become more and more impressed with the reality of Ultimate Reality, which some people call "God."

The Historical Background of Physical Science

The acquisition and systematizing of positive knowledge is the only human activity which is truly cumulative and progressive. Our civilization is essentially different from earlier ones, because our knowledge of the world and of ourselves is deeper, more precise and more certain, because we have gradually learned to disentangle the forces of nature, and because we have contrived, by strict obedience to their laws, to capture them and to divert them to the gratification of our own needs.[1]

GEORGE SARTON

INTRODUCTION

Physical Science is the study of inanimate nature. Indeed, the word *physics* is derived from the Latin *physica* or the Greek *physis*, both of which mean nature. Early man undoubtedly studied nature somewhat as a young child does today. He was curious, and wanted to know more about the things around him. He learned many things by experience just as a child learns that something hot will burn. The important characteristic of these early experiences is that they were not planned.

The cave man did not understand nature. He saw the moon change its appearance, and the sun rise and set. He was familiar with wind, and the furies of the tornado or hurricane. Lightning and thunder were attributed to the wrath of gods. Eclipses and earthquakes, shooting stars and volcanoes must have been sources of fear. The seasons came and went but he did not know why.

Because early man did not understand the causes of these displays of the forces of nature he invented myths to explain them. He invented

gods which he endowed with human characteristics, emotional and susceptible to bribes. He attributed natural forces to various gods, and practiced such religious rites as animal or human sacrifices to appease the gods. Many early men, not understanding the sun, but recognizing its importance, became sun worshipers.

RECENT HISTORY OF MAN

The recent history of man may be organized in terms of the things which he left behind as follows: (1) the Stone Age, dating back about one million years; (2) the Bronze Age, dating from about 4000 to about 2000 B.C.; and (3) the development of modern western civilization which dates from about 2000 B.C. It had its beginnings in the northern subtropical regions in Egypt, along the Nile river, and in Babylonia and Chaldea, along the Tigris and Euphrates rivers. At about the same time, other great civilizations were being founded in China, in the valley of the Yangtze river and in India, in the valleys of the Indus and Ganges rivers.

The invention of writing, which made it possible to accumulate a store of knowledge, came

---

[1] *Introduction to the History of Science*, Vol. I, pp. 3–4. Williams and Wilkins, 1927.

into use in Egypt about 3000 B.C. This invention was followed by the invention of papyrus, a paper-like material, which thus provided something to write upon.

THE FIRST TYPES OF KNOWLEDGE

When people began to live together in communities they began to specialize—some making pottery or building dwellings, others engaging in agriculture or trade. They began to sell their products to each other, so the first types of knowledge to develop had to do with measurements of weight, capacity, and length. The foundations of arithmetic and geometry were started in Babylonia, in connection with building activities. The Egyptians developed these tools further during the great pyramid age (2980–2475 B.C.). The Egyptians employed fractions and quadratic equations about 2000 B.C. In Egypt, glass making and the weaving of linen cloth were developed by 1500 B.C.

The story of the early observations and conclusions of the Egyptians and Babylonians concerning the change from night to day, the changes of the seasons, and the apparent motion of the sun, moon, and stars will be found in Chapter 12.

THE GOLDEN AGE OF GREEK REASONING

Ancient civilization reached its peak in Greece, where important advances were made in mathematics, but the greatest contributions of the Greeks were in the realm of logic and the rules of reasoning. It should be kept in mind that this Golden Age of Greek learning occurred at a time when physical labor was done by slaves or servants, and that anything involving physical work or dirtying of the hands was considered to be beneath the Greek upper classes. For that reason, the Greeks failed to experiment; but they were very successful in the study of astronomy, where observations did not require experiments. The reasoning developed by the Greeks is an important step in the modern scientific method, but it cannot lead to useful conclusions unless it is based on adequate observations.

One of the outstanding Greeks was Aristotle (384–322 B.C.). He understood the laws of levers and the law of floating objects, and even anticipated the laws of motion and some of the properties of light and sound. In fact, he made such important contributions to knowledge that for the next thousand years, the Dark Ages, his teachings were considered to be the last word.

THE RISE OF EXPERIMENTAL SCIENCE

Undoubtedly, the renaissance in Religion represented a gradual departure from reasoning by authority, which characterized the Dark Ages, and laid the foundations for the renaissance in Science. The new freedom of thought in religion thus fostered the modern age of Science. In some respects, this freedom of thought resembled that of the Greeks. This new Golden Age added the all-important contribution of experiment to the Greek rules of reasoning.

Modern experimental science began in the Renaissance with the work of Copernicus, Kepler, and Galileo, whose contributions were chiefly in the field of astronomy. They will be studied in Unit II.

Sir Francis Bacon (1561–1626) was an early exponent of experimentation. He recommended the formulation of conclusions based on extensive observations and experiments suggested by them.

Antoine Lavoisier (1743–1794), the "father of modern chemistry," laid the foundations for the tremendous growth of chemistry which has taken place during the past century and a half, and especially during the past fifty years. In this very short period of time, man has learned how to transform such common materials as air, water, salt, and coal into a host of useful things. These advances were based on quantitative experiments, in which the use of the balance, introduced by Lavoisier, was a basic technic.

Luigi Galvani (1737–1789) and Alessandro Volta (1745–1827) made the first contributions to the field of electricity. Galvani observed the twitching of a frog's leg as it came into contact with a metal, thus leading to Volta's first chemical cell for the production of an electrical current. How can one account for the tremendous developments of this modern age of electricity from this small beginning? Again the answer is *experimentation,* as when Benjamin Franklin (1706–1790) drew down sparks from the clouds during a thunderstorm by flying a kite into them. It was the basic experiments of only a few pioneers in the field of electricity which led to such modern devices as electrical generators and motors, vacuum tubes, and transistors, which made possible huge industries, such as those based on the radio, the telephone, the telegraph, and the generation and distribution of electrical power. The development of our knowledge of electricity during the past century and a half is but one of the interesting stories told in this book.

Sir Isaac Newton (1642–1727) made enormous contributions to physical science, laying the foundations of mechanics with his laws of motion and gravitation, and of optics with his study of light. In fact, the field of physics was dominated by Newton's ideas up to the beginning of the twentieth century.

THE NINETEENTH CENTURY— THE INDUSTRIAL REVOLUTION

The nineteenth century witnessed the development of the knowledge of mechanics and heat, on which was based the invention of power-driven machinery which ushered in the industrial revolution. The invention of the steam engine made possible railroads, steamships, and power-driven machines to operate such factories as textile mills. Toward the close of the nineteenth century, the invention of the internal combustion engine laid the foundation for the revolution in transportation brought about by the automobile and the airplane.

Michael Faraday (1791–1867), an English genius, was one of the most important scientists of the nineteenth century. He made basic discoveries in both chemistry and physics, but perhaps his most outstanding contribution was the basic principle of the electrical generator, which made it possible to harness power-driven machines to electrical generators.

THE TWENTIETH CENTURY— THE NUCLEAR AGE

It was during the period starting with the turn of the nineteenth century, as mentioned above, that the science of chemistry reached a mature development. As the result of the experimental work of thousands of scientists, many "better things for better living" such as dyes, drugs, perfumes, plastics, synthetic rubber, and new fibers and textiles poured out of huge chemical plants. The growth of modern chemistry is another one of the fascinating stories to be told in this book.

However, the outstanding story of the present age is the discovery of a new source of power hidden in the atomic nucleus, the possibilities of which are almost beyond the imagination. Since you are living in the nuclear age, you are not only aware of atomic (nuclear) energy; you also cannot help being concerned about its impact on modern life.

The groundwork for the development of the atomic bomb and atomic energy, now preferably spoken of as nuclear energy, was laid in 1905 by Albert Einstein (1879–1955), when he published a new theory of the Universe in the form of his "General Theory of Relativity." Einstein's theory of relativity suggested an equivalence between matter and energy that laid the foundation for the discovery of nuclear energy.

On October 4, 1957, Russian scientists lofted Sputnik I into orbit around the world, thus ushering in a new dimension of Science. For the first time, man could think seriously of exploring space. Since October 4, 1957, many rapid advances have been made in space technology, such as communication and weather satellites, and the placing of men in orbit around the earth.

PHYSICAL SCIENCE IN THE NINETEEN-SIXTIES

It has been stated that 90 per cent of all of the scientists who ever lived are alive today. This statement is in line with the facts but, of course, the percentage is merely an approximation. The growth of physical science during the past few years has resulted in the snowballing of knowledge at such an increasing rate that it will require modern electronic brains to keep up with it.

Today is truly the age of Science, especially physical science. Large sums of money are spent in scientific research. The United States government earmarks about one-tenth of its huge budget for research and development. Many industrial companies employ thousands of scientists and spend from 5 to 10 per cent of their incomes on research.

To be living in this age of physical science and not be familiar with its basic foundations is unthinkable. One of the objectives of this text is to provide a background which will help the non-science major to adjust to his modern scientific environment.

THE REALM OF PHYSICAL SCIENCE

The terms, Science, physical science, and chemistry have been introduced without having been defined. It is high time that we back up and define Science and the branches of Science.

SCIENCE DEFINED

The word, **Science,** is derived from the Latin word, *scientia,* which means knowledge. Webster's Dictionary defines Science as *"knowledge amassed, severely tested, coordinated, and systematized, especially regarding . . . the laws of nature."* In this text, **Science** will be spelled with a capital *S* when it is used as a general term to refer to *all organized knowledge, the method by which it is obtained, and the scientific attitude.* However, there are many subdivisions of Science which are called sciences, in which the word science is spelled with a small *s.*

THE SUBDIVISION OF SCIENCE

Knowledge becomes significant when it is organized. Because of man's inability to comprehend present knowledge in toto and in order to save time and effort, Science has been classified into a number of subdivisions. The main divisions of Science are defined and classified as follows, employing the usage given in the Encyclopedia Britannica in most cases:

I. The Physical Sciences, *the sciences dealing with matter and energy, apart from life.*

1. **Astronomy**—*the science of the universe outside of our own planet*
2. **Physics**—*the science of matter and energy*
3. **Chemistry**—*The science of the composition of matter*
4. **Mineralogy**—*the science of minerals*
5. **Geology**—*the study of the structure of the earth*
6. **Geography**—*the study of the earth's surface and economic products, and their relation to living creatures, especially man*
7. **Meteorology**—*The study of climate and weather*

Physics and chemistry are the fundamental physical sciences. The other physical sciences are special composite applications of these two fundamental sciences.

II. The Biological Sciences, *the sciences dealing with living organisms.*

1. **Botany**—*that portion of the science of biology which relates to plants*
2. **Zoology**—*that portion of the science of biology which relates to animals*
3. **Paleontology**—*the science of extinct forms of life*
4. **Bacteriology**—*that portion of the science of biology which relates to bacteria*
5. **Physiology**—*the science of the functions of living organisms*
6. **Hygiene**—*the science of preserving health*

III. The Psychological and Social Sciences, *the sciences dealing with man.*

1. **Psychology**—*the science of the mind*
2. **Language**—*the science of verbal communication*
3. **History**—*the science of past events*
4. **Anthropology**—*the science of the natural history of man*
5. **Ethnology**—*the science of man as a racial unity*
6. **Archaeology**—*the science of antiquities*
7. **Political Economy (Economics)**—*the science of wealth and mediums of exchange*
8. **Sociology**—*the science of human society*

9. **Education**—*the science of deliberate direction and training*
10. **Theology**—*the science of religion*
11. **Naturalistic Philosophy**—*the science of explaining all natural phenomena*

The order in which these sciences are listed represents fairly closely the order of their historical development, and to a certain extent the order in which they are studied, as would be expected.

Arithmetic, mathematics, logic, and **metaphysics** are sometimes classified as sciences, but *they are chiefly concerned with the method by which knowledge is obtained and expressed rather than with its content*, and are therefore not included in the above classification.

Literally hundreds of sciences could be added to the above list as subtitles under the above more inclusive titles.

THE FUNDAMENTAL DIVISIONS OF PHYSICAL SCIENCE

Physics

Physics is the basic physical science because it provides the technics of observation and the language for expressing observations concerning inanimate matter, and the changes which it undergoes. **Physics** *deals only with those changes in matter which do not involve a change in its composition* (with the exception of that no-man's-land known as nuclear physics). Physics specializes in the study of various forms of energy, and the transformations of one form of energy into another. Physics is usually subdivided into the study of mechanics, heat, sound, light, and electricity. Mechanical, civil, and electrical engineering are branches of applied physics.

Chemistry

The word **chemistry** is a shortened form of the word **alchemistry,** a pseudo (false) science of the Dark Ages, *which was chiefly devoted to the search for a method of creating gold from cheaper metals*, an ancient get-rich-quick scheme. While no alchemist ever succeeded in converting base metals—such as iron or lead—into gold, the alchemists added much to the knowledge of matter, because they carried out many changes in the composition of matter in connection with their experiments designed to produce gold. **Chemistry** *deals with the changes in the composition of matter,* such as the burning of fuels, the cooking of foods, or the conversion of petroleum into plastics. Changes in the composition of matter involve a change in **chemical properties,** *which describe the composition of matter.* For example, when we state that wood may be burned to produce various gaseous products and ashes, we are stating a chemical property of wood.

All changes in matter, both chemical and physical, are accompanied by energy changes, so chemistry and physics are concerned with energy as well as matter. Since we are living in an age in which one of the greatest achievements is the conversion of matter into energy, the borderline between physics and chemistry has nearly disappeared. Of course, it was an arbitrary border in the first place. There is little difference between a nuclear physicist and a nuclear chemist, although it is true that the chemist may be engaged in the analysis of the products of the changes in the atomic nucleus, while the physicist is concerned with the changes which produced these products.

A college physics laboratory differs a great deal from a college chemistry laboratory. In the chemistry laboratory, the student is engaged in chemical changes, which often yield offensive fumes and sometimes even unexpected explosions. There is a frequent washing of glassware dirtied by the chemical reactions. Acid fumes quickly corrode metallic surfaces in a chemistry laboratory, and it must be well ventilated to preserve the health of the instructor and students. What a different situation is found in the college physics laboratory! The air is clean, and the metallic surfaces of the apparatus retain their sheen, unless the physics laboratory is near the chemistry laboratory. The student uses the apparatus to learn the fundamental physical properties of matter, and to study such forms of energy as heat, light, sound, electricity, and motion. With care, the apparatus remains unchanged at the end of the experiment.

The other physical sciences—i.e., geology, mineralogy, astronomy, geography, and meteorology—employ the fundamental principles of physics and chemistry to the study of special bodies—such as the stars, the earth, minerals —and such changes as earthquakes, volcanoes, and winds, or the seasons.

SUMMARY

1. Science is knowledge and the method by which it is obtained. Knowledge is essential to the attainment of the goal of humanity.

2. Science, through invention, has brought about important changes in our culture and has thus created many problems.

3. Experimentation is an important basis for the success of modern Science.

4. A knowledge of physical science is essential to the solution of many problems of everyday life in this modern age of Science.

Study Questions

1. DEFINE: Science, science, chemistry, physics, geology, astronomy, meteorology.
2. List the three main divisions of Science, and indicate how they differ from each other.
3. Give the derivations of the words *Science* and *physics*.
4. How did the learning experiences of early man differ from those of modern man?
5. What was the outstanding contribution of the Greek philosophers to the scientific method?
6. Why did the Greek philosophers fail to make greater progress?
7. Why was little progress made during the Dark Ages?
8. Relate the renaissance in Religion to the renaissance in Science.
9. Where did western civilization have its beginnings?
10. Name an outstanding man in each of the periods of the development of modern knowledge, and give his chief contributions.
11. When did modern experimental science have its beginnings?
12. List some of the basic discoveries of the eighteenth and nineteenth centuries.
13. What discoveries ushered in the industrial revolution?
14. Differentiate between the sciences of chemistry and physics.

The Scientific Attitude and Method

The future of our civilization depends upon the widening spread and deepening hold of the scientific habit of mind.

JOHN DEWEY

The acquisition and systematizing of positive knowledge is the only human activity which is truly cumulative and progressive.

GEORGE SARTON[1]

INTRODUCTION

If a radio station were to broadcast a realistic presentation of an imaginary mass bombing of American cities by enemy airplanes using nuclear bombs, bedlam and bloodshed on our highways would result.

Perhaps you would not be so frightened by such a radio broadcast, but do you buy your soap, hair tonic, depilatory, cigarettes, medicines or breakfast food on the basis of the radio or television announcer's advice? Do you believe that a statement is true just because it is printed? In general, do you have the scientific attitude?

Do you use the scientific method in the solution of your problems? Perhaps you will be able to answer this question better after studying this chapter.

THE SCIENTIFIC ATTITUDE

Science is an activity where honesty is absolutely essential for success. Briefly, the **scientific attitude** *is the truth-seeking attitude.*

An **attitude** *is simply a habitual way of*

[1] *Introduction to the History of Science,* Vol. I, Williams and Wilkins, Baltimore, 1927.

looking at things, or a state of mind. It is largely emotional in nature, and motivates and determines conduct and behavior. The scientific attitude causes one to seek to control primitive emotions by rational appeal to fact rather than by superstitions, prejudices, traditions, customs, precedents, dogmas, and intolerant self-conceit.

The Truth Seeker Cultivates Certain Habits of Mind

1. He Realizes that Truth as Discovered by Man is never Absolute—The truth seeker cannot hope to discover finality in a universe in which change is one of the dominant characteristics. The quest for truth is endless, and no human problem is ever finally settled. The best that one can do is to reach a tentative conclusion based on all of the data available.

2. He Believes in the Orderliness of Natural Processes—The truth seeker does not believe that events happen capriciously, nor does he believe in magic, astrology, fortune-telling, or "lady luck." The student of nature soon discovers that our universe is one of law and order. He knows that behind every result there is a cause, and that the same causes will always produce the same results, under the same conditions.

3. He Is Curious—The truth seeker is definitely curious about the world in which he lives. He is never a disinterested bystander.

4. He Is not Prejudiced—He is willing to lay aside lifelong convictions, the traditions of history, and the morals and customs of his generation, long enough to see whether or not a new fact will change his point of view.

5. He Is Open-Minded—He does not want merely to obtain support for his preconceived notions, but he wants to know the truth. He never laughs at new ideas.

6. He Is Aggressively Tolerant—The truth seeker must be ready to admit that other people may know more than he does, and that they may be right and he may be wrong. He seeks to discover the elements of agreement and disagreement between himself and others, in an effort to discover the truth. He does not ask others to accept his point of view.

7. He Does Not Accept Conclusions Unless They Are Supported by Adequate Evidence—The truth seeker is definitely skeptical. Skepticism is not cynicism or suspicion, but it does involve the scrutinizing of every belief, custom, and conclusion, to discover the data, if any, upon which it rests. He reaches conclusions, but he does not jump at them.

8. He Is Able to Recognize Fellow Truth Seekers—It is hopeless to attempt to repeat and verify all of the scientific work of past ages, and it therefore becomes necessary to depend upon the work of others for most of his information. He judges authorities by the evidence presented for their conclusions, rather than by their fame or wealth.

9. He Is Undaunted in His Pursuit of Truth—It takes a great deal of painstaking effort, patience, and perseverance, even to begin to discover the facts necessary to solve a problem. The truth seeker keeps trying, even after many failures. Work for him is a pleasure, because it leads to one of life's greatest satisfactions—that of discovering new knowledge, or of solving problems.

10. He Does Not Subscribe to the Adage, "What You Don't Know Won't Hurt You"—He has learned from experience that it is usually what he does not know that causes most of his difficulties.

11. He Cultivates Accuracy of Observation and Precision of Statement—The truth seeker knows that no detail is too small to be of importance. Deliberate dishonesty, distortion of truth, the selection of facts which support a preconceived point of view, inaccurate measurement, the dishonest or ignorant use of statistics, and careless observations are obstacles blocking the pathway to truth.

12. He Is Optimistic—The truth seeker never says that a thing cannot be done, but rather he says "give me a chance at it." The fact that a thing has never been done presents a challenge.

The Scientific Attitude Requires Conscious Effort for Its Cultivation

No truth seeker possesses all of the above attributes. They represent goals toward which one should strive, but which will never be attained to perfection. No one is born with the scientific attitude. Those who have acquired it, have done so by conscious effort and much self-discipline.

THE SCIENTIFIC METHOD

The scientific method is important because it provides a reliable method for the solution of problems by scientists and non-scientists alike. Whether or not such a person is really a scientist depends upon the extent to which he exhibits the scientific attitude and uses the scientific method in the solution of problems. As ordinarily used, the term, *scientist*, refers to a person whose avocation or vocation is devoted to the scientific pursuit of new knowledge.

The scientific method may be considered to be man's greatest discovery, because it represents a sure method of discovering new knowledge.

There is no simple definition of the **scientific method.** *In general, it is the method found by scientists to be successful in the solution of their problems.* Different problems are solved in different ways by different people. Nevertheless, there are characteristics common to many scientific investigations to which we will refer as the scientific method. **The steps in the scientific method,** as the authors understand them, are summarized as follows:

1. *The location and definition of a problem.*
2. *Search or research.*
3. *Organization and evaluation of data.*
4. *Formation of a hypothesis,* i.e. a possible or tentative solution to the problem.
5. *Testing and verifying the hypothesis.*

The Location and Definition of a Problem

Many of the problems that arise as a part of everyday living are the result of felt needs. In such problems, the location and definition of the problem is very important. The problem may not be what we think it is at first. Many questions will arise, and frequently the problem cannot be adequately defined without obtaining additional information.

Search or Research

Often a search of literature or a contact with people (authorities) who are likely to have the required information turns up a solution to the problem, or suggests possible fruitful approaches to its solution. Many times, the problem can be solved without research, because search alone yields sufficient information. It is characteristic of most scientific investigations that search precedes research. Much time can be wasted by research that yields information already published.

Research generally refers to the *obtaining of data through experiments, which are controlled so as to yield meaningful results. Careful records of observations* are called **data.** Data are obtained by (1) **bare observations,** i.e., observations made under uncontrolled conditions, and (2) **experimental observations,** i.e., observations made under controlled conditions. **Controlled observations** *involve the altering of one factor at a time, while other factors are kept constant.* Uncontrolled experiments are seldom useful. Both types of observations must be capable of being repeated and verified by others. Observations must not only be controlled, they must also be checked to insure their reliability.

At best, man's senses are very limited, and differ widely among individuals. Because of this fact, the senses often yield false or misleading information. Therefore, many measuring instruments have been devised to aid the senses.

However, instruments can yield incorrect data if they are not working properly. Errors due to faulty instruments may be eliminated by **calibrating** them—i.e., *by correcting or adjusting them*—or by checking the results obtained with them against the results obtained with other instruments.

The reduction of errors in observation is one of the major problems in the search for truth. The senses may be made more reliable through training. In fact, one of the most important objectives of laboratory work in the training of scientists is to train them to make accurate observations, with and without instruments.

In spite of the determination to do so, no one can be alert to everything that goes on around him, and every man will be influenced in making observations by his interests. Such errors, due to the personality of one observer, may be eliminated by having his observations repeated by other observers. Mistakes are avoided in banks, stores, hospitals, and scientific laboratories by checking and rechecking. No information should be accepted as being reliable until it has been checked.

Organization and Evaluation of Data

A great deal of the time required for the preparation for work in the physical sciences must be devoted to the mastery of mathematical tools. Mathematics provides methods of arriving at general conclusions, based upon certain arbitrarily chosen definitions. Inasmuch as many scientific generalizations are obtained by mathematical reasoning based on arbitrarily chosen assumptions, it is quite evident that there is no absolute generalization in Science, and that hypotheses, and even scientific laws, are subject to change when new data indicate that original assumptions were not justified. A knowledge of mathematics is essential in interpreting many data, but a knowledge of statistics is of equal importance, because statistics enables one to determine what data to use.

Every measurement involves some error and, for this reason, it is extremely important that the amount and significance of these errors always be taken into consideration. This is another problem of statistics. Too often, conclusions based on data are mere nonsense rather than truth, because statistics was not employed.

Formation of a Hypothesis

There are two approaches to the formulation of possible hypotheses. One approach, called the **inductive method,** *starts with data obtained by observation, and uses these data as the basis for the hypothesis.* In another approach, called the **deductive method,** *one starts with the hypothesis, and then obtains data to check the assumptions on which the hypothesis was based.* Do not concern yourself too much about induction and deduction; both methods are equally valid. The important thing is not which comes first, but rather the fact that both can be subjected to the same tests and checks.

Inductive thinking dates from the time of Galileo. His new philosophy came to be called "Science" (from the Latin word, *scientia,* meaning knowledge). It was Galileo's idea that there could be no such thing as ultimate truth, because new knowledge often makes it necessary to revise old generalizations. Perhaps Galileo's greatest contribution was the substitution of induction for deduction. He built his conclusions on observations, rather than on a set of generalizations. Furthermore, he challenged the validity of any generalization which had not been tested by experiment. Thus, Galileo's viewpoint was directly opposite to that of the ancient Greeks—which had held sway up until the Renaissance—in that it starts with particular facts and leads to general conclusions.

The formation of a hypothesis is a mental process. The ability to formulate hypotheses that are justified by the data available comes with training and experience. Very often conscious mental effort fails to result in a tentative solution to a problem. Many research workers have found that if they give up further work on the problem and turn their attention to something else, the solution comes to them as a "flash of genius" when they are least expecting it. This "flash of genius," or scientific hunch, is always preceded by a felt need for a solution to a problem, and by charging the mind with information concerning it, either by search or research, just as a lightning flash is preceded by a charged cloud. This process, whereby the unconscious mind works out a solution to a problem, is given the technical name of **seren-dipity,** which may be defined as the *conscious stimulation of unconscious processes.*

Classical examples of solutions to complicated problems in which the possibilities are almost infinite—and in which it is almost humanly impossible to accumulate sufficient data even by laborious observations—are the explanation of the motion of the heavenly bodies by Isaac Newton, and Charles Darwin's theory of evolution. Darwin wrote in his autobiography, "I can remember the very spot in the road, whilst in my carriage, when to my joy, the solution came to me."

When Einstein announced his generalization relating space and time, he stated that "the idea occurred to him while sick in bed."

The conditions for this unconscious leap beyond the boundaries of experimental evidence seem to be:

(a) **Great interest in the problem.**

(b) **The problem must be well defined.**

(c) **The mind must be charged with pertinent information.**

(d) **After attacking a problem for some time, abandon it.**

(e) **A sense of freedom from interruptions and pressing problems.**

Sometimes, attacking or reviewing a problem before bedtime will start the unconscious mind working on it, and the solution is ready the next morning.

The Mental Side of Problem Solving— Crooked Thinking—The mental side of problem solving is concerned with initial planning, devising changes in plans in the light of unexpected difficulties or developments, and finally, interpreting the data obtained. While thinking is an important part of the scientific method, it is an art; and, like all arts, it must be learned and perfected by practice.

Perhaps a brief survey of the following common errors in the mental approach to problems will help one to understand the scientific method better by comparing it with crooked thinking:

a. *Confused Thinking*—The majority of differences of opinion may be traced to differences in meaning attached to common words by different people.

The language of Science is filled with thousands of words especially coined to express new ideas. These new words have very precise meanings, and give a great deal of trouble to beginning students until they learn to use them correctly.

b. *Pseudo-Statistical Thinking*—Many people are rightly very skeptical of statistical reasoning, because they have seen so many examples of data which have been carefully selected so as to lead to a predetermined conclusion. The important source of crookedness in statistical thinking is the failure to obtain and use all of the data.

c. *Speculative Thinking*—The danger of speculative thinking is that it is easy to conclude that the speculation which *may* be true, actually *is* true.

d. *Repetition*—Advertisers depend upon repetition a great deal, knowing that even falsehood will be accepted by the majority of people if it is repeated often enough, because repetition is often confused with proof.

e. *Rationalization*—Prejudices lead to that kind of crooked thinking which is often called rationalization. Rationalization represents reasoning at its worst, because the information furnished the mind has been carefully selected on the basis of emotions. Prejudices are personal obstacles which make us unwilling to think straight. When our hidden desires lead us to accept a given idea, our minds invariably furnish us with a set of reasons to support it.

f. *Incautious Conclusions*—It is very easy to arrive at extreme conclusions not justified by available data. Overstatements should be avoided.

g. *Compromise*—Compromise is often expedient, but not necessarily straight thinking. Many people decide upon a course of action after studying only what other people do under similar circumstances, and then try to steer a middle course. Such a procedure avoids controversy, but it does not represent an honest attempt to arrive at the truth.

h. *"Either–Or" Thinking*—Nature cannot be pigeon holed. No person is wholly sane or insane, good or bad, intelligent or unintelligent, conservative or radical.

i. *Reasoning by Authority*—As previously pointed out, from the time of the Golden Age of Greek learning down to the Renaissance, most of the reasoning was based on premises established by authority rather than experience. It is a common practice to try to support a given conclusion by referring to authorities.

j. *Inconsequential Arguments*—A certain lubricating oil for automobiles is advertised to "last longer and reduce knocks." The inference that one is supposed to reach is that this oil would be the best lubricant available for the engine. Actually emery powder would last longer, and lead tetraethyl would be a better remedy for knocks, but neither would serve as a lubricant.

k. *Reasoning by Analogy*—Many people reason by analogy: if a person has a strong jaw, he has a strong character, or is quite determined.

"One can predict as successfully whether a motor is good, bad, or absent, by examining the hood as he can tell whether an individual is a genius, lunatic, or imbecile by examining the skull."—Moss.

Testing and Verifying Conclusions

In Science, a conclusion is tentative; it is something to be tested. Such tests involve the collection of additional data. New generalizations are thus obtained, and so the process continues. A generalization is tested by figuring out what ought to happen if the generalization is true, and then observing whether or not these predictions are verified by further experiment.

Generalizations differ in reliability. A **hypothesis** *is a tentative conclusion,* or generalization. *Generalizations that stand the tests of time and experience come to be accepted as true, and are called* **laws.** Most of our scientific laws have been revised repeatedly as additional information showed that they were inaccurate or inadequate. Scientific laws differ from civil laws in that the latter involve a command or duty, while a **scientific law** *is a description of a regularity in nature.*

The Grand Theories of Physical Science— Theories are integrating explanations that knit together large bodies of facts, hypotheses and laws. They constitute the most useful portion of scientific knowledge. An important contribution of theories is that they suggest new generalizations.

The Greek philosophers wondered what would happen if matter could be subdivided. Two schools of thought developed. One group of thinkers considered that matter could not be broken down into ultimate particles, but is continuous. The other school thought that if matter were subjected to processes of subdivision, there would finally be found ultimate particles which would not yield to further subdivision.

The grand theories of physical science are those which suggest that both matter and energy consist of small units. At the beginning of the nineteenth century the atomic theory was advanced. This theory was that chemical reactions take place between *ultimate, small particles of different types of matter called elements*. These particles were called **atoms**. Later evidence suggested that most of the matter with which we come into contact consists of compounds of these elements, or mixtures of these compounds, and that the *smallest portions of a compound which can exist and still retain its properties* are **molecules**. Later, it was found that atoms are not ultimate particles, but consist of *negatively charged particles* called **electrons** surrounding a positively charged nucleus. It was found that atoms or molecules could gain or lose electrons to yield electrically charged particles called **ions**. Eventually it was found that the nuclei of atoms, in turn, are not ultimate, but consist of smaller, positively charged particles called **protons**, and neutral particles called **neutrons**. Thus, the grand theories of physical science deal with the idea of particles. These theories, the atomic theory, the molecular theory, the electron theory, the ionic theory, and the nuclear theory, explain most of the facts and laws of physical science, and will constitute an important part of this book.

At the beginning of the twentieth century, the idea that energy also occurs in the form of discrete units called **quanta** (singular, quantum) was advanced in the form of the quantum theory. To this list of theories should be added Einstein's basic theory, which shows the relationship between matter and energy.

SUMMARY

1. The scientific attitude is essential to the satisfactory solution of problems. It is the attitude of the truth seeker. Truth seekers are honest, curious, tolerant, skeptical, discriminating, industrious, and accurate.

2. The supreme contribution of Science to humanity is its method of solving problems, which consists of (1) definition, (2) search or research, (3) organization and evaluation of data, (4) the formation of a hypothesis, (5) testing the hypothesis.

3. The essence of the scientific method is that observations and conclusions are subjected to thorough checking.

4. The grand theories of physical science deal with the ultimate nature of matter and energy. Matter may be subdivided to yield atoms, molecules, ions, electrons, neutrons and protons. Energy also exists in the form of particles called quanta.

Study Questions

1. DEFINE: scientific attitude, scientist, induction, deduction, serendipity, hypothesis, law, theory, search, research, data, calibration, statistics, atom, molecule, bare observation, experimental observation, controlled observation.

2. What are the characteristics of the truth seeker?

An Introduction to Matter and Energy

The things that any science discovers are beyond the reach of direct observation. We cannot see energy, nor the attraction of gravitation, nor the flying molecules of gases, nor the forests of the Carbonaceous era.

C. S. PIERCE

INTRODUCTION

A course in Physical Science consists of a study of matter and energy. Matter and energy are everywhere in our environment—in fact, they *are* our environment. It is impossible to visualize a single material substance or a single activity that is not concerned with matter or energy. It does not matter whether we are examining our environment on the subatomic level or on the level of the Universe,[1] matter and energy are always present.

It would also seem impossible that anything as unlimited in its scope as matter and energy would escape the prying eyes of Science. In spite of the tremendous amount of fundamental research, Science has yet to "uncloak" matter and energy so that their ultimate nature may be revealed. But this is not a failure of Science. The very nature of matter and energy renders any such attempt futile.

Science is concerned with what it *can* do—i.e., the determination of the properties of matter and energy, and their application to the development of a better life on earth.

As you study this chapter and the following two chapters, you will find frequent references

to chapters that occur later in the text. Since a study of Physical Science is a study of matter and energy, these three chapters serve as an introduction to the remainder of the text. The purpose of these three chapters is to present an overview of matter and energy, with emphasis on: (1) a development of a *working* definition of matter and energy, (2) a description of the general properties of matter and energy, and (3) a classification of the forms of matter and energy.

ULTIMATE REALITIES

Most scientists, realizing the apparent hopelessness of attaining a true understanding of matter and energy, accept the concepts of matter and energy as postulated fundamentals, and proceed from there. For the purpose of this text, the authors also assume that matter and energy are irreducible entities. There is not a single shred of evidence that these two elusive realities were born of something else during the primordial past, nor that they will decay (or grow) into something different during the eons which are to come.

In other words, matter and energy represent true beginnings, the same now as they have been since creation. Apparently, matter and energy cannot be reduced to anything simpler. Therefore, we shall assume that they are ulti-

---

[1] Universe is capitalized when it refers to the sum of all heavenly bodies. It is not capitalized when it refers to a galaxy such as the Galaxy of which the earth is a member.

17

mate realities. Philosophers and theologians have used the existence of these two physical ultimate realities to show the relationship (and the division) of Science and Religion. They point out that if these fundamental entities are manifestations of God, then there can be no doubt of the existence of God. Or, if matter and energy were created by a Supreme Creator, their very existence shows the presence of God. The following passage shows the relationship between Science and Religion:

> There cannot be any issue between faith and science, for science and faith mutually exclude one another; not in the sense that the one renders the other impossible, or vice versa, but rather that so far as science extends, faith does not exist, and faith begins where science leaves off. It cannot be denied that beyond this limit there may be real objects to be embraced by faith. It is, therefore, not the object of science to destroy faith, but rather to define the boundaries to which knowledge extends, and within these to establish a uniform system.
>
> Rudolf Virshow

If we accept the position of Rudolf Virshow, then the task of Science is to attempt to discover the properties of the postulated funda-mentals (ultimate realities) and, once the properties are discovered, to apply them toward a better life for mankind on earth. In their own way, both Religion and Science are seeking more knowledge (and application) of their own respective ultimate realities.

We will follow the traditional path, and discuss matter and energy in terms of their properties and functions. For the moment, we will submit the following definitions for matter and energy: **Matter** is *that which occupies space and has inertia.* **Energy** is the *capacity for performing work.* The remainder of this chapter and the following two chapters are devoted to the expansion of these two simple definitions.

HISTORICAL ASPECTS OF MATTER AND ENERGY

The Greek philosophers believed that all matter could be reduced to a few elementary forms. By deductive reasoning, they concluded that all materials were made up of varying proportions of four fundamental "elements"—earth, air, fire, and water. Figure 3-1 illustrates the relationship of these fundamental "ele-

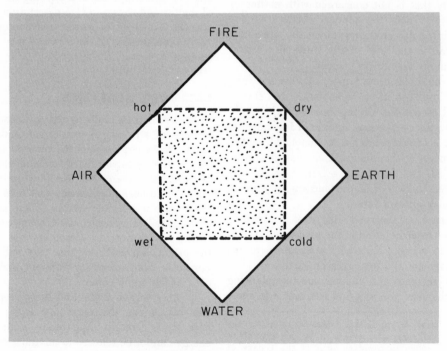

Figure 3–1. The four elements and the four properties according to the Greek philosophers.

ments." Bones were considered to be composed of two parts of fire and one part each of earth and water. Flesh consisted of equal parts of all four "elements." Angels were composed of fire alone.

The four "elements" gave rise to the "properties" of matter—hot, dry, wet, and cold. Thus, water had the properties of being wet and cold; fire, on the other hand, was hot and dry.

Empedocles (490–430 B.C.), the Sicilian philosopher, taught that the four "elements" acted under the influence of love or hate to form more complex substances. Love served to bring them together, and hate caused them to separate. Thus, he seems to have been the first philosopher to associate changes of matter with energy. Empedocles also gave us the basis for our conservation laws. According to Empedocles, there was no creation nor absolute destruction of the four "elements." They could only be changed to different forms.

THE DUALITY OF MATTER AND ENERGY

Until 1905, matter and energy were considered to be separate entities. Albert Einstein (1879–1955) suggested that matter and energy were related much like a coin which presents different faces to the viewer. His idea was that of a duality, in which matter-energy is present under one set of conditions and becomes the material substance of the universe-matter; and under different circumstances it becomes energy. By elaborate mathematics, Einstein showed that energy (E) is proportional to the amount of matter (m) times the velocity of light squared (c^2). This is the famous equation: $E = mc^2$, the only mathematical expression included in this text. Since "c^2" is a tremendously large number, 900 billion billion, even if the amount of matter which may be changed into energy is very small, the resulting quantity of energy is very large. For example, the energy in a level teaspoonful of sugar, if utilized in the normal metabolism, would provide only sufficient energy to sustain a person for approximately ten minutes. But if this same amount of sugar were converted entirely into energy, it would meet the energy requirements of more than a thousand persons for their entire lifetime. The energy released in the Hiro-

shima atomic bomb explosion represented the change of only one gram (1/28 ounce) of matter into energy.

THE CONSERVATION LAWS

The conservation laws are the backbone of theoretical science; they are essentially an "accounting system." If something disappears from the credit side of the ledger, a corresponding amount must appear on the debit side. We will be concerned with four conservation laws: (1) conservation of matter, (2) conservation of energy, (3) conservation of mass-energy, and (4) conservation of momentum.

During the 1770's, the foundations of the first conservation law, the law of conservation of matter, were being established. Antoine Lavoisier (1743–1794) had discovered that weight was a fundamental property of matter, and he had devised the chemical balance to measure weight. He conducted many experiments dealing with the nature of combustion (burning), from which he concluded that the sum of all of the weights of the starting materials of a combustion reaction was equal to the weights of the end products. This conclusion was contrary to the widely held belief that a substance, phlogiston, escaped during a burning process, with the result that there was a decrease in weight.

Based on his experiments, Lavoisier formulated his "law of the indestructibility of matter." This law was later called the law of **conservation of matter,** and it was stated as follows: *there is no perceptible gain or loss of matter during any chemical change.* With the advent of nuclear reactions, in which matter was changed into energy, the above law was restated as follows: *In all non-nuclear changes in the composition of matter, there is no weighable gain or loss of mass.* In 1793, Lavoisier met his death on the guillotine, in spite of his great services to his country, because he was a member of the aristocracy and had been associated with a tax-collecting company that was hated by the people. C. S. Minot said of his death at the hands of the French revolutionists:

Compared with the growth of Science, the shiftings of Governments are minor events. Until it is clearly recognized that the gravest crime of the French Revolution was not the execution of the King but the execution of Lavoisier, there is no right measure of values, for Lavoisier was one of the three or four greatest men France has produced.

Somewhat later, a similar law of conservation was formulated for energy. With the advent of Einstein's theory relating to matter and energy, Science again formulated a new conservation law, known as the law of **conservation of mass-energy,** which states that *the total amount of mass-energy of the universe is constant.*

MEASUREMENT

Aristotle said, "All men by nature desire to know," but it remained for Johann Kepler (1571–1630) to add: "to measure is to know." Measurements of high precision are prerequisite to the mass production of modern machines with their interchangeable parts. The growth of modern Science can be attributed largely to the invention of thousands of machines that make it possible to make more exact and accurate observations.

The numbers that we use in Science are of two types. One is the result of counting, in which the objects themselves are counted. The other is the result of measurement which, even at best, is an approximation. For example, an agronomist might be given a sample of wheat, for which he could count the actual number of grains. After some time spent in counting, he would announce that the sample contained 4,326 grains. But suppose that he had used a measure to determine the number of grains. If the measuring cup had a capacity of 400 grains, he would announce the number to be 4,400 grains, plus or minus 200 grains. This is the correct method of reporting results using a measuring instrument—a correct reading to the nearest whole measure, plus or minus half a measure. The same procedure is used regardless of the type of measure. The measurer must either specify the precision of his measuring instrument or specify the tolerances, as the agronomist did. We must realize that practically every measure, whether it be for amperes of electricity, grams of mass, or light years of length, always has an inherent error. The precision of our measuring instruments might reduce the error, but it can never be eliminated. We will never be able to measure the length of a pencil and give its exact length.

Measuring Devices

The first chapter of this text pointed out the necessity of measurements as soon as man began to live in social communities. Of course, the earliest measurements were mere comparisons. Who is the tallest? Who has the longest club? But soon, the simple comparisons were not adequate and man began looking for a system of measurement based on units. For the units, he used his own body just as he used his fingers and toes for counting. Many of the units that we use today have their origins based on anatomical lengths. For example, the cubit of the early Egyptians was the length from the elbow to the outstretched middle finger. The fathom was the distance between outstretched hands, and the hand was the breadth of four fingers.

By the end of the Renaissance, the need for a standard for measurements was felt, and there were many attempts at standardization. For instance, Henry I of England decreed that a yard would be the distance from *his* nose to the end of *his* thumb when *his* arm was outstretched. An old German attempt at the standardization of a rod (16 ½ feet) was:

Stand at the door of a church on Sunday morning and bid sixteen men to stop, tall ones and short ones, as they leave the church; then make them put their left feet one behind the other, and the length thus obtained shall be a right and lawful rod to measure and survey land with, a sixteenth part of it shall be a right and lawful foot.

Today, our measurements are carefully standardized, but unfortunately the English-speaking countries, which use the English system of measurement, do not agree on some of the units. For instance, the Canadian quart and gallon are larger than those used in the United States. To complicate matters more, the United States uses a *dry* quart to measure vegetables and berries, and a *liquid* quart to measure milk and other liquids.

The Metric System

The present world standard of measurement, the metric system, which is based on a unit of length called the meter, had its beginnings in 1670, when the French mathematician, Gabriel Moulton, suggested the adoption of a new standard of length based on the earth's circumference. But it was more than a century later, as a result of the urgings of such famous scientists as Lavoisier, LaGrange, and LaPlace, that King Louis XVI decreed the establishment of the new metric system. The Academie des Sciences was sanctioned to set up the necessary committees and to carry out the work of establishing the new system. On March 19, 1791, the committee recommended to the French Assembly that the new measurement system be based on a length equal to one ten-millionth part of the earth's quadrant. To simplify the surveying, it was decided to measure a ten-degree segment (about 700 miles) of the quadrant that passed through Paris. Four years later, on April 7, 1795, the final report was presented, but the re-checking of the system continued for a number of years. The work was declared finished in 1799, and the system was made permissive in 1812 and compulsory in 1820. The United States *officially* adopted the metric system in 1893, and the yard was defined as 3,600/3,937 meter.

The **meter,** *as recorded on a platinum-iridium alloy bar preserved at the Palais des Archives in Paris, has always been the distance between two scratches on the bar when measured at 0° C.* Today, a much more readily available and more exacting standard for the *length of one meter is the total distance of 1,650,763.73 wavelengths of a particular light emitted by Krypton 86.* The concept of wavelength will be discussed in Chapter 5.

The meter, the basic measure of the metric system, is subdivided into smaller units by dividing by multiples of ten (10, 100, 1,000). The units larger than a meter are obtained by multiplying by multiples of ten. The scheme of either dividing or multiplying by multiples of ten provides an easy method of changing from one unit or another, since it uses the decimal system. It eliminates the cumbersome process of changing from one unit to another, typical of the English system. The decimal system employed in the metric system uses the prefixes deci- (1/10), centi- (1/100), milli- (1/1000), and kilo- (1000 x).

From the basic unit, the **meter,** other basic measurement units are derived. The liter (the unit of volume) and the kilogram (the unit of mass) are based on the meter. Thus, the **liter,** *the unit of volume,* is *the volume of a cube, each side of which is 1/10 meter.* This volumetric unit was subdivided into smaller units by dividing by multiples of ten, the most common smaller unit being the **milliliter.** The milliliter is the same as the **cubic centimeter.** *The unit of weight,* **the kilogram,** is *the mass of one liter of water when measured at 3.98° C.* Subdivisions of the kilogram are the **gram** and **milligram.**

TABLE 3-1

COMMON METRIC UNITS

Dimension	Fundamental Units	Multiples or Submultiples
Length	meter (m)	kilometer (km)
		centimeter (cm)
		millimeter (mm)
		Angstrom (10^{-8} cm)
Area	square meter (m^2)	square centimeter (cm^2)
Volume	cubic meter (m^3)	cubic centimeter (cm^3)
	liter (l) (cubic decimeter)	milliliter (ml)
Mass	kilogram (kg)	gram (g)
		milligram (mg)

Inasmuch as there are two widely used systems of measurement in use throughout the world, the English system and the metric system, one should be able to compare the fundamental units of one system with those of the other system. Table 3-2 shows these important comparisons.

TABLE 3-2

COMPARISON BETWEEN ENGLISH AND METRIC UNITS

1 inch = 2.54 centimeters
1 meter = 39.37 inches
1 kilometer = 0.62 mile
1 kilogram = 2.2 pounds
1 liter = 1.057 U.S. liquid quart, or 0.8799 British liquid quart
1 pound = 453.6 grams

Nearly every country in the world has adopted the metric system as the legal standard, but the English-speaking countries are

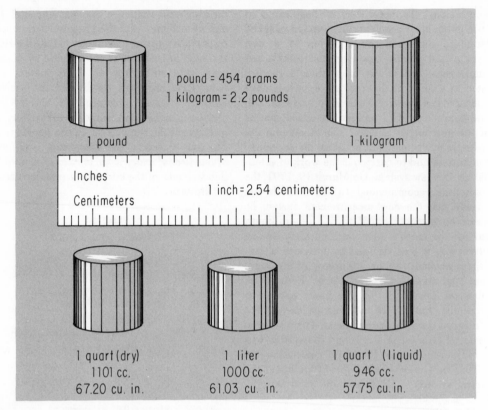

1 pound = 454 grams
1 kilogram = 2.2 pounds

1 pound

1 kilogram

Inches

Centimeters

1 inch = 2.54 centimeters

1 quart (dry)	1 liter	1 quart (liquid)
1101 cc.	1000 cc.	946 cc.
67.20 cu. in.	61.03 cu. in.	57.75 cu. in.

Figure 3–2. A comparison of English and metric units. The U.S. dry quart measure is larger than the liter, but the U.S. liquid quart is slightly smaller. The liquid quart in Canada is larger than the U.S. liquid quart.

very slow in accepting it for everyday use. The metric system should be employed universally because: (1) a single system would simplify world communications and world trade. Even the standardizing of English units would help. For instance, there are more than a hundred different "bushels" to measure everything from oats to apples. (2) The metric system would save a great deal of time in education. Since the metric system is based on the **denary** (*decimal*) system of counting, changing from one unit to another is merely the matter of shifting the decimal point. The laborious method of changing feet to miles, or square yards to acres requires considerable arithmetical skill.

Many writers and speakers have argued for the change from the English system of measurement to the metric system. One of the most outspoken was Lord Kelvin:

I believe I am not overstating the truth when I say that half of the time occupied by clerks and draughtsmen in engineers' and surveyors' offices—I am sure at least one-half of it—is work entailed upon them by the inconvenience of the present farrago of weights and measures.

In 1965 Britain announced a change to the metric system to take place gradually over a ten-year period in order to be in line with the nations of Europe which use the metric system exclusively.

SUMMARY

Matter and energy are considered to be irreducible entities or ultimate realities.

The ancient Greek philosophers considered four "elements," earth, air, fire, and water, to be fundamental. These elements were considered to have the properties of hot, wet, cold, or dry.

Matter and energy are now considered to be

equivalent, according to the equation: $E = mc^2$. A small amount of matter is equivalent to a tremendous amount of energy.

The conservation laws are essentially an accounting system. The laws are stated as follows:

The Law of Conservation of Mass—In all non-nuclear changes in the composition of matter there is no weighable loss or gain in mass.

The Law of Conservation of Mass-Energy—The total amount of mass-energy in the universe is constant.

Scientific numbers are of two kinds, (1) those based on counting, and (2) those based on measurement. There are always errors in even the most precise measurements.

The metric system is a simple system because it is based on multiples and submultiples of ten.

Study Questions

1. DEFINE: ultimate reality, meter, gram, liter, denary.

2. In the mathematical equation $E = mc^2$, what is the meaning of each term?

3. Give a modern statement for the law of conservation of matter. Why does it differ from the older form?

4. State the law of conservation of mass energy.

5. What were the "elements" and their properties according to the Greek philosophers?

6. Why was the chemical balance so important in the development of Science.

7. Give examples of numbers that are the result of counting.

8. Give examples of numbers that are the result of measurement.

9. What is meant by a system of measurement based on anatomical units?

10. Why was the metric system established?

11. What is the fundamental unit of the metric system? What does it represent?

12. What is meant by the denary system of counting?

13. Why has the metric system not been universally adopted?

14. In what regards is the metric system of measurement superior to the English system?

An Introduction to Matter

The object of all science is to coordinate our experiences and bring them into a logical system.

ALBERT EINSTEIN

INTRODUCTION

In the previous chapter matter was introduced as an ultimate reality. Therefore, it would be futile to try to define matter in terms of anything simpler, or to discuss its ultimate nature.

One area of fundamental research includes an attempt to discover the ultimate, smallest particle or particles. Even the Greek philosophers debated the existence of such particles. Some of the philosophers held that by a process of dividing, a sample could be reduced eventually to small particles which could not be again divided. Quantum-field theorists now believe that there are many such indivisible particles. In some respects the neutrino is as remarkable as anything that particle research has discovered. Elusive and mysterious, the **neutrino** (meaning: *little neutron*) *has no charge and apparently no mass*. It can travel through large thicknesses of lead and emerge without colliding with a single lead nucleus. These elusive properties of the neutrino make it the most difficult to detect of any of the elementary particles. The device with which the neutrino was discovered was nicknamed the "perhapsatron"—perhaps it would be able to find the neutrino.

PROPERTIES OF MATTER

A **property** *refers to the way in which materials affect our senses or our instruments, and also the way the materials behave under certain conditions.* In this chapter some very general properties of matter are discussed. Throughout the text, special properties, such as electrical conductivity or chemical activity, will be presented. Scientists spend much of their time observing, measuring, and devising methods of applying the properties of matter. For instance, geologists are interested in the properties of metals that determine their **occurrence**—*i.e., where they are found, in what form, and how abundantly.* Gold is found uncombined because it does not readily combine with other substances. This is a chemical property, specific for gold and several other metals. Usually, gold is found in the bottom of a pocket of sand or gravel because it is more dense than sand or gravel. In this case, we are dealing with a physical property of gold, i.e., its density. Gold can *be rolled or hammered into very thin sheets*. This characteristic of gold is another physical property, known as **malleability.**

A special property of the compound, methyl butyrate, is its pleasing odor which resembles the odor of pineapple. Odor is a chemical property. The odor of certain substances, called mercaptans, is so unpleasant and so powerful that it can still be detected after dilution with 50 billion times as much air.

GENERAL CHARACTERISTICS OF MATTER

Three general characteristics of matter are: (1) matter has inertia, (2) matter occupies space, and (3) matter can be influenced or caused to undergo chemical changes by energy.

Inertia

To illustrate the concept of inertia, let us consider three balls of the same size and appearance, say about the size of a basketball—one being made of lead, another of wood, and a third an ordinary basketball. The problem is to determine which of the balls has the most inertia. **Inertia** is defined as *that property of matter that causes it to resist any change in its state of motion.* A good hard kick with the foot should be sufficient to test the inertia in each case. Needless to say, the basketball would readily move a considerable distance, the ball made of wood would not move so far, and the net result of kicking the lead ball might be a broken toe, but little motion, because of its high inertia. See figure 4-1.

Mass is sometimes defined as *a measure of the inertia, or amount of matter.* The term, **weight,** is sometimes confused with the term,

mass, but *weight refers to the effect that gravity has on matter. Mass is a non-varying characteristic of matter*, whereas *weight will vary*, depending upon the particular gravitational field that is acting on it. Gravitational fields will be discussed in the next chapter.

In order to measure the mass of an object, it may be compared with a standard mass, called a "weight," by means of a device called a balance. The process is called "weighing," but actually it is the mass that is being determined, rather than the weight. The principle of the balance is that it involves the balancing of an unknown mass with a standard mass (a weight), using the principle of the see-saw.

A spring scale is used to measure weight directly, because it indicates the pull of gravity for an object. Since the pull of gravity will vary from place to place on the earth, the weights of an object obtained with a spring scale will also vary. Note, however, that the mass has not changed as the weight changed. On the other hand, if the mass of an object is measured with

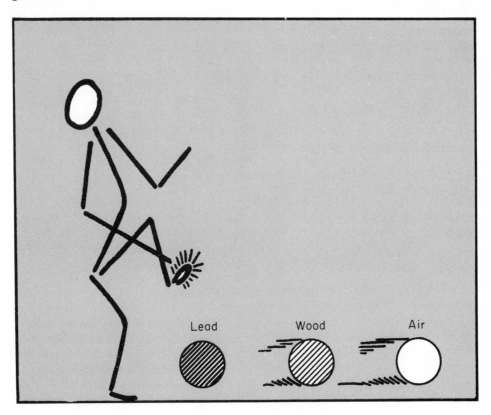

Figure 4–1. An illustration of inertia.

a balance, it will always be the same, regardless of where it is measured. The reason for this fact is that the gravitational attraction for the known mass (the weight) on one side of the balance is exactly the same as for the unknown mass on the other side of the balance.

Space

In a later chapter, it will be pointed out that the particles that make up the atom are separated by relatively large spaces. It is possible, therefore, to mix a pint of water with a pint of alcohol and have less than a quart of the mixture, because the water molecules have occupied some of the space between the alcohol molecules and vice versa. In no case, however, do two atoms of matter occupy the same space at the same time.

In the definition of matter given in the previous chapter, it was stated that matter is that which occupies space. This statement requires augmentation. Space, like matter and energy, is considered to be an ultimate reality. It has the following characteristics:

1. Space apparently extends endlessly. Science does not know of any limit or boundaries of space.

2. Space may be subdivided endlessly. There is no smallest particle of space.

3. Space may be either occupied or unoccupied by matter.

The Effect of Energy on Matter

The various effects of energy on matter will be introduced in the next chapter. An example is the effect of heat on water: water may be changed from a solid (ice) to a liquid or a gas by heating it.

THE ANALYSIS OF MATTER

Robert Boyle (1627–1691) introduced the term, *analysis*, which refers to the process of determining the composition of a sample of material by separating it into the various kinds of substances in the sample, thus making it possible to identify each substance. Robert Boyle defined elements as follows:

I mean by elements certain primitive and simple, or perfectly unmingled bodies; which not being made of any other bodies, or of one another, are the ingredients of which all those called perfectly mixt bodies are immediately compounded, and into which they are ultimately resolved.

Robert Boyle, early in his life, became a member of the *Invisible College,* a group of men who met together in England from time to time to discuss philosophical and scientific questions. They adopted the experimental and inductive method advocated by Francis Bacon:

being satisfied that there was no certain way of arriving at any competent knowledge unless they made a variety of experiments upon natural bodies.

This group of learned men was similar to other groups which sprang up at about the same time in Germany, France, and Italy. Later, these English scientists formed the Royal Society, one of the greatest scientific societies in existence today.

In the process of analysis, it will become apparent that some samples of materials are **heterogeneous,** i.e., *they are made of two or more different kinds of substances. Heterogeneous materials* are called **mixtures.** A mixture of sugar and salt, while it might appear to be **homogeneous**—i.e., *every portion having the same composition*—would be found to be heterogeneous if the grains were separated from each other and tasted.

If a sample of matter is found to be heterogeneous, the first problem in the analysis is to separate the mixture into its ingredients. As an illustration, consider a mixture of sand, sugar, and iron filings that has been prepared without any regard for proportions. By the use of a magnifying glass, a pair of forceps, and extraordinary patience, the particles of sand, sugar, and iron filings could be separated into individual piles. A simple approach would be to dissolve the sugar with water, since the sand and iron filings are not soluble in water. Then the water, containing the dissolved sugar, could be separated from the sand and iron filings by filtration. Upon evaporation of the water solution, sugar would be obtained as a residue. By use of a magnet, the iron filings could be pulled out of the mixture, because sand is not attracted as iron is by a magnet. In the separation of this mixture, such physical processes as dissolving and evaporation were used. Physical properties, such as magnetic attraction and light reflection, were likewise employed. The properties of the sand, sugar, and iron filings were the same after the separation as they were before they were mixed. **Physical processes (physical changes)** are *those processes which do not involve a change in the composition of the ingredients in a mixture.*

A **chemical process (chemical change)**, on the other hand, *does involve a change in the composition of a substance.* Examples of chemical processes are the burning of wood, the digestion of food, the baking of a cake, or the setting of cement. The study of chemistry is largely one of examining the chemical properties of matter, and the chemical changes that various types of matter will undergo.

In the analysis of a homogeneous sample, one might attempt to break it down into smaller portions. If this process were to be continued, it would be found that there would be obtained an ultimate, small particle, called a **molecule,** *which could not be broken down into a smaller particle and still retain the properties of the substance.* There are as many kinds of molecules as there are kinds of matter.

If the molecule is broken down into its component parts, new units of matter, the atoms, would be obtained. The **atom** is defined *as the smallest particle of an element which can exist and still retain the properties of the element.* An **element** is defined as a *substance that cannot be decomposed into a simpler substance by any nonnuclear chemical or physical process.*

Table 4-1 shows how matter may be classified on the basis of analysis.

ELEMENTS

If a sample of matter, composed of every kind of matter present in our universe, were to be analyzed, millions of different kinds of compounds would be found. If the molecules of these compounds were to be broken down into atoms, only 89 different kinds of atoms would be obtained, because all compounds are composed of different combinations of these basic 89 kinds of atoms, called elements.

TABLE 4-1

A CLASSIFICATION OF MATTER

MATTER—that which occupies space

SUBSTANCE	Homogeneous—contains only one kind of particle throughout. Inseparable into component parts by physical processes.
ELEMENT	Cannot be decomposed into simple substances by any non-nuclear process.
COMPOUND	Contains elements in a fixed ratio. Can be separated into component parts by chemical processes.
MIXTURE	Heterogeneous—does not have a fixed composition. Usually, separable into component parts by physical processes.
COARSE MIXTURE	Particles of such a size that they can be seen with the unaided eye.
COLLOID	Aggregates of molecules, where particle size is larger than a single molecule.
FINE DISPERSION	Aggregates of a large number of molecules. Larger than colloidal particles.
SOLUTION	Homogeneous mixture of molecules. Particle size is that of a single molecule.

To the list of basic elements, atomic physicists have added a number of artificial or man-made elements, making a total of 103 different elements as of 1964.

Of the 89 naturally occurring elements, only about two dozen are used to a very large extent. Table 4-2 shows that about 99 per cent of the terrestrial matter (elements making up the earth's crust, water, and air) is made up of 12 elements.

TABLE 4-2

OCCURRENCE OF ELEMENTS IN THE EARTH'S CRUST (percentage by weight)

Oxygen	50.02	Potassium	2.28
Silicon	25.80	Magnesium	2.08
Aluminum	7.30	Hydrogen	0.95
Iron	4.18	Titanium	0.43
Calcium	3.32	Chlorine	0.20
Sodium	2.36	Carbon	0.18

The number of elements which occur in appreciable amounts in the human body is also quite small. Table 4-3 shows the approximate percentages of the elements found in the human body.

TABLE 4-3

THE COMPOSITION OF THE HUMAN BODY (percentage by weight)

Oxygen	65.0	Potassium	0.35
Carbon	18.0	Sulfur	0.25
Hydrogen	10.0	Sodium	0.15
Nitrogen	3.0	Chlorine	0.15
Calcium	2.0	Magnesium	0.05
Phosphorus	1.1	Iron	0.004

Source: modified from H. C. Sherman and C. S. Langford, "Essentials of Nutrition," third edition, The Macmillan Company, 1951.

Naming the Elements

Many of the names of the elements were either given to them by the ancients, or were derived from ancient languages. For example, hydrogen is derived from the Greek words meaning water-producing, and chlorine comes from the Greek term for yellowish green, the color of chlorine. Some elements were named after the localities in which they were discovered: the name of strontium came from Strontian, Scotland.

COMPOUNDS

It is not always easy to tell whether a substance is an element or a compound. For example, it is very difficult to decompose sand (white quartz) by heating it, and consequently one might consider quartz sand to be an element. Methods have been found, however, by which sand can be decomposed into its two constituent elements, silicon and oxygen, thus proving that sand is a compound. In 1790, Lavoisier drew up a list of substances that he considered to be elements. This list included elements such as sulfur, carbon, and iron, but it also included eight substances that are now recognized to be compounds. Among these were sand and compounds of oxygen with certain metals such as calcium and magnesium —which, like sand, could not be decomposed by any method known to Lavoisier.

The rearranging of atoms in molecules, the decomposing of molecules, or the making of new molecules belong to the realm of chemistry.

MIXTURES

Mixtures are classified according to the size of the particles into coarse mixtures, fine dispersions, colloidal mixtures, and solutions (molecular mixtures). In 1861, Thomas Graham (1805–1869) found that certain substances in a solution would pass through parchment paper, while others would not. *Those substances that passed through the membrane* he called **crystalloids** and *those that did not* he called **colloids.** The properties of colloids are more the result of their **size** than of their **chemical nature.**

A characteristic of colloids can be demonstrated by the **Tyndall effect,** named after the eminent Irish scientist, John Tyndall (1820–1893). He observed that *the path of a beam of light becomes visible when it is passed through a colloidal mixture,* similar to the illumination of the path of light from a motion picture projector as it passes through dust or tobacco smoke. Figure 4-2 shows a photograph of the Tyndall effect taken in King Solomon's Temple, Jerusalem.

In 1827—long before Graham coined the word *colloid*—another Scotch scientist, Robert

Figure 4–2.   The Tyndall effect.

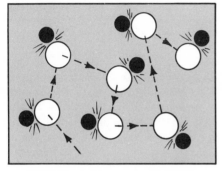

Figure 4–3.   The Brownian movement.

Brown (1773–1858), noticed peculiar movements of pollen grains in water when he examined them with a microscope. *This constant zigzag motion,* characteristic of colloids, was later called **the Brownian movement,** in honor of the man who first observed it. *This motion has been attributed to the bombardment of colloidal particles by molecules,* and it has been used as evidence for the existence of molecules.

THE MICRO WORLD OF MATTER

The particles in a coarse mixture are large enough to be seen with the unaided eye, or at least by the use of an ordinary microscope; but when it comes to colloids, the particles are too small to be seen with an ordinary microscope. However, they may be made visible by an **ultramicroscope,** *which employs special lighting to make them visible.*

By using a beam of electrons which may be focused by means of electromagnets, magnification in the range of 100,000 times is possible with the electron microscope, as compared with a range of about 200 times for the ordinary microscope. Figure 4-3 shows a photograph of some very large molecules taken with an electron microscope.

Figure 4–4. A photograph of large molecules of deoxyribonucleic acid (DNA) taken with an electron microscope. The white sphere is a bit of polystyrene used as a measuring standard. (Courtesy, Julius Marmur and Paul Doty)

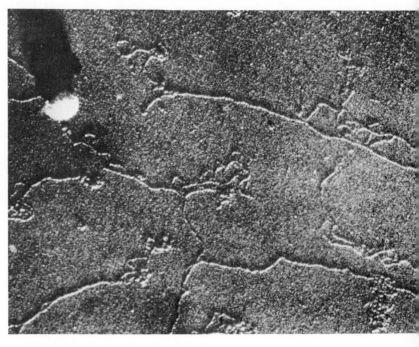

Figure 4–5. A photograph of the atoms of a tungsten crystal taken with a field-ion microscope. Magnification of this reproduction is approximately 2,800,000 times. (Courtesy, Erwin W. Müller and The Pennsylvania State University)

Another more powerful microscope, with a magnification of approximately 2.8 million times—the field-ion microscope—was used to photograph the actual atoms of a tungsten crystal as shown in Figure 4-4.

HOW SMALL ARE MOLECULES?

The British physicist, F. W. Aston, provided the following illustration of the size of molecules:

If you make a hole in an ordinary evacuated light bulb which would allow molecules of air to pass in at a rate of one million per second, it would take about a hundred million years before the bulb would be filled.

SUMMARY

Space is an ultimate reality. It extends endlessly, can be subdivided endlessly, and may or may not be occupied by matter.

Properties of matter refer to the ways in which matter affects our senses or our instru-ments, and how one kind of matter interacts with other kinds of matter.

Characteristics of Matter

Matter has three general characteristics: (1) it occupies space, (2) it possesses inertia, and (3) it can be affected by energy to bring about a change in physical or chemical prop-erties. Mass is a quantitative measure of in-ertia. Inertia is the property of matter that causes it to resist any change in the state of motion. Weight is the measure of the gravita-tional attraction for matter. Mass is measured with a balance and does not change. Weight is measured by a spring scale, and changes with changes in gravitational attraction from place to place.

Classification of Matter

Matter may be classified as to composition as heterogeneous (mixtures) and homogene-ous (elements or compounds). It may also be classified as to the size of particles. A mixture is classified according to the size of the parti-cles as coarse, fine dispersion, colloid, or solu-tion.

Processes

A physical process does not involve a change in composition, whereas a chemical process does involve a change in composition.

Study Questions

1. DEFINE: property, chemical property, physi-cal property, physical process, chemical pro-cess, inertia, element, compound, mixture, weight, mass, atom, molecule, analysis, space, solution, colloid.
2. Differentiate between a solution and a sub-stance.
3. List the characteristics of space.
4. How may inertia be measured?
5. Compare the weight and mass of an object. Under what conditions will they be the same? Under what conditions will they dif-fer from each other?
6. What device is used to measure mass?
7. Classify matter as to composition.
8. Classify matter as to the size of particles.
9. Differentiate between physical and chemical processes.
10. What are the three general characteristics of matter?

CHAPTER 5

An Introduction to Energy

Energy will do anything that can be done in this world; and no talents, no circumstances, no opportunities, will make a two–legged animal a man without it.

GOETHE

INTRODUCTION

Anthropologists tell us that if there has been a single thing that has liberated man from his animal heritage, it has been his conquest of energy. Since the time he lost his mortal fear of fire and made it work for him by providing warmth, by cooking his food, and by providing a natural shield to place between his cave and the beasts on the outside, he has been using energy other than that generated by his own body. In the United States, we are utilizing about eighty times as much energy as our bodies could supply.

The word, energy, creates a strange paradox for scientists. It is a term used to describe something that no one knows very much about. Yet it is a term which has universal usage. First-grade youngsters are described as bundles of energy. Certain foods, such as pastries, are said to be rich in calories (a measurement of heat energy). An atomic bomb is noted for the tremendous amount of energy that it releases. Still we do not know what energy is.

In Chapter 3 it was suggested that energy is an ultimate reality, and that Science cannot hope to resolve it into anything simpler. However, Science can determine the properties of energy, and can study the transformations of one form of energy into another.

It was also mentioned in the previous chapters that the concept of energy is a "newcomer" in Science as compared to the concept of matter. The early Greek philosophers reasoned that everything tends to find and settle in a "natural place." They were not concerned with the force or activity which directed the object to its "natural place." Aristotle was the first philosopher to be concerned about such a force, and he suggested that there was an "unmoved mover" who kept things in the heavens from falling to the earth. He was undoubtedly concerned with the problem of what keeps the moon in its orbit.

Galileo helped to lay the foundations for the study of energy as a result of his fascination with the action of a pendulum. Born during the year of Galileo's death, Sir Isaac Newton (1642–1727) placed the study of energy on the footing that has continued down to the present time. Surprisingly, the laws of Newton have stood the test of time, and are as valid in light of present-day scientific knowledge as they were when Newton formulated them.

FORCE AND MOTION

The concept of force is a very old one, and it makes itself known to us constantly. The force of a hurricane or an earthquake is tremendous. The human body can exert forces, varying from the playing of a piano to lifting it. **Force** is defined as: *any influence which can produce, or tends to produce a change in the motion of a body*. The dictionary defines force as *that which produces or tends to produce change*.

The phrase "change in the motion of a body" has several meanings. For example, let

31

us observe a pitcher during a baseball game. During the windup the ball remains in the pitcher's hand, and the motion of the ball is being increased from a standstill (zero relative velocity) to a velocity of 100 miles per hour. This is the velocity attained by a "fast" ball thrown by a major-league baseball pitcher. **Velocity** means two things, the *speed* of the ball (100 miles per hour) and the *direction* in which it is traveling (toward home plate). *If one is concerned only with the rate of travel,* **speed** would be the proper term.

The moment the ball leaves the pitcher's hand, it begins slowing down, because of the resistance of the air to the passage of the ball. Also, as the ball travels through the air, it will drop slightly because of the pull of gravity. This illustration represents three primary changes in the motion of an object—**acceleration,** *when the rate of motion is being increased;* **deceleration** (or negative acceleration), when *the rate of motion is being decreased;* and **curvature,** when *the direction of motion is being changed.*

WORK

The term, work, is another scientific word that is often misused in everyday conversation. If one should attempt to pick up a piano he would say that he was doing work even if he could not move the piano. In preparing for an examination a student would say that he is doing mental work. According to the scientific definition of work, work was not accomplished in either of the two cases mentioned above, because nothing was moved. The definition of **work** requires that *an object be moved by a force.* It is important to note that both *a force and a distance are involved.* If either one is absent, no work has been accomplished. Stated mathematically, **work** is *proportional to force times distance.*

It is also important to note that *there is no time element involved in* the definition of **work.** A piano that is moved up a flight of stairs requires the same amount of work regardless of the speed of the motion. If one is interested in the *rate of doing work,* then he is concerned with what is known as **power.**

Work and power are discussed in more detail in Chapters 22 and 23.

THE CLASSIFICATION OF THE FORMS OF ENERGY

The classification of the forms of matter as presented in the previous chapter proceeded by a logical series of steps, but energy does not lend itself as readily to logical classification. The difficulties arise primarily from the very nature of energy—its forms tend to overlap. The following table presents the basic subdivisions of the forms of energy that are most common. There are other forms of energy concerning which so little is known that it would be impossible to fit them into a scheme of classification. Each form of energy will be discussed briefly in the remainder of this chapter, which is intended to serve only as an introduction to energy. These forms of energy will be discussed in detail in later chapters in this text.

THE FORMS OF ENERGY

I. Potential Energy
   A. Arising from an object being placed in a potential field,
      1. gravitational
      2. electrical
      3. magnetic
   B. Arising from the composition of matter,
      1. chemical
      2. nuclear
   C. Arising from elastic deformations
II. Kinetic energy
III. Mechanical energy
IV. Radiant energy

Energy Arising from the Placing of an Object in a Field (Potential Energy)—If a person should drop a bowling ball on his toe, he might blame the ball or his own clumsiness. But a scientist would not blame the bowling ball. He would blame the law of gravity, which is responsible for so many of our everyday mishaps. The bowling ball merely acted in accordance with natural laws, and functioned as a material object should, when placed in a gravitational field. Similarly, every material object is influenced by gravitational fields, and at the same time it provides a gravitational field of its own. This concept, while very revolutionary, holds for all material objects—from the smallest subatomic particle to the largest star.

The term, field, is a common word in physical science, and it warrants additional explanation. A **field** is a *portion of space surrounding a source of potential energy, and throughout which the force of attraction (or repulsion) is governed by the inverse square law.* The source might be one that gives rise to a gravitational field, a magnetic field, or an electrical field. While the exact method of conveying the energy from the source to the object placed in the field is not known, it is well established that the strength of the field, or intensity, is greatest nearest the source and falls off rapidly as one moves away from the source.

This "diminishing of energy" can be shown by the operation of a paint sprayer shown in Figure 5-1. Issuing from the nozzle is a certain amount of paint. For example, suppose that one ounce of paint is sprayed per minute and that the paint is sprayed on a piece of cardboard one foot square, held one foot from the nozzle. It is assumed that all of the paint that comes from the nozzle will be sprayed on the cardboard. As the distance is increased to two feet, i.e., twice as far, the sprayer will cover an area of four square feet. The amount of paint sprayed will still be the same, one ounce per minute, but the amount of paint on each square foot is now only one-fourth as much. If the distance is increased to three feet, the paint deposited on each square foot will be one ninth as much as in the first case. These observations can be stated mathematically in the form of the **"inverse square law"**: The amount of paint per square foot will *vary inversely as the square of the distance from the source.*

The inverse square law applies to gravitational, electrical, and magnetic fields. In a **gravitational field,** the *force of gravity is directly proportional to the masses, but inversely proportional to the square of the distances between any two objects.* Similarly, in electrical and magnetic fields, the force is inversely proportional to the square of the distance.

As the distance separating two objects increases, say a thousand times, the total force between them may become exceedingly small —practically nonexistent—but the force never becomes zero for a field obeying the inverse square law. Therefore, astronomers conclude that no matter what distance separates the constituents of the universe, every part is under some influence of these types of potential-energy fields.

Returning to the bowling ball, in which the toe was the instrument which measured the

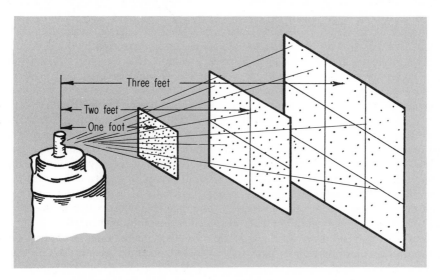

Figure 5–1. The paint sprayer demonstrates the inverse square law.

amount of energy resulting from releasing the ball in the gravitational field of the earth, the bowling ball had its own gravitational field. As a result of its gravitational field, the bowling ball attracted the earth toward it. Since the amount of motion of both the bowling ball and the earth is inversely proportional to their respective masses, the bowling ball did most of the moving, while the earth, for all practical purposes, remained unmoved. From the definition of energy—the capacity to do work—an object located in a potential-energy field could perform work if it were free to move as the forces of the field dictate, but the moving is not necessary; only the *possibility of moving need exist*, insofar as **potential energy** is concerned.

Each of the three potential energy sources will be discussed in later chapters in this text.

Chemical and Nuclear Energy—Forms of Potential Energy—By virtue of the arrangement of the atoms in a molecule, the molecule possesses a certain amount of potential energy. By causing a chemical reaction to take place, a rearrangement of the atoms within the molecules will result, and some of the potential energy may be changed into some other form of energy—such as heat or light. In other chemical reactions, energy may be absorbed and stored in the molecules in the form of potential energy. Some molecules, like those of trinitrotoluene (TNT), possess large amounts of potential energy, which may be released violently. In some instances, more than one kind of molecule is involved. In every case, *the change in arrangement of atoms within molecules is the result of a gain or loss of potential energy*. When a jet of natural gas is burned, the molecules of methane (natural gas) and the molecules of oxygen (from the air) undergo changes. The resulting molecules of carbon dioxide and water contain less chemical energy than the methane and oxygen molecules contained, and the potential energy thus lost is changed into heat and light.

A chemical reaction resulting in the release of energy may be more subtle. For example, the rusting of iron releases small amounts of energy very slowly. The iron and oxygen molecules contain more chemical potential energy than the iron oxide (rust) molecules formed.

Energy transformations in which various forms of energy are changed into chemical potential energy are very common. Plants convert water and carbon dioxide molecules into carbohydrate molecules, in which the sugars and starches formed contain much more chemical energy than the water and carbon dioxide from which they are formed. The source of this energy is sunlight.

Nuclear energy, on the other hand, *is the energy liberated when a portion of the nuclei of atoms are changed into energy*—i.e., in which mass is changed into energy. Chapters 62 and 63 will take up the study of nuclear energy.

Kinetic Energy—Energy of Matter in Motion

In contrast with potential energy, **kinetic energy** *requires that a material object be moving.* Kinetic energy is possessed by any moving object, no matter what the size of the object or the reason for its motion. The object might be reacting to a force received, for example, a ball hit by a baseball bat; or it may be a falling body, reacting to a gravitational field. Kinetic energy will be discussed in the next chapter.

Mechanical Energy—The Sum of Potential Energy and Kinetic Energy

Galileo was the first man to put the study of energy on an experimental basis. He became interested in energy (according to legend), while being distracted by the rhythmic to-and-fro motion of a hanging lamp. For a timing device, Galileo used his own pulse beat; but it occurred to him that a pendulum could serve as a timing device. He made a pendulum and timed its swing, noting the varying positions and the changing velocity of the pendulum. Thus he was unknowingly examining the mechanical energy of the pendulum. In the drawings in Figure 5-2, notice the changing amounts of potential and kinetic energies, and note also that the sum of the two kinds of energy remains unchanged.

Another good example of the relationship between potential and kinetic energies is in the dropping of an object as shown in Figure 5-3.

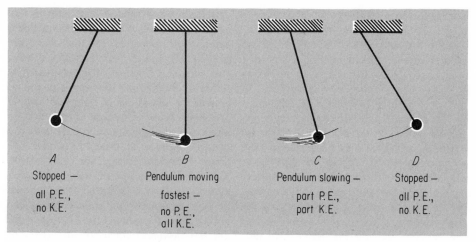

Figure 5–2. The pendulum. Note that the sum of the kinetic and potential energies remains the same.

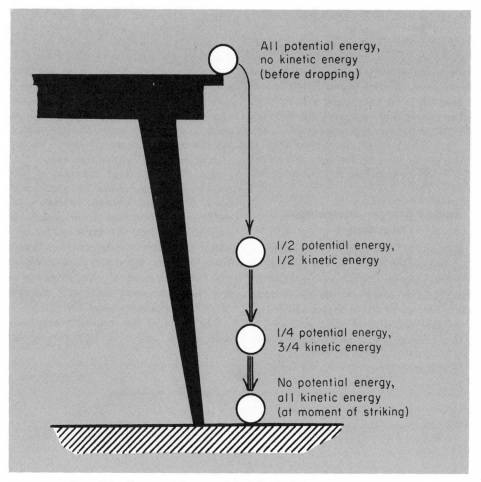

Figure 5–3. The potential energy of the falling ball changes to kinetic energy.

When the mechanical energy of an ordinary system is measured after the system has been in operation for a time, there is a decrease in the amount of mechanical energy. The pendulum in Figure 5-2 never returns to the same height unless additional energy is applied. A ball will not continue to bounce at the same height. The reason for the decreases in motion is **friction.** While in some cases friction is advantageous, in others it is a hindrance. Engineers are constantly trying to find new methods of reducing friction by making better bearings, better lubricants, or by reducing the number of moving parts. It is impossible to eliminate friction completely. However, astronomical, atomic, and nuclear systems do not experience friction.

Friction *causes some of the mechanical energy to be transformed into heat energy.* Even a rubber ball will become a little warmer after being used in a vigorous game. But, should a perfectly elastic ball ever be made, mechanical energy would be conserved, and the ball would bounce to exactly the same height each time. We know that this is impossible. However, it is considered that material particles, atomic and molecular in size, are capable of achieving perfectly elastic collisions. They rebound with the same energy as they had before the collision, and apparently they can continue to collide and rebound endlessly.

Radiant Energy—Energy Apart from Matter

Radiation is considered to *represent a method of energy travel, i.e., a method of transferring energy from one location to another.* Thus the energy of the sun is transferred to the earth by radiation. Radiation does not give rise to itself. For instance, the light that reaches one from an incandescent light bulb when lighted originates in the filament of the bulb. The heat from a fire originates from a chemical reaction of a fuel with oxygen. The energy from certain sources, radiated to specific neural receptors—such as the retina of the eye, or the nerves in the skin—creates the sensations of light and heat. There are many types of radiant energy that do not affect neural receptors; therefore, we are completely unaware of them. Examples of such types of radiant energy are radio waves and X rays. The concept of wave formation, by which energy is transferred from one place to another, is basic to an understanding of radiant energy. Familiar types of wave motion are the rhythmic waves of an ocean, or the waves formed when a stone is thrown into a still pool of water. Figure 5-4 shows a cross-section of a wave. The *most important property of waves* is their **length.** The wave length may be extremely short, a thousandth of a billionth of a billionth of an inch in length, or it could have a length of half of the distance across the United States. It is important to note that as the wave length is changed, however little, the characteristics of the wave will also be changed. For example, small differences in the wave length of light may cause the different sensations of color. This concept will be discussed later in the text.

One of the unifying concepts of physical science is the concept that the great variety of kinds of **radiant energy** (waves)—such as radio waves, light, heat waves, gamma waves, etc.—*are basically the same insofar as their nature and mode of transmission is concerned. Their primary difference is in wave length.* The complete array of wave lengths is called the "electromagnetic spectrum," an example of which is shown on page 376.

The speed of any radiant energy wave is that of the speed of light, approximately

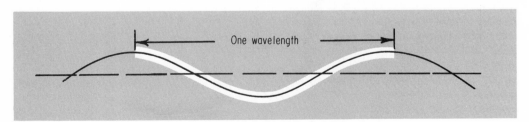

One wavelength

Figure 5–4. A cross section of a wave.

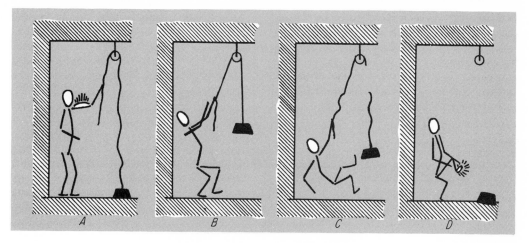

Figure 5–5. Some energy transformations.

186,282 miles per second. This speed is the speed of light in space (i.e., a perfect vacuum), but it varies considerably in different media such as air, water, or glass. The speed of light is almost incomprehensible. It is so great that light could travel around the earth seven times in one second.

It will be noticed that a discussion of sound waves is conspicuously absent from this brief discussion of energy. This does not mean that sound waves are less important than other types of energy, but rather that there is no need to introduce them at this time in order to understand the chapters which follow. Sound waves differ from electromagnetic waves in that they are vibrations in matter. Sound waves are discussed in Chapters 38, 53, 54, 55, and 56.

THE PROPERTIES OF ENERGY

Energy has been previously defined as the ability to do work. Energy and work are expressed by the same units.

An important **general property of energy** is *the capacity of one form of energy to be transformed into another form.* Figure 5-5 shows the following series of energy transformations: (a) Chemical energy is being changed into kinetic energy in the muscle. (b) Kinetic energy is being transformed into potential energy. (c) The rope breaks, and potential energy is changed back to kinetic energy. (d) Kinetic energy is transformed

into heat energy as the cement block strikes the floor (and the toe). In this case, again, the broken toe is the measure of the amount of energy transformed.

Another **general property** of all forms of energy is *that the law of conservation of energy is obeyed in all energy transformations.* This law is a part of the more general law of the conservation of mass-energy discussed in Chapter 3. If one is concerned with energy apart from the change of matter into energy or vice versa, the **law of conservation of energy** states that *in all non-nuclear energy transformations the total amount of energy is constant, regardless of the kind of energy transformation.* As in the discussion of the properties of matter, energy likewise has many **specific properties,** *which differentiate one form of energy from another.* These particular properties of the different forms of energy will be discussed in various portions of this text.

SUMMARY

Energy can be classified as (1) potential, (2) kinetic, and (3) radiant.

Potential energy is classified as (1) field energy (2) chemical and nuclear energy, and (3) elastic.

Potential fields include (1) gravitational, (2) electrical, and (3) magnetic.

A field is a portion of space surrounding an energy source, throughout which the force of attraction or repulsion is governed by the inverse square law, which states that the force varies inversely as the square of the distance from the source.

Energy may be changed from one form into another without gain or loss in all nonnuclear energy transformations.

Study Questions

1. DEFINE: energy, force, work, motion, acceleration, deceleration, potential energy, field, wave length, kinetic energy, radiant energy, chemical energy, nuclear energy, mechanical energy, power, speed, velocity.
2. Distinguish between force and work.
3. Distinguish between speed and velocity.
4. Show how the inverse square law works in the operation of a paint sprayer.
5. How far does a gravitational field extend?
6. Classify the various forms of energy.
7. How does sound energy differ from electromagnetic waves?
8. Explain the energy changes which are illustrated by a child's swing.

The Kinetic-Molecular Theory

Nothing in Nature is more ancient than motion, and the volumes that the philosophers have compiled about it are neither few nor small; yet have I discovered that there are many things of interest about it, that have hitherto been unperceived.

GALILEO

The value of any working theory depends upon the number of experimental facts it serves to correlate, and upon its power of suggesting new lines of work.

LORD RUTHERFORD

INTRODUCTION

It was not until the kinetic-molecular theory was advanced about one hundred years ago, that many puzzling questions could be answered concerning the behavior of gases, liquid and solids, and the changes from one of these states to another. The **kinetic-molecular theory** *postulates that matter exists in the form of tiny, invisible particles, called molecules, moving at speeds which depend upon their temperature.*

THE KINETIC-MOLECULAR THEORY

The kinetic-molecular theory, like any theory, consists of a number of basic assumptions as follows:

The Existence of Molecules

Evidence for the existence of molecules was presented in the previous section.

The Size of Molecules

Molecules are very small, too small to be seen with a light microscope.

The Masses of Molecules

The masses of molecules, like their sizes, are very small.

The Motion of Molecules

The basic law of **kinetic energy** states that: *kinetic energy is equal to one half of the product of the mass of the molecules times the velocity squared.* This is a technical way of saying that at a given temperature, molecules of larger mass move more slowly than molecules of smaller mass, and vice versa.

The speed of molecules depends upon their absolute temperature.

Molecular motion is frictionless; molecules must be frictionless, because their motion is heat, and heat cannot produce more heat.

Collisions Between Molecules

Molecules of gases very frequently collide with each other, the duration of a collision being negligible as compared with the time interval between two collisions. A hydrogen molecule, traveling at a speed of one mile per second, travels an average distance of only 1/60,000 centimeter before hitting another hydrogen molecule. As a result of the collisions between fast-moving and slower-moving molecules, a given volume of a gas will eventually acquire a uniform temperature. **Molecules are perfectly elastic.** Their collisions would result in no change in the kinetic energy of molecules traveling at the same speed, if their masses were the same.

Ideal Gases versus Real Gases—If the above assumptions were all that there is to the kinetic-molecular theory, the gas laws would be found to be exact laws. However, the gas laws are only approximate laws, because they apply to real gases. Ideal gases do not exist. Real gases require the following additional assumptions for the kinetic-molecular theory:

Attractive Forces between Molecules

There are attractive forces between the molecules, which are stronger than the forces that would be the result of gravitational forces. These forces are stronger at close range and become weaker at greater distances.

The Finite Volumes of Molecules

Molecules have a finite volume apart from the space that they occupy. In gases at low pressures the actual, finite volume of the molecules, compared to the space occupied by the molecules, is practically negligible; but in the case of liquids and solids, where the molecules occupy much less space, the finite volume of the molecules becomes significant.

In liquids and solids, the molecules are so close to each other that practically all of the space occupied by the liquid or solid represents the finite volumes of the molecules.

THE EXPLANATION OF THE CHARACTERISTICS OF GASES BY THE KINETIC-MOLECULAR THEORY

The Pressure of Gases—Boyle's Law

A characteristic of gases is that they may be squeezed into a smaller volume by applying pressure, as shown in Figure 6-1.

When one increases the pressure in an automobile tire, the volume of the tire remains about the same, but the volume of the gas that is squeezed into the tire is decreased. Robert Boyle expressed this characteristic of gases in the law that bears his name: *At constant temperature the volume of a given quantity of a gas is inversely proportional to the pressure.*

Like the other gas laws, this law is not exact because it does not take into consideration the actual, finite volume of the molecules. Furthermore, it does not account for the fact that the attraction between the molecules results in a small decrease in volume.

In terms of the kinetic-molecular theory, pressure represents the bombardment of the walls of a container by molecules, as shown in Figure 6-2.

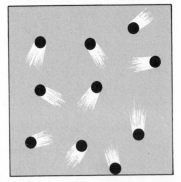
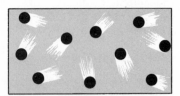

Figure 6–1. Boyle's law as explained by the kinetic molecular theory. As the volume of the container is decreased there are more molecules in a given volume and, therefore, the pressure on the walls of the container is increased. Expansibility and compressibility are the result of the facts that molecules of gases are relatively far apart and have a high velocity.

If the number of molecules in a given container is increased, the pressure is increased.

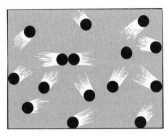

Figure 6-2. The pressure of a gas is the result of the bombardment of the walls of a container by molecules.

The Expansion of Gases—Charles' Law

Jacques Alexander Caesar Charles (1746–1823) observed that gases expand with an increase in temperature. This observation was stated in the form of the law named after him as follows: *Under constant pressure the volume of a gas is very nearly proportional to the absolute temperature.* A corollary of this law is that under constant volume the pressure of a gas is very nearly proportional to the absolute temperature.

An increase in the temperature of a given volume of gas increases the pressure, because the kinetic energy of the molecules is increased. They hit the walls of the container more often, and with increased speeds. Charles' Law, like Boyle's Law, is not an exact law.

The Diffusibility of Gases

The diffusibility of gases is expressed by *Graham's Law.* Thomas Graham stated that: **Gases diffuse at rates which are inversely proportional to the square roots of their densities.** Since the kinetic energy of molecules depends upon their masses and velocities, it is easy to understand that the definition of kinetic energy could be derived from Graham's Law, or vice versa. In simple terms, the law states that *light molecules travel faster than heavy molecules.*

Gases will diffuse through other gases just as if the other gases were not present, because the molecules are so far apart. ·

Dalton's Law of Partial Pressures

The pressure of a mixture of gases is equal to the sum of the pressures of each of the gases according to Dalton's Law, discovered by John Dalton (1766–1844), who originated the atomic theory as a result of his investigations of gases. If a given amount of a gas were to be placed in a given container it would exert a pressure on the walls of the container. Additional gases added to the container would occupy the spaces between the original molecules, and each gas would thus add molecules, which would increase the bombardment on the walls of the container.

The Liquefaction of Gases

The gas laws do not explain why gases will liquefy when compressed and cooled. An ideal gas would remain gaseous right down to absolute zero, but actual gases liquefy when compressed and cooled because of the attraction between the molecules, which becomes relatively more important as their kinetic energy is decreased. These attractive forces must differ for different kinds of molecules because some gases are much more readily liquefied than others.

An increase in pressure makes it possible to liquefy gases without cooling them so much as would otherwise be necessary. This is because the attractive forces between the molecules increase as the molecules are brought closer to each other by increasing the pressure.

THE EXPLANATION OF THE CHARACTERISTICS OF LIQUIDS BY THE KINETIC-MOLECULAR THEORY

Density

Liquids are much more dense than gases, because their molecules are much closer to each other. The term, **dense,** or **density, refers** to *the mass per unit volume.* As a result of the attractive forces between the molecules, liquids maintain a constant volume at a given temperature and pressure, but these attractive forces are not sufficient to cause the liquids to have a fixed shape. As a result, they take the shape of the container in which they are placed. Liquids are only very slightly compressible because there is very little space between the molecules in liquids.

Surface Tension

The attractive forces between molecules of liquids also accounts for their **surface tension,** which may be defined as *the unequal attraction of the molecules at the surface of a liquid.* See Figure 6-3. Surface tension will

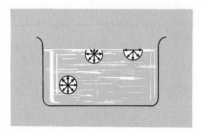

Figure 6–3. The unequal attractions between the molecules within the liquid and those at the surface is the cause of surface tension.

cause liquids to rise in capillary tubes if the liquids wet the surface. The extent of the rise can serve as a measure of surface tension.

Viscosity

Liquids exhibit **viscosity,** which is *the resistance to flow of a liquid.* As a rule, the more dense the liquid, the greater is the viscosity. **Viscosity** *represents a measure of the attraction between the molecules within a liquid.* It can be determined by measuring the time required by various liquids to flow through a given orifice or tube at a given temperature. The viscosity of a liquid decreases with an increase in temperature, because the increased kinetic energy of the molecules enables them to partially overcome the attractive forces. For the same reason, a rise in temperature will increase the volume of a liquid.

THE EXPLANATION OF THE CHARACTERISTICS OF SOLIDS BY THE KINETIC-MOLECULAR THEORY

The **chief characteristics of solids** is that *they have both a definite volume and a*

definite shape. They are very slightly compressible. Their volumes may generally be increased by increases in temperature, but only to a small extent.

The molecules of crystalline solids are held together in regular patterns characteristic of different substances. Crystalline solids have a definite, sharp melting point, because a definite temperature is required to overcome the forces which hold the crystals together.

It is because of the shape of water molecules, that solid ice crystals exhibit forces which tend to keep the molecules apart. The density of ice is therefore slightly less than that of water near the freezing point. The consequence is that ice floats.

THE EXPLANATION OF PHYSICAL PROCESSES BY THE KINETIC-MOLECULAR THEORY

Figure 6-4 shows the relationships between the chief physical processes. For example, it shows that energy is liberated when a gas is changed into a liquid or a solid. This energy is the kinetic energy of the molecules, which must be removed by cooling in order to effect

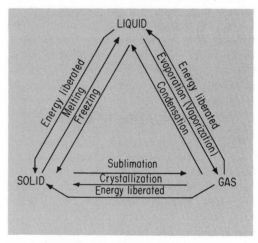

Figure 6–4. The chief physical processes.

the change. In all of these physical processes, the changes are produced by temperature changes, which increase or decrease the kinetic energy of the molecules. Thus solid, liquid, and gaseous states differ chiefly in regard to how closely the molecules are

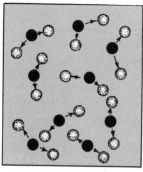 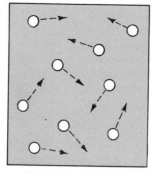 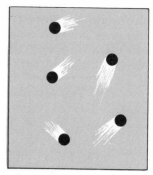

Molecules of a solid vibrate about fixed positions.

Molecules of a liquid move about freely.

Molecules of a gas are far apart and move rapidly.

Figure 6–5. Molecular motion in solids, liquids, and gases.

packed, how great their attractive forces are, and how much a given change in temperature affects the kinetic energy of their molecules. Figure 6-5 shows graphically the difference between the solid, liquid, and gaseous states.

Evaporation

Evaporation takes place below the boiling point of a liquid, because of the differences in the kinetic energy of the molecules in the liquid. Some of the molecules with higher kinetic energy are able to break away from the attractive forces of the other molecules at the surface. Evaporation takes place more rapidly on a warm day, because more molecules attain sufficient kinetic energy to escape. A windy day will dry clothes faster than they would dry on a quiet day, because the wind carries the molecules away from the surface of the water as they escape, and thus prevents the atmos-

phere above the liquid from becoming saturated.

On a damp (humid) day, water evaporates less rapidly than on a dry day, because there are more water molecules in the atmosphere above the liquid water on a damp day than on a dry day. When the **relative humidity is 100 percent**—i.e., *when the atmosphere is completely saturated with water vapor*—just as many molecules return to the surface of the water as leave it, as shown in Figure 6-7.

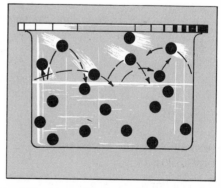

Figure 6–7. Evaporation in a 'closed container soon reaches a state of equilibrium in which the number of molecules leaving the surface of the liquid is balanced by the number of molecules returning to the surface.

Thus there is an equilibrium between the processes of condensation and evaporation.

BOILING AND BOILING POINT

When liquids are heated, evaporation takes place, but the molecules in the air retard the

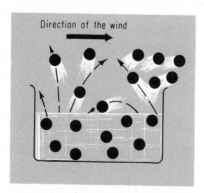

Figure 6–6. Evaporation of molecules into the atmosphere. Note that the wind carries most of the molecules away from the surface of the liquid.

process because of collisions of the escaped molecules with the molecules of the atmosphere, as shown in Figure 6-8. If one continues to heat the liquid, the rate of evaporation is gradually increased until the liquid begins to boil. The vaporization then con-

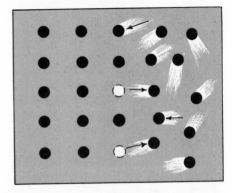

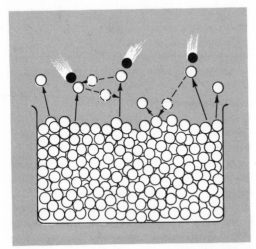

Figure 6–8. The molecules above the liquid (black) strike molecules escaping from the liquid (white) and cause some of them to return to the liquid, thus retarding evaporation.

Figure 6–9. Melting and freezing. At equilibrium, as many molecules leave the solid crystal as return in a given time.

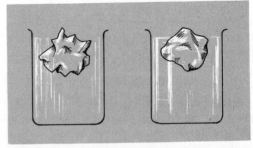

Figure 6–10. Evidence for the equilibrium between the solid and liquid states at the freezing point of water. If the temperature is maintained at 0° C. the jagged piece of ice will become smooth, but the weight will remain the same.

tinues at a rate that depends upon the amount of heat applied, but the temperature does not rise. *When the tendency of the molecules of a liquid to escape just exceeds the atmospheric pressure,* the liquid **boils.** *The temperature required to just start the boiling is called the* **boiling point.**

LE CHATELIER'S LAW OF EQUILIBRIA

The equilibria between different physical changes were explained by Henri Louis Le Chatelier (1850–1936). For example, if heat is applied to a mixture of ice and water, some ice will melt but the temperature will not be changed. Similarly, when heat is removed, some water will freeze but as long as some water remains, the temperature will not change. Figure 6-9 shows a molecular picture of the equilibrium between ice and water, which represents a **dynamic equilibrium,** i.e., *a balance between two opposing processes.* In simple terms, **Le Chatelier's Law** states

that nature is conservative—or, in other words, *when an attempt is made to disturb a system in equilibrium, changes will take place that will resist the attempted change.* This law is of great importance to an understanding of all systems of dynamic equilibria—physical, chemical, physiological, and perhaps even economic or social. In terms of molecules, the equilibrium in each case is really the result of the difference in the total energies of the different molecules.

Figure 6-10 shows how a jagged piece of ice in equilibrium with ice water would grow smooth, thus providing dramatic evidence that the equilibrium is dynamic rather than static.

CHARACTERISTICS OF SOLUTIONS

The molecules in a true solution—whether it be a solution of a gas in a gas, a gas in a liquid, a liquid in a liquid, or a solid in a liquid—do not settle out. Once the **solution** has been prepared, it is *homogeneous*, but *its composition can be varied considerably.*

The characteristics of solutions are explained by the kinetic-molecular theory on the basis that a solute particle in a solution is molecular in size. A **solute** is *the substance that is dissolved. The substance in which it is dissolved is the* **solvent.** The molecules distribute themselves uniformly throughout the solution because of their kinetic energy, just as gas molecules completely fill any container in which they are placed. There are attractions between the solute and solvent molecules that depend upon the chemical nature of the substances in question. This fact explains the great differences in the solubilities of different substances.

Solubility is the *concentration of a solute in a given amount of solvent, when the solution is saturated at a given temperature.* A **saturated solution** represents *a condition of equilibrium, in which molecules of dissolved solute are in equilibrium with the molecules of undissolved solute.*

If crystals of a solid are in contact with a saturated solution of the solid in a liquid, the larger crystals will grow larger at the expense of the smaller crystals. This is true because the smaller crystals expose more surface relative to their mass than do the larger crystals and, as a result, the small particles dissolve faster than the larger particles. Keep in mind that the equilibrium is between the surface molecules and the solute molecules.

SUMMARY

The Laws

Boyle's Law: The volume of a given quantity of gas is inversely proportional to the pressure, provided that the temperature remains constant.

Charles' Law: Under constant pressure, the volume of a gas is very nearly proportional to the absolute temperature.

Dalton's Law of Partial Pressures: Each gas in a gaseous mixture exerts the same pressure as it would if it occupied the whole space alone.

Le Chatelier's Law states that when a system in equilibrium is subjected to a stress, the equilibrium is disturbed and a change takes place in the direction that tends to relieve the stress, until the system once more reaches a state of equilibrium.

Kinetic-Molecular Theory

Matter is composed of very small, discrete particles called molecules, far apart relative to their size, moving in all conceivable directions. The average kinetic energy of each kind of molecule is the same at a given temperature. Light molecules move more rapidly than heavy molecules. The molecules are perfectly elastic. Gas pressures are due to bombardments by molecules. Molecules have a small finite volume. There are attractive forces between the molecules.

Study Questions

1. DEFINE: gas, liquid, solid, density, viscosity, surface tension, melting, freezing, evaporation, solubility, solute, solvent, saturated solution.
2. Contrast the different states of matter.
3. What are the physical changes that absorb heat?
4. What are the physical changes that evolve heat?
5. Make a diagram of the chief physical processes and indicate the heat changes involved.
6. State Boyle's and Charles' Laws.
7. List the main assumptions of the kinetic-molecular theory.
8. What assumptions of the kinetic-molecular theory explain the very slight compressibility of liquids and solids?
9. What assumptions of the kinetic-molecular theory account for the properties of real gases as contrasted with those of ideal gases?
10. Why are the gas laws only approximate laws?
11. State Graham's Law and try to give an illustration based on your experience.

Particles Smaller than Molecules

All science has one aim, namely to find a theory of nature.

RALPH WALDO EMERSON

INTRODUCTION

The kinetic-molecular theory, outlined in the previous chapter, explained most of the physical changes of matter quite satisfactorily, but it did not explain chemical or nuclear changes. In this chapter, we will introduce the particles that are smaller than molecules— i.e., **atoms, ions,** and **subatomic particles.** Later in the text, especially in Chapters 30, 31, 62, and 63, the atom will be discussed in more detail. Keep in mind that this chapter, like those that precede it, is introductory in nature.

DALTON'S ATOMIC THEORY

The ten years between the time of the formulation of the law of conservation of mass and the close of the nineteenth century were especially fruitful for the science of chemistry. Joseph Louis Proust (1755–1826) in 1799 stated the **law of definite proportions** as follows: *If two or more elements combine to form a new chemical substance, they do so in such a manner that the ratio of the weights of the elements will always be the same.* For example, when hydrogen reacts with oxygen to form water, the ratio of the weights will always be one part of hydrogen to eight parts of oxygen. If any other ratio prevails, the product will not be water.

During the first few years of the 1800's, John Dalton (1766–1844) announced his famous atomic theory. He recognized that the law of definite proportions would apply to the small particles involved in chemical changes

which he called atoms. The fact that Dalton used the term, atom, suggests that he was familiar with the ideas of Democritus, who first suggested the existence of atoms.

The main assumptions of **Dalton's atomic theory** are as follows:

1. *The smallest particles of elements are atoms.*

2. *Atoms are very small.*

3. *Atoms are indestructible; they cannot be created nor destroyed.*

4. *All atoms of a given element are alike in properties, but atoms of different elements have different properties.*

5. *Atoms have mass. All atoms of one element have the same mass, but atoms of different elements have different masses.*

PHYSICAL CHARACTERISTICS OF THE ATOM

To say that atoms are extremely small does not begin to tell how incomprehensibly small they really are. The diameter of an atom is about one hundred-millionth of an inch. All atoms are of about the same size, the largest being only about ten times the size of the smallest ones. If a row of atoms were to be placed across a penny, about 900 million would be required. If all of the people in the United States were reduced to the size of atoms, they could stand in a space the size of the eye of Lincoln on a penny.

Scientists are more interested in the distances between the centers of atoms than in their actual size. In fact, it is almost impossible to measure the exact diameter of an atom.

The masses of atoms are likewise extremely small. For example, the mass of the lightest atom, the hydrogen atom, is approximately 0.000,000,000,000,000,000,000,001,66 gram. The heaviest naturally-occurring atom is about 240 times heavier than the hydrogen atom.

THE STRUCTURE OF THE ATOM

In Chapters 29, 30, and 31 the historical development of our present ideas concerning the structure of the atom will be presented. Our present mental picture of an atom is that of a very small, massive nucleus, which is surrounded by electrons, numbering from one to more than one hundred. These electrons are considered to move very rapidly around the nucleus in gyrating, random paths. The speed of these electrons is so rapid, and their motion is of such a highly random nature, that physicists refer to the electrons as clouds.

Within the atomic nucleus, several kinds of subatomic particles are found. At present, we shall consider only two of these particles—the protons and neutrons. The protons, neutrons, and electrons are about equal in size, but the protons and neutrons are about 1,840 times heavier than the electrons. Protons and neutrons have approximately the same mass.

One of the outstanding characteristics of the structure of the atom is that it is almost empty space. If the atom could be enlarged to the size of a basketball, the subatomic particles —i.e., the protons, neutrons, and electrons— would be the size of almost invisible dust particles. If it were possible to compress these particles so that there would be no empty space between them, an extremely dense material would be produced. For example, if water molecules were to be so compressed, almost two cubic miles of water would occupy the volume of a safety-match box. Certain stars, as we shall learn in the next few chapters, have extreme densities. For example, Van Maanan's star has a mass of almost 18 tons per cubic inch.

THE FUNDAMENTAL ELECTRICAL CHARGE

The third fundamental physical characteristic of the atom and of subatomic particles is that of electrical charge. An electrical charge may be regarded as an ultimate reality. For a lack of a better notation, the *two opposite kinds of electrical charge are designated as positive and negative.* This designation means nothing more than that the two types of charges are opposite in nature. In Chapters 30 and 40 the historical development of our knowledge of electrical charges will be presented.

Arbitrarily, the **proton** is *assigned a unit positive charge,* and the **electron** is *assigned a unit negative charge.* The magnitudes (sizes) of the opposite charges are exactly the same. The **neutron** has *neither a positive nor a negative charge,* and it is therefore said to be *neutral.*

An **atom** is a *neutral particle, containing the same number of positive and negative charges—i.e., protons and electrons.* For instance, the hydrogen atom consists of one proton and one electron. Copper atoms, on the other hand, contain 29 protons, and 29 electrons in the electron cloud.

Of the many kinds of elementary, subatomic particles in the nucleus, the most important is the proton. **The number of protons that are in a nucleus** *determines the kind of atom in which they are found.* For example, if the nucleus contains only one proton, the atom is a hydrogen atom. If the nucleus contains two protons, the atom is a helium atom, and if the nucleus contains three protons, the atom is a lithium atom. It may seem to be surprising that protons alone determine the nature of an atom. Electrons can be added or subtracted without any effect on the kind of atom. The number of neutrons or other nuclear particles can also be altered, within limits, without changing the nature of a given atom.

The number of protons in the nucleus *governs the chemical properties that a given element will exhibit.* The electrons are directly involved in chemical transformations, but the number of protons in the nucleus holds the key to the reacting capabilities of the electrons.

The **number of neutrons** has *very little influence on the chemical behavior of an atom.* While **neutrons** *add weight to an atom, their chief function appears to be that of stabilizing the nucleus.*

ATOMIC AND MOLECULAR WEIGHTS

Since chemists work with relatively large numbers of molecules, they are seldom interested in the masses of single atoms or molecules. An atomic mass scale (usually called an atomic weight table) was devised—the standard being carbon, with a value of 12.0000. The **atomic weight of an element** is *the weight of an atom of the element relative to the weight of a carbon atom.* The **molecular weight of a compound** is *the sum of the atomic weights of the atoms that make up the molecule.* Hydrogen atoms, with one proton as the nucleus of each atom, weigh one-twelfth as much as the standard carbon atom, which contains six protons and six neutrons. It is assigned an atomic weight of 1.0000. Oxygen atoms, whose nuclei contain eight protons and eight neutrons, have an atomic weight of 16.0000. On the same scale, a water molecule has a molecular weight of 18.0000. Electrons are so light in comparison to the masses of the nuclear particles, that their weights are disregarded in atomic weight comparisons.

ISOTOPES

In 1919, the British physicist F. W. Aston (1877–1945) discovered that all of the atoms of neon gas do not have the same mass. His experiments showed that 90.5 per cent of an average sample of neon gas consisted of atoms with an atomic weight of 19.999; 9.2 per cent had an atomic weight of 21.998; and 0.3 per cent had an atomic weight of 20.999. Note that the atomic weights of these three different kinds of neon atoms were nearly 20, 22, and 21 respectively. Further studies showed that practically every sample of any given element consists of mixtures of atoms having different masses. Since the atoms of a given element must contain the same number of protons, it was concluded that a nuclear particle contributes mass to the atom without changing its

chemical properties. Aston called these different forms of the same element **"isotopes"** (from the Greek word, *"in the same place"*). Later, when the neutron was discovered, it was shown that the mass of an atom could be altered, without changing its chemical properties, by altering the number of neutrons in the nucleus. **Isotopes** are defined as *different varieties of a given element having the same atomic number, i.e., the same number of protons, but different atomic weights; they differ in the numbers of neutrons in the nuclei.*

THE ELECTRON CLOUD

We are accustomed to seeing the "planetary" representation of the electronic structure of the atom, as shown in Figure 7-1, which shows the structure of two isotopes of lithium. The nucleus is positioned in the center of the drawing, and the electrons occupy specific circular orbits or shells outside of the nucleus. While a drawing such as this is excellent for describing certain chemical characteristics, the drawing is an oversimplification. The distances between the nucleus and the electrons are much greater than shown, and the paths of the electrons are much more complicated than the perfectly circular movements that are traditionally pictured. Physicists, not interested in the mechanisms of chemical reactions, draw a "probability" representation of the atom as shown in Figure 7-2, in which the fine lines represent the positions where most of the electrons will be found. This figure

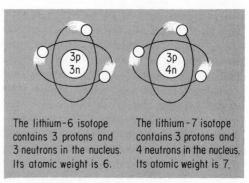

The lithium-6 isotope contains 3 protons and 3 neutrons in the nucleus. Its atomic weight is 6.

The lithium-7 isotope contains 3 protons and 4 neutrons in the nucleus. Its atomic weight is 7.

Figure 7–1. The only difference between these two isotopes of lithium is that there is an extra neutron in the heavier isotope. Both isotopes have the same atomic number, i.e., 3, but their atomic weights differ.

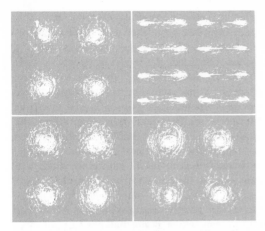

Figure 7–2. The electronic cloud concept. These figures show the different ways in which the electrons in the atoms in different kinds of molecules may or may not have overlapping electron clouds.

shows some of the different relations of atoms in different kinds of molecules, and it will be referred to later.

THE BOHR THEORY OF ATOMIC STRUCTURE

In 1913, Niels Bohr (1885–1962) proposed the theory that deals with the electronic structure of atoms, as follows:

1 *Electrons are restricted in their motions to certain permitted or specific orbits.*

2 *If electrons are traveling in these permitted orbits, they will not radiate any of their energy.*

3 *When an atom is "excited" the electrons gain energy and move to orbits farther from the nucleus, depending upon the amount of energy received.*

4 *When electrons return to their normal orbits they emit energy in packets of electromagnetic radiation known as quanta.*

According to the Bohr theory, the amount of energy contained in a photon of radiant energy determines how far the new orbit will be from the **ground state,** i.e., *the unexcited state,* when it is intercepted by an electron. After a short time, usually about 0.001 second or less, the electron returns to the orbit of its ground state, in one or more jumps, emitting a quantum of energy with each jump. See Figure 7-3.

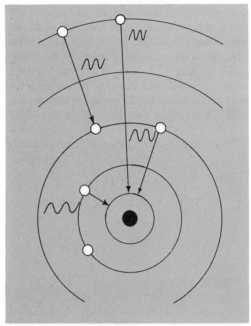

Figure 7–3. The Bohr Theory. In jumping from an outer orbit to an inner orbit the electron emits radiant energy. The bigger the jump the shorter the wavelength of the radiated energy will be. The electrons can revolve in definite orbits only.

THE CHEMIST'S MODEL OF ELECTRONIC STRUCTURE

Chemists visualize the electrons as traveling in particular shells around the nucleus. The electrons travel in specific orbits, and a shell may contain several orbits. A particularly stable configuration of electrons results if a shell is filled, i.e., if all of the orbits within a shell are filled with electrons. The first shell is filled if two electrons are traveling in it. The remainder of the shells are filled if the outermost shell contains eight electrons. Atoms having a large number of electrons may have more than eight electrons in the inner shells.

Figure 7-4 shows the chemist's picture of the electronic structure of some of the lighter elements. The hydrogen atom is shown to have one electron in its only shell. The helium atom has two electrons in its shell, which represents a very stable configuration; as a result helium is chemically inactive. Lithium has three electrons, two in the filled inner shell and one in the outer shell. As we progress from lithium to the succeeding elements, an additional electron is added to the outer shell for each element. Neon has a filled inner shell and a filled outer shell, and exhibits a chemical inactivity similar to that of helium. The next element, sodium, contains one electron in the third or outer shell; and another series of elements is formed by adding one electron in the outer

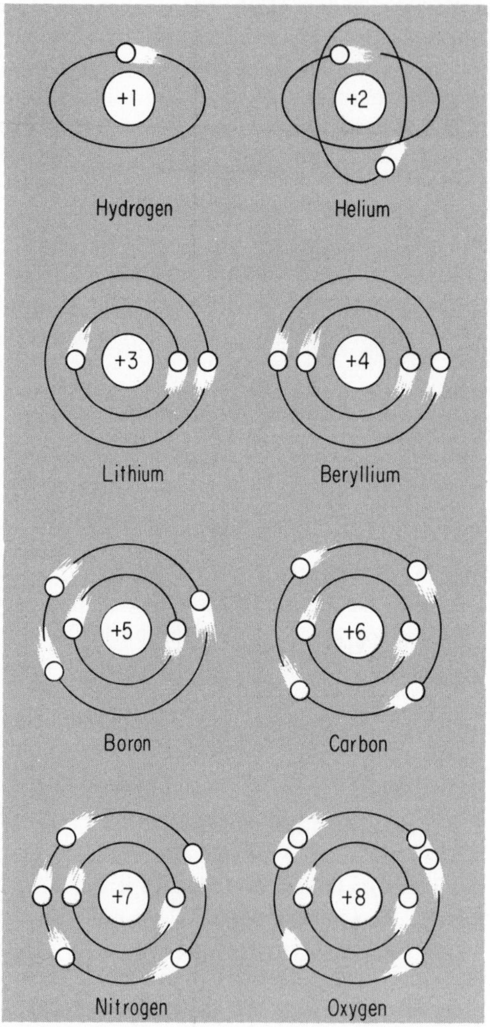

Figure 7-4. The composition of some of the lighter elements. The composition of the nuclei is not given, but the net positive charge on the nucleus, i.e., the atomic number is shown. Each nucleus is surrounded by a number of electrons equal to the atomic number. The electrons are pictured as occupying a series of orbits around the nucleus. The orbits are not in one plane and their direction of motion probably varies. The spatial arrangement of the electrons in the helium atom is shown but it is too difficult to show it for the more complex atoms.

orbit for each succeeding element until this outer orbit has been filled with eight electrons.

Atoms of the different elements have a tendency to form stable arrangements of their electronic structures by gaining or losing electrons from other elements in order to fill the outer shells. This gain or loss of electrons results in an electrical imbalance within the atoms, in which the number of protons does not equal the number of electrons. Sodium, with one electron in its outermost shell, will readily give up this electron to another atom, resulting in a filled outer shell. It thus acquires one positive charge, because it now has one proton which is not balanced by an electron. Chlorine, with seven electrons in its outermost shell, will readily accept one electron so as to fill its outer shell. When a pellet of heated sodium metal is dropped into a jar of chlorine gas an explosion results, because of the great attraction that chlorine has for electrons and the readiness of sodium to give up electrons. A white powder, sodium chloride, results from the above explosion; it is common table salt. The transfer of a single electron from sodium to chlorine—both of which are highly harmful to the human body —thus produced a new substance, which the body must have in order to sustain life.

Atoms that have gained or lost electrons, as illustrated by the sodium and chlorine atoms above, are called **ions.** *Chemical reactions in which ions react with each other, or in which ions are produced are* called **ionic reactions.** Such reactions will be discussed in Chapters 32, 33, and 34.

NATURAL RADIOACTIVITY

In 1896, Antoine Becquerel (1852–1908) discovered that certain substances spontaneously emitted invisible rays that would affect photographic plates as if they had been exposed to light. Later, it was found that the rays emitted by these substances could be separated by means of electrically charged plates. Figure 7-5 shows the three types of rays produced.

Natural radioactivity is associated with events occurring within the nucleus, and the products of the radioactive decay of elements are specific for each kind of radioactive nu-

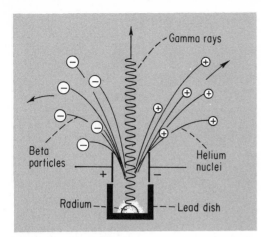

Figure 7-5. The disintegration products of radium. The gamma rays are depicted as moving straight from the radium because they, like light, are not deflected by an electric field. The beta particles, being negative, are attracted by a positively charged plate or they may be repelled by a negatively charged plate. Just the opposite deflection takes place with the helium nuclei (alpha particles). Various lighter elements are left in the lead dish when the radium gives off these rays and particles.

cleus. Only a few naturally occurring atomic nuclei are radioactive. However, many artificially produced radioactive nuclei have been obtained by the bombardment of various atomic nuclei with high-speed particles.

Some radioactive nuclei decay in less than a second, while others decay very slowly. The term, half-life, is used to describe the time required for a given radioactive change to take place. The **half-life** is *the time required for half of a given sample to undergo radioactive decomposition.* Radioactivity will be discussed in more detail in Chapters 31 and 62.

SUMMARY

The Atomic Theory

The smallest division of an element is the atom, which is the unit of chemical change. Atoms do not change in chemical reactions. Atoms of different elements differ in mass and other properties, while atoms of a given element have the same average mass and similar chemical properties. Compounds are formed by combining definite whole numbers of atoms.

The Electron Theory

Atoms consist of positively charged nuclei surrounded by negatively charged electrons, the number of electrons being equal to the number of protons in the nucleus.

The Bohr Theory

The electrons outside of the nuclei of atoms are relatively far apart, and are arranged in orbits having different energy levels. When excited, electrons move to orbits or levels farther from the nucleus. When the electrons return to inner levels, they emit energy. The energy gained or lost by electrons is in the form of *definite packets or bundles,* called **quanta.**

The Ionic Theory

Some atoms may gain or lose electrons and thus form negatively or positively charged ions.

The Nuclear Theory

Atoms are composite in nature. They consist of a positively charged nucleus made up of neutrons and protons, surrounded by a number of electrons outside of the nucleus that is equal to the positive charge on the nucleus. This number is the **atomic number.** Atoms which possess differing nuclei but the same number of electrons outside of the nucleus are called isotopes. The nucleus of an atom contains most of the mass of the atom. The number of protons in the nucleus is equal to the number of electrons outside of the nucleus. In all radioactive changes it is the nucleus which is affected.

Study Questions

1. DEFINE: proton, isotope, neutron, electron, atomic number, atomic weight, molecular weight, half-life, ion.
2. Outline the main points of Dalton's atomic theory. What type of facts does it explain?
3. What fundamental difference in the structure of atomic nuclei is responsible for different kinds of atoms?
4. What types of radiation are obtained from radioactive elements?
5. Show how the Bohr theory accounts for the electronic structures of the eight lightest elements.

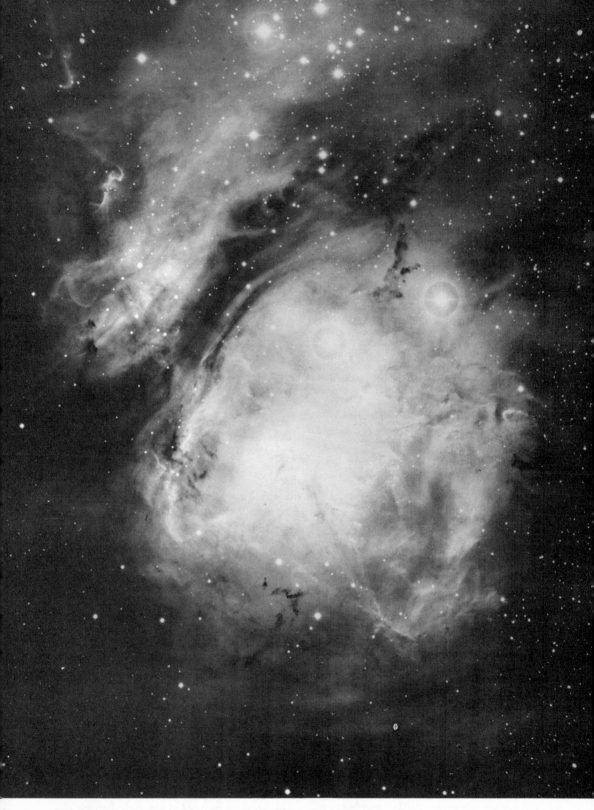

Lagoon Nebula. This nebula is a hydrogen cloud which probably represents a new star in the early stage of formation. (Courtesy, Mount Wilson and Palomar Observatories)

The Vast Universe
of Energy and Matter

And Nature, the old nurse, took
*   The child upon her knee,*
Saying "Here is a story-book
*   Thy Father has written for thee.*
"Come wander with me" she said,
*   "Into regions yet untrod;*
"And read what is still unread
*   "In the manuscripts of God."*
And he wandered away and away
*   With Nature, the dear old nurse*
Who sang to him night and day
*   The rhymes of the universe.*

LONGFELLOW

THE EARTH, our home in the Universe, is a tiny member of the great cosmos of matter and energy, a beautiful system of stars and galaxies, seemingly endless and timeless.

This unit deals with matter and energy on a large scale—the astronomical scale. It portrays the Universe as revealed to us by modern astronomy, one of the oldest of the physical sciences.

Probably there are not more than two thousand professional astronomers in the world, but these astronomers have extended man's vision farther and farther out into space as a result of their toil, night after night. As Longfellow suggested in the above poem, the "rhymes of the universe" were discovered by astronomers during the night, while their companions slept. Was this nightly toil in the cold air of the astronomical observatory worthwhile to the astronomers? Yes. Few men have been able to experience the pure joy of discovery such as has been the reward of astronomers. But, has the work of astronomers been of any practical value to the rest of mankind? Yes. It was the theoretical study of the source of the energy emitted by the sun and other stars that led to the development of nuclear energy, perhaps the greatest scientific discovery to date.

As man's knowledge of the Universe has expanded, the earth has shrunk in prominence to the point where it has become an inconspicuous speck in the cosmic scheme of things. And what is man's position in this vast scheme of things? It is true that a study of astronomy will administer a rude shock to man's conception of his relative importance. However, it is well to keep in mind that although, astronomically speaking, man is very small—still astronomically speaking, he is the astronomer.

The study of astronomy cannot help leaving the student with a very much greater appreciation of the Universe and its Creator.

As we conquer peak after peak we see in front of us regions full of interest and beauty, but we do not see our goal, we do not see the horizon; in the distance tower still higher peaks, which will yield to those who ascend them still wider prospects, and deepen the feeling, the truth of which is emphasized by every advance in science, that "Great are the Works of the Lord."

Sir J. J. Thomson

Astrology and Astronomy, the Counterfeit and the Genuine

Knowledge advances by steps, and not by leaps.

MACAULAY

The greatest and noblest pleasure which men can have in this world is to discover new truths; and the next is to shake off old prejudices.

FREDERICK THE GREAT

INTRODUCTION

Astronomy is one of the oldest of the sciences; its beginnings are lost in antiquity. The origin of the arbitrary division of the calendar into weeks has been lost, but the fact that the days of the week were associated with heavenly bodies is well attested by their names; Sunday (sun's day), Saturday (Saturn's day), etc.

Very early in this history of civilization, man must have felt the need for methods of reckoning time, and it is probable that astronomy developed out of this need. Ancient Chinese, Babylonian, and Egyptian records show that considerable attention was given to the study of the heavenly bodies which were visible to the naked eye.

The Egyptians and Babylonians observed the same heavenly bodies that we see as we turn our gaze to the sky. They recognized that the heavenly bodies seemed to revolve about the polar star, and they thought of the Universe as a star-studded dome, resting on a flat earth, similar to the impression that one might gain today from a visit to a modern planetarium. **Astrology**—*a false science, which started in Babylon*—*was based on the*

idea that the motion and positions of the heavenly bodies controlled the fortunes and destinies of man. "Wise men" were employed by ancient rulers to study the heavens, and to provide guidance based on an interpretation of the positions of the heavenly bodies. Today, many people buy astrology magazines and base their important decisions on horoscopes. Webster's Dictionary defines a **horoscope**

"as a . . . scheme of the twelve signs of the *zodiac* (the broad belt of constellations which the sun traverses during the year) in which is marked the disposition of the heavens at a given time, and by which astrologers formerly told the fortunes of persons, according to the position of the stars at the time of their birth."

It does not seem possible that this persistence of superstition and magic could exist in this day of modern Science. Modern astrology, like modern quackery in medicine, shows the need for a much greater emphasis on the scientific attitude in our schools.

Although astrology was based on superstition, it nevertheless made significant contributions to the foundations of modern astronomy, a genuine science.

55

THE IDEAS OF ANCIENT ASTROLOGY

Early explanations of natural phenomena centered around the idea that everything had a soul like that of man. Every object, animate or inanimate, was considered to have thoughts and feelings, and to be friendly or unfriendly to man. This concept called for the medicine man, or the priest, to evolve and perform certain occult rites to keep these thousands of unseen forces friendly. Gradually the belief grew that these priests were endowed with the power of foretelling future events and, as soothsayers and intermediaries between man and the unseen forces, they became the valued advisers of the people's rulers. Even today, people will flock to hear men who claim to have the gift of prophecy.

It is not surprising that man came to consider the stars and planets to be living deities who controlled the destinies of man, and that he worshiped them as such.

Long before the time of Christ, astronomical measurements were made to determine the time for annual national and social events, and to predict positions of the stars favorable for important undertakings. This growth of astronomy naturally led to the early high development of those parts of mathematics (geometry especially) which are useful to astronomy.

Even in this enlightened age, so many people believe in astrology and horoscopes that many newspapers print daily columns devoted to this ancient counterfeit science.

The code of Standard Astrology states that

a precise astrological opinion cannot honestly be rendered with reference to an individual unless it is based upon a horoscope for the year, month, day, and time of day, plus corrected geographical location of the place of birth of the individual.

How, then, could forecasts in newspapers or magazines be of any value? On the other hand, are such horoscopes any less valuable than those specially prepared for individuals? One of the many errors of astrology is that it requires that planets with a considerable degree of similarity affect human affairs in entirely dissimilar ways.

MODERN ASTROLOGY

The following statements were taken from a report of the Executive Council of the Society for Psychological Study of Social Issues:

The principal reason why people turn to astrology and to kindred superstitions is that they lack in their own lives the resources necessary to solve serious personal problems confronting them. Feeling blocked and bewildered they yield to the pleasant suggestion that a golden key is at hand—a simple solution and ever-present help in time of trouble. . . .

By offering the public the horoscope as a substitute for honest and sustained thinking, astrologers have been guilty of playing upon the human tendency to take easy rather than difficult paths.

ANCIENT VIEWS OF THE NATURE OF THE UNIVERSE

The Babylonians pictured the Universe to be a closed chamber, with the earth as its floor. Around the earth lay a moat of water, beyond which stood high mountains supporting the dome of the heavens. The Babylonians recognized eclipses, and predicted the times that they would occur. They even fixed the length of the year at 365¼ days, which represented an error of about eleven minutes.

The Hebrews' concept of the Universe, probably influenced by the Babylonians, was that there was a heavenly expanse resting on pillars and containing windows through which waters that surrounded the firmament could reach the earth. It is obvious that their ideas were based on less information than we have available today.

THE IDEAS OF THE GREEK PHILOSOPHERS RELATIVE TO ASTRONOMY

No doubt there were many thinkers among the primitive astronomers of Chaldea, Babylonia, China, Egypt, and India, but their ideas have not come down to us.

Thales of Miletus, Greece (about 640–548 B.C.) has been called the founder of Greek astronomy. Thales was a merchant, statesman, engineer, mathematician, and astronomer. He taught the Greek sailors to guide their ships by the polar star, and observed the natural division of the year into four seasons by the regular recurrence of the longest and shortest days of the year, and of the two intervening days, when the days and nights were of equal length. He successfully predicted an eclipse of the sun. He believed the stars to be self-luminous bodies, and the moonlight to be light reflected from the sun. He taught that the earth was a flat disk floating on water.

Anaximander (611–547 B.C.), a contemporary of Thales, was the first man to recognize that the heavens revolve around the polar star, and to teach that the visible dome of the sky is half of a complete sphere, whose center is the earth. For many centuries after his time, the earth was considered to be the center of the Universe. Anaximander is also said to have introduced into Greece the sundial, consisting of an *upright rod* (stile, or **gnomon**) *placed on horizontal ground.*

Pythagoras (566–470 B.C.) considered the earth to be a sphere, whose rotation explained the apparent rotation of the heavenly dome.

Aristotle (384–322 B.C.) was one of the greatest organizers and generalizers the world has ever known. His *Encyclopedia of Knowledge* was so great that he was looked upon as the final authority in many fields of knowledge for nearly two thousand years. Aristotle improved nearly every field of learning that he touched, except those of physics and astronomy. He considered the earth to be a sphere in the center of the Universe, and taught that the planets were supernatural beings entirely unlike the earth.

Aristotle interpreted twilight and dawn as the reflection of sunlight by the atmosphere.

Aristarchus of Samos (circa 250 B.C.) held the most modern ideas of all the Greeks, but perhaps because his ideas were different from those of Aristotle, they were not accepted. He taught that the earth was spherical, and that it and the other planets revolve about the sun. He accounted for the relatively stationary positions of the stars by assuming that they were at greater distances from the earth than the sun. Aristarchus was the first man to declare that the sun, not the earth, was the center of the solar system. He declared that the earth rotates on its axis and that the sun

is much larger than the earth. He concluded that the sun was about twenty times more distant from the earth than the moon. The actual ratio is about 1 to 400, but his errors were due to inadequate instruments; the principles of his experiments were sound.

Eratosthenes (died about 195 B.C.) was the first man to measure the size of the earth on the assumption that it was a sphere. He noted that at noon on June 21 at Syene, Egypt, the sun was directly overhead; and that exactly a year later at Alexandria, the sun was a little more than 7 degrees south of the line passing directly overhead. He concluded that this was due to the fact that the earth was round. Inasmuch as the distance between these two cities (about 480 miles by his measurements) represented 7/360 of the entire circumference of the earth, he calculated the circumference to be about 24,000 miles, which is within about 900 miles of the present accepted value for the circumference at the equator.

Hipparchus (190–120 B.C.) was the last of the great Greek astronomers. He catalogued about 1,080 stars, classifying them according to their brightness; and mapped the course of the sun among the stars. His measurements of the size of the moon and its distance from the earth were within about 10 per cent of present-day values. He discovered the precession of the equinoxes (to be studied later), and determined its amount.

Claudius Ptolemy (circa the second century, A.D.), a Greek born in Egypt, made observations in Alexandria, the center of Hellenic culture for centuries. On the basis of these observations, he worked out a system of astronomy that dominated the minds of men for the next thirteen centuries. His great contribution was the compilation of his *Almagest,* or encyclopedia of astronomy, which preserved the work of Hipparchus.

Ptolemy believed that the earth was the center of the Universe. He also erroneously believed that the earth was stationary, but he was correct in his assumption that the earth is a sphere, balanced without supports in space. He concluded that the fixed stars were fastened to the inside of a vast dome that revolved about the earth once every twenty-four hours. The planets supposedly moved in

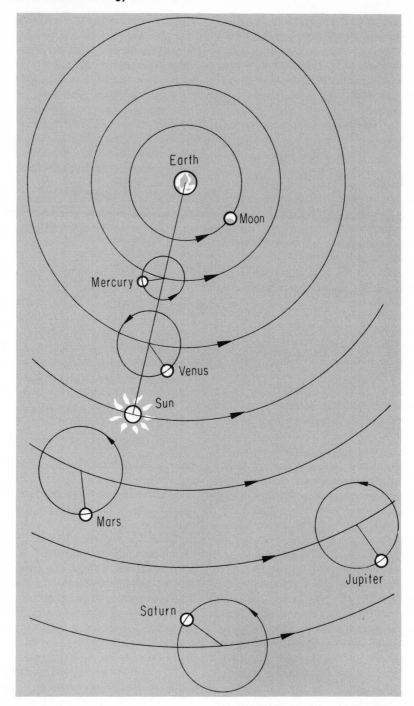

Figure 8–1. Ptolemaic system of the Universe. The dome of the stars lies outside of Saturn.

independent orbits between the earth and this star-studded dome. His system was so satisfactory that it was widely accepted, and never seriously challenged until the time of Copernicus, thirteen centuries later.

For thirteen hundred years following Ptolemy there was a period of retrogression, in which people returned to the old astrology, and, forgetting the relatively advanced teachings of Ptolemy, generally considered the earth to be flat—an idea which persisted down to the twentieth century in the minds of many people who refused to accept the evidence of modern Science to the contrary.

COPERNICUS, THE FIRST OF THE RENAISSANCE ASTRONOMERS

Nikolaus Copernicus (1473–1543) was a skilled painter and student of medicine, mathematics, and astronomy. He taught from the still-dominant *Almagest*, and was greatly influenced by the teachings of Aristarchus. Fortunately, he did not accept traditional theories without question but made observations of the stars for himself. He found so many errors in the Ptolemaic tables that he came to distrust all of Ptolemy's teachings.

In 1507, he wrote his famous book *De Revolutionibus Orbium Caelestium* "Concerning the Revolutions of the Heavenly Bodies"). His main thesis was that the sun is the center of the solar system, and that the earth is but one of the planets revolving around the sun. He also advanced the modern concepts that the moon revolves around the earth—accompanying it in its revolution around the sun—and that the earth turns on its axis from west to east, thus accounting for day and night and the apparent motion of the stars.

OTHER RENAISSANCE ASTRONOMERS

Bruno (1548–1600), Copernicus' follower, went even farther, and stated that the universe is infinite, and that the stars are scattered throughout space.

Bruno was brought before the Inquisition for his teachings, and was burned at the stake. His executioners really believed that they were preserving truth by this act.

Tycho Brahe (1546–1601), whose interest in astronomy was aroused by an eclipse of the sun coming at the exact time predicted in 1560, spent his life making untiring and much more accurate measurements of the positions of the stars and planets than had before been made. He designed and built a large observatory and equipped it with the best instruments then available.

The fundamental principles of Copernicus were not proved to be true until long after his time. Tycho Brahe understood that if the earth moved around the sun, the stars ought to show an annual displacement of position on account of being viewed from different positions. He failed to detect such a displacement and therefore rejected the idea of the earth's motion.

Johann Kepler (1571–1630), one of Tycho Brahe's students who fell heir to his observations, became a convert to the Copernican system. Kepler's main contribution was the discovery of three laws of planetary motion which laid the foundation for the great work of Newton. See Chapter 12.

Galileo—The intellectuals of this time (circa A.D. 1600) found their teachings challenged by the concept of the Copernican system and, not being open-minded, brought pressure to bear on the not unwilling churchmen for a protest. Therefore, Galileo Galilei (1564–1642), the first of the moderns, met with much opposition.

Galileo's great contribution to astronomy was the construction of the telescope, and its application to the study of the heavenly bodies. It is quite probable that he got the idea for it from a Belgian spectacle maker, Lippershey, who had invented combinations of lenses to magnify distant objects. By applying his knowledge of optics, Galileo built a telescope for himself, which would magnify 33 diameters. He established the validity of the Copernican theory by his discovery of the revolution of Jupiter's four largest moons. He discovered mountains on the moon and spots on the sun, by which he could detect its rotation. And what a thrill it must have been when he first saw Saturn's gorgeous rings!

Galileo rightly concluded that the stars were far away and very hot, because they appeared as points of light rather than as disks typical of the planets. He also found that stars are much more numerous than had been previously suspected. He wrote:

To the three stars of Orion's Belt and the six of his Sword I have added eighty other stars recently discovered in their vicinity . . . near the six stars of the Pleiades there lie more than forty others invisible to the naked eye.

Galileo saw "innumerable stars planted together in clusters" when he observed the Milky Way with his telescope, and thus solved the mystery of the Milky Way.

THE CALENDAR AN ANCIENT PROBLEM OF ASTRONOMY

The records of earliest civilizations indicate that attempts were made to work out calendars in terms of such readily observed changes as day and night and the phases of the moon.

The basic problem in working out any calendar is that of trying to fit it into the period of rotation of the earth (a day); the time for the moon to pass through its phases, 29½ days (a month); and the time required for the earth to travel around the sun, 365¼ days (a year).

As previously mentioned, the Babylonian observations of the sun led to a fairly accurate basis for a year. Our calendar of today is an inheritance from the past, to which early astronomers made valuable contributions. However, our modern holidays and holy days come on different days from year to year, and testify to the fact that we do not have a modern calendar. For example, in 325 A.D. the Council of Nice adopted the rule for Easter, which fixes it as the first Sunday after the 14th day of the nearly full moon, which occurs on or immediately after March 21. This plan insured adequate moonlight for the pilgrims' travel to the locations of their yearly Easter celebrations. Many Christian leaders now favor a fixed date for Easter Sunday.

THE ILLOGICAL BASIS FOR OUR PRESENT CALENDAR

Julius Caesar, in 45 B.C., introduced the Julian calendar invented by Sosigenes. He used 365¼ days as the year, and invented the leap year to take care of the quarter-days. The Julian year is too long by 11 minutes and 14 seconds. In 400 years, this variation amounted to 3 days. In the sixteenth century, this error had increased to 11 days. Pope Gregory, at that time, dropped 10 days from the calendar, but not without considerable opposition.

The Gregorian calendar provides that century years are not leap years unless they are divisible by 400, thus making another such radical revision of the calendar unnecessary, because our present year is too long by only 26 seconds. Thus the Gregorian calendar provides for fewer leap years than the Julian calendar.

The Gregorian calendar was adopted by England in 1752, and several people were killed in riots which resulted from this calendar change. One can imagine that a good many people thought that they had been cheated, because interest, rent, and wages could not be collected for the days dropped. Russia dropped 13 days when it adopted the Gregorian calendar in 1918.

Before Julius Caesar's time, March was selected as the standard for the calendar, because that was the month in which the sun started to move north of the equator. The names of the months of September, October, November, and December came from the Latin names for the numerals 7, 8, 9, 10. These names designated the number of months after March. The Roman Senate honored Julius Caesar by naming the fifth month, July. His calendar provided that all even-numbered months should have 30 days except February, which was to have only 28 days, except in leap years; while odd-numbered months were to have 31 days.

Later, Augustus Caesar had the month of August named after him and changed the length of the month to 31 days in order to have it equal Julius Caesar's month in the number of days. This change unbalanced the length of the quarters, so a day was taken from the months of September and from November and added to the months of October and December. Such is the illogical basis for our present calendar.

CALENDAR REFORMS

Many people believe that we are about due for a calendar reform. Our present calendar, handed down to us by the Caesars and Pope Gregory, possesses the following disadvantages: months, quarters, and half-years are not of equal length and do not contain whole numbers of weeks—thus making calculations of salaries, rents, interest, and other business transactions inaccurate when based on monthly, quarterly, or semi-yearly periods. The calendar is not perpetual, and holidays and other principal events occur on different days of the week from year to year.

Many improvements in the calendar have been recommended. One of them is a year of 13 months—28 days each—the 13th month to be named Sol, and New Year's Day to be the extra day not belonging to any month; in leap years another day would be added between February and March.

The World Calendar represents one basis for reform that has received considerable support. It would consist of 12 months of 30 days each, except that the first month of each quarter would have 31 days. At the end of each year, there would be added an extra day called "World's Day." In leap years an extra day, called "Leap Day" would be added to the end of June.

Perhaps the most popular reform in this day of the automobile is the calendar that would provide for long weekends, with holidays on Mondays.

SUMMARY

Astronomy is one of the oldest of the sciences. It was originally associated with a great deal of superstition, but received the support of powerful rulers because of the belief that man's undertakings are influenced by the relative position of the heavenly bodies. This false concept, which is basic to the pseudo-science of astrology, caused rulers to support astrologers, who were thus enabled to devote their lives to the study of astronomy, while they maintained themselves by means of fortune-telling. The early astrologers left a heritage of real value—but astrologers of the present age, instead of contributing to astronomical knowledge use it to exploit ignorant people who still believe in magic, offering horoscopes as substitutes for the intelligent use of the scientific method in solving problems.

The Greeks arrived at many correct conclusions concerning the heavenly bodies, but their failure to test their conclusions left preference as the only criterion of the relative value of their different conclusions; and it was the authority of Aristotle that decided nearly every question up to the time of Copernicus and Galileo, who dared to substitute observation and experiment for authority and thus ushered in a new day for astronomy.

Copernicus should be remembered for his modern concept of the solar system.

Kepler should be remembered for his three laws of planetary motion.

Galileo should be remembered for his application of the telescope to astronomy, and especially for his scientific attitude, which challenged the solving of problems by reference to ancient authorities.

Our calendar is an inheritance from the past.

Study Questions

1. DEFINE: astrology, horoscope, zodiac.
2. What were the Babylonian ideas concerning the stars?
3. Give a brief outline of your present conception of the Universe.
4. List some of the astronomical ideas of the Greeks.
5. What new concepts concerning the nature of the Universe did Copernicus introduce?
6. What led Copernicus to reach his conclusions concerning the solar system?
7. What led Galileo to reach his conclusions concerning the solar system?
8. Why were the ancient conceptions of the Universe so inaccurate?
9. Upon what observations did Thales recognize a natural division of the year into four seasons?
10. How did Thales account for the luminosity of the moon?
11. What was the most important contribution of Galileo to Science?
12. What is meant by the statement that astrology is a pseudo-science?
13. What are the major ideas of astrology?
14. Differentiate between astronomy and astrology.
15. Why does Easter come on different dates from year to year?
16. What was Pope Gregory's provision for a leap year?
17. What was the basis for the numbers of days in the different months?

CHAPTER 9

The Tools of the Astronomer

Like buried treasures, the outposts of the universe have beckoned to the adventurous from immemorial times. Princes and potentates, political or industrial, equally with men of science, have felt the lure of uncharted seas of space, and through their provision of instrumental means the sphere of exploration has rapidly widened.[1]

GEORGE ELLERY HALE

INTRODUCTION

Nowhere is man's ingenuity shown to better advantage than in his invention of instruments to aid him in making observations. Galileo's application of the telescope to astronomy was very significant, because it extended man's observations of the heavenly bodies. Modern telescopes, made possible by modern technology, have greatly expanded man's knowledge of the Universe, and the end is not in sight.

The astronomer now has available many instruments which supplement the telescope. Some of the most important of these instruments will be described in this chapter.

TELESCOPES

Astronomers are able to observe distant stars by the use of telescopes, not because they magnify the image of stars so much as because of their light-gathering power. Cameras supplement the eye in using telescopes for most observations because they can make a record of the light gathered over a considerable period of time.

Observations made with telescopes, supplemented by the camera, thus provide informa-

[1] *Signals from the Stars*, Charles Scribner's Sons, New York, 1931.

tion concerning the existence and location of stars and their brightness. They also help to determine the distance of the nearer stars.

The two main types of telescopes are the refractors and the reflectors. These telescopes are supplemented by the Schmidt telescope, which combines the principles of refractors and reflectors. All of these telescopes are used to observe the light from distant stars. It has been found that many stars emit electromagnetic radiations in the range of radio waves, so light telescopes are now supplemented by radio telescopes.

Refracting Telescopes

A **refracting telescope** is so called because *it changes the path of light as it passes through a double convex lens* as shown in Figure 9-1. This *lens,* called the **objective,** *brings the light to a focus, and thus concentrates the light from a distant object, which would be too faint to be seen otherwise.*

The principle of the refracting telescope is shown in Figure 9-2. The larger the diameter of the objective lens, the more the amount of light thus brought to a focus. *The distance between the lens and the point at which the light passing through the lens is brought to a focus* is the **focal length** of the lens. The larger the diameter of the objective, the less

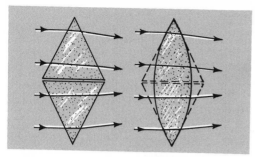

Figure 9–1. Lenses behave like two prisms in refracting light.

is its curvature and the longer is its focal length—provided the thickness of the lens remains the same.

The microscope is similar to the telescope, except that it is intended to be used to view small, close objects, and therefore has an objective lens of relatively short focal length. The chief purpose of a telescope, unlike the microscope, is not to secure great magnification, but to gather and focus light.

Large objectives are used in telescopes, not only to increase their light-gathering power, but also to increase their **resolving power**— i.e., *their power to distinguish between two objects that are close to each other.*

A *second double convex lens,* called the **eyepiece,** *functions like a magnifying glass to magnify the image.* The focal length of the eyepiece, in relation to the focal length of the objective, determines the magnifying power of the telescope, and the amount of magnification may be changed by merely changing the eyepiece.

The largest refractor in the world is in the Yerkes Observatory at Williams Bay, Lake Geneva, Wisconsin. It has an objective lens which is 40 inches in diameter. It will collect about 25,600 times as much light as the eye, and thus renders visible stars that are 160 times too distant to be visible to the naked eye. There are more than forty large refractors in use throughout the world.

The image formed by a simple lens is subject to a number of *defects,* called **aberrations;** for example, light of different colors is refracted by different amounts, with the result that these *different colors are not brought to a focus at the same point.* Another type of aberration, known as **spherical aberration,** is *the blurring of an image toward the edge of the field of view.* Both of these aberrations may be reduced by use of a **compound lens,** which is *made up of a number of different lenses ground to different shapes.* Compound lenses increase the loss of light both by absorption and reflection; and, of course, the larger the lens the thicker it becomes, and the greater is the amount of light absorbed.

Most of the objections to larger refracting telescopes could be dealt with satisfactorily today; but larger telescopes would be very unwieldy, and the cost of construction would be prohibitive. Refractors are the best type of telescopes as far as smaller instruments are concerned.

Reflecting Telescopes

Sir Isaac Newton constructed the first reflector. It was similar in principle to the one shown in Figures 9-3 and 9-4.

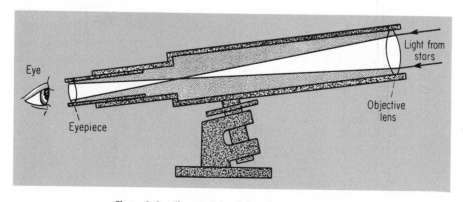

Figure 9–2. The principle of the refracting telescope.

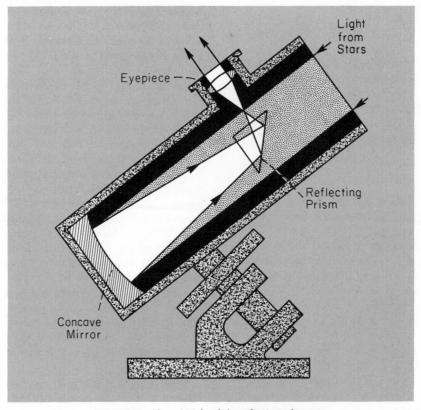

Figure 9–3. The principle of the reflecting telescope.

The largest telescopes *employ concave mirrors—which reflect the light rather than refract it as do the refracting telescopes—*and thus less light is lost by absorption. All of the colors are reflected at the same angle, so that there is no chromatic aberration in reflecting telescopes. The spherical aberrations are more pronounced in reflecting telescopes than in refracting telescopes, but they are partially overcome by proper grinding of the surface of the mirror to a special shape. The reflecting telescope is never as good as a refracting telescope for photographing large areas of the sky because of this spherical aberration. It is, however, better for photographing small areas.

Reflectors are less costly to construct and house than refractors of the same power, because they are much shorter. The construction

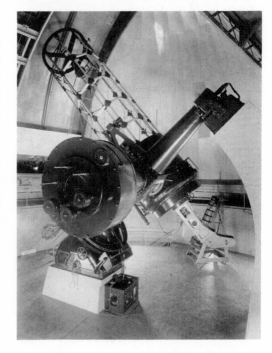

Figure 9–4. The 74-inch reflecting telescope of the David Dunlap Observatory, Richmond Hill, P.O. Ont. (Courtesy, David Dunlap Observatory)

of reflecting telescopes is much simpler than that of refracting telescopes because only one surface has to be shaped rather than four or more surfaces, as in the compound lens; and the color or transparency of the glass is of no importance, because the light does not pass through it. A mirror may be supported from the back, while a refracting lens has to be supported at the edges.

The first giant reflector, equipped with a 72-inch mirror, was constructed by Lord Rosse in Ireland, in 1845. A crude, unwieldy affair, it had none of the automatic mechanisms of modern telescopes. It had to be twisted about by hand, and was kept focused on the object in the same way.

The mechanism of modern telescopes enables them to be kept focused on an object in any predetermined position in the sky with great precision, by means of mechanisms regulated by clocks that move the position of the telescope at the same rate that the earth turns, so as to keep the object in view.

The astronomer of today merely presses buttons which set electric motors into action to move the telescope, revolve the dome, and raise or lower the floor surrounding—but independent of—the telescope and even the platform on which the observer reclines.

The Giant Reflectors

The 200-inch reflecting telescope ranks as one of the greatest technical achievements of this generation. It is the result of the efforts of George Ellery Hale, who died in 1938 before it became a reality. It was his dream of a 200-inch telescope that brought the $6,000,000 gift from the International Education Board, financed principally by John D. Rockefeller, Sr. This giant telescope is located on Mount Palomar, in southern California. It explores a volume about eight times greater than that previously accessible.

The world's second largest telescope in 1965 was the 120-inch reflector of the Lick Observatory located on Mount Hamilton, California. However, two larger mirrors made from fused quartz, due for completion in 1966, will eventually be the second and third largest reflectors. The 151-inch reflector is to be housed in the Kitt Peak observatory in Ari-

zona. The 140-inch mirror will be used for a European Southern Observatory in the mountains of Chile. It is sponsored by five European nations.

The Schmidt Telescope

In 1931, Bernhard Schmidt, of Hamburg-Bergedorf Observatory, invented the telescope named in his honor. This telescope is a *hybrid instrument, half reflector and half refractor,* possessing the advantages of each. It consists of a spherical mirror and a thin lens, called a "correcting plate," which eliminates spherical aberration.

The advantages of the Schmidt telescope are that it covers a relatively large area of the sky and takes sharply defined pictures in relatively short periods of time. It will photograph an area five hundred times larger than is possible with an ordinary reflecting telescope, in about one-tenth of the time. The 48-inch Schmidt telescope at Palomar Observatory is expected to advance astronomy as much as the 200-inch reflector at the same Observatory. Employing the Palomar Schmidt telescope, the National Geographic Society sponsored a survey of the visible sky which was photographed on about one thousand plates in a period of four years, using red and blue filters to give information concerning the color of stars. The color of a star is a rough measure of its temperature. Thus, blue-white stars have a surface temperature range of 40,000° F to 60,000° F, while red stars have a range of 4,000° F to 6,000° F. By using a blue filter, all light except blue light is screened out. Similarly, a red filter allows only red light to pass through it. Photographs taken without filters would not enable astronomers to tell which stars are blue-white or red. The temperature of a star is important in determining its type. It is estimated that astronomers will be kept busy for fifty years tabulating and interpreting the information contained on these plates.

The Radio Telescope

Short radio waves from space may be received by very sensitive radio receivers, the antennae of which correspond to the functions of the refractor or reflector. The energy received is changed into an electric current, which is amplified and recorded graphically.

The source of the radio waves received from outer space is a matter of conjecture. However, it is known that hydrogen gas emits radiations having a wavelength of 21 cm. The first hydrogen radiation from space was observed at Harvard University in 1951, thus stimulating the construction of radio telescopes of various types throughout the world. Unsuspected clouds of hydrogen gas have been revealed by the radio telescope.

THE LOCATION OF OBSERVATORIES

Just as light is bent as it passes from air through glass, so it is bent by passing from less dense into more dense air (cold or hot). Variations in the moisture content likewise cause bending of light. To reduce this error as far as possible, telescopes are located preferably on mountains, where the light from cities will not interfere, and where the least number of cloudy days will be experienced.

A good telescope cannot be kept in a heated dome in winter, because the warm air escaping through the opening in the dome would produce a wavering in the air that would make observations impossible. Furthermore, it is important that the temperature of the instruments be kept as constant as possible.

MODERN TELESCOPES HAVE EXTENDED MAN'S KNOWLEDGE OF THE UNIVERSE

With modern telescopes man has been able to bring into photographic view about thirty billion stars, or ten million stars for every star that is visible to the unaided eye. The Palomar telescope penetrates space to a distance of 2 billion **light years** (*a light year is the distance that light travels in one year at the speed of 186,282 miles per second.*)

SPECTROGRAPHS

The principle of the simple spectrograph is shown in Figure 9-5.

Figure 9-6 shows how a ray of light is bent by a prism.

The prism of a spectrograph **disperses** the light, i.e., *separates it into its different wave-*

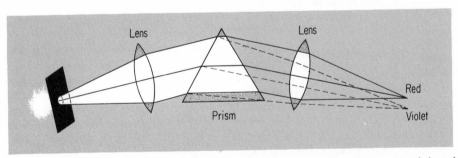

Figure 9–5. The principle of the optical spectrometer. Light from a source such as sunlight is passed through a slit and a lens, then through a glass prism which disperses the light into its component colors. The second lens brings the light rays to a focus. The colors of the visible spectrum represent wavelengths to which the color receptors of the eye respond. Note that the wavelengths at the violet end of the spectrum are refracted more than the wavelengths at the red end of the spectrum.

Figure 9–6. Refraction of a light ray by a glass prism. The two angles shown are intended to be the same.

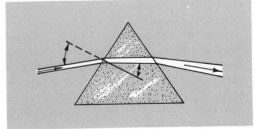

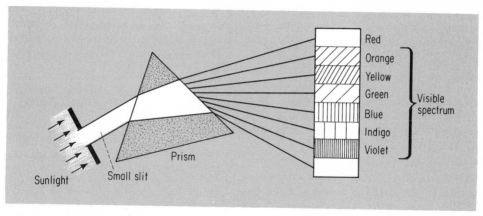

Figure 9–7. A prism disperses white light into the colors of the spectrum. The shorter wavelengths at the violet end of the spectrum are refracted most.

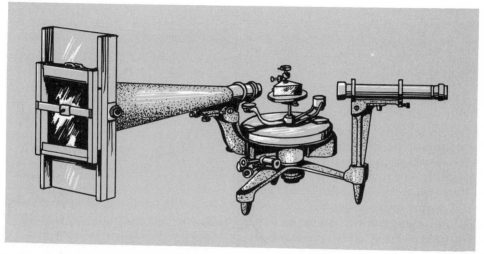

Figure 9–8. A simple Spectrograph. The light from a light source passes through a narrow slit in the tube to the right, known as the collimator. Then it passes through a prism which separates the light into its component colors. The tube to the left is a small telescope which brings the light from the prism to a focus on a photographic plate contained in the plate holder to the far left. If the eye replaces the photographic plate the instrument is known as a spectrometer or a spectroscope depending upon the presence or absence of a device to measure the wavelength of the lines.

lengths. Each different color, representing a different wavelength, is differently refracted by the prism, the shorter wavelengths being refracted more than the longer wavelengths. See Figure 9-7.

Solids or liquids, when heated to incandescence, yield *an unbroken band of colors* called a **continuous spectrum,** similar in appearance to a rainbow. Incandescent gases usually yield *bright lines or bands,* called **bright line spectra.** The wavelengths of these bands recorded on a photograph may be

measured. When portions of a continuous spectrum are intercepted by a transparent medium—such as a gas, a liquid, or a solution —*dark bands, the* **Fraunhofer lines,** *are found at the positions where the medium would have yielded bright lines had it been heated to incandescence. Such a dark band spectrum is known as an* **absorption spectrum.**

The dark lines of an absorption spectrum of a star correspond to the Fraunhofer lines in the sun's spectrum. These dark lines are found to differ in intensity for different stars, and by checking the distances of these stars by the **method of parallax**,[1] it was found that there is a correlation between the intensities of these lines and the distances of the stars. In other words, these dark lines reveal the intrinsic or actual brightness of a star. Knowing the apparent brightness of a star and its actual brightness, it is easy to estimate star distances.

By comparing the spectrum of an unknown substance with spectra of known substances, the composition of the unknown may be determined. For example, the spectrum of the light from the sun showed lines not characteristic of any element known on the earth. This element was called helium. Later it was discovered on the earth.

The intensity of the energy present determines the extent to which molecules break down to form atoms, or the extent to which molecules or atoms become ionized. Thus, the temperatures of stars can be determined roughly from spectra.

The astronomer can deduce from the spectrum of a star not only the composition of its atmosphere, but also its temperature and direction of motion relative to the observer. As explained by the Quantum theory below, red-hot stars emit their most intense radiation in the red part of the spectrum, while white-hot or blue-hot stars emit more radiation in the blue portion of the spectrum. Thus the spectrum of a star reveals its temperature.

When a star is approaching the observer, the wavelengths of the spectral lines appear to be decreased, whereas they are increased for receding stars. A shift toward the red end of the spectrum indicates that the light source is receding. This *shift in the wave-*

---

[1] The *method of parallax* is used to determine star distances, using the principle employed by surveyors in determining the distances across lakes, etc. If a given star is observed at two intervals, six months apart, so that the observations are made on opposite sides of the earth's orbit, and the angle of the telescope relative to the plane of the earth's orbit is measured, then by trigonometry the distance from the earth to the star can be determined. This method is accurate only for the nearer stars. The angles are so small for more distant stars that results are unreliable for stars more than 300 light-years away.

length is known as **the Doppler effect.** By measuring the displacement of the lines, the speed and direction of motion of a star can be determined.

ELECTRICAL AND ELECTRONIC TOOLS

The photoelectric cell shown in Figure 9-9 is employed in the photoelectric photometer, which can be used to determine the apparent brightness of a star, and aid in determining star distances. By using photoelectric cells in connection with powerful electronic devices, such as the image converter, instruments of great light sensitivity have been designed. According to theoretical calculations,

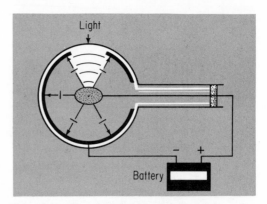

Figure 9–9. The photoelectric cell. When light strikes the potassium-coated electrode in the center electrons are emitted and stream to the positive electrode.

an ideal image converter, when combined with the 200-inch telescope at Palomar, would enable the telescope to "see" as far into space as an unaided 2,000-inch reflector could penetrate. The **image converter,** like the **photoelectric cell,** *converts the light of faint stars into electrons, which may then be accelerated and focused on a photographic plate.*

SUMMARY

The four types of telescopes are refractor, reflector, Schmidt, and radio. The first three types gather light and focus it to give a sharp image. This image is magnified by the eyepieces. Radio telescopes depend upon the reception of radio waves from distant sources.

The spectrograph enables the astronomer to make the following observations:

Type of observation	Value
Number and position of the lines	Composition—both elements and compounds
Variation in width of Fraunhofer lines	Intrinsic brightness—star distances
Direction of shift	Motion of stars
Variation in intensity of lines of different wavelength	Star temperatures

Fraunhofer lines are *the dark bands on a continuous spectrum, which represent the absorption of light of the wavelength that the absorbing medium would have emitted, had it been luminous.*

Study Questions

1. DEFINE: refractor, reflector, refraction, objective, eyepiece, light year, focal length, resolving power, continuous spectrum, bright line spectrum, Doppler effect, Fraunhofer lines, image converter, absorption spectrum, disperse, Schmidt telescope, compound lens, spherical aberration.
2. Give the principles of the two main types of telescopes.
3. Why are the largest telescopes reflectors rather than refractors?
4. What are the relative advantages and disadvantages of reflecting and refracting telescopes?
5. What are the functions of the objectives in telescopes?
6. What is spherical aberration, and how is it overcome?
7. Why are very large refractors less practical than very large reflectors?

CHAPTER 10

The Stellar Universe

Twinkle, twinkle, little star—
How I wonder what you are.
Up above the world so high,
Like a diamond in the sky.

"Angel, I will go no further; for the spirit of man acheth with his infinity. Insufferable is the Glory of God. Let me lie down in the grave and hide me from the persecution of the Infinite, for end I see there is none. . . ." The Angel lifted up his glorious hands to the heaven of heavens, saying, "End is there none to the universe of God. Lo! also, there is no beginning!"

JEAN PAUL RICHTER

INTRODUCTION

Our **sun** is *but one of the untold billions of stars. It is a typical, single, average type of star,* composed of virtually the same elements as other stars examined with the spectrograph. Like other stars, it is composed of a mass of very hot gases held together by gravitational attraction. It is visible because of the tremendous amount of energy that it generates in the visible part of the spectrum. The heat of the sun overhead on a hot summer day testifies to the energy of the sun, and this is only one 2-billionth of the sun's output.

Even with the naked eye it is possible to see that the stars differ in color. Do they differ in other regards? How do they compare with the sun as to size, mass, density, temperature, and energy? What is the source of their energy? How old are the stars? Are they all of the same age, or do they go through a life cycle? Such are the questions that arise as our eyes turn to the heavens.

ARRANGEMENT OF THE STARS

One of the first things that one observes as he turns his eyes to the sky is the Milky Way. The **Milky Way**, when viewed by a telescope, turns out to *be a vast disk-like system of stars about 80,000 light years in diameter and about 10,000 light years in thickness.* Our sun is located in the plane of the Milky Way near one edge, as shown in Figure 10-1.

When we view the Milky Way in the sky, we are looking toward the edge, and see many more stars than when we look toward either face of the disk. The Milky Way would appear as a brilliant band of light if it were not for the presence of great amounts of dust which obstruct our view.

This giant system of stars is a **typical spiral nebula, or galaxy.** The total number of galaxies which have been observed is about 1 billion. The number of stars in our galaxy has been estimated to be over 100 billion. Multiply this figure by the number of

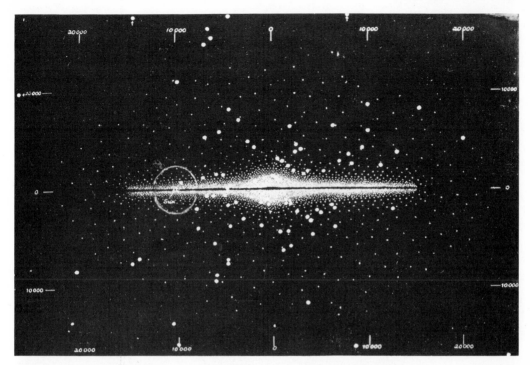

Figure 10–1. Diagram of our Galaxy by Oort. The solar system is located at the center of the circle at the left. The large dots are globular star clusters. (Courtesy, Dominion Astrophysical Observatory)

known galaxies and you will obtain an estimate of the number of stars in the known Universe: a number beyond our comprehension.

Galaxies will be studied in Chapter 14.

Spiral nebulas are often called **universes** or **island universes.** In this text the word **universe** will be capitalized when referring to the sum of all of the universes and will be referred to as **"the Universe."** When speaking of our island universe we will refer to it as **"the Galaxy"** to distinguish it from the other galaxies.

STAR CLUSTERS

The stars in our galaxy are not evenly distributed. Sometimes they are grouped as star clusters, like the cluster in *Hercules*, shown in Figures 10-4 and 10-5; or sometimes as open clusters, such as the Pleiades ("Seven Sisters"), shown in Figure 10-6.

The great *Hercules* star cluster radiates one thousand times as much energy as is radiated by the sun. Figure 10-5 gives the impression that these stars are close to each other, but appearances are deceiving because this star cluster is so far distant. Actually, the average distance between these stars is about 100,000 times the distance from the earth to the sun. There is plenty of room for each of these stars to have many planets revolving about it, but planets would be too small to be seen even with the most powerful telescopes, so there is no evidence that other stars do or do not have systems of planets.

There are 93 globular clusters such as the star cluster in *Hercules*. These clusters are intrinsically very bright, because they are composed of so many stars; about 100,000 in the Hercules star cluster, which is faintly visible to the naked eye. The globular clusters are not found in the Milky Way, but they are still considered to be members of the stellar system of which the Milky Way is a portion. The nearest cluster is estimated to be 18,000 light years distant, while the most distant one discovered so far is estimated to be 184,000 light years away.

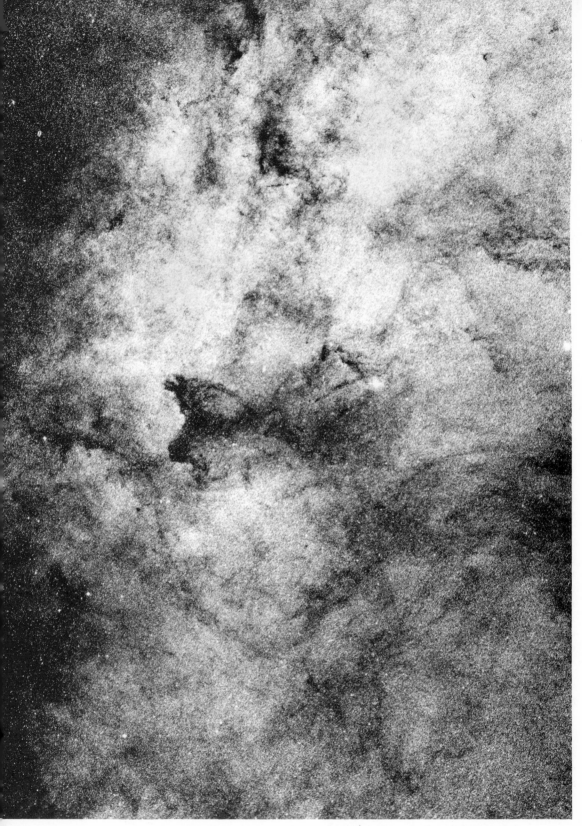

Figure 10–2.   Milky Way in Sagittarius. (Courtesy, Mount Wilson and Palomar Observatories)

Figure 10–3. Milky Way near Rho Ophiuchi. (An astronomical photograph from the Yerkes Observatory, reprinted by permission of the Chicago University Press)

Figure 10–4. Great globular cluster in Hercules, Messier 13, photographed with the 24-inch reflecting telescope, Yerkes Observatory. (An astronomical photograph from the Yerkes Observatory, reprinted by permission of the Chicago University Press)

Figure 10–5. Great globular cluster in Hercules, Messier 13, photographed with the 200-inch telescope, Mount Palomar. Compare this figure with figure 10–4. (Courtesy, Mount Wilson and Palomar Observatories)

It would be possible for a single star to pass through a globular star cluster. More than a million years would be required for the passage of a star through such a cluster, and yet these stars in the cluster are so far apart that it would happen only once in thousands of millions of years that two stars would come close enough to each other to bring about a cosmic collision. Estimates based on the laws of probability indicate that a collision between stars may occur about once every million billion years. There are more than 300 open clusters such as shown in Figure 10-6. The *"Seven Sisters"* of the Pleiades group can be seen with the naked eye, but there are actually about 500 stars in the group. All but two of the *"Big Dipper"* stars are a part of an open cluster known as the Ursa Major group, which is about 80 light years distant. *Sirius*, the "Dog Star," visible in the southern sky, is a member of the same group.

Figure 10–6. Nebulosity in the Pleiades. (An astronomical photograph from the Yerkes Observatory, reprinted by permission of the Chicago University Press)

STAR CLOUDS

The sun is a member of a star cloud, known as the local star cloud, which appears to be a flattened group of stars lying at a slight angle to the plane of the Milky Way.

MULTIPLE STAR GROUPS

Many stars are associated in groups, such as *double* (binary), and *multiple* (from three to six). At least one-half, and perhaps three-fourths of the stars in our galaxy are composite, binary, or multiple stars.

A typical double star is Sirius—which consists of a blue-hot star, the *"Dog" star;* and a cooler, less massive companion, the *"Pup,"* which revolves about it once every fifty years. Each of these stars can be seen with a telescope, but the evidence for more distant double stars is the periodic fluctuations in the amount of light received from them. These fluctuations are assumed to be the result of the eclipse of one of the stars by its companion.

The "Pup" is dimmer than the "Dog" star, and it is most unusual in that it has a mass approximately equal to our sun, but it has a diameter only 1/32 of the sun. Spectrographic data indicate that it is as hot as its bright companion. The larger of the two stars is twice as large as the sun, and is very bright. How can the smaller companion be much smaller than the sun and still have about the same mass as the sun? The conclusion must be that this star is very dense, its mass being packed into a volume of about 16,000 miles in diameter. For this to be possible, it must have a density nearly 3,000 times that of platinum. A tablespoonful of its material would weigh more than a ton on the earth.

Algol is a well-known eclipsing pair of stars, which decreases in brightness every three days —the dark phase lasting about nine hours. Half a cycle later the dimming is repeated, but to a lesser extent, probably because one of the two stars is much more luminous than the other.

Periodic shifts in spectral lines furnish evidence of the existence of at least a thousand double stars.

STAR CONSTELLATIONS

The constellations of the stars have no scientific significance except as an aid in naming and locating stars. The **constellations** *are merely groups of stars that ancient man imagined to fall into definite groups whose formations traced the lines of various objects, in which animals predominated.* Thus a swan (*Cygnus*), a ram (*Aries*), and a dragon (*Draco*), and a bull (*Taurus*) are among the nearly 100 constellations. The *Big* and *Little Dippers* are the most familiar figures.

Today, the brighter stars are usually referred to by name. Thus *Vega*, *Arcturus* (made famous by the Century of Progress Fair at Chicago), *Betelgeuse, Polaris, Sirius,* etc., are well-known stars. Since common names would soon run out and would be of no value in locating stars for scientific purposes, the stars are named either by Greek letters according to their magnitude in generally-accepted constellations; or they are simply numbered according to their position in a given section of the sky.

THE MOTION OF STARS

The velocity of stars varies considerably; some stars move with a velocity of 200 miles per second, and others move less rapidly. The average rate is about 18 miles per second. Our own sun is moving toward the constellation Hercules at the leisurely speed of 12 miles per second. So great is the distance of the stars from the earth, however, that any two of the more distant stars moving apart at the rate of 600 million miles per year (characteristic of the speed of many stars) would not show any appreciable change of position within a thousand years.

COLOR AND TEMPERATURE OF STARS

Telescopic observations of stars with the eye instead of a camera show that the stars vary in color: yellow, orange, red, blue, white, etc. Because most of the astronomical photographs are made with black and white film, we do not generally think of stars as having color. However, when the heavens are photographed with color film, gorgeous coloring is revealed. The differences in the colors are chiefly due to the differences in temperatures.

THE SIZE AND DENSITY OF STARS

From the knowledge of the temperatures of stars and other data, it seems to be certain that some stars are merely volumes of very hot gases, so rarefied that they would pass as a good vacuum on earth, while other stars are more dense than anything known on earth. Stars do not appear to differ as much as a hundredfold in mass, but they may differ in size (volume) as much as a hundred millionfold.

NOVAS AND SUPERNOVAS

One of the early startling observations was the appearance of what seemed to be new stars. Hipparchus observed such a star in 134 B.C. In 1054, a new star, surpassing Venus in brightness was visible for weeks in daylight. Figure 10-7 shows the present view of this star which is called the *Crab Nebula*. In 1572, Tycho Brahe observed another brilliant new star, and wrote a book about it, entitled *De Nova Stella*. Thus the modern term, *Nova*, originated for a *"new star."* Eventually, telescopic observations proved that novas are not new stars at all, but merely faint stars which have suddenly produced greatly increased amounts of energy, as typical in an explosion. After an explosion, a nova settles down to its original state, but it is surrounded for months or years with an expanding glowing shell of gases, as shown in Figure 10-8. Some of the novas have been observed to repeat their explosive outbursts several times and are called recurrent novas. Other novas, called permanent novas, seem to resemble a continuous, huge volcano.

Some novas are so much more brilliant than others that they are called **supernovas.** Probably the "new stars" observed by ancient astronomers were supernovas. They may attain brightness equal to 100 million of our suns,

and release as much energy in a day as our sun gives off in a million years.

Supernovas are explained as the explosions of stars which, as a result of interior changes, suddenly collapse. The very high temperature generated by the tremendous increase in pressure due to this collapse is high enough to cause a fusion type of nuclear reaction between the hydrogen atoms not yet used up. *After the explosion, resulting from the fusion reaction, the core of the star is a* **white dwarf.** Eventually a white dwarf grows dimmer, and finally becomes a black, nonluminous body.

NEBULOUS MATERIAL IN OUR GALAXY

It is thought that the dark splotches formed against a background of stars in the Milky Way, such as shown in Figure 10-9, do not represent an absence of stars in these regions, but rather a blotting out of the light from stars by masses of cosmic dust. The luminosity of the nebulous material shown in Figures 10-3 and 10-6 is probably caused by the light reflected from cosmic dust.

THE LIFE HISTORY OF A TYPICAL STAR LIKE THE SUN

Astronomers have evidence that leads them to conclude that stars have been in various

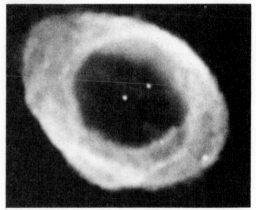

stages of creation ever since the Universe began (if it did have a beginning), and that they are being created today. Signs of extreme youth are found near extreme old age, in the same star clouds. The oldest stars date back as far as the Universe does, while the youngest stars are less than a million years old.

It has been estimated that there is as much matter in the space between the stars as there is in all of the stars put together, most of it hydrogen. Stars probably start with this hydrogen. Eventually the star generates sufficient heat in the center, as a result of condensation, to start a fusion reaction which continues as long as there is an abundance of hydrogen fuel. Perhaps the helium atoms formed by the fusion of hydrogen atoms will now fuse, liberating more energy and forming heavier elements.

Another source of new stars may be the tremendous amounts of energy radiated by the stars into space. Perhaps this energy becomes matter again—somehow, somewhere.

SUMMARY

Stars occur in our galaxy in the form of single, binary, or multiple stars. They may also occur in such star groups as open-cluster, globular clusters, or clouds.

Our galaxy or universe, the Milky Way, is but one of 100 billion known universes, the total being called the Universe.

Within our galaxy are patches of dark or luminous matter which probably consist of clouds of gases and dust particles.

Stars differ in temperature, mass, density, and color. They are considered to pass through a life cycle which results in changes in density and temperature.

Study Questions

1. DEFINE: binary star, multiple star, nova, universe, Universe, constellation, supernova, Galaxy, galaxy.
2. How fast do stars move?
3. How can a nova be accounted for?
4. What is meant by the statement that many stars are multiple?
5. Compare the variations of stars in density and mass.

Figure 10–9. "Horsehead" nebula in Orion. (Courtesy, Mount Wilson and Palomar Observatories)

6. Are collisions between stars likely to be of frequent occurrence? Discuss.
7. What is the estimated number of stars in our galaxy?
8. What form does our galaxy take?
9. What is the size of our galaxy?
10. What is thought to be the nature of a nebular cloud?

The Sun—The Nearest Star

Astronomy, more perhaps than any other science, teaches the imperfection of human understanding, and hesitates to set limits to the planes which may be attained in the future. Celestial things are rarely what they seem.

SIR RICHARD GREGORY

INTRODUCTION

If man wanted to find some object in the universe to worship, the sun would probably be selected—because it is the source of our light and heat, and because our food, clothing, and housing could never have been formed without its valuable rays.

The sun is the only star in the Universe close enough to permit a study of its surface and other characteristics. Therefore, the study of the sun enables us to know much more about the nature of stars than would otherwise be possible.

In a sense, we live in the sun's outer atmosphere, and the earth is enveloped at times in particles emitted from the sun's surface. Auroras, disturbances in radio transmission, and perhaps variations in the weather and other profound influences result from the huge eruptions on the surface of the sun.

CHARACTERISTICS OF THE SUN

Size

The sun is about midway between the smallest and largest stars in size. The largest known star, *V V Cephei,* has a radius about 1,220 times that of the sun; while the smallest stars are about 1/100 the size of the sun.

The diameter of the sun is 865,400 miles, about 100 times the diameter of the earth. See Figure 11-1.

Mass

The sun is about average in mass. The largest stars are not more than a few hundred times the mass of the sun, while the least massive stars are about 1/60 the mass of the sun. The mass of the sun is 333,400 times the mass of the earth.

Density

The sun lies about midway between the other stars in density, some of them having a density about one million times the density of the sun, and others having a density of about one-millionth that of the sun.

An average cubic inch of the most dense star would weigh about 620 tons on the earth. On the other hand, the average density of a huge star like **Betelgeuse** would represent a good vacuum on the earth, about 1/2,000 that of the atmosphere at sea level. The average density of the sun is about 40 per cent greater than water. The density of the earth averages about four times that of the sun.

Thus it appears that the sun is an average star as to size, mass, and density, but that it is more luminous than other average stars.

Luminosity

The sun has been referred to as an average type of star, but in luminosity it is about 13 thousand times brighter than most of the average type of stars.

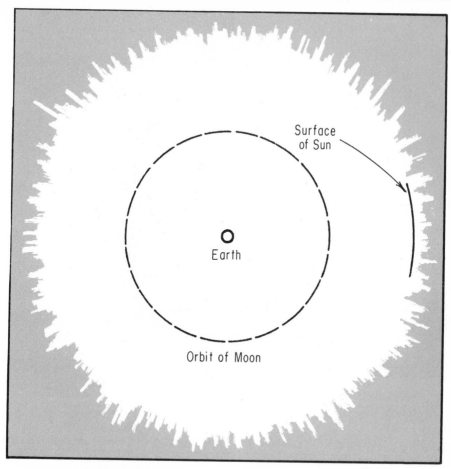

Figure 11-1. The size of the sun in comparison with the earth and the orbit of the moon.

Temperature

It is a common observation that the temperature of a hot body can be indicated by its color, which may vary from a dull red to a bluish white.

The temperature of the sun's surface may be determined by spectrographic measurements, which show the relative intensities of the different wavelengths. Such data give a surface temperature of about 5,700° C. It is estimated that the interior temperature of the sun is about 20 million degrees C.

Distance of the Sun from the Earth

The average distance of the sun from the earth is about 93 million miles, but because the orbit of the earth's path around the sun is an ellipse, it is closer at one time than at another time. As shown in Figure 11-2, the distance at aphelion is greater than the distance at perihelion. The terms aphelion and perihelion are used so much today, in discussing the orbits of man-made satellites, that we introduce them here. **Aphelion** refers to *the point at which the earth is farthest from the sun,* and the **perihelion** is *the point where it is closest to the sun.* Because the sun is closer to the earth in December, the earth receives about 7 per cent more heat in December than in June. For this reason, the weather in the northern hemisphere is tempered slightly, while the southern hemisphere should experience colder winters and hotter summers. However, because of the large expanse of the southern oceans and other factors, the temperatures experienced by the southern

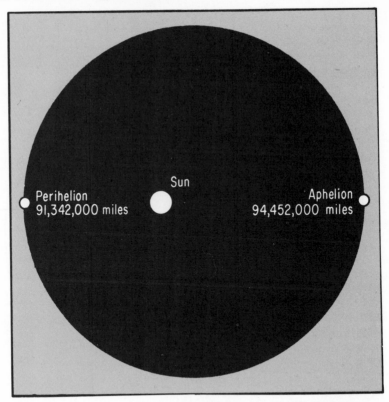

Figure 11–2. The distance of the earth from the sun at aphelion and perihelion.

hemisphere are not markedly different from those of the northern hemisphere.

Composition

Spectrographic data show that 66 of the 92 elements found in the earth are present in the sun. The surface atmosphere is composed largely of hydrogen mixed with small amounts of helium and oxygen, plus minute amounts of metallic vapors.

The Outer Layers of the Sun

The sunlight that we see on the earth comes from *the surface layer of the sun,* which is called the **photosphere,** because it is *the sphere of light.* The **photosphere** *is a layer of gases about 200 miles thick, which emits a continuous spectrum of visible-light wavelengths.*

Figure 11-3 shows that the surface of the sun appears to be granular in nature, the size of each granule ranging from 150 to 900 miles in diameter.

Next to the photosphere is the **chromosphere,** a *turbulent layer of less dense gases about 5,000 miles thick.* The term, **chromosphere,** *is based on the fact that the colored lines of the bright line spectrum originate in this layer.*

Outside of the chromosphere is *the extensive envelope of gases* called the **corona.** Figure 11-4 shows how it appears during an eclipse. It is not visible to the naked eye, except during eclipses. The corona extends outward from the sun, a distance about one-third its diameter. Radio waves originating in the corona indicate that its temperature is about 1 million degrees C.

Sunspots

The most conspicuous objects on the sun's disk are *the dark areas* called *sunspots,* which usually occur as groups, as shown in Figure 11-5. Sunspots were discovered by Galileo. Some sunspots have been observed to be so large that their diameter exceeds the diameter of the earth. They usually range between 500 and 50,000 miles in diameter. Most of the sunspots continue for only a few days, but some large ones may be seen for several months.

Sunspots represent relatively cool areas, which have a temperature of about 4,000° C, as compared with 6,000° C, which is the temperature of the hottest outside portions of the chromosphere. It is thought that these areas of lower temperatures—characteristic of sunspots—are the result of tremendous solar cyclones, which increase to a maximum and then for some unknown reason decrease periodically every 11 years.

Heinrich Schwabe (1789–1875) made observations with two telescopes little larger than spyglasses, over a period of 10 years, in which he found that sunspots show a periodic rise and fall of activity. The average interval between maximum and minimum activity, for a 200-year period, has been about 11 years, varying 9 to 13.6 years.

Studies of annual tree rings show that they vary in a similar 11-year cycle. When these solar disturbances are at their maximum, magnetic disturbances occur on the earth that interfere seriously with telegraphic, telephonic, and radio communication. The aurorae are also more brilliant at such times.

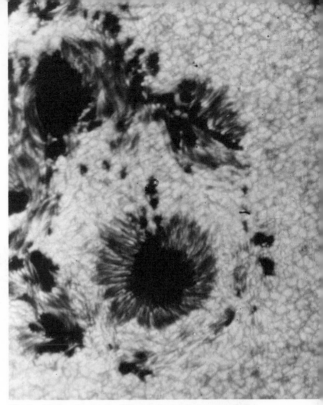

Figure 11–3. Sunspots. This photograph is one of the sharpest ever taken of the sun's surface. It was taken from a balloon-observatory where photographs could be made free from the distortion caused by the earth's atmosphere. The camera was controlled by radio and the telescope was aimed and focused by the use of television. (Project Stratoscope of Princeton University, sponsored by the Office of Naval Research and the National Science Foundation)

Figure 11–4. Solar Corona, photographed at the total eclipse of June 8, 1918, Green River, Wyoming. (Courtesy, Mount Wilson and Palomar Observatories)

Figure 11–5. Sunspots of August 13, 1917. (An astronomical photograph from the Yerkes Observatory. reprinted by permission of the Chicago University Press)

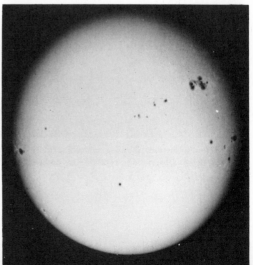

Observations of the snowfall, rainfall, relative occurrence of icebergs, and the number of storms have shown a relationship between them and sunspot maxima and minima; but more data must be obtained before definite conclusions are justifiable.

Some observers consider that wet and dry cycles on the earth result from changes in the temperature of the earth, the rate of evaporation of water and the amount of cloudiness, and the rainfall, which in turn are related to sunspot activity. For example, the annual rings in trees are wider during sunspot activity because of more favorable growing conditions.

Unusual weather (and what weather is not unusual!), wet and dry cycles, wars, panics, epidemics, and other periodic occurrences have been blamed on sunspots; but no sure conclusions are justified by present evidence, often conflicting in nature.

These disturbances on the earth may be due to increased streams of electrons and ions or

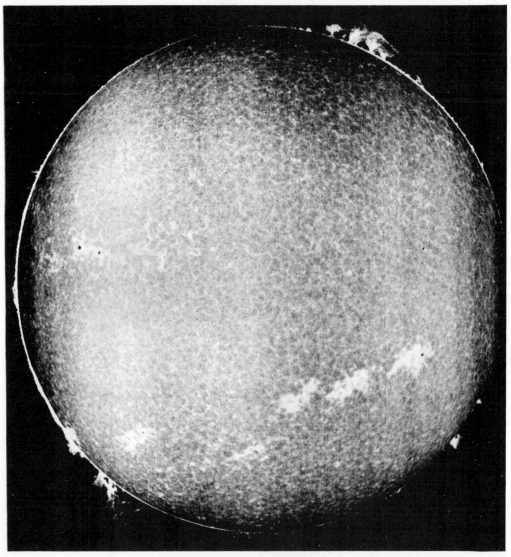

Figure 11–6. The sun, showing unusual activity in both flocculi and prominences. (An astronomical photograph from the Yerkes Observatory, reprinted by permission of the University of Chicago Press)

increased ultraviolet radiation coming from the sun, as a result of changing solar conditions.

Perhaps periodic effects on the earth, and the periodic changes in sunspots and prominences do not represent a cause-and-effect relationship, but are the result of profound nuclear changes within the sun.

In 1896, Pieter Zeeman (1865–1943) observed that luminous vapor, when placed in a powerful magnetic field, produced spectrum lines having an abnormal band-like appearance. Spectra of sunspots have this same appearance, and lead to the conclusion that each sunspot is a center of a magnetic field, which increases with increasing sizes of the spots. Spots in groups vary in polarity, but the polarity reverses at the beginning of a new cycle.

A great magnetic storm occurred in April 1938, in which energy was expended at the rate of 2 billion kilowatts for a two-hour interval, according to A. G. McNish of the Carnegie Institution. This storm was accompanied by obstruction of transatlantic radio communication, numerous interruptions in wired communications services, and interference with the operation of electric power systems. The International Geophysical Year was timed to coincide with a period of maximum sunspot activity, and the sun reciprocated by putting on one of its greatest displays of sunspots.

The sun rotates about its axis in the same direction as does the earth; but not being a solid, it does not rotate uniformly as a whole. Thus spots on the sun's equator rotate in about 24.6 days, as compared with a rotational period of 34 days or more near the poles.

Prominences

Prominences, such as shown in Figures 11-6 and 11-7, may be seen during an eclipse of the sun by the moon, or by use of special devices to screen out the bright disk of the sun. These features of the surface of the sun have received a great deal of study. Although they have far-reaching effects on the earth, they still are not fully understood. These **prominences** are *great flares of glowing hydrogen gas, often shooting out from the sun very rapidly, forming an arch and returning to the sun.* One prominence was observed to move with a velocity of 450 miles per second. These flares may billow out from the sun a distance of from 30,000 miles to even 1 million miles, at times. They average about 6,000 miles in thickness, and 30,000 miles in height.

In many cases, the prominences appear to be vast quantities of luminous gases pouring into the sun. They usually last for only a few days. Brilliant flares are often accompanied by fade-outs of high-frequency radio transmission, and even electrical transmission by telegraph.

Figure 11–7. A tremendous prominence—June 4, 1946. (Courtesy, High Altitude Observatory, Boulder, Colorado)

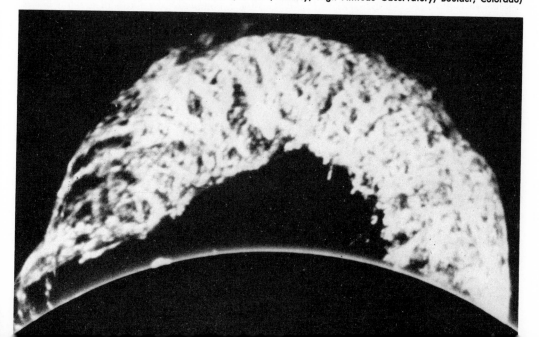

THE ENERGY OF THE SUN

The amount of the sun's energy that finally reaches the earth is very large, but it is only one two-billionth of the sun's total output. Measured by the pyrheliometer, it is found that the earth receives 230 trillion horsepower continuously, or about 160,000 horsepower for every human being. The amount of energy radiated by the sun would be sufficient to melt a 40-foot shell of ice around the sun within one minute. The generators at Hoover Dam, when operated at maximum capacity, are able to generate 834 thousand horsepower—thus harnessing about 1/275 millionth of the sun's energy which reaches the earth.

Records preserved in the rock layers of the earth indicate that there has been no noticeable permanent change in the amount of energy that the earth has received during the past billion years. This observation indicates either that there is so much energy in the sun that the relative amount lost in a billion years is negligible, or that there are changes taking place within the sun which liberate energy to compensate for the energy that is lost.

The outstanding thing about most stars is that they can be seen or photographed, because, like our sun, they generate their own energy. At one time, this energy was accounted for by the contraction of stars. While contraction may be an important source of energy at various times in the life history of a star, it cannot account for the huge, continuous outpouring of energy typical of our sun. When radioactivity was discovered toward the close of the nineteenth century, it was at first considered to be the final explanation. However, the spectra of the sun did not reveal the presence of the radioactive elements; and again, even the large amounts of energy thus liberated would be inadequate to account for the energy liberated by the stars. When Einstein, in 1905, proposed his relationship between matter and energy, calculations showed that the amounts of energy generated within the stars could be accounted for in terms of the conversion of mass into energy.

At the high interior temperature of the sun, it is believed that only atomic nuclei could exist. It would appear, therefore, that the source of the sun's energy would be a fusion type of nuclear reaction—triggered by its very high temperature—in which light hydrogen nuclei fuse to form helium nuclei. Since the gases of the sun are composed largely of hydrogen and helium, this conclusion would seem to be reasonable. The energy liberated by the reaction would be sufficient to keep the reaction self-sustaining, and at a constant temperature.

It has been calculated that 564 million tons of hydrogen are converted into 560 million tons of helium every second. In this reaction, the 4 million tons of matter left over represent the amount of matter converted into energy. If the sun continues to consume hydrogen at this rate, there will be enough to last about 100 billion years, and there is evidence that the sun is constantly pilfering space to supplement its supply. The sun loses about 350 billion tons of mass per day, but it has an amount sufficient to keep on losing it at this rate for billions of years.

SUMMARY

The sun is an average star in terms of mass, size, and density; but it is brighter than most stars of its type. It is a giant sphere of glowing gas. Its surface, the photosphere, is surrounded by the chromosphere, outside of which is the corona.

Sunspots are probably giant magnetic storms on the surface of the sun, and are often accompanied by flares of glowing gases, called prominences.

Periodic minima and maxima of sunspot activity occur about every eleven years.

The source of the sun's energy is probably one or more types of fusion reactions in which hydrogen and helium serve as the fuels.

The sun is about 5 billion years old, and has enough fuel to last at least 100 billion years more.

Study Questions

1. DEFINE: sunspot, photosphere, chromosphere, corona, prominence, aphelion, perihelion.
2. How far is the sun from the earth?
3. Is the sun gaseous, liquid, or solid? Give reasons for your answer.
4. Discuss the temperature of the sun.

5. Compare the sun and the earth as to density.
6. What is a possible source of the sun's energy?
7. What is thought to be the nature of the sunspots?
8. How do the sunspots influence the earth?
9. What are the indirect ways of using the sun's energy?
10. Give some data to show how much energy is received from the sun by the earth each day.
11. How much longer can the sun continue to pour out energy at its present rate?
12. Discuss the periodic nature of sunspot activity.

13. In what respects is the sun an average star?
14. In what respect does the sun differ from most average stars?
15. Compare the sun and the earth as to diameter.
16. What is the nature of the sun's corona, and when may it be observed to best advantage?
17. Why does the distance of the earth from the sun vary from time to time?
18. At what time of the year is the earth closest to the sun?
19. Why does the southern hemisphere not have such extremes of temperature as one would expect it to have?

CHAPTER 1 2

The Solar System

An isolated fact can be observed by all eyes; by those of the ordinary person as well as of the wise. But it is the true physicist alone who may see the bond which unites several facts among which the relationship is important, though obscure. The story of Newton's apple is probably not true, but it is symbolical; so let us think of it as true. Well, we must believe that many before Newton had seen apples fall, but they made no deduction. Facts are sterile until there are minds capable of choosing between them and discerning those which conceal something and recognizing that which is concealed; minds which under the bare fact see the soul of the fact.

HENRI POINCARÉ

INTRODUCTION

The solar system consists of the sun at the center, around which revolve nine planets and their satellites. Figure 12-1 shows a natural grouping of the planets into two groups: (1) the **terrestrial,** *small, inner, earth-like planets,* and (2) the larger planets more distant from the sun. In addition to the nine planets, there are 31 **satellites** (*moons*) of the planets, more than 30,000 *minor planets* (**planetoids**), and vast quantities of meteors, comets, dust particles and gases. The planets, planetoids, and satellites shine only because of the sunlight which they reflect.

The ancient Babylonians, Egyptians, and Greeks recognized five "wanderers" besides the sun and the moon, but it did not occur to them that the earth was a sixth such wanderer or planet.

With the exception of the smaller objects, including the comets and meteors, the larger bodies exhibit some important regularities. All of the planets except Pluto revolve about the sun in a nearly flat plane which is that of the sun's equator. The planets revolve in nearly circular orbits, although these circles are slightly elongated to form ellipses. All of the planets (with the possible exception of Pluto) revolve about the sun in a counter-clockwise direction. All of the planets with the exception of Pluto and Uranus rotate about their axes in counter-clockwise direction, the same direction as the direction of rotation of the sun about its axis. All of the satellites, with the exception of Triton (a satellite of Neptune), revolve about their planets in a counter-clockwise direction, and in the planes of their planetary equators.

Such regularities suggest a common origin of all of the members of the solar system, including the sun. Pluto, the exception mentioned above, may not even be a planet. It has been suggested that it is a runaway satellite of Neptune. "Wrongway" Triton, like Pluto and Uranus and its satellites, may have had its direction changed by some kind of cosmic accident.

THE ORIGIN OF THE SOLAR SYSTEM

Newton suggested that the solar system might have been formed by the **condensa-**

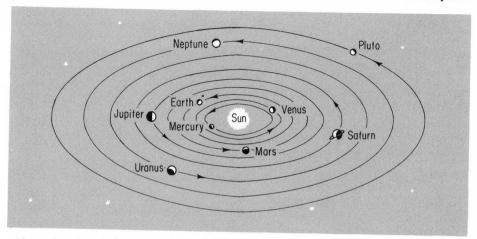

Figure 12–1. The solar system consists of the sun and nine planets. The planets travel in slightly elliptical (elongated) circles in a plane parallel to the sun's equator.

tion of clouds of gas and dust particles.
As the mass of the nucleus grew, its gravitational attraction increased, thus hastening the process.

Pierre Simon de Laplace (1749–1827) advanced the **nebular hypothesis** in which the starting point, as in Newton's hypothesis, was a vast cloud of gases and dust particles (the forerunner of the sun), but he added the idea that this cloud was rotating.

The nebular hypothesis was discarded for a time in favor of the idea that the solar system was the result of a near collision of two stars which resulted in pulling off a large mass of gases, perhaps by tidal action (hence the name, **Tidal theory**), which then condensed to form the planets and their satellites. Today, however, the nebular hypothesis has been revived; and Newton's ideas, with variation, are generally accepted.

It is now considered that the planets were never a part of the sun, but that they were probably formed from an accumulation of dust particles and gas molecules drawn toward the sun as it passed through vast dust clouds.

MOTIONS OF THE PLANETS

Johann Kepler undertook the determination of the path of Mars, based on fairly accurate measurements made by his predecessor Tycho Brahe. After fourteen years of labor, he found that an ellipse, with the sun at one of the two foci, fitted the data. After six more years, he was able to state his famous three laws of planetary motion:

1. Elliptical Orbit Law

A planet revolves about the sun in an elliptical orbit, the sun occupying one of the foci of the ellipse.

2. Law of Areas

If a line is drawn between the planet and the sun, the line sweeps equal areas in equal time intervals. The motion of a planet is fastest when it is nearest to the sun, and it is slowest when it is most distant from the sun.

3. Harmonic Law

The square of the time for one complete revolution of a planet about the sun is proportional to the cube of the mean radius of its orbit. Planets with the smallest orbits revolve about the sun at the greatest speeds.

It was the genius of Newton that provided the explanation of these laws with his famous law of gravitation. Newton's calculations led to the conclusion that the paths of the planets should be in the form of ellipses, and thus confirmed Kepler's conclusions.

NEWTON'S LAW OF GRAVITATION

About a half century after Kepler stated his three laws, Newton announced his **law**

of gravitation, which may be stated as follows: *Every particle of matter in the Universe attracts every other particle, with a force that is proportional to the product of their masses and inversely proportional to the square of the distance between them.*

A popular account of Newton's discovery of the law of gravitation was that he got his idea when an apple fell out of a tree under which he was lying and hit him. As Poincaré pointed out in the quotation at the head of this chapter, this story is probably not true.

The important idea that occurred to Newton was not that objects are attracted to the earth—this fact was common knowledge—but that every object in the Universe exercises an attraction for every other object in the Universe.

In developing his law of universal gravitation, Newton set out to see whether or not the motion of the moon corresponded with his predictions which were based on the law. He met with difficulties at once, because different parts of the earth and the moon were not equally distant from the center of each. Newton finally solved this problem by using a new kind of mathematics, calculus, which he had invented for the purpose. Calculus has been of inestimable value to modern science in solving a wide variety of problems.

Newton presented his law of gravitation and his laws of motion in the *Principia,* published in 1686. His ideas form the basis of mechanics, and are important in the successful placing of modern satellites in orbit, or in hitting a target 5,000 miles away with a rocket.

NEWTON'S LAWS OF MOTION

The First Law of Motion

This law was first stated by Newton as follows: *"Every body perseveres in its state of rest or of uniform motion in a right (straight) line, unless it is compelled to change that state by forces impressed thereon."* It is common experience that every body "stays put" unless something causes it to move. It is also a matter of common knowledge that a body in motion will continue to move in a straight line with undiminished speed unless something is done to interfere with this motion. Of course, the motion of objects with which we are familiar gradually diminishes due to friction. One of the basic principles of putting man-made satellites into orbit is that their motion will continue undiminished, once they get out of the earth's atmosphere.

The Second Law of Motion

Newton stated his second law as follows: *The alteration of motion is ever proportional to the motive force impressed; and is made in the direction of the right (straight) line in which that force is impressed.*

A more modern statement is as follows: *The change in velocity of a body, multiplied by the mass of the body, is proportional to the force and the time for which it acts, and is in the direction of the applied force.* To understand this statement, we need to know that the **velocity** with which an object moves is *the distance it travels in a given direction divided by the time it takes to travel that dis-*

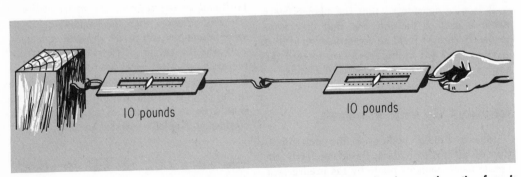

Figure 12–2. Newton's third law of motion. The two scales show the same reading because the action force is equal to the reaction force.

tance. The second law tells what happens when a force changes the velocity of a body.

The Third Law of Motion

Newton stated the third law as follows: *To every action there is always opposed an equal reaction;* or *the mutual actions of two bodies upon each other are always equal, and directed to contrary parts.* Today, a simpler statement of this law is: *To every force there is an equal and opposite reaction.* Thus, if you pull on a spring, it develops a force which pulls you, as illustrated in Figure 12-2. When one rows a boat he exerts a force against the water. But the water exerts a force on the boat in the opposite direction, and it moves forward.

Figure 12–3. Newton's third law of motion. The reaction force of the water against the nozzles causes the sprinkler to rotate.

THE PLANETS

The Terrestrial Planets

Mercury, the Most Interesting Planet—This planet is seldom seen at night, because it sets soon after the sun does and rises in the morning with the sun. Its mass is too small to hold an atmosphere. The temperature on its sunny side is above 315° C.

Venus, the Mysterious Planet—Venus passes through phases like that of Mercury and the moon. It is the brightest object in the sky after the sun and the moon, and it resembles the earth more than any other planet. Its surface is covered with clouds, and as a result it remains an enigma.

The Earth and Its Satellite, A Double Planet—Many aspects of the earth will be studied in Chapter 15. The moon will be studied in the next chapter.

The diameter of the earth is 7,913 miles, but it bulges somewhat at the equator and it is somewhat pear-shaped. It is probably solid to the core.

Mars, the Most Talked-About Planet—Mars is the only planet which could support life, and this life would be limited to primitive vegetation. The existence of some water is indicated by the thin layers of frost on the polar caps and by occasional clouds. Some astronomers claim to have observed canal-like markings on Mars, which they ascribe to intelligent beings; but such canals or any other evidences of life on Mars were not revealed by photographs taken by Mariner IV in July, 1965.

Pluto, the Most Distant Planet—Pluto is noted chiefly for its relatively great distance from the sun. Pluto is nearly forty times as far away from the sun as the earth is, and it takes 248 years to travel once around the sun. It is so far distant from the sun that its temperature must not be higher than −350° F.

The Major Planets

Jupiter, the Largest Planet—Of the major planets, Jupiter is the brightest. It shines brilliantly as an evening star. It is the largest planet, larger in both mass and volume than all of the other planets put together. However, all of the major planets are less dense than the earth. Jupiter has twelve satellites, four of which may be seen with good binoculars. With one exception, these satellites are larger than the earth's moon.

Saturn, the Ringed Planet—Saturn (see Figure 12-4) is famous because of its three

Figure 12–4. Saturn. (Courtesy, Mount Wilson and Palomar Observatories)

rings, one foot thick and 45,000 miles in width, consisting of myriads of small meteoric particles. Saturn has nine satellites whose orbits lie outside the rings.

Uranus, the Accidental Planet—Uranus and Neptune, like the earth and Venus, are twin planets. Uranus is about one-fourth as dense as the earth, and is barely visible to the naked eye on a dark night. An odd thing about its satellites is that they rotate in a direction contrary to the motion of those of the other planets. Sir William Herschel (1738–1822), on the night of March 13, 1781, discovered Uranus when he happened to observe the portion of the sky occupied by that planet.

Neptune, the Mathematical Planet—Uranus followed its predicted path until 1831, when its deviation began to be marked enough to observe. By 1841, the discrepancies were so great that one of two conclusions had to be drawn: either Newton's laws were not correct, or there was an unknown body influencing the path of Uranus. Two mathematicians—J. C. Adams and U. J. J. Leverrier—working independently, calculated the position of this unknown body; and in 1846, the German astronomer, J. G. Galle, whom Leverrier asked to look for it, after a half-hour's search discovered the planet Neptune less than a degree distant from the predicted position. This was a great triumph for Newton's laws, and greatly increased man's belief that his universe is one of cause and effect.

At the beginning of the twentieth century, small irregular motions of Uranus were observed, which suggested the existence of another planet more distant than Neptune. After years of searching, *Pluto* was discovered in 1930.

OTHER MEMBERS OF THE SOLAR SYSTEM

The Planetoids (Asteroids)

The planetoids follow elliptical orbits between those of Mars and Jupiter. Perhaps they represent the products of the disintegration of a planet that came too near to Jupiter. *The planetoids are of relatively small mass*—Ceres, the largest, having a mass about 1/8,000 that of the earth.

Comets

Several hundred comets have been observed, but most of them are visible only with a telescope. Halley's comet makes its journey around the sun once every 74 years, and its appearances have been recorded since 240 B.C. It last appeared in 1910, when it was readily visible to the naked eye.

The heads of **comets** consist of *swarms of meteors, which are surrounded by an envelope of gas,* so rarefied that stars can be readily seen through it. As a comet approaches the sun, its speed is increased, its head contracts, and a tail forms. The tail probably consists of gas particles, which are driven outward by the pressure of the radiations from the sun.

Sometimes, the heads of comets disintegrate, and form swarms of meteors. Biela's comet, which appeared in 1846, later was replaced by the Bielid meteors (Andromedids), which revolved in the same orbit and and gave spectacular showers of meteors in 1872 and 1885.

Meteors

The so-called shooting stars, properly called meteors, *consist of small chunks of rock and metal ranging in size from small pebbles to huge masses weighing many tons.* When this cosmic debris reaches the earth's atmosphere, its motion is accelerated as it approaches. This rapid motion produces heat, due to the friction of the atmosphere; and this heat causes all but the larger particles to burn up when they reach the oxygen-rich atmosphere. Most meteors are heated to incandescence and burned to form gases and dust before they reach the solid surface of the earth. Meteors are not seen until they reach the earth's atmosphere. Usually they first appear at a height of about 68 miles, and shoot across the sky, leaving a burning stream of particles. Sometimes they explode, and produce brilliant blue or green light flares which can be seen for many miles. Most meteors are entirely consumed by the time they have come within an average distance of 54 miles of the earth's surface.

As mentioned above, a possible source of meteors is the disintegration of comets. Per-

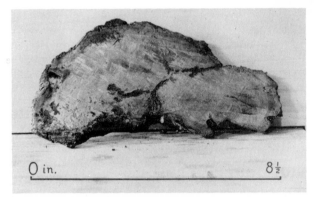

haps they are the leftovers from the great cosmic event which produced the planets and their satellites. And, perhaps they come from interstellar space.

It has been estimated that at least 100 million meteors reach the earth's atmosphere every twenty-four hours. At times of periodic meteor showers, this number must be larger.

Meteorites

The larger meteors, which reach the solid surface of the earth, are called **meteorites.** It is estimated that an average of one meteorite reaches the earth's surface every twenty-four hours. There have been reports of damage to buildings, and there is a record of at least one person having been struck by a meteorite. There have also been some close misses. A meteorite, weighing more than 50 tons, still lies where it fell in Southwest Africa. A very large meteorite is believed to have struck in Arizona, where a huge crater is now visible. See Figure 12-7. This crater is 4,200 feet in diameter and 570 feet deep.

Figure 12–7. Meteor Crater, Arizona. (Courtesy, U.S. Air Force)

All of the various kinds of meteorites that have been found fall into **three general types**: *those of metal,* called the **siderites**; those of *stone,* called the **aerolites**; and those which are *mixtures of metal and stone,* called **siderolites.** The siderites are iron alloys which usually contain 5 to 20 per cent nickel, and individual specimens are uniform in composition. They can be identified by the unique pattern of crossed lines, which show up when they are etched with acid. There are historical records of the use of siderites by ancient man to make tools.

The largest meteorite known in modern times fell in Central Siberia on June 30, 1908, and completely devastated an area of over 1,000 square miles. It was seen at a distance of 4,000 miles. Nearly 50 miles away, people were burned by its heat.

SUMMARY

All of the planets, their satellites, and the planetoids, probably have a common origin.

TABLE 12-1

DATA CONCERNING THE PLANETS

Name	Diameter in Miles	Number of Satellites	Revolution Period	Rotation Period
Mercury	3,100	0	87.97 d.	88 d.
Venus	7,700	0	224.7 d.	?
Earth	7,913	1	365.26 d.	1 d.
Mars	4,250	2	687 d.	24.5 h.
Asteroids	?	—	3–6 y.	—
Jupiter	86,830	12	11.86 y.	9.91 h.
Saturn	71,520	9	29.46 y.	10.63 h.
Uranus	31,700	5	84.02 y.	10.77 h.
Neptune	31,000	2	164.8 y.	15.8 h.
Pluto	?	?	248 y.	?

The present theory is that all of these bodies were formed from clouds of dust and gases.

The Laws

Kepler's laws of planetary motion
Newton's law of universal gravitation
Newton's three laws of motion

The discoveries of Neptune and Pluto were great triumphs for Newton's laws.

Study Questions

1. DEFINE: planetoid, comet, satellite, meteor, meteorite, siderite, aerolite, siderolite, planet.
2. Why does the earth not travel in a straight line through space relative to the sun?
3. Name and classify the planets.
4. What keeps planets in their orbits?
5. If Pluto and the earth were exactly the same size, which one would revolve around the sun the faster?
6. What peculiar feature is associated with Saturn?
7. In what respect were the discoveries of Neptune and Pluto a triumph for Newton's laws?
8. How do the terrestial planets differ from the outer planets?
9. Which is the most distant planet?
10. Would an object fall more rapidly toward the moon or toward the earth? Why?
11. How does a star differ from a planet?
12. What causes the tail of a comet?
13. What is the composition of a comet?
14. Why do meteoric showers occur periodically?
15. Suggest three different sources of meteors.
16. How do meteorites differ from meteors?
17. Compare the composition of the three kinds of meteorites.
18. Suggest a reason for believing that the members of the solar system, exclusive of the sun, have a common origin.
19. Upon what two things does the attraction between two bodies depend?

CHAPTER 13

The Moon

I saw the new moon late yestreen
Wi' the auld moon in her arm;
And if ye gang to sea, Maister,
I fear we'll come to harm

Sɪʀ Pᴀᴛʀɪᴄᴋ Sᴘᴇɴs

INTRODUCTION

There are many superstitions concerning the influence of the moon on man and his affairs. Many farmers believe that certain crops should be planted in the dark of the moon and other crops in the light of the moon. Some fishermen think that fish bite best during the days of the month when there is the least amount of moonlight at night. Still other people think that the moon influences the weather, as indicated in the excerpt from the "Ode to Sir Patrick Spens" given above. The actual facts are that the moon has little influence on the earth beyond that of causing tides and eclipses.

THE EARTH AND MOON—A DOUBLE PLANET

Our moon is so much larger than the satellites of the other planets in relation to the sizes of their primaries that it may be considered as a small planet.

The diameter of the moon is somewhat more than $\frac{1}{4}$ the diameter of the earth. Its actual diameter is 2,160 miles. The mass of the moon is about $\frac{1}{81}$ the mass of the earth. Its density is $\frac{3}{5}$ of the density of the earth. The average distance to the moon is 238,857 miles; but because the moon has an elliptical path, the distance varies from 221,463 to 252,710 miles. The moon moves around the earth at an average speed of 2,287 miles per hour.

The light received by the earth from the moon is reflected sunlight. It reflects about 7 per cent of the light that falls on it. Full moonlight is 1/600,000 as bright as full sunlight.

ROTATION AND REVOLUTION OF THE MOON

The moon does not appear to rotate in respect to the earth, but since it keeps the same face toward the earth at all times, it must rotate about its axis once a lunar month. In other words, the period of rotation is the same as the period of revolution about the earth, i.e., 29 days, 12 hours, 44 minutes, 2.78 seconds.

THE GRAVITATIONAL FORCE OF THE MOON

The gravitational force of the moon is only $\frac{1}{6}$ of the gravitational force of the earth. This is another way of saying that an object would weigh only $\frac{1}{6}$ as much on the moon as it does on the earth. A broadjumper could easily jump 100 feet, and a high jumper could jump 35 feet high.

This gravitational force is not sufficient to

93

hold gas molecules to its surface, with the possible exception of such heavy molecules as the rare gases, xenon and krypton. Both the absence of erosion on the moon's surface and spectrographic evidence indicate the absence of any atmosphere.

The absence of an atmosphere on the moon accounts for the temperatures on its surface. On the light side, the temperature is about 248° F, somewhat above the temperature of boiling water, and hotter than the highest temperatures recorded in Death Valley or the Sahara Desert. On the dark side of the moon, the temperature is lower than −200° F., which is much colder than the lowest polar temperatures. The lack of an atmosphere also means that there can be no sounds on the moon, because an atmosphere is necessary to transmit sound waves to the ears. One could not talk or be heard on the moon. The complete lack of an atmosphere accounts for the fact that there is no life on the moon.

The almost complete vacuum on the moon would have a disastrous effect on an unprotected person. His eardrums might break, and he might experience a nosebleed and other complications. Special suits and helmets would be required to take care of this problem.

Again, the lack of an atmosphere would permit dangerous ultraviolet light or high-energy cosmic rays to reach the moon's surface. Finally, the lack of an atmosphere would allow all meteors to reach the moon's surface.

THE SURFACE OF THE MOON

Large telescopes apparently bring the moon so close that objects only 300 feet long can be seen on its surface. The visible surface of the moon has been carefully photographed and studied, and its high mountains and wide plains named. The striking difference between the surface of the moon and that of the earth is the former's abundance of craters, ranging from a quarter of a mile or less to 140 miles in diameter. The mountain chains and the crater walls rise three, four, and even five miles. The cause of these lunar craters is uncertain. The craters on the moon look like the craters of volcanoes on the earth, but they do not appear to be the result of mountain-building activity. A possible cause of the craters might be the explosions of meteorites upon impact. The relationship between the width and depth of the craters is similar to that of man-made bomb craters. Probably the craters on the moon are the result of both meteorite and volcanic activity.

There is evidence that the surface of the moon is covered by a thin layer of powdered rock or dust.

EARTHSHINE ON THE MOON

The earth is a much better reflector of light than the moon is, because of its atmosphere and clouds. The moon reflects about 7 per cent of the light that falls on it, while the earth reflects 39 per cent. Because the surface of the earth is larger than that of the moon, and because of its higher reflecting power, it gives 78 times as much light to the moon as the full moon gives to the earth. At new moon, the dark side of the moon is faintly lighted by

Figure 13–1. The Caucasus and Apennine mountains on the moon at eighteen days. (An astronomical photograph from the Yerkes Observatory, reprinted by permission of the Chicago University Press)

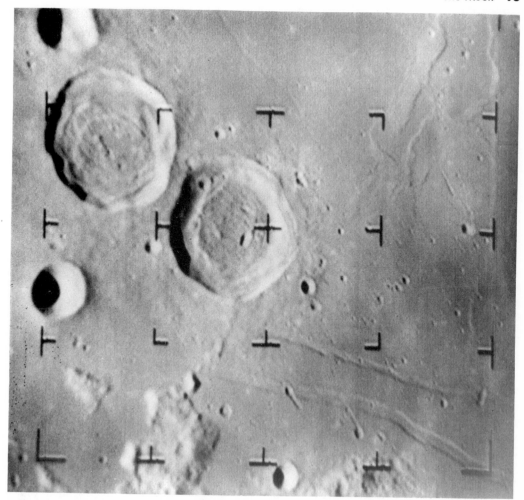

Figure 13–2. Television picture of a portion of the moon taken by Ranger VIII prior to impact on February 20, 1965, at an altitude of 151 miles above the moon, 2 minutes and 15 seconds before impact. This photograph shows the southwest corner of Sea of Tranquility, showing large flat-bottomed craters Sabine and Ritter. (Courtesy, Jet Propulsion Laboratory, California Institute of Technology)

the earthshine. This effect is often called "the old moon in the new moon's arms."

THE PHASES OF THE MOON

Figure 13-3 shows that the cause of the phases of the moon is its monthly motion around the earth. When the moon is between us and the sun, its unlighted side is toward us. On the other hand, when the earth is between the sun and the moon, the full side of the moon facing the earth is lighted. The phases of the moon between dark and full are shown in Figure 13-3. The horns of the old

crescent are turned up in a direction opposite to that of the young crescent. The full moon rises at about sunset and sets at about sunrise.

ECLIPSES

An **eclipse** is *caused by the shadow of one body falling across another body. When the earth lies between the sun and the moon,* a **lunar eclipse** results. Such eclipses last about four hours from start to finish, the total eclipse lasting about two hours. A total lunar eclipse can be seen any place where night

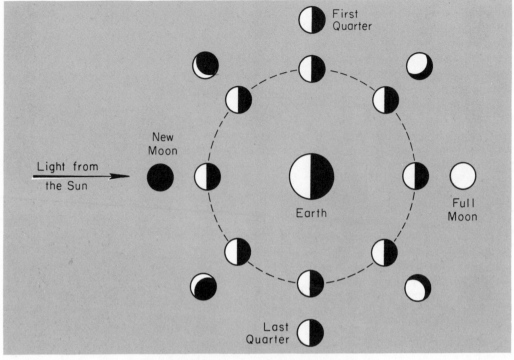

Figure 13-3.   The phases of the moon.

occurs during the time of the eclipse, and is therefore visible over more than half of the earth. It can occur only when the moon is full. In some years there are no lunar eclipses, and in other years there may be as many as three eclipses.

As the moon comes between the sun and the earth it will partially or wholly blot out the surface of the sun. The shadow cast by the moon is cone-shaped, and its path is never more than 168 miles wide. **Solar eclipses** can come only at the time of the new moon. The maximum duration of a total solar eclipse is 7 minutes, 40 seconds. The position of the moon determines the duration of the total solar eclipse. In the latitude of North America, it lasts about 100 seconds. There are always at least two eclipses of the sun each year, but never more than five.

Partial eclipses of the sun by planets, caused by their passage between the sun and the earth, are rare events called **transits.**

Total eclipses of planets or stars, caused by the passage of the moon between them and the earth are called **occultations.** The occulta-

tions of the brighter planets—Venus, Mars, Jupiter, and Saturn—are very spectacular.

THE TIDES

The gravitational force of both the sun and the moon causes tides in the atmosphere, the oceans, and the solid earth. Tides in the solid earth at the equator amount to about eight inches.

The moon is the principal cause of the tides. The sun's tide-raising force is only about $\frac{2}{5}$ that of the moon, inasmuch as the sun is 400 times as far from the earth as is the moon, and inasmuch as the attraction varies inversely as the square of the distance and only directly as the masses. Twice each lunar day this attraction acts to increase the depth of the water in the oceans at different times in different localities. The fact that the tides are synchronized with the lunar day rather than with the solar day proves that the moon is chiefly responsible for the tides.

The waters on the side of the earth nearest the moon are drawn toward it, while those on the other side are attracted least of all and tend to rise, because the earth is attracted more than the water. Thus high tides occur on the sides next to and opposite the moon, while low tides are found at positions just midway between these points.

The **"spring"** tides are the *highest* because *they occur when the pull of the sun and moon are acting together,* in other words, when the sun and moon are on the same or opposite sides of the earth. The term "spring" in this case is not related to the season known as "spring."

The **"neap"** tides *occur when the gravitational pull of the sun exerts the maximum neutralizing effect on the gravitational pull of the moon.* The physiographic features of the earth's surface modify the intensity of the tides, delaying their arrival at different points. Figure 13-4 shows how spring and neap tides are formed. The highest tides known are in the Bay of Fundy, between Nova Scotia and New Brunswick, where they vary from 60 to 70 feet. Here, rivers empty and fill up twice every twenty-four hours. In most places, there are only a few feet between high and low tides.

Tides come about an hour (51 minutes) later each day, because the lunar day does not coincide with the solar day. The highest tides occur at times of the new moon and full moon.

TIME

From ancient times, the moon has been a timekeeper. In fact, the term, month, was derived from "moon." The lunar month ceased to be a natural unit back in the times of the Caesars. To measure time, it must be divided into suitable intervals by some repetitive process. Until recently, the rotation of the earth about its axis provided the basis for the measurement of the day. The revolution of the earth about the sun, in turn, provided the basis for a year.

Sun Time

Sun time is confusing. *It is the time that one would obtain with a sundial.* Accurate clocks coincide with sun time only four times a year, April 15, June 12, September 1, and December 24. During two quarters sundial time is slower than clock time, while it is faster during the other two quarters.

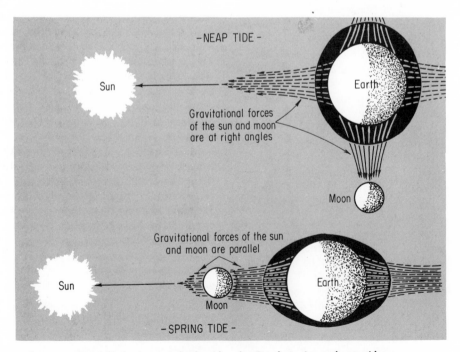

Figure 13–4. Lunar and solar tides, showing the spring and neap tides.

Sidereal Time

Since sun time is variable, astronomers set up a new system for time measurements, based on the apparent motion of the stars. This star time, or sidereal time is the official time used by astronomers, but it is not satisfactory for everyday use.

Mean Solar Time

We use as our timekeeper, not the actual sun, but an imaginary sun called the **mean sun,** *whose apparent motion is uniform.* **Mean solar time** *is the time used in everyday life.*

The Measurement of Time

Precise time measurements require periodic effects of much smaller duration than the rotation of the earth, so clocks were invented. However, the best of them are inadequate for some scientific purposes. The first atomic clock depended upon the frequency of vibration of quartz molecules, but later, more precise clocks used ammonia molecules, cesium, or rubidium vapor. The cesium clock will not gain or lose as much as a second in 1,000 years.

Two jet airliners one mile apart, traveling toward each other at ten miles per minute, would collide in three seconds. The control of jet flights has become a matter of accurate time measurements.

The tremendous speeds of artificial satellites, and the need to determine or control their courses with great accuracy, requires unprecedented accuracy in time measurements. The Goddard Space Flight Center in Washington, D.C. keeps fourteen tracking stations synchronized within a thousandth of a second. Soon, millionths of seconds will be the required accuracy.

Present-day physics is concerned with nuclear particles, whose entire existence is much less than a second, and must be measured in terms of millionths of seconds.

Because electric clocks are controlled by the 60-cycle frequency of alternating-current electricity, it is important to maintain a constant frequency. The cycles are maintained within a maximum deviation of one-tenth of a second. The cycles of many electrical generators in a large power system are controlled with Bureau of Standards radio time. Electric clocks can give no more accurate time than the control of the frequency of power cycles permits.

Standard Time

Clocks would become four minutes slower with each degree of longitude (about 60 miles) moving westward. In 1884, not long after the building of a transcontinental railroad, the inconvenience of a whole succession of local times was eliminated by dividing the United States and Canada into five time belts as shown in Figure 13-5. One hour is added as one moves eastward from one zone to another.

These lines are roughly about $\frac{1}{24}$ of the circumference of the earth, or about 1,040 miles apart on the equator. Actually these time belts are irregular, because changes have been made at different points to suit local business conditions.

A traveler going westward sets his watch back an hour at certain intervals. Obviously, this process involves a day's change at some point. By international agreement, a line was chosen as the **"international date line"**; it is in the Pacific Ocean, and *ships crossing it westward must skip a day.* If it is Monday at 3 P.M. when the ship reaches the line sailing westward, it will be Tuesday at 3 P.M. when the ship has crossed it. *When traveling eastward, the same day is counted twice.* Thus one may read in a Monday newspaper about events in Japan dated Tuesday.

In 1884, 26 nations joined in establishing a uniform system of time and longitude for the entire world. *Zero longitude was fixed as the* meridian running through Greenwich, England. Twenty-four time intervals, 15° apart, were set up starting with the above **prime meridian.**

SUMMARY

The earth and moon constitute a double planet, because the moon is such a large satellite.

The moon causes solar and lunar eclipses.

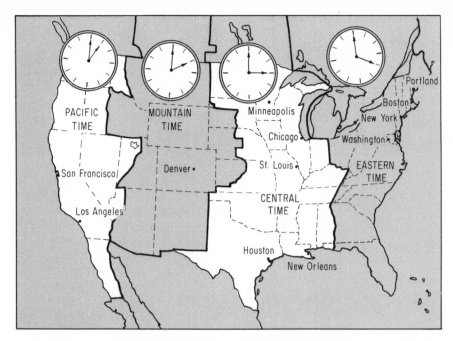

Figure 13–5. The time zones of the United States.

The gravitational forces of the sun and moon cause tides in the solid earth, its atmosphere, and its oceans.

The lack of an atmosphere on the moon means that a visitor would have to provide oxygen, water, food and protection against ultraviolet radiation, meteors, cosmic particles, and lack of pressure.

There are four kinds of time: sidereal, true or apparent solar, mean solar, and standard. **Standard time** is *a system of timekeeping in which all of the timepieces in a given zone are set to read noon, when places located in the central part of the zone have the sun on the meridian at noon.*

Because of the standard-time belts one must set his timepiece ahead one hour for each time belt passed over while traveling westward.

A day is added at the international date line, when traveling eastward.

Study Questions

1. DEFINE: neap tide, spring tide, solar eclipse, lunar eclipse, transit, occultation, standard time, mean solar time, sun time, international date line.
2. Why is the earth-moon called a double planet?
3. Would it be possible to see a skyscraper on the moon with a modern telescope?
4. Why is it that a high jumper could jump thirty-five feet on the moon?
5. Why are the mountains on the moon steep and jagged?
6. What is a possible cause of the craters on the moon?
7. Describe some of the unusual conditions of theoretical life on the moon.
8. Explain the phases of the moon.
9. What causes eclipses?
10. What is the average duration of a total eclipse?
11. What are the four times used today?
12. Why is the international date line necessary?
13. What is standard time?
14. How many standard time belts are there in the United States? Name them.
15. Is the time set forward or backward as one moves westward? Why?
16. What kind of time is measured by ordinary electric clocks?
17. Differentiate between apparent sun time and mean sun time.
18. Why did standard time become a necessity with the advent of the machine age?
19. What type of time is obtained with a sundial?

20. What is the evidence that there is no atmosphere on the moon?
21. Why does the moon always expose the same face to the earth?
22. Explain the phases of the moon.
23. In what regards does the moon affect the earth?
24. Why can one never see a star between the horns of a crescent moon?
25. How can one tell the difference between a new moon crescent and a last quarter crescent?
26. Where are the highest tides found?
27. Why is it important to be able to measure time accurately?
28. When is a day subtracted at the international date line?

Galaxies and Galactic Clusters

I do not expect to make of you philosophers like Newton, astronomers like Kep-
ler, or mathematicians like Laplace, but I hope to open your eyes and your
understanding of the wonderful lessons of the Universe. We shall grow larger if
we accustom ourselves to contemplate great objects—we shall broaden with the
effort to grasp great truths, even if we fail to envisage them.

MARIA MITCHELL

INTRODUCTION

Maria Mitchell (1818–1889), the first woman astronomer in America, and teacher of Astronomy at Vassar College, expressed her teaching philosophy in the above quotation.

The Universe, as pictured in this chapter, is much greater than Maria Mitchell ever dreamed of. Not many people can experience the sheer joy of "thinking God's thoughts after him" as one astronomer put it. This joy is rivaled only by that of scientists working with matter at the other end of the scale of the sizes of particles, as they delve into the secrets of atoms and molecules.

CONFUSION OF NAMES

About 1800, the French astronomer, Charles Messier, (1730–1817) cataloged a number of *luminous patches*, called **nebulas** (from the Greek for "cloud"). Many of these nebulas are still known by his name and numbers. See Figures 14-1, 14-2, 14-5 and 14-7 for such nebulas.

Many **nebulas** are definitely *clouds of gases and dust in the Milky Way*. The most dramatic of the earlier observed nebulas was a spiral-shaped nebula in *Andromeda*, shown in Figure 14-1. Was the Andromeda nebula a similar gaseous nebula, or a vast collection of stars outside of the Milky Way? It was not until 1924 that a photograph of Andromeda, made with the 100-inch telescope, showed that it consists of billions of stars. **Cepheid variables** discovered in Andromeda, enabled astronomers to fix its distance at 2 million light years. Soon it was recognized that Andromeda represents what the Milky Way would look like when viewed at a distance of 2 million light years. Andromeda is a giant spiral, with arms like a pinwheel extending out from the center (the hub).

Astronomers generally refer to **spiral nebulas** outside of the Milky Way as *galaxies,* or *extragalactic nebulas.*

The name, **galaxy,** is derived from the Greek word, gala, meaning *"milk."*

SHAPES OF GALAXIES

Galaxies vary widely in texture and shape, from irregular groups of stars such as the diffuse nebulas, to symmetrical systems such as the elliptical galaxies.

About 20 per cent of the galaxies are elliptical, and 2 to 3 per cent are irregular. The rest of the galaxies are spiral nebulas of many forms. Some have only two principal arms extending from opposite sides of the hub, as

101

Figure 14–1. The great spiral nebula of Andromeda. (An astronomical photograph from the Yerkes Observatory, reprinted by permission of the Chicago University Press)

Figure 14–2. Barred spiral nebula in Eridanus. Photographed by the 200-inch telescope. (Courtesy, Mount Wilson and Palomar Observatories)

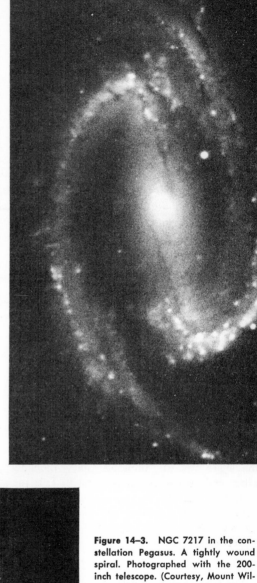

Figure 14–3. NGC 7217 in the constellation Pegasus. A tightly wound spiral. Photographed with the 200-inch telescope. (Courtesy, Mount Wilson and Palomar Observatories)

shown in Figure 14-4. In some galaxies, the arms are tightly wound around the hub, as shown in Figure 14-3. Others, like the galaxies shown in Figure 14-5, have quite loosely wound arms. About 30 per cent of the spirals are "barred," consisting of a bar-like hub with arms extending from each end, as shown in Figure 14-2.

Nearly all of the **spirals** have *flat wheel-like centers with their arms lying in the same plane*, as clearly shown in photographs of spirals edge-on, as shown in Figures 14-6 and 14-7. Such photographs reveal a thin cross-section of dark, obscuring material against the luminous central disk. which represents the arms of the spiral.

NUMBER AND DISTRIBUTION OF GALAXIES

About one billion galaxies lie within the range of the 200-inch telescope. These galaxies are not distributed evenly throughout space, but are grouped somewhat as the stars are grouped in a galaxy. In the constellation *Coma Berenices*, for example, there is a large ellipsoidal cluster of about 11,000 galaxies, about 2 million light years in diameter.

Figure 14-4. Spiral nebula in Pisces, Messier 74. Photographed by the 200-inch telescope. (Courtesy, Mount Wilson and Palomar Observatories)

Figure 14-5. Whirlpool nebula, Messier 51. One of the most beautiful galaxies known. Its two parts are about 3,500 light-years distant from each other and about three million light-years distant from the sun. This spiral was recognized by Lord Rosse in 1845, who thought that it represented a spiral system of stars lying outside of our galaxy. Photographed by the 200-inch telescope. (Courtesy, Mount Wilson and Palomar Observatories)

Our own galaxy is a part of a "local cluster" of sixteen galaxies, which includes the *Magellanic Clouds* and the *Andromeda galaxy*. This cluster may, in turn, belong to a *larger system of galaxies traveling through space as a unit*. Such a system is called a **supergalaxy.**

Most of the galaxies in a condensed cluster, such as *Coma Berenices,* shown in Figure 14-8, have a flattened-disk shape characteristic of the centers of spirals, but they lack the arms and clouds of gases typical of spirals.

GALACTIC COLLISIONS

Using radio telescopes, astronomers detected two powerful radiowave sources at points in the sky where no conspicuous objects had been noticed. One of these sources, *Cygnus A,* when photographed by the 200-inch telescope turned out to be two galaxies in collision. Stars in colliding galaxies rarely hit each other, because they are relatively small and far apart. However, the huge gas clouds in spiral galaxies do collide. Colossal amounts of energy are liberated at the site of this collision, in the form of very powerful radio waves. At the same time, the temperatures of these gas clouds are raised to millions of degrees. Such collisions are infrequent, except in the more closely packed groups. Figures 14-7 and 14-9 show galaxies in collision.

NATURE OF OUR GALAXY

The most difficult galaxy to see with the exception of the very distant ones, is our own galaxy, because we are too much a part of it to have the proper perspective. The solar system is located far from the center of our galaxy in one of the spiral arms which contains many luminous clouds of gases and dust as well as dark patches, as shown in the

Figure 14-6. Spiral nebula in Virgo, seen edge on (Messier 104). Photographed by the 200-inch telescope. (Courtesy, Mount Wilson and Palomar Observatories)

"*Horsehead Nebula,*" Figure 10-9. The fact that only spiral nebulas contain such clouds of gases proves that our galaxy is a spiral.

The spiral arms of our galaxy have been deduced from spectrographic data which show portions of our galaxy to be similar to the arms of Andromeda, our closest neighbor among the galaxies. These arms extend a distance of 10,000 light years. The radio telescope has made it possible to trace out these arms, as the result of the radio emissions from the hydrogen contained in them. This evidence shows the existence of several more arms than had been previously suspected. It also shows that the Galaxy rotates once every 200 million years.

The velocity of rotation indicates the strength of the centrifugal forces acting on the spiral's arms. These forces must be balanced by a gravitational force, which may be used to calculate the total mass of a spiral. The total mass of our spiral is estimated to be

Figure 14–7. Giant-type SO Galaxy, NGC 5128 in collision with a spiral galaxy on edge. Type SO galaxies are similar to elliptical galaxies in that they lack spiral arms, but otherwise they resemble spirals. Photographed by the 200-inch telescope. (Courtesy, Mount Wilson and Palomar Observatories)

Figure 14–8. Spiral nebula in Coma Berenices, seen edge on. Photographed by the 200-inch telescope. (Courtesy, Mount Wilson and Palomar Observatories)

Figure 14-9. Two colliding galaxies, NGC 4038 and 4039. A 48-inch Schmidt photograph. (Courtesy, Mount Wilson and Palomar Observatories)

estimate the age of the earth, such as the time required for the deposit of rock strata, or the time required for rivers to wash out the salts in the land and carry them to the ocean in the quantities now found there.

The various methods of estimating the age of the earth placed it at millions of years, but it was not until the discovery of radioactivity that an accurate measuring stick was obtained. The times required for the radioactive disintegration of different elements show that the age of some of the oldest rocks on the earth is about 3 billion years. Present estimates are that the age of the earth is about 4.5 billion years.

Now, if the earth was formed at the time that the sun was, it means that the sun is about 4.5 billion years old. But, as pointed out in the previous chapter, the sun is considered to be a relatively young star. So the age of the Universe must be older than that of the sun. At the time that this text was written, the figure generally agreed upon was about 8 billion years, but some estimates placed it as high as 24 billion years.

200 billion times that of the sun, equally split between the stars and interstellar matter. If our sun is an average star, which we consider it to be, there must be at least 60 billion stars in our galaxy. The hub of our galaxy consists of about 2 billion stars grouped into a lens-shaped, flattened sphere, having a diameter of about 10,000 light years and a thickness of about 1,000 light years.

AGE OF THE UNIVERSE

Up until the eighteenth century, it was generally accepted that the creation of the Universe took place about 6,000 years ago. In 1785, James Hutton (1726–1797) advanced the idea that such processes as mountain building and erosion, which are observed to be very slow, operated at the same rate throughout the earth's history, thus providing the basis for the idea that the earth was millions of years old. He was derided, but the geologist Charles Lyell (1797–1875), presented irrefutable evidence concerning the time involved in geological processes. Since that time, many methods have been used to

SUMMARY

The known Universe consists of about 1 billion galaxies similar to our galaxy, the Milky Way, and the end is not in sight.

Galaxies may exist as diffuse nebulas, elliptical, irregular, or spiral. Spiral galaxies may be tightly wound, or loosely wound, or may be bar-shaped.

Galaxies are sometimes found in groups, called supergalaxies.

Collisions may take place between galaxies.

The age of the Universe is estimated to be between 4 and 24 billion years.

Cepheid variables in exterior galaxies provide a method of estimating their distance from the sun.

Man is very small in this vast scheme of things, but the fact that he can explore the Universe, suggests that his mind is in tune with the Infinite.

Study Questions

1. DEFINE: supergalaxy, spiral nebula, extragalactic nebula, nebula, galaxy.

2. Discuss the distribution of galaxies.
3. What evidence do we have for galactic collisions?
4. How does the age of the Galaxy compare with the age of the Universe?
5. Outline the reasoning behind the idea that the Universe is older than the Galaxy.
6. What is the estimated age of the earth?
7. How many galaxies are estimated to exist?
8. List some of the shapes of galaxies.
9. What is the name of the spiral nebula closest to the Galaxy? What is its distance from us?
10. How was the distance of Andromeda from our Galaxy determined?
11. What are the relative percentages of the different kinds of galaxies?
12. Give two methods for estimating the age of the earth.
13. What is the nature of our galaxy?

The Grand Canyon of the Colorado River. (Courtesy, Union Pacific Railroad)

Our Restless, Provident Earth

> *The hills are shadows, and they flow*
> *From form to form, and nothing stands;*
> *They melt like mists, the solid lands;*
> *Like clouds they shape themselves and go.*
>
> ALFRED, LORD TENNYSON
> *In Memoriam, cxxiii*

AN EXPLORATION of the earth soon reveals that it is constantly changing. Mountains are raised, worn down, and raised again. Sheets of ice cover vast portions of continents, melt away, and return again. Oceans have covered large sections of continents and receded to leave inland salty seas, which evaporated and left layers of salt hundreds of feet deep. Volcanoes spew forth lava flows covering areas of thousands of square miles. Earthquakes are evidences of continuous changes in the earth's surface. This unit is concerned with the continuous changes in the earth's surface, which have brought about the conditions, which made possible the development of man.

The changes in the earth's surface have provided the soil that supports the growth of plants which furnish our food, clothing and housing. They have produced the vast deposits of coal, petroleum, and natural gas, which serve as our major sources of energy to heat our homes, cook our foods, and furnish power for our machines. The changes in the earth's surface have also segregated minerals to furnish the metals to build our skyscrapers, our trains, automobiles, airplanes, and machines. It requires our best scientific brains and many cunning instruments to discover their secret hiding places. Yes, Mother Earth is a provident earth. It pays to get acquainted with her.

In this unit, we are introduced to two important physical sciences, geology and meteorology. A study of geology presents two striking features. First, geologic events are very slow, for the most part. To the average person, it would seem as if cataclysmic events have been responsible for the bent, folded, upturned rocks that we see during a drive in the mountains. And yet, so slow are the processes of Nature that we could come back a thousand years from now and see very few changes in the landscape. A second striking feature of the study of geology is that very little is known concerning the interior of the earth.

The study of meteorology is included in this unit because it is the evaporation of water from the oceans, caused by the energy received from the sun; and the transportation of this water vapor to the land areas by the winds, which have caused weather phenomena, and have also caused erosion of the land, one of the chief sources of the changes in the earth's surface.

The Earth as
an Astronomical Body

The heavens are calling you, and wheel around you,
Displaying to you their eternal beauties,
And still your eye is looking on the ground.

DANTE

INTRODUCTION

Following World War II, it came to be realized that we knew too little about the planet on which we live. Many maps were inaccurate, and some parts of the world had not been mapped. An intensive program of mapping the world was undertaken. Later, in 1957, the International Geophysical Year (I.G.Y.) represented the combined efforts of scientists of 66 nations to make an intensive study of the earth. Four thousand major outposts were set up, and many instruments were carried by balloons, rockets, and satellites to aid in this modern exploration. The result was that so much was learned concerning the earth that long-cherished theories had to be revised or discarded. More questions were raised than were answered, but that is typical of scientific investigation. Some of the new information, like the Antarctic bulge, is contained in this chapter.

THE SHAPE OF THE EARTH

It is a popular belief that Columbus was the first man to proclaim that the earth is spherical. However, as already pointed out, Aristotle taught this idea; and Ptolemy, in his *Almagest*, written about 150 A.D., summarized the reasoning that supported this idea. He based his reasoning on the observa-

tions that the sun, the moon, and other heavenly bodies rise and set at different times at different places on the earth. Similar reasoning applied to eclipses. Ptolemy showed that such observations could not be accounted for in terms of any shape other than that of a sphere. He also called to mind that ships at sea seemed to disappear at the horizon.

Today, photographs of the earth taken from high altitudes show its curvature. The earth is a typical planet, and all planets, when viewed through telescopes, are spherical.

However, the earth is not perfectly round. It is slightly bulged at the equator to the extent of about 27 miles, probably due to the centrifugal force produced by the rotation of the earth about its axis. Studies of the earth's orbits also show that the earth is slightly pear-shaped, being slightly raised at the arctic and slightly bulged at the antarctic regions.

The off-center weight of ice at the Antarctic is about 25,000,000,000,000 tons. This ice cap spreads over an area of about 6 million square miles, and has an average depth of about 1 mile. The center of this mass is about 300 miles from the south pole, and does not lie on the axis of rotation. This off-center weight may cause the pear-shaped bulge in Antarctica, and its centrifugal force could cause shifts in the earth's crust.

There is likewise a 45-foot bulge at the

111

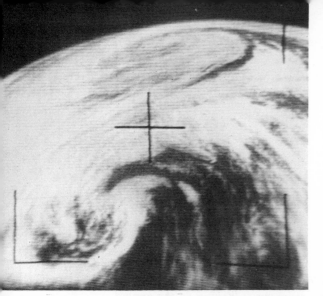

Figure 15–1. Photograph of the Earth by Tiros VI— September 28, 1963—shows a double cloud vortex, and the curvature of the earth. (Courtesy, National Aeronautics and Space Administration)

north pole, which may be due to the large Arctic ice-cap.

THE MASS OF THE EARTH

According to Newton's law of universal gravitation, the force of attraction between two bodies depends upon their masses and the distance between them. By measuring the attraction of the earth for an object of known mass, the mass of the earth is calculated to be 6×10^{27} (6 followed by 27 zeros) grams, or 66×10^{20} tons.

THE CIRCUMFERENCE OF THE EARTH

Astronomical measurements show that a star overhead changes in elevation by 1 degree for every 69.5 miles we travel over the surface of the earth. For 360 degrees, the circumference of the earth would thus be 360 x 69.5, or 25,220 miles. From this circumference the diameter could be derived, and it would come out to be about 8,000 miles. Eratosthenes used this method, and obtained a value within 1 per cent of the present accepted value. The same method of measurements shows that the circumference at the equator is slightly more than the circumference north and south. The equatorial diameter is 7,927.0 miles, while the polar diameter is 7,900.4 miles, a difference of 26.6 miles.

THE TEMPERATURE OF THE EARTH'S INTERIOR

Our knowledge of the interior of the earth is very meager. Before the study of the earth by the behavior of earthquake waves, it was generally thought that the earth was molten inside. Holes drilled deep into the earth have shown that the temperature increased at the rate of 1 ° F. for each 60 feet downward. It was only natural to conclude that volcanic eruptions, accompanied by lava flows, represented the escape of material from the molten interior of the earth. Chapter 16 points out that it seems to be likely that volcanic activity is local in nature and that the heat is generated near the surface of the earth, rather than from the core. One theory of the origin of the heat in the earth's crust is that it is produced by radioactivity.

THE ROTATION OF THE EARTH

If we were to make a slow motion picture of the stars in the vicinity of the North Star, *Polaris,* we would find that the stars would describe circular paths about Polaris. A similar picture could be taken in the southern sky. From such photographs, one could develop the concept that the earth rotates about an imaginary axis, which now points toward the North Star.

A classical experiment, which proves that the earth rotates, is that of the pendulum. In 1851, Leon Foucault (1819–1868) hung a long pendulum with a heavy bob from the top of the dome of the Pantheon in Paris, and set the pendulum swinging. The direction of the swing was carefully marked. In a short time, it was observed that the swing changed its direction at the rate of about eleven degrees per hour. The pendulum could not have changed the direction of the swing without a force acting on it. However, no force had been applied, so the only conclusion was that the earth, as a result of its rotation, changed its position relative to the pendulum and thus caused the apparent change in the direction of the swing of the pendulum.

PRECESSION

If the earth were perfectly spherical, its axis of rotation would maintain a constant direction in space. However, the bulge at the equator results in an uneven gravitational pull on the earth by the sun and moon. The consequence is that the axis of rotation of the earth is always inclined at approximately the same angle to the earth's orbit. It would trace a large circle in the heavens in about 25,800 years. Figure 15-2 shows that the extended axis describes a vertical cone.

This *displacement of the direction of the axis of rotation* is called **precession,** or the **precession of the equinoxes.** The rotation of the earth is eastward, but precession is westward.

As previously mentioned, the **equinox** is *the time when the day and night are of exactly the same length.* The spring, or vernal equinox, occurs on or about March 21, while the autumnal equinox occurs on or about September 22. The March equinox occurs twenty minutes earlier each year. *This regular shift in the dates of the equinoxes* is called the **precession of the equinoxes.**

Today, Polaris misses being directly over the earth's axis by 1 or 2 degrees, and a few thousand years from now, another star will serve as the polar star. However, about 28,000 A.D. it will again become the North Star.

The gyrocompass is a useful modern invention that is free from the defects of the magnetic compass, which is particularly troublesome on iron vessels. The rotation of the earth causes precession of the gyroscope, and its axis therefore always points to the true geographic north pole rather than to the magnetic north pole.

THE CAUSE OF THE SEASONS

Figure 15-3 is based on observations that the axis of the earth is always inclined at an angle of 23½ degrees to the plane of the earth's orbit. For this reason, the north pole is inclined toward the sun for half of the year, and the south pole is inclined toward the sun during the other half of the year. The two

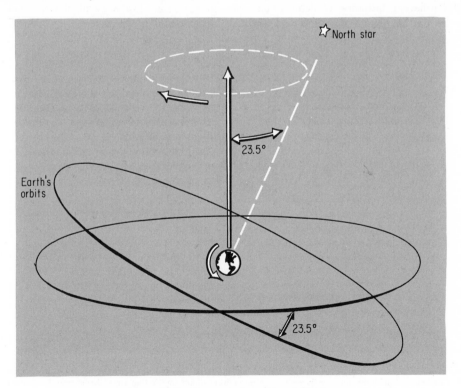

Figure 15–2.   The precession of the equinoxes.

extreme positions occur on June 21 and December 22.

The four seasons do not exist at the equator, where the days and nights are of the same length. North of the equator, the days become shorter from June 21 to December 22, while they become longer during the same period in the southern hemisphere. The diagram shows that the day is twenty-four hours long at the Arctic Circle on June 21, and the night is twenty-four hours long on December 22.

The coldest period in the northern hemisphere at present is that time when the earth is closest to the sun, but every 13,000 years, this condition is reversed because of precession. The distance from the earth to the sun varies from 91,500,000 miles to 94,500,000 miles, because the earth travels in an elliptical path. The seasons in the southern hemisphere are more extreme; and in the northern hemisphere, it is warmer during the winter and cooler during the summer than it would otherwise be, because the earth is closest to the sun when it is winter in the north.

The amount of heat received by the earth in the different latitudes is determined not only by the lengths of the days and nights, but also by the angle at which the sun's rays strike the earth. Thus, the winter is not as hot as the summer, just as the evening is not as hot as the noonday. See Figure 15-3.

In the tropics, there are no well-defined seasons as far as temperature is concerned; but the rainfall does vary, and wet and dry seasons are recognized. In the arctic and antarctic zones, summers are short and winters are long, whereas spring and autumn are of brief duration. Near the poles, the chief difference between the seasons is in the amount of light received; here one would refer to the light and dark seasons. In the temperate zones, the four common seasons of varying temperature and length of day (i.e., winter, spring, summer, and autumn) are well known. This change in the seasons is one of the major factors in producing changes in weather, and will be discussed in Chapter 19.

The unequal distribution of the sun's heat between the equator and the poles is the cause of the most widespread variations in climate. The equatorial regions receive more radiant energy from the sun than do the polar regions; it is always warm at the equator and always cold at the poles.

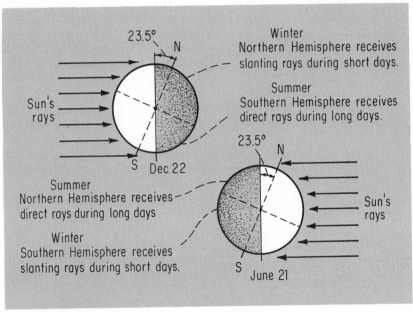

Figure 15–3. The inclination of the earth's axis is the cause of the seasons because it results in changes in the number of hours of sunlight per day as well as changes from direct to slanting rays. Direct rays heat a given area more than slanting rays because there is more radiation received by a given area.

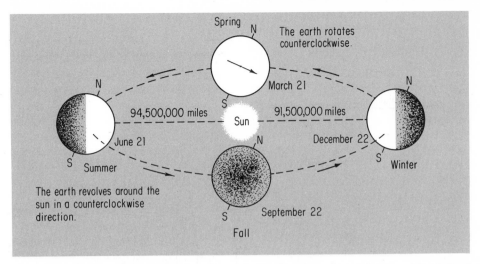

Spring
N
The earth rotates
counterclockwise.

N
March 21
S
94,500,000 miles   Sun   91,500,000 miles

N
N
June 21   December 22
S   S
Summer   Winter

The earth revolves around the
sun in a counterclockwise
direction.   S   September 22

Fall

Figure 15–4. The revolution of the earth around the sun causes the seasons in part because of the inclination of the earth's axis, but also because the distance of the earth from the sun varies from time to time during the year.

THE TEMPERATURE LAG

On June 21 or 22, the sun reaches its most northerly position and turns southward again. In spite of this fact, the hottest month in the United States is July. The earth loses heat by the process of radiating it to interplanetary space; and the higher the temperature the greater is the rate of radiation.

Even after the days begin to shorten, more heat continues to be received from the sun than is lost by radiation. The earth has not yet warmed up to the temperature at which the rate of loss is as great as the rate of gain. As the temperature of the earth's surface increases, and the days keep on shortening, the rate of loss finally becomes as large as the gain, and the temperature ceases to increase.

Because of the continual redistribution of heat by winds, ocean currents, etc. and because of the different thermal properties of different kinds of surfaces, the duration of the lag of highest and lowest temperatures behind the longest and shortest days is widely different at different places on the earth. In southern Arizona and New Mexico, the highest normal daily temperatures come only 10 days after the longest day. Around the Gulf of Mexico and the Atlantic coast, the lag is about 40 days. In the central states, the lag is about 30 days, and in San Francisco, it is 100 days,

although at Sacramento, less than 100 miles inland, the lag is 37 days.

THE SEISMOGRAPH

The **seismograph** is a *delicately adjusted instrument, extremely sensitive to vibrations, whose amplitude it records.* There are two general types of seismographs in common use. The first consists of a heavy pendulum, which holds a delicate penpoint against a moving sheet of smoked paper, and makes waves in the lines thus formed, according to the amplitude of the vibrations. The second type of instrument employs a small mirror mounted on a balanced weight, which causes a beam of light to move on a moving piece of photographic paper. Another recent device converts the beam of light into an electric current, which, in turn, is used to move a recording pen.

The essential part of the seismograph is similar to a pendulum, the bob of which tends to remain stationary in space, while everything attached to it moves. It is impossible to attach the pendulum in such a way that it does not move to a certain extent with the earth, but this motion may be corrected so as to obtain the true motion of the earth relative to it.

Figure 15-5 shows how the paths of earthquake waves in the earth are deflected by the

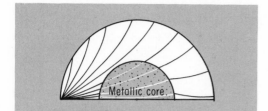

Figure 15–5. The path of vibrations through the earth indicates that it has a dense, metallic core.

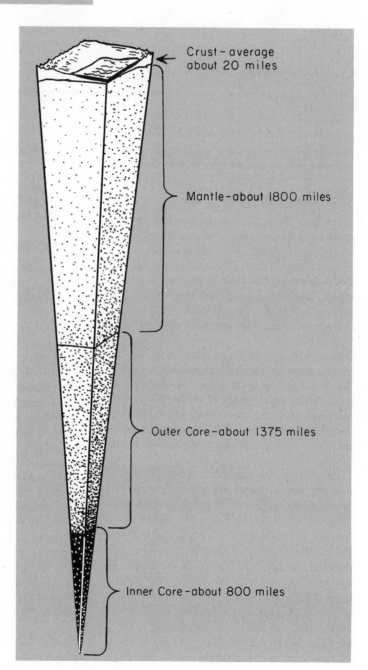

Figure 15–6. The inferred composition of the interior of the earth. Not drawn to scale.

Crust – average about 20 miles

Mantle – about 1800 miles

Outer Core – about 1375 miles

Inner Core – about 800 miles

core of the earth. Earthquake waves show abrupt changes in speed at a depth of about 1,800 miles, which suggests that the core, or centrosphere, consists of metals—probably iron and nickel.

THE INTERNAL STRUCTURE OF THE SOLID EARTH

Data obtained with the seismograph and other lines of evidence suggest that the earth has an outer crust of soil and rock, varying from 3 miles in thickness under portions of the oceans to 37 miles in thickness on the continents. *Beneath this layer* is the **mantle** *about 1,800 miles thick* which, in turn, consists of layers. The top layer, about 950 miles in thickness, probably consists of compounds of iron, magnesium, and silicon. In the lower layer the percentage of iron and nickel probably increases. Below the mantle there is the metallic core, consisting of iron and nickel, having a diameter of about 4,400 miles.

The average density of the earth is 5.5 times that of water, although the average density of the crust is only 2.7 times that of water. The core makes up about ⅙ of the volume of the earth, but almost ⅓ of its mass. The remaining ⅔ of the mass is due to the mantle and the crust. The crust makes up only about 1/250 of the earth's mass.

The rate at which vibrations pass through different media is well known; and from this information it is concluded that the metallic core is in the form of a rigid solid, rather than molten metals.

THE "MOHOLE" PROJECT

In 1909, a Serbian geologist, Andrya Mohorovicić observed a change in the velocity of earthquake waves on a line about 20 miles below the surface. This line is now called the Mohorovicić discontinuity. It is a layer which separates the crust from the mantle. The **"Moho"** or **"Mohole" project,** as it came to be known, *is to drill a hole into the earth's mantle.* The plan at the time this text was written was to drill a hole in the floor of the ocean in a location where the ocean is about 15,000 to 18,000 feet deep, and where the crust is thought to be only 3 or 4

miles thick. A hole drilled about 16,000 feet below the ocean floor should reach the above discontinuity. It should help to answer many questions concerning the earth's composition, magnetism, radioactivity, and geologic history, and it may change current theories concerning the nature of changes in the earth's crust.

LATITUDE AND LONGITUDE

Figure 15-7 shows the basis for latitude and longitude.

The lines drawn parallel to the equator are known as **parallels.** *At any point on a parallel,* the **latitude** *would be the same.* By observing the position of the North Star, or by measuring the height of the sun above the horizon by use of the sextant, the latitude of any position may be obtained. The sextant is simply an instrument to measure angles. A *Nautical Almanac* would be necessary to make the calculation of the latitude from the above observations.

As previously mentioned, *the line drawn north and south between the poles* is called a **meridian,** and *the meridian that passes through Greenwich, England* is the **prime or**

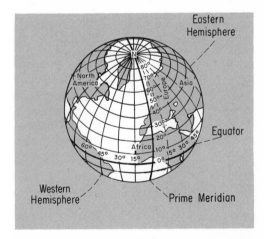

Figure 15–7. Latitude and longitude. Parallels of latitude are shown along a meridian at intervals of 10°. Each line is parallel to the equator and is therefore called a parallel. The angular distance at any point measured along a meridian is the latitude of that point. A change in 1° of latitude equals a distance of 69 miles.

Meridians of longitude are measured in degrees **east** or **west** from the prime meridian (0°).

zero meridian. **Longitude** is the *angular distance of any point on a parallel from the prime meridian,* and it is measured east and west from the prime meridian. In order to obtain the longitude at any given point, one would need an accurate clock set at Greenwich time, or a radio that could receive time signals from Greenwich. One would note the Greenwich time, at noon. By noting the number of hours that the sun is fast or slow in comparison to Greenwich time, and by multiplying this time difference by 15°, the longitude may be obtained.

SUMMARY

The earth is a slightly pear-shaped sphere. The bulge at the equator is responsible for precession. The inclination of the earth's axis and the elliptical nature of the sun's orbit account for the seasons. There is a lag in the heating and cooling of the earth.

Latitude and longitude are used to describe the position of any point on the earth's surface.

Study Questions

1. DEFINE: latitude, longitude, "mohole" project, precession, equinox, seismograph, mantle.
2. What was the purpose of the International Geophysical Year? What was accomplished by it?
3. What are the bases for the conclusion that the earth is nearly round?
4. How could you prove that the earth rotates?
5. What causes the bulge of the earth at the equator?
6. What is the consequence of the earth's bulge at the equator?
7. What causes the bulges at the earth's poles?
8. What is the probable consequence of the earth's bulge at the poles?

Stresses in the Lithosphere

Every valley shall be lifted up,
and every mountain and hill be made low;
the uneven ground shall become level,
and the rough places plain.

ISAIAH *40, verse 4*

INTRODUCTION

Gradation refers to *leveling off processes in which high places are worn down and low places are filled up.* In the next chapter we shall outline the eroding action of running water, ocean waves, glaciers, ground water and other agents of gradation, which should have leveled off the surface of the earth long ago. However, mountains exist and are being formed today. It is the purpose of this chapter to outline the facts of diastrophism and volcanism, two forces which tend to lift up land areas and thus balance the forces of gradation.

Diastrophism refers to *all movements of the outer layers of the earth.* **Volcanism** *refers to all phenomena that are connected with molten rock material* (**magma**) *and its movements;* the term is derived from *Vulcanis,* the Roman god of fire, who was supposed to dwell in a volcano. A **volcano** is a *vent in the earth's crust, from which molten or hot rock, steam, gases, cinders, and ashes issue.*

THE EARTH'S CRUST HAS ITS UPS AND DOWNS

Some portions of the earth's surface are being elevated gradually. For example, the northern part of the Scandinavian Peninsula has been rising for several thousand years. Shore lines have been raised 1,000 feet above the sea in northern Sweden. On the other hand the coast in the far eastern United States has been gradually sinking, with the production of islands and channels where hills and rivers once prevailed.

In addition to the elevation and sinking of shore lines, the fact that strata of sedimentary rocks such as limestone are found high in many mountains, indicates that these rocks are products of the sea and were once covered by seas. The fossils found in many of these strata are marine in nature, and thus confirm this conclusion.

THE LOCATION OF MOUNTAINS

There is an almost continuous belt of mountains encircling the Pacific Ocean, from Antarctica north through South and North America, and South through New Zealand, The Philippines, and Japan. This belt of mountains has been called the "Circle of Fire," because of the large amount of volcanic activity associated with it. These mountains are unlike such mountains as the Appalachians, which were uplifted by diastrophic movement and then eroded by the action of running water. They represent large blocks of rock which have been pushed upward. Other similar mountain belts, such as the Himalayas-Caucasus-Alpine system, also border on

119

Figure 16–1. An elevated shoreline, Point Harford, California. (Courtesy, U.S. Geological Survey, G. W. Stose)

Figure 16–2. Thrust fault, Shuger's Glen, Schuyler County, New York. (Courtesy, U.S. Geological Survey, V. H. Barnett)

oceans. At one time, it was considered that the beds of the oceans were level except for occasional volcanoes. Today, especially as the result of the observations made during the International Geophysical Year, we know that this is not true. The greatest discoveries made during this intensive effort were found in the 71 per cent of the earth that lies under water. Scores of mountains as tall as Mt. Whitney were discovered. Mountain ranges extending all of the way around the earth, and huge chasms and trenches were found. In the Pacific Ocean, southwest of Guam, there is a trench 35,630 feet deep, called the Marianas Deep. The floor of the Pacific Ocean was found to be split by four gigantic east-west cracks, up to 30 miles wide and 10,500 feet deep. A ridge, 25,748 feet in height was found in the South Atlantic Ocean.

In many places, faults and folds may be observed. A **fault** is *a fracture along which movement has taken place*. Movements along faults take place in a series of small displace-

Figure 16–3. A fold in a rock stratum. (Courtesy, U.S. Geological Survey, Walcott)

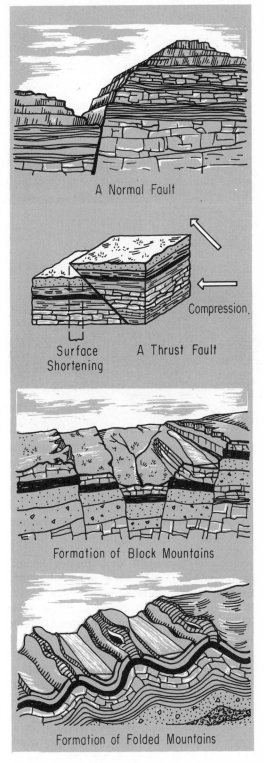

A Normal Fault

Compression.

Surface Shortening   A Thrust Fault

Formation of Block Mountains

Formation of Folded Mountains

Figure 16–4. Faults and mountains.

ments. Cliffs, and even steep mountain fronts such as the eastern slope of the Sierra Nevada or the Grand Tetons, are the result of motion along a fault.

Folds must have been caused by a shrinkage in the earth's crust. Some mountains were formed by folding, in which *one part was bent or laid on another*.

VOLCANISM

Many mountains are of volcanic origin, as can be determined by their conical shapes.

Volcanic eruptions occur on the land and under the oceans. Sometimes new islands are thus formed. For example, the island called "Old Bogoslof" in the Bering Sea was raised to an elevation of nearly half a mile by volcanic activity during the period 1796–1823. In 1883, a second island, "New Bogoslof," appeared, while a third island was raised in 1906.

Only about 430 volcanoes have been active within the time of recorded history. Many of the very numerous prehistoric volcanic activities were not the explosive types with their typical spouting of rocks and ash, belching of gases, flames, and smoke from cones, as found in modern volcanoes; but rather they more closely resembled the great lava flows of Iceland. In 1783, a series of earthquakes in Iceland preceded two great rivers of **lava** (*molten rock*) that poured out of fissures, 24 miles one way and 40 miles in the opposite direction, covering 200 square miles of land.

Parts of Ireland, the Hebrides, and large

Figure 16–5. Cinder cone and lava flow of Mount Vesuvius. The cinder cone consists of ashes, rock fragments and particles of magma which have been blown into the air and cooled to the solid state before reaching the earth. This volcano exploded without warning in A.D. 79, burying the Roman towns of Herculaneum and Pompeii. A recent eruption in 1906 was very spectacular.

Most of the extensive mountain ranges and high mountains in the oceans appear to be volcanic in origin. Volcanic action occurs around the rims of oceans where mountains are being formed, but it also occurs in the middle of oceans.

The lavas flowing from these fissures, such as occurred in Iceland and the Hawaiian Islands, are dark in color, because they are rich in iron but poor in silica. They flow freely for a long distance and do not cool rapidly, and gases readily escape through the lava.

The lava that flows from the conelike volcanoes is much hotter, but cools very quickly to form masses through which gases cannot pass; explosions generally occur, and steep cones are produced. The light-colored lavas are rich in silica but poor in iron. Tremendous pressure may be built up in such volcanoes over long periods of time before they explode. A volcano in the Tyrrhenian Sea erupted in 1786, pouring forth enormous quantities of cinders and ashes for fifteen days. Then it returned to its former death-like calm, only to explode again a century later.

Mount Vesuvius is another volcano that

Figure 16–6. Dikes cutting the flat-lying Eocene strata near Spanish Peak, Colorado. These dikes are intrusions of lava which were uncovered by erosion. (Courtesy, U.S. Geological Survey, G. W. Stose)

sections of Greenland were formed in this way, and 200,000 square miles of northwestern United States were covered with lava flowing from cracks. Some of these flows were nearly a mile deep and leveled off the landscape. The Deccan plateau in India was once covered by lava flowing from fissures out over nearly 250,000 square miles, to a thickness of 10,000 feet in places. Similar plateaus have been found in South America and South Africa.

The Hawaiian Islands were formed by layer upon layer of lava flows, extending seven miles above the ocean floors, two miles of which are above the sea.

explodes almost without warning. The eruption of A.D. 79, buried the Roman towns of Herculaneum and Pompeii. In 1906 its most recent eruption was very spectacular. With a tremendous roar, a great gas blast shot eight miles into the air before it began to spread out to form a huge cloud. Mount Vesuvius has been active ever since 1913, and is due to erupt again within a few decades.

Krakatoa, which had lain dormant in the Dutch East Indies for many years, in 1883 blew more than four cubic miles of its cone into the air. The eruption was heard more than 2,000 miles away. Tens of thousands of people were killed, and the dust that shot into the air went around the earth.

The eruption of Katmai in Alaska, in 1912, blew five cubic miles of volcanic ash into the air, and produced clouds so dense that the country for a hundred miles around was in darkness for two days. Six inches of ash covered the land as far as 160 miles away.

Tamboro, off the island of Java, is estimated to have blown out 38 cubic miles of material.

Seasons of unusual cold have been experienced after tremendous volcanic explosions that throw volcanic ash to great heights. This dust is not carried down by the rains, because it is carried far above them and around the world by the upper air currents. The dust reflects and absorbs much of the sun's heat. The eruption of Tamboro in the East Indies was followed by "The Year without a Summer"—1816. In New England, snowstorms occurred in June, July, and August of that summer. Similar cool seasons followed the explosion of Krakatoa in the East Indies, in 1883, and of Katmai in Alaska, in 1912.

Some of the most noted mountains in North America are volcanic in origin. Among these are Mount Hood, Mount Shasta, and Mount Rainier. Mount Lassen is the only active volcano in the United States, not including Hawaii and Alaska. The fumaroles, geysers, and hot springs of Yellowstone National Park are characteristic of the final stage of volcanic activity. These volcanic activities observed on the surface are merely slight indications of the inner turmoil which causes them.

Many lava flows, which did not reach the surface, *filled in fissures between rocks*, forming **dikes** of *hard rock that protrude above the softer rocks around them, when they are exposed to weathering conditions.* The Palisades of the Hudson were formed by *intrusions of lava between beds of rock*, forming thick **sills.** In several areas, intrusions cause *the upper layers of rock to bulge upward into dome-shaped hills or mountains*, called **laccoliths.** The Black Hills are typical **laccoliths.** *Lava-filled tubes of volcanoes* are called **necks.** *When lava cools so quickly that it does not have time to crystallize, volcanic glass*, or **obsidian,** is the result.

Figure 16–7. A volcanic plug, Shiprock, New Mexico. This plug was a neck of a volcano which filled up with lava. Later, the retaining crater was eroded away. (Courtesy, U.S. Geological Survey, W. T. Lee)

EARTHQUAKES

Earthquakes are *vibrations in the earth produced by movement along faults, or by explosions.* During the past fifty years, the world has known many disastrous earthquakes. Japan has experienced three such earthquakes—in 1891, 1896, and 1923. The last earthquake killed more than 140,000 people, and destroyed property worth billions of dollars.

California has had four great earthquakes during the same period. San Francisco was all but destroyed by the fire following the great earthquake in 1906. A violent earthquake occurred in the Yellowstone National Park region on August 15, 1959. Nearly a hundred thousand people were killed in Messina, in Sicily, by an earthquake that occurred in 1908. The great earthquake of 1964 in Alaska destroyed several cities and many fishing boats, setting back the economy by several years.

Earthquakes, small or large, are occurring at some place on the earth's surface all the time; and they have been taking place since history began to be recorded. There are probably about 150 large earthquakes a year, although very few of them make the front pages of newspapers because most of them occur under the sea. The majority of earth-

quakes are caused by the sudden slipping along fractures of portions of the earth's crust, or by the fractures themselves.

Sometimes great blocks of material, separated from others by cracks, are elevated or lowered along faults. In 1899, a block of forest on the Pacific coast of the United States was submerged into the sea, whereas a neighboring block was elevated 47 feet. The great San Andreas fault, 600 miles long, was the location of the shifting in the earth's surface that produced the earthquake causing the San Francisco fire. The main stresses in the earth's surface today lie along fractures bordering the Pacific Ocean and a path that reaches through the Mediterranean, the Himalayas, and the East Indies.

Some earthquakes in or near oceans cause seismic waves in the oceans, which do tremendous damage. Seismic waves in the oceans have been given the scientific name of tsunamis.

PINPOINTING EARTHQUAKES BY SEISMOGRAPHS

An earthquake is a vibration in the earth's crust and it may be recorded by seismographs in such a way as to show its relative severity.

There are about 350 seismographic stations located at various places on the earth's surface to record earthquakes. Each station must have at least three seismographs arranged at right angles to each other. The seismographs enable the scientist to determine the approximate location of the larger earthquakes, even when their centers are thousands of miles away. The majority of earthquakes originate in the earth's outer crust, but the resulting vibrations travel throughout the globe. Some travel around the surface, while others travel to the center where they are deflected by the dense cores. The time intervals between the arrivals of the different waves are noted at three different stations. See Figure 16-8.

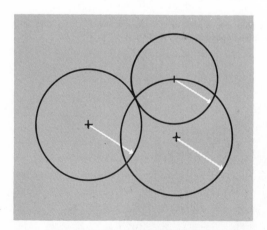

Figure 16–8. The center of an earthquake is determined by information obtained from three observatories. A circle is drawn around each observatory, with a radius equal to the estimated distance to the earthquake. The location of the earthquake is at the intersection of the three circles.

THEORIES OF CRUSTAL MOVEMENT

There are several theories of crustal movement, and this fact alone indicates that there is no single satisfactory theory. Perhaps crustal movements are of several different kinds, each of which requires a different theory for its explanation. In any case, a theory must be consistent with the facts of volcanism and diastrophism, and should attempt to account for the forces involved.

Most of the theories assume that there is a shell of rocky material, plastic in nature, which covers the solid layers below it. Over this plastic layer the crust of the earth is relatively free to move. Radioactivity is assumed to be the source of the heat in the mantle.

The Cooling and Shrinking Theory

This theory assumes that the center of the earth is very hot, and that the earth is gradually cooling and shrinking. This shrinking would cause wrinkles in the earth's crust.

The Expansion Theory

Today, a popular idea is that the earth is gradually heating up due to radioactivity. Less dense rocks float upward to form extensive domes or uplifts along faults. Cracks would form at weak places such as the junctures between continents and oceans, and in the middle of thin ocean floors, where the main faults in the crust are found.

The Theory of Isostasy

Almost all theories incorporate **isostasy,** *the theory that the earth's crust floats on solid rock, which because of the high temperature and pressure is plastic enough to act as a liquid. The core of this theory is that there is a condition of equilibrium between the different portions of the earth's crust.* At a depth of about 70 miles there is assumed to be a level of compensation, in which shifts of the rocks will take place so as to return adjoining areas of the surface to a condition of equilibrium. Every portion of the earth above the level of compensation must have the same weight.

Erosion carries tremendous quantities of material from one place to another, decreasing the weight over one area and increasing the weight over other areas.

The heavier lowlands reach a state of equilibrium with the lighter highlands; but erosion unbalances the equilibrium, with the result that the lowlands become heavier and the highlands lighter. This difference in pressure causes the solid rocks to move in such a way as to restore the equilibrium. The lowlands sink as rock materials are forced out from under them, while the highlands are forced still higher.

The present gradual elevation of the region north of the Great Lakes is thus explained by this principle of isostasy, or balancing of weights. When the Great Lakes' region was covered with heavy glaciers, it must have sunk because of the increased weight due to the glaciers. Then, when the ice melted and the water drained off, an opposite movement was produced to restore the equilibrium.

SUMMARY

Mountains may be formed by erosion of high plateaus, but most mountains are the results of diastrophism or volcanism. Diastrophism may produce mountains by folding or by isostatic readjustments. Volcanism may form cone-shaped volcanic mountains, or it may form domes by intrusions of magma. Earthquakes may be caused by volcanic explosions, or by faulting and folding.

Diastrophism may be accounted for by isostasy and cooling or heating the earth's crust, which may result in folds or cracks.

The heat required for volcanic activities may result from either diastrophism or radioactivity, or both.

Study Questions

1. DEFINE: diastrophism, gradation, volcanism, dike, neck, isostasy, earthquake, fault, fold, lava, volcano, sill, laccolith, obsidian.
2. What processes offset the results of gradation?
3. What is isostasy?
4. What is an earthquake?
5. Why do earthquakes often occur along certain seacoasts?
6. What is a fault, and how is it produced?
7. Why have the eroding and transporting action of the various processes of gradation not brought all land areas below sea level?
8. What processes bring about a shift in weight and pressure on the earth's surface?

9. Explain how earthquake centers may be located.
10. What is the cause of volcanoes?
11. Is there any reason why earthquake regions should also be volcanic regions?
12. What are the causes of earthquakes?
13. Why do earthquakes occur more often in California than in the Mississippi Basin?
14. Give several examples of very destructive explosive volcanoes.
15. All of the known ice ages occurred either during or soon after continental uplifts and mountain building. Thus the earth may be said to manufacture its own ice ages. Volcanic activity was also very great during these mountain-building periods. Is there any evidence in this chapter that would support the above idea that the earth manufactures its own ice ages?
16. Explain the present gradual elevation of the Great Lakes region.
17. Differentiate between the behavior and nature of the two types of volcanoes.
18. Are there any evidences of present volcanic activity in continental United States, with the exclusion of Alaska?
19. Mention some well-known topographic features that are volcanic in origin.
20. What is diastrophism?

CHAPTER 17

Rocks and Minerals

True knowledge can only be acquired piecemeal, by the patient interrogation of nature.

SIR EDMUND WHITTAKER

INTRODUCTION

The collection, cutting, and polishing of rocks and minerals is a very satisfying hobby for many people. It is inexpensive, a stimulant to learning, a very fine incentive for outdoor exploration, as well as a fascinating pursuit for rainy days and winter evenings.

A visit to a mineral collection in a museum enables you to see many beautiful crystalline specimens that you would not be likely to see in nature, unless you knew where to find them. Evidently, these specimens differ from ordinary rocks. They are called minerals.

A **rock** is a *general term that refers to any part of the earth's crust.* A **mineral** is *a homogeneous material of definite chemical composition, often crystalline in nature, which is found in rocks. The rock containing a mineral is called* an **ore** *if it is commercially valuable.*

Today, as you visit various scenic spots such as Yosemite Valley, and see huge walls of granite a mile high, or perhaps the beautiful scenery of the Canadian Rockies in British Columbia with their jagged peaks exposing many strata of rocks, you begin to realize that rocks differ very much from place to place. Ultimately, you learn that the solid portion of the earth is made up of three classes of rocks: igneous, sedimentary, and metamorphic.

Igneous rocks *are produced by the solidification of molten magma.* **Sedimentary** *rocks are formed by deposition (by water or wind).* **Metamorphic rocks** *are the result of changes in the above two types of rocks, usually caused by heat and/or pressure.*

IGNEOUS ROCKS

James Hutton, a Scotch doctor and farmer, became interested in the study of rocks, and finally devoted his life to their study. He did not go along with Werner's theory that all rocks were deposited from a muddy sea, the heavier granite depositing first. One day he came upon a stratum of limestone overlying a bed of red granite. This granite extended up into cracks in the limestone. At once, he realized that the granite must have been in a liquid state in order to be forced up into these cracks. Most of the igneous rock of today undoubtedly represents forms of rock which were liquefied below the surface and returned to the surface again by lava flows, volcanic activities, or isostatic readjustments.

This *molten rock,* called **"magma,"** generally contains superheated steam and other gases, whose rapid expansion in a volcanic eruption causes the magma to spray out into the air, where it cools quickly to form volcanic dust. When the slower moving bodies of magma work their way up through fissures in the rocks, they solidify to form layers of lava on or beneath the surface, or dikes as shown in Figure 17-2.

Figure 17–1. Half Dome in Yosemite National Park. An example of granite rock. (Courtesy, U.S. Geological Survey, Calkins)

Figure 17–3. An example of igneous rock. Close-up of Devil's Post Pile National Monument on San Joaquin River, Sierra National Forest, California. (Courtesy, U.S. Forest Service)

Figure 17–2. Dikes in stratified rock, Alamille Creek, Socorro County, New Mexico. (Courtesy, U.S. Geological Survey, N. H. Darton)

Pumice is formed by the cooling of the froth produced in the magma by the rapid expansion of dissolved gases, as the result of the lowering of pressure on reaching the surface. If certain lavas cool quickly, volcanic glass or "obsidian" is formed, as has been previously mentioned. Slower cooling produces fine-grained, igneous rocks. The crystal, or grain, is larger if the magma cools still more slowly. A distinguishing characteristic of igneous rocks is their massive and uniform structure. There are two forms of igneous rocks, which are quite well known, namely, granite and basalt. Granites, which have been formed slowly, have large quartz and feldspar crystals that give a coarse texture, while other, more rapidly cooled granites, have small quartz and feldspar crystals, and consequently a fine texture. Basalt contains crystals which are microscopic in size, and therefore presents a homogeneous appearance. The basalts are denser than the granites and are found chiefly under the oceans.

Figure 17-3 shows giant six-sided columns of basalt.

SEDIMENTARY ROCKS

Sedimentary rocks can be identified by characteristic strata, formed by deposition of eroded material from water. The layers are produced by the uneven rate of sedimentation; thus a full, rushing stream of early spring carries more materials and larger particles farther than the shallow stream of late fall. Layers of sediment are cemented together by minerals removed chemically from the water; and as these layers become buried by layer after layer of rock, up to a thickness of thousands of feet, the resulting pressure makes them more compact.

Conglomerates are *sedimentary rocks made from the coarser gravel and sand.* Sand, often nearly pure quartz, produced from the disintegration of granite, is cemented together to form sandstone. The smaller sedimentary particles (i.e., the silt and clay) form the characteristic laminated shales. Limestone is another type of sedimentary rock, formed from the remains of the shells of mollusks, coral, and other invertebrate animals, by the action of certain algae and bacteria, and also by chemical methods. Sedimentary rocks can be readily recognized as such, because they are usually stratified, and may be broken apart along the bedding planes separating the different layers.

METAMORPHIC ROCKS

Metamorphic rocks are produced by the action of heat and high pressures on other forms of rocks. Slate is a good example of a metamorphic rock; it is produced by the combined effect of heat and pressure on shale. It is easily split into sheets, which are valuable for blackboards and roofing.

Marble is produced by the effect of high pressures and temperatures on limestone. In this process the fossil shells may lose their identity, and part of the calcium carbonate crystallizes; the small crystals give marble its typical appearance.

HOW ORES ARE FORMED

The first discovery of **smelting** (i.e., *extraction of metals from their ores*) was probably made when lumps of iron or copper ores were reduced in a wood fire. Since that time, man has been searching for new ore deposits and working out new methods of separating metals from their ores. Ore deposits consist of minerals which have been segregated.

The lighter elements—oxygen, silicon, and aluminum—account for about 90 per cent of the earth's crust. All of the other elements would scarcely be noticed, and would be very costly to separate, if provident nature had not separated them in the form of valuable ores in a variety of ways.

Magmas are the sources of nearly all mineral deposits. As they cool, the least soluble, or the highest melting-point compounds, crystallize first. Such compounds generally are compounds of the heavy metals. They settle out, or are injected into fissures. Some of the world's richest ore deposits are formed in the veins thus formed.

Pegmatites *represent the last stage in the crystallization of magma.* They include most of the gem stones and beautiful mineral crystals that one sees in museum collections.

Gases, vapors, and fumes rise through the

magma, and carry with them large quantities of low melting-point metals such as lead, zinc and copper. These metals may combine with oxygen or sulfur and deposit in fissures and cracks. Water may react with these metals or their compounds to form hot solutions from which minerals crystallize. The ores of such metals as gold, silver, cobalt, arsenic, antimony, bismuth, mercury, and the platinum metals are often found in veins.

Once the magma cools, surface action takes place. Erosion breaks down the ores, and *the heavy minerals or metals deposit in the beds of rivers and streams*. They are called **placer deposits.** Gold and silver are found in such deposits.

Some metallic compounds dissolve in chemically active solutions, and combine with other elements to form insoluble compounds, which precipitate out. Such deposits include iron, uranium, manganese, and aluminum. The huge iron-ore deposits of the Mesabi Range in Minnesota were formed in this way. In this case, a variation of the process might have taken place in which the soluble materials in magma were dissolved, leaving the insoluble iron oxide behind.

Organic materials may also form deposits of coal and phosphate rocks. Even iron and vanadium are segregated by some organisms.

VAST DEPOSITS OF USEFUL SALTS

Some salt deposits were formed under conditions which caused the different salts in the ocean water to separate out one at a time.

At some places, Epsom salts and gypsum (magnesium and calcium sulfates) have been formed. At other locations, borax and soda have been deposited. Some of the richest deposits of borax and soda in the world have been located in the ancient lakes of the Mojave Desert, which acted as great catch basins for the water from the surrounding mountains.

Twenty billion tons of valuable potassium salts were created by the evaporation of a great inland sea to form the present great Stassfurt deposits in Germany. Similar deposits have been found far underground extending for many miles under portions of Oklahoma, Texas, and western Canada.

Another exceedingly valuable product, common salt, is obtained in some sections of the world today by the evaporation of ocean water, desert lakes, or salt water pumped from wells. Huge deposits of solid salt have been laid down in many parts of the world by the evaporation of inland seas. It has been estimated that if the salt in the ocean were separated by evaporation, there would be an amount sufficient to cover the surface of the earth to a depth of 112 feet.

PRECIOUS STONES

During all recorded history, man has valued jewels and precious stones for their beauty, and he has often endowed them with imagined powers for good or evil. A **gem** is *any mineral, precious or otherwise, which has been polished. When a gem has been cut and mounted in some kind of setting*, it is called a **jewel.**

Only three minerals possess the requirements—beauty, durability, and rarity—which characterize precious gems; the precious gems are diamond, corundum, and beryl. The ruby and sapphire are varieties of corundum, while the emerald is a variety of beryl. Beauty is associated with such factors as color, luster, transparency, and sparkle. The value of the diamond is due to all three of the above factors, while the beauty of the emerald is due chiefly to its green color.

Most of the precious stones may be synthesized today. With the discovery of this synthesis, superstition surrounding precious stones has decreased, and their values have changed. Now they are valued for what they are rather than for their rarity.

IDENTIFICATION OF MINERALS

It is clear that one may have to examine a great many properties of minerals before a sure identification can be made. This is why a knowledge of chemistry is always a useful and sometimes a necessary supplement to microscopic examination and physical tests. However, the interested person can soon learn to identify most of the minerals with the aid of a good book on minerals.

Quartz resembles calcite in appearance, but

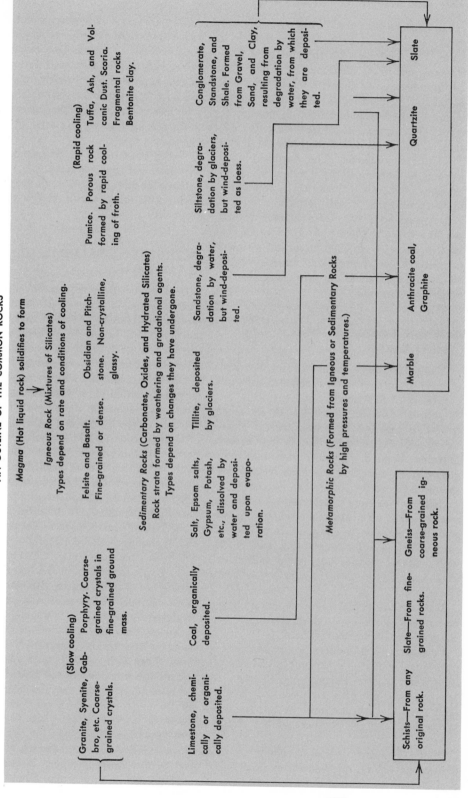

TABLE 17-1

AN OUTLINE OF THE COMMON ROCKS

Magma (Hot liquid rock) solidifies to form

Igneous Rock (Mixtures of Silicates)
Types depend on rate and conditions of cooling.

(Slow cooling)

		(Rapid cooling)
Granite, Syenite, Gabbro, etc. Coarse-grained crystals.	Porphyry. Coarse-grained crystals in fine-grained ground mass.	Felsite and Basalt. Fine-grained or dense.	Obsidian and Pitchstone. Non-crystalline, glassy.	Pumice. Porous rock formed by rapid cooling of froth.	Tuffa, Ash, and Volcanic Dust. Scoria. Fragmental rocks Bentonite clay.

Sedimentary Rocks (Carbonates, Oxides, and Hydrated Silicates)
Rock strata formed by weathering and gradational agents.
Types depend on changes they have undergone.

| Limestone, chemically or organically deposited. | Coal, organically deposited. | Salt, Epsom salts, Gypsum, Potash, etc., dissolved by water and deposited upon evaporation. | Tillite, deposited by glaciers. | Sandstone, degradation by water, but wind-deposited. | Siltstone, degradation by glaciers, but wind-deposited as loess. | Conglomerate, Standstone, and Shale. Formed from Gravel, Sand, and Clay, resulting from degradation by water, from which they are deposited. |

Metamorphic Rocks (Formed from Igneous or Sedimentary Rocks by high pressures and temperatures.)

| Schists—From any original rock. | Slate—From fine-grained rocks. | Gneiss—From coarse-grained igneous rock. | | Marble | Anthracite coal, Graphite | Quartzite | Slate |

131

calcite can be scratched with a knife, and quartz is too hard to be scratched with a knife. The hardness of a mineral is of considerable aid in its identification. The Moho hardness scale is as follows: 1, talc; 2, gypsum; 3, calcite; 4, fluorite; 5, apatite; 6, orthoclase; 7, vitreous pure silica; 8, quartz; 9, topaz; 10, garnet; 11, fused zirconia; 12, fused alumina; 13, silicon carbide; 14, boron carbide; 15, diamond. The hardness of a mineral is determined by finding which of the above minerals will scratch it, and which of these minerals it will scratch.

The **specific gravity** of a mineral, i.e., *its weight relative to the weight of an equal volume of water,* is another important physical property. Color, luster, and the manner in which minerals break are frequently used in describing minerals.

COMMON ROCK-FORMING MINERALS

About 2,000 minerals are known, but most of them are rare. The most common minerals are described as follows:

Quartz (silicon dioxide), in six-sided prisms, is colorless or milky, with a glassy luster, and will scratch glass. It is abundant in veins. Colored varieties, such as smoky quartz, rose quartz, and amethyst, are precious stones.

Calcite (calcium carbonate), next to quartz, is the most abundant mineral. Limestone and marble are largely composed of calcite. It has a hardness of 3, and reacts with acids to produce bubbles of carbon dioxide gas. The crystals split easily in three directions.

Dolomite is similar to calcite, except magnesium carbonate is its chief constituent. It is somewhat harder than calcite.

Feldspar (aluminum silicates containing potassium, sodium, or calcium), consists of rectangular crystals having good cleavage. It is colorless, white, grey, or pink. It is harder than glass, but not as hard as quartz; and makes up about 60 per cent of the earth's crust.

Mica (aluminum silicates containing hydrogen, potassium, magnesium, or iron), has perfect cleavage and is quite soft. It occurs in the form of cleavable sheets.

Clay (silicates of hydrogen and aluminum with varying small amounts of potassium or iron) consists of microscopic crystals of dull luster, and is very soft, and of low density. Kaolin, a pure clay, is used to make pottery and porcelain ware.

Gypsum (calcium sulfate), has a hardness of 2. It is used to make plaster of paris and wallboards.

Halite (table salt) is characterized by its salty taste and cubical crystals.

Hornblende, consists of six-sided crystals, having a hardness of 5 or 6. It may occur as needle-like crystals.

PETROLEUM, NATURAL GAS, AND COAL

Coal and petroleum (crude mineral oil) came from plant and animal remains, which were compacted and covered over with rock strata. Natural gas and petroleum usually occur together, and probably originated chiefly from plant-like micro-organisms.

Once petroleum and natural gas are formed, they tend to migrate through porous rock strata and collect in domes with impervious caps, as shown in Figure 17-4. Huge amounts of petroleum are found in shale, but the separation of the petroleum from shale is relatively expensive. These shale deposits represent vast reservoirs of petroleum, which may be tapped after other sources of petroleum have been exhausted. Oil shale deposits, underlying 16,500 square miles in Colorado, Utah, and Wyoming, have a potential yield of 25–300 billion barrels of oil.

Coal was formed from the luxurious plant growth in swamps during periods of warm, moist climate. Cellulose, the basic material produced by plants, is a compound of carbon, hydrogen, and oxygen. Cellulose, sugars, and starches are typical compounds containing these three elements. If such carbon compounds are compressed and heated, they decompose to an extent that depends upon the conditions of temperature and pressure. **Peat,** *found in bogs, represents the first stage in coal formation.* It has been subjected to little or no pressure or heat. **Lignite,** *brown coal, has been slightly compacted.* **Bituminous (soft) coal** is *harder than lignite, and contains less hydrogen and oxygen, and little*

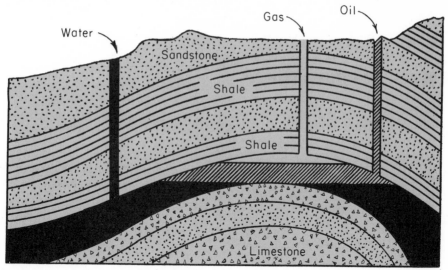

Figure 17–4. This diagram of a dome-like formation shows the proper locations for gas or oil wells.

water. **Anthracite (hard) coal** *is very hard, and contains about 85 to 95 per cent carbon.* Coal beds may be a few inches to more than 100 feet in thickness.

SUMMARY

There are three types of rocks, igneous, sedimentary, and metamorphic. Igneous rocks were produced by the cooling of magma. Sedimentary rocks resulted from sedimentation, and metamorphic rocks were formed from the first two types of rocks by the action of heat and/or pressure. Igneous rocks are uniform in structure, while sedimentary rocks show bedding planes.

A mineral is a pure substance that occurs in nature. Beautiful, durable, and rare precious stones are gems. Cut and mounted gems are jewels. An ore is a portion of the earth's crust that contains a mineral in large enough concentrations to be of economic value. Minerals have probably been segregated into ores by (1) crystallization from hot magma, from water solutions, or from hot gases; (2) sedimentation; (3) precipitation; (4) activity of living organisms; and (5) gravity.

Minerals are identified by their hardness, color, specific gravity, luster, and manner of breaking, aided by microscopic examination and chemical tests when necessary.

Coal, petroleum, and natural gas owe their origin to plant and animal deposits. Peat, lignite, bituminous coal, and anthracite coal represent steps in the decomposition of plant and animal residues. Petroleum probably originated in marine life.

Study Questions

1. DEFINE: rock, mineral, ore, gem, jewel, igneous rock, sedimentary rock, metamorphic rock, conglomerate, smelting, pegmatite, placer deposit, specific gravity, lignite, bituminous coal, anthracite coal.
2. What is an igneous rock?
3. Why are some granites fine-grained and other granites coarse-grained?
4. What are the characteristics of igneous rocks?
5. What are the characteristic features of sedimentary rocks?
6. Give some examples of igneous rocks formed by volcanic activities.
7. What is a metamorphic rock?
8. Give some examples of metamorphic rocks.
9. Account for the different types of coal.
10. Account for the occurrence of heavy minerals in high mountains.
11. What is the probable source of petroleum and natural gas? Give the reasons for your conclusion.
12. Why are precious stones "precious"?
13. What natural processes have concentrated ores from igneous rocks?
14. How are veins formed?
15. How are minerals identified?
16. What processes segregate minerals?

CHAPTER 18

The Busy Hydrosphere

For Nature Time is nothing. It is never a difficulty: she always has it at her disposal: and it is for her the means by which she has accomplished the greatest as well as the least results.

LAMARCK

INTRODUCTION

If we were to visit Niagara Falls, Yellowstone National Park, or Yosemite Valley and then return ten years later, few changes except those wrought by man would be observed. However, a visit to the Grand Canyon shows what one river can do and is doing. Given time, nature will obliterate all of these landmarks. In considering the processes of erosion and sedimentation, we must keep in mind that these are the long, slow processes by which nature grinds down and disintegrates the high places, and fills in the low places.

Most of the processes of erosion and sedimentation could not happen without water. But water would accomplish little if it were not transferred in the form of water vapor by wind. In brief, there would be no wind and no water if there were no atmosphere. Water and atmosphere do their work because of the energy furnished by the sun.

So we have a splendid combination of sun, atmosphere, and water. What more could we ask for in order to have an earth that would support plant and animal life? A moment of reflection would suggest that soil must be present to support plant growth. We may look upon **soil** as *the end-point of erosion.*

Millions, yes billions, of years were required by the slow processes of nature to squeeze water to the surface, forming the seas, before erosion could get underway. It took a lot of work to get the earth ready for man, and much of it was done by the busy hydrosphere.

EROSION

Erosion is *a general term that includes all processes by which rocks are disintegrated and worn away.* Weathering is one kind of erosion. However, the most active agents of erosion are wind, waves, running water, ground water, and glaciers. Running water is by far the most important of the agents of erosion.

WEATHERING

Weathering *is a process of disintegration and decomposition of rocks by both chemical and mechanical action.* Water alone may dissolve certain portions of rocks, but aided by such gases as carbon dioxide or sulfur dioxide, it may exert chemical as well as solvent action. For example, it is the carbon dioxide that is dissolved in ground water that enables it to dissolve limestone to form huge caves in natural limestone formations.

Water may also disintegrate rocks by lodging in cracks where it freezes and expands, thus acting as a wedge to pry rocks apart. Plants may take seed in crevices, and develop to a point where their roots likewise wedge rocks apart.

Temperature changes may make minor contributions to weathering. Gravity plays an important part in pulling disintegrated portions of rocks of mountains or cliffs to the slopes below, thus exposing new surfaces to weathering. Likewise, gravity aids streams to transport rocky debris. Finally, gravity is important in sedimentation.

WINDS

Strong winds wear down rocks, due to the abrasive action of sand or dust which they carry. They also serve to transport large quantities of sand and dust from one place to another. Sometimes, a single wind storm in the southwest portion of the United States will pick up a million tons of dust and scatter it over a dozen states.

Figure 18–1. A rock worn by wind-borne particles. (Courtesy, U.S. Geological Survey, Erdman)

DISINTEGRATION OF OCEAN SHORE LINES

More than three-fourths of the earth's surface is covered by oceans to an average depth of two miles. Oceans constantly pound their way into rocky shores, wearing down the rocks to form sandy beaches. It is the ocean waves which do the work of erosion, and the larger the waves are the greater is the amount of erosion. Violent storms often do serious damage to highways and houses near ocean shore lines.

LAKES

As a rule, the waves in lakes are smaller than those in the oceans, and therefore subject their shore lines to a more gentle pounding. On the other hand, lakes in cold climates freeze over, and the expanding ice grinds the shore lines.

Many lakes occupy low spots on the land that have resulted from sinking of certain areas under the pressure of glaciers, as in the case of the Great Lakes of North America, or from the water's carving action, as in the case of oxbow lakes in the wide valleys of old rivers. Lakes may be formed by glaciers whose forward walls have melted in a valley as fast as they have progressed down the valley, with the result that *the terminus of the glacier has remained in the same place, and gradually piled up large heaps of rocks and other rocky debris,* called **moraines.** These terminal moraines may then dam up a valley and form a lake.

GLACIERS

There have been periods in the earth's history when large portions of the surface were covered with *ice sheets,* called **glaciers.** Glaciers a mile deep once extended over two million square miles of Europe. Similar glaciers spread over four million square miles of North America, moving over mountain ranges, such as the Adirondacks in New York, and rounding them off to produce the typical New England scenery. These huge masses of ice gouged out the hollows, now filled with water, to make the numerous lakes of Canada, and carried the resulting debris to the northern part of the United States, where deposits several hundred feet deep were left.

The last ice age was in full retreat about 10,000 years ago. Evidence of previous ice ages, many millions of years ago, both in the southern and northern hemispheres, have been found in some older rocks.

Mountain glaciers are rivers of ice formed from the winter snows that fail to melt completely in the summer, and pile up year after year, gradually changing to ice as a result of the heat of the sun and the pressure of the accumulating mass.

Mountain glaciers, often many hundreds of feet thick, move a few inches or feet per day, grinding rocks in their path with their tremendous frictional force. This force is increased by rocks, ranging in size from the smallest pebbles to boulders weighing many tons, which have become incorporated into the bottom and sides of the glacier, to make a very effective grinding surface. This grinding action produces colloidal materials that cause milkiness in streams in glacial regions.

Glaciers produce typical amphitheater-like or U-shaped valleys. The best evidences of glaciation, however, are the scratches that are left on the surfaces of rocks.

GROUND WATER

Ground water, i.e., *water below the surface of the ground,* seeps through porous layers and into cracks. Here it dissolves out soluble substances. Eventually, ground water emerges as springs, carrying with it the dissolved materials that are transported by rivers to the sea. Billions of tons of dissolved matter, nearly a quarter of the material transported by rivers, are thus carried to the sea every year.

When water falls on the ground, it soaks in until the ground is saturated. *The level at which the ground becomes saturated is called* the **water table.** Sometimes it is near the surface, and sometimes it becomers lower and lower, as a result of widespread pumping of water from wells. Water seeps into wells when they are driven below the water table. When streams cut below the water table, springs occur along the banks. In some places, portions of land lie below the water table, and a swamp or lake will form.

Artesian wells are produced when pipes are

Figure 18–2. Nabesna Glacier and Mt. Blackburn (16,140 feet) in the Wrangell Range, Alaska. (Courtesy, Museum of Science, Boston)

Figure 18–3. Thousand Springs, Snake River Canyon, Idaho. Outlet for ground water flowing through porous lava. (Courtesy, U.S. Geological Survey, C. F. Bowen)

sunk into ground water that is under pressure. *Occasionally, the pressure of the steam formed in the lower portions of fissures causes the water to shoot upwards suddenly as a* **geyser.** This action of geysers may occur regularly, as in the case of Old Faithful, in Yellowstone National Park, or irregularly, as in the case of Eaimangu, in New Zealand, which has spouted streams of mud and water as high as 1,500 feet at the most unexpected times.

Springs carry many kinds of dissolved substances from under ground. Spring water may contain sulfur compounds, carbon dioxide, iron and calcium compounds, soda, epsom salts, borax, acids, alkalies, rare gases, or even poisonous salts in solution. The hot waters from springs often precipitate their mineral freightage when they reach the surface and are cooled, thus forming interesting deposits like those found in Yellowstone National Park.

STREAM EROSION

The erosive action of running water depends upon its volume, the speed of flow, and the amount and kind of debris which it carries with it. It is increased about 64 times for each time the velocity is doubled.

Young streams are characterized by rapids and falls. It is their high velocity that enables them to carry large amounts of debris such as sand, gravel, and even boulders, which are their cutting tools. The Colorado River is an example of a rampant young river, and the Grand Canyon testifies as to its cutting action. The aging of streams is a slowing-down process, in which the rate of flow decreases.

Mature streams would not be found in young mountains, but rather in low lands, which have been leveled. In mature streams, downcutting decreases and lateral cutting increases. The V-shaped valleys of young rivers become U-shaped, and their floors are widened. Many tributaries develop.

When rivers reach old age, they flow very slowly; they meander and squirm through wide valleys which have been filled up by sediments carried down in their more youth-

Figure 18–4. A young stream. (Courtesy, U.S. Geological Survey, Jackson)

ful days. The old rivers are large, and the number of tributaries is reduced. The vast valley of the Mississippi River is an example of the valley of an old river.

The youth or maturity of a given region can be determined by observing the rivers and valleys. A new uplift will have few valleys, and those will be in the form of canyons. Older topography will be characterized by a fretwork of ridges and valleys. These ridges gradually become gentler hillsides, and eventually the region becomes almost level.

Sometimes old streams experience a second youth, as the areas through which they flow are gradually lifted up (by diastrophic processes), and thus form steeper slopes and swift-flowing streams, because the hard rocks are lifted up more rapidly than the streams can wear them away.

Other streams cut down the rising mountains as fast as they form, producing tremendous gorges; the Columbia River cut a seventy-mile path through the Cascade Mountains, which were uplifted long after the Columbia River established its course. Such rivers are called **antecedent rivers.** Less rapid currents of water are slower in their action, but no less effective in the long run. They constantly round off the boulders and rocks as they jostle them against each other and against the rocky canyon walls, and transport the lighter particles thus formed farther down stream. The Mississippi River carries a million tons of silt and sand to the Gulf of Mexico every twenty-four hours. Large deltas are formed by such rivers as the Mississippi,

the Nile, and the Yangtze, as they dump their debris into the sea.

SEDIMENTATION

The debris is sorted out by size and density as the speed of the streams slackens. Larger-sized particles are the first to settle out. At one place there may be formed a gravel bank, and farther down stream, a sand bar. Floods carry vast quantities of silt and deposit it in broad valleys. Alluvial fans are found where water is carried out of steep valleys into plains. **Sedimentation** is *the process of settling out of solid materials from water.*

SOIL

Where there is no vision, the people perish.—Proverbs 29:18.

What shall it profit a nation to gain all the gold in the world and suffer the loss of its soil? —Walter G. Lowdermilk.

The production of soil is a slow and complicated process. First, the rocks must be disintegrated by erosion into fine particles of sand, clay and other materials; but plants will not grow in powdered rock. The rocks must first be decomposed by weathering. Then bacteria, to the extent of ½ million to 10 million per gram of soil, get to work. Bacteria have been called nature's chemists. Some bacteria take nitrogen from the air and store it in the form of soluble compounds in the soil. Various other chemical changes necessary for the liberation of plant nutrients are carried out

Figure 18–5. The meanders of an old river. (Courtesy, U.S. Geological Survey, Walcott)

by the bacteria. Now plants can grow. As they grow and die, they contribute organic matter to the soil, which furnishes food for other bacteria and for animal life, which help to keep the soil in a porous condition.

Early pioneers came to America as conquerors, exploiting its rich natural resources and its native population, taking what they wanted, and destroying the rest. Confronted by seemingly inexhaustible resources of plant and animal life, they killed huge herds of buffalos for their hides, ruthlessly cut down the world's greatest forests, and burned the wood to obtain charcoal or wood ashes, as if these natural resources were man's worst enemies. Of course, their object was to provide fields for crops and pastures for animals. Sod, which had been thousands of years in the making, was plowed up with considerable difficulty; and as soon as a piece of land was denuded of its soil by erosion, plows moved on to new virgin territory. By this time, however, the machine age had multiplied man's destructiveness a thousandfold, so it was not long until the scene of the marvelous golden wheatfields in the Middle West became the desolate graveyard of the machines which made the wheatfields possible; and the dust bowl witnessed the exodus of some of our best citizens, who had unwittingly helped to bring about the permanent loss of an alarmingly high percentage of the priceless soil.

When the natural processes of erosion are disturbed, soils, which take centuries to deposit, may be removed in only a few years. This process is called **accelerated erosion.**

If one were to visit a desert region such as Death Valley, he would see examples of maximum erosion. Here it seldom rains, but when there is a cloudburst typical of the desert, a tremendous amount of erosion can take place very quickly, because the ground deposits consist of clay and other materials which offer little resistance to erosion. However, if one were to visit hilly country, which receives much more rain, little erosion is noticed if the land is covered by forests or other vegetation. One should keep in mind that a freshly-plowed field resembles the hills of the desert, in that it may offer little resistance to erosion.

When forests are cut down on watersheds, water is no longer detained but runs off quickly, robbing the land of its precious soils, and forming flooded streams that continue their costly path of destruction down to the oceans. Semi-arid lands are quickly ruined by plowing them up and planting grain, for the protective sod no longer soaks up water to store for dry spells. Soon a drought comes, and the winds blow the soil away. Hills must be kept covered with vegetation to prevent the rapid formation of deep gullies that will quickly ruin good pasture land.

It has been estimated that 3 billion tons of solid soil materials are washed from our farms each year. If we could locate a large soil deposit somewhere, and transport it back to our farms by railroad trains, it would require trains almost a mile long, leaving every minute throughout the year, to return this soil to its rightful place.

Loss of soil can be prevented only by avoiding such overexploitation of the soil as overcutting of forests, overgrazing of range lands, and overtilling of fertile lands. The past few years have witnessed an aggressive attack on this problem. Thousands of dams have been built to check the formation of deeper gullies and to collect silt that would otherwise be washed away. Natural vegetation has been restored, and increased vigilance against disastrous forest and range fires has been established.

Water conservation involves the maintenance of forests and grassy lands in water sheds. It also requires the storage of water behind dams that reduces the rate of flow of streams, and eliminates floods. Thus, water conservation and soil conservation go hand-in-hand.

SUMMARY

Highlands are torn down by the decomposing and disintegrating action of erosion, and low places are filled up by sedimentation. The net results of these two processes would be to level the surface of the earth.

Agents of erosion are weathering, winds, waves, ground water, glaciers, and running water, the latter being the most important one.

Weathering is the result of mechanical action (such as freezing), and the chemical action of water or water solutions.

Glaciers are of two kinds, ice sheets, such as are found in the polar regions at present, and mountain glaciers. Glaciers owe most of their erosive action to the rocky debris which has become embedded in them. Glaciers leave rounded-off hills, polished and scratched rocks, U-shaped valleys, terminal moraines (accumulations of rocky debris), and lakes.

Ground water removes tremendous amounts of salts by solvent and chemical action. It is responsible for limestone caves.

The erosive action of streams depends upon their volume and speed of flow and the kinds of rocky debris which they carry.

Sedimentation tends to sort out rocky debris into deposits of gravel, sand, clay, silt, etc.

Soil is a precious heritage, produced by slow processes. Much soil is lost due to natural processes, but this erosion may be increased by unwise use of land. Soil and water conservation go hand in hand. Both are essential for the production of food.

Study Questions

1. DEFINE: erosion, sedimentation, weathering, water table, glacier, ground water, antecedent river, soil, moraine, geyser, accelerated erosion.
2. Account for springs.
3. How can one recognize glaciated topography?
4. Give the chief characteristics of young rivers.
5. What are the characteristics of the aging of rivers?
6. How can one tell the age of a given mountain range?
7. How are rivers rejuvenated?
8. What is an antecedent river? Give an example.
9. What happens to shore lines as land areas sink and lift?
10. To what do glaciers owe their erosive action?
11. Show how the atmosphere is an ultimate cause of erosion.
12. What is the most active agent of erosion?
13. Explain the formation of caves such as the Carlsbad Caverns.
14. Explain the formation of U-shaped valleys such as Yosemite Valley.
15. How do glaciers bring about erosion?
16. Explain the existence of swamps.
17. Explain the formation of lakes.
18. Give a possible explanation of hot springs and geysers.
19. List the most important weathering agents.
20. How does gravity aid in erosion and sedimentation?
21. Outline briefly the steps involved in the evolution of soil.
22. Why does it take so long to evolve good soil?
23. Outline the functions of bacteria in soil production.
24. What are the causes of soil erosion?
25. Outline the most important methods of combating soil erosion.
26. Give examples of the way in which the United States has squandered its natural resources.
27. Why has the United States not conserved its natural resources to a larger extent?

The Turbulent Troposphere—
Our Weather Maker

Let me first understand the facts, and then we may seek the cause.

ARISTOTLE

INTRODUCTION

We live at the bottom of an ocean of air, the atmosphere, which surrounds the earth and travels with it through space. It is the turbulence in the *lower layer of the atmosphere,* called the **troposphere,** in which we live, that is responsible for our weather and climate. This turbulence is caused by the heat of the sun, the geographic features of the earth's surface, and the motions of the earth about its axis and around the sun. This chapter is devoted to the study of the **weather,** i.e., *the short-range changes in atmospheric conditions;* and **climate,** i.e., the *long-range average conditions of the atmosphere at a given locality.*

THE STRUCTURE OF THE ATMOSPHERE

Figure 19-1 shows an arbitrary division of the atmosphere into several layers. This division is determined by temperature, pressure, and other properties rather than the depth of each layer. *The first layer,* called the **troposphere,** varies in depth from 5 miles at the poles to 10 miles at the equator. *Above the troposphere* is the **stratosphere,** *which has a depth of about 70 miles. Beyond the stratosphere* is the **ionosphere,** *which extends outward for another 500 miles.* As its name implies, it consists of ionized molecules and has several layers, which will be referred to later.

Information radioed to the earth by Explorer VII, indicates that beyond the ionosphere there is a halo of helium about 900 miles thick. *An additional layer of particles,* called the **magnetosphere,** *reaching out 60,000 miles,* was discovered during the International Geophysical Year. Above this layer, highly rarified hydrogen extends into interplanetary space.

THE TEMPERATURE OF THE ATMOSPHERE

The temperature of the atmosphere decreases up to an altitude of about 30 miles, dropping 1°, Fahrenheit, for a rise of 300 feet. At an altitude of 5 miles, the temperature is 20° below zero, Fahrenheit. In the upper atmosphere the temperature rises to 4,000° Fahrenheit, a temperature high enough to melt iron. Temperature is a measure of the motion of the particles; in the very rarefied atmosphere at high altitudes, the particles move almost unhindered, because they are so far apart. They obtain their energy by absorption of high-energy, ultraviolet radiation from the sun.

THE WEIGHT OF THE ATMOSPHERE

The total weight of the atmosphere is about 5,900 trillion tons, more than half of which is in the lower 3½ miles. The first 18 miles contain 97 per cent of the atmosphere.

141

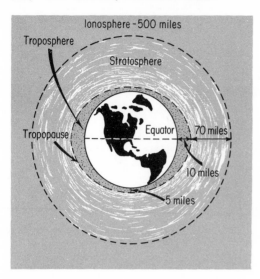

Ionosphere – 500 miles
Troposphere
Stratosphere
Tropopause
Equator
70 miles
10 miles
5 miles

Figure 19–1. This diagram is not drawn to scale. Actually the atmosphere amounts to about the thickness of a coat of paint on a classroom globe. Note that the atmosphere bulges at the equator.

THE COMPOSITION OF THE ATMOSPHERE

The lower atmosphere is composed mostly of nitrogen (about 79 per cent) and oxygen (about 21 per cent), and its composition remains the same throughout the troposphere. The lower portion of the troposphere also contains varying amounts of carbon dioxide and water vapor.

THE PRESSURE OF THE ATMOSPHERE

The atmosphere exerts a pressure of about 15 pounds per square inch at sea level. The pressure of the atmosphere decreases by approximately one half for each 3.5 miles increase in altitude.

CLIMATE

Continental climates show greater temperature ranges, less frequent rainfall, and more sunshine than marine climates. Desert climates represent the extreme of continental climatic conditions with their hot days, relatively cool nights, and low average rainfall. Large bodies of water experience relatively small or slow temperature variations, because of the high specific heat of water, as has previously been explained. In the daytime, a large portion of the sunlight is lost by reflection from the surfaces of bodies of water, while much of the energy of the light which is absorbed is used up by evaporation. The amount of energy that is absorbed is insufficient to raise the surface temperature of the water of the ocean even a degree in a day, because of the high specific heat of water and the cooling effect of evaporation. Land areas, on the other hand, reflecting less heat than water areas and being composed of materials of relatively low specific heat, become heated or cooled rapidly. Heat is also distributed by motions within the water, whereas land is immobile. The climate on the western shores of continents in the temperate zones is generally more equable than that on eastern shores, due to the effect of the prevailing winds from off the oceans. The prevailing winds vary because of seasonal changes, and differ from place to place; but in general, they blow from westerly directions in the temperate zones, because of the effects of the rotation of the earth on the circulation of the atmosphere.

THE GREAT WIND SYSTEMS

Air rises at the equator and pushes out from the polar regions. As a result, there is a flow of air from the polar regions toward the equator. Figure 19-2 shows the most important prevailing winds on the earth.

Winds blowing toward the equator from higher latitudes are deflected westward; *these prevailing northeasterly and southeasterly winds of the tropical regions are* called the **trade winds.**

There are belts of comparative calm at about 30° latitude north and south, between the trade winds and the prevailing westerlies. Here the atmosphere forms high-pressure belts, particularly over the oceans. These latitudes are called **horse latitudes** because sailing vessels carrying horses from New England to the West Indies were obliged to throw a part of their cargo overboard when water became scarce because of slow progress due to the lack of winds. In these latitudes, one would expect to find the chief desert regions of the world.

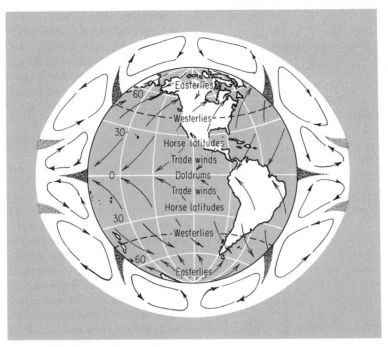

Figure 19–2. The general circulation of the atmosphere. The vertical loops are considered to be responsible for the north-south circulation of the atmosphere as well as at least a portion of the differences in the prevailing surface winds. The dotted lines represent polar fronts. The dark gray areas represent low-pressure regions, and the light gray areas represent high-pressure regions.

The prevailing westerly winds are especially well developed *in the southern hemisphere,* where, free to blow with great violence, they are known as the **roaring forties.**

The area of equatorial calm, called the **doldrums,** shifts north and south with the seasons.

Near the poles, the atmosphere is cooled and flows away from them.

The net result of the rotation of the earth is the creation of a pattern of little whirls and big whirls, as shown in Figure 19-2. Between these whirls at *higher altitudes, narrow, undulating, high-velocity streams of air,* called the **jet streams,** are set in motion.

ATMOSPHERIC CIRCULATION— THE CAUSE OF WEATHER

The circulation of the atmosphere is one of the primary factors in bringing about weather changes.

The so-called general, or planetary circulation of the atmosphere, brought about by the unequal heating of the earth's surface at different latitudes and modified by the rotation of the earth, is not as simple as it seems, because many factors alter this general picture. For example, the unequal heating of land and water areas during the day and the unequal cooling at night cause disturbances. In the temperate zones, in the summer, the atmosphere over the land areas becomes heated and the pressure becomes less; the atmosphere over the ocean has a correspondingly low temperature and high pressure. During the winter season these conditions are reversed. Mountain ranges also greatly influence the currents in the atmosphere. The preceding effects are especially marked in the northern hemisphere, because of the preponderance of land there.

Most important of all, however, are the frequent storms of middle latitudes, which continually disturb the general circulation. The interlatitudinal circulation of air between the heated equatorial regions and the cold polar regions does not take place in a regular, unvarying manner, but rather, as great, irregular disturbances, caused by powerful jet airstreams in the upper atmosphere, in the temperate zones.

WATER VAPOR IN THE ATMOSPHERE

Water continually evaporates from living organisms and from moist soil as well as from the surface of bodies of water. Evaporation is more rapid when winds are blowing, because they carry off the vapor and keep the space unsaturated; evaporation is especially rapid when a hot, dry wind is blowing, because the *tendency for water to evaporate* (**vapor pressure**) increases with rising temperatures. The maximum amount of water vapor that can exist in a given volume of air increases with a rise in temperature. The more humid the air, i.e., the more water vapor that is already present, the less rapidly will more water evaporate into this space.

Sometimes, as much as 5 per cent of the total volume of air in a given locality is water vapor. An observation of steam rising from a teakettle, or of fog rising from the surface of a lake on a cold day, shows that moist air rises. It rises because moist air is less dense than dry air. This difference in density is due to the fact that water molecules are lighter than oxygen or nitrogen molecules.

CONDENSATION AND PRECIPITATION

When warm, humid air is cooled, saturation is eventually reached. Any additional cooling will then cause condensation of some of the water vapor. *The temperature at which condensation will take place* is called the **dewpoint.** The number of degrees that the temperature must fall to reach the dewpoint depends upon the relative humidity. **Relative humidity** refers to *the ratio between the percentage of water vapor in the atmosphere, as compared with the amount in air that is saturated with water vapor at the same temperature.*

Dew does not "fall," but condenses from the atmosphere on objects on the earth's surface, which, because of loss of heat by radiation,

have cooled more rapidly than the surrounding atmosphere. If the relative humidity is low, there may be no dew. Still, cloudless nights favor dew formation. Clouds radiate heat back to the earth, so that dew is less likely to form. Winds keep the atmosphere stirred up, and prevent local cooling of the various objects and the adjacent air.

Fogs and clouds are formed when the temperature of the free atmosphere falls below the dew point. The nucleus for nearly every droplet is a dust particle, on which the water condenses. In the mountains, one may climb up into a cloud, which is then called a fog, because it is at ground level. Condensation leading to fogs and clouds may be brought about when a current of warm, damp air strikes and partially mixes with a current of cold air. The most important cause of condensation, and the only important cause of rain or snow, is the cooling that results from expansion of warm, humid air when it is caused to ascend. Heated air at the ground rises because heating makes it less dense, and it is forced up by the surrounding cooler air, much as a cork is forced up in water; air expands as it rises, because of the lower pressure upon it at higher altitudes. Remember that expansion always uses up heat and thus lowers the temperature, unless further heat is added. Vertical ascent and *descent of air* are called **convection.** Convection is also produced when air is forced to flow over mountain ranges, or when a current of warm air flows up over a current of cold air. When upward convection of humid air is on a large enough scale, some of the minute cloud particles may grow larger, until they become so heavy that they fall as rain or snow. Sometimes rain evaporates before it reaches the earth as it descends to lower altitudes.

So minute are the particles of water in a cloud, that a fair-sized cloud would contain less moisture than a glassful of water. It has been estimated that eight million ordinary cloud particles contain the same amount of water as one ordinary raindrop.

The size of raindrops depends upon the conditions under which they are formed. When moist air rises slowly, very small droplets will fall in the form of a drizzling rain. Sometimes, however, there are strong currents of air moving upward, carrying the droplets with them, catching them up again as they fall, and carrying them up time after time, until they grow very large, and fall in large splashes. Such large drops are often observed just in advance of the downpour of a thunderstorm.

THUNDERSTORMS

Thunderstorms result from powerful, upward, convection currents of highly humid air, and are likely to follow a very hot day of strong, ascending air currents. There are about 44,000 thunderstorms per day throughout the world.

Violent thunderstorms form frequently on the windward side of mountains, because the strong winds are deflected upwards by the mountain slopes. Hail often accompanies thunderstorms. The irregular, powerful, convection currents carry drops of water into the upper cold layers of air, where they freeze and gather coatings of snow and frost; but, as they are tumbled about by the turmoil within

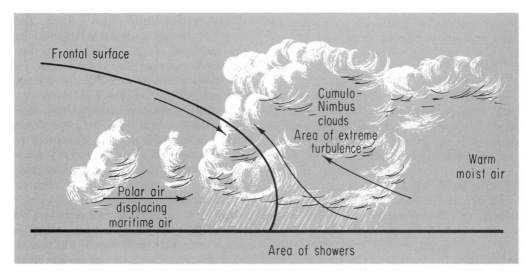

Figure 19–3.   A cold front.

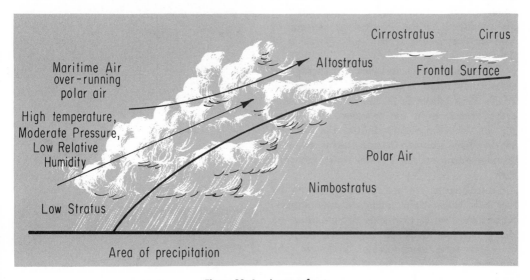

Figure 19–4.   A warm front.

the cloud, they fall back to where the temperature is above freezing and get coatings of water. Then, they are again carried up, and so they move up and down, gathering additional coatings on each trip, until they become too heavy to be supported any longer, and fall as hailstones. When a hailstone is split open, the concentric layers are easily seen as alternate layers of clear and cloudy ice.

Hail is a feature of intense thunderstorms that occur in the spring and summer. Some hailstones have been found that show as many as 25 layers, and are as large as baseballs. One hailstone, weighing 1½ pounds, had a circumference of 17 inches. Hailstones may be very destructive—ruining crops, killing livestock, and breaking windows.

There are two kinds of thunderstorms: the local thunderstorm generally follows an extremely hot day and moves in no certain path, although the prevailing winds determine its direction somewhat; the more severe thunderstorm is the result of a great current of cold air, often hundreds of miles across, flowing against a current of moist hot air, and lifting it bodily by sliding in under it.

Figures 19-3 and 19-4 show two kinds of **fronts,** i.e., *contacts between warm, moist air masses and cold, dry air masses.*

Thunder squalls, or line squalls, are often very destructive, because of the great velocity of the wind. This wind results from the motion of the huge air mass in part, but is due chiefly to the outward and downward rush of air produced by the descending current of cold air that results from the evaporation of the rain.

Thunderstorms occur very frequently in certain mountain regions; for example, on Pike's Peak, there is a thunderstorm nearly every afternoon in the summer. Hot, moist regions, like those surrounding the Gulf of Mexico, have frequent thunderstorms, whereas thunderstorms on the Pacific coast are very rare.

Cloudbursts are sometimes produced by the conditions that attend thunderstorms. Sometimes rain is prevented from falling by rising currents until extraordinary amounts of water have accumulated. Suddenly, the supporting force weakens, and the water descends as a so-called cloudburst. At Cher-

rapuaje, India, 40.8 inches of rain fell in one day, on June 14, 1876. Here, the average annual rainfall is 426 inches, amounting to about 50,000 tons per acre.

TORNADOES AND WATERSPOUTS

Sometimes upward convection leads to a whirling motion of the ascending column, which may produce according to circumstances an ordinary whirlwind, a tornado, or a waterspout. A **tornado** *originates at the general cloud level, and bores downward toward the ground; the vortex is visible as a writhing, funnel-shaped cloud.* It is the most violent of all storms; the wind velocity has been estimated, from its effects, to have reached 500 miles per hour in some cases. The rapid whirling leads to a considerable decrease in the atmospheric pressure at the center; and as the center passes over buildings, they sometimes burst outward, because of the sudden decrease in external pressure. Tornadoes are small, ranging from a few feet to 1,000 feet in diameter; and generally travel from the southwest to the northeast at 20 to 40 miles per hour, rarely more than 25 miles.

The West Indian **hurricanes,** and the Chinese **typhoons** are *atmospheric whirls on a larger scale,* but less intense than tornadoes, having diameters of from 50 to 500 miles.

Figure 19-5. A tornado. (Courtesy, U.S. Department of Commerce, Weather Bureau)

Figure 19–6. A waterspout. (Courtesy, U.S. Department of Commerce, Weather Bureau, and John R. Lambert III)

Figure 19–7. The tremendous force of a hurricane is demonstrated by this piece of timber that was driven through the trunk of a palm tree. (Courtesy, U.S. Department of Commerce, Weather Bureau)

They are usually more destructive, because they are much more widespread and last longer.

SUMMARY

Climate refers to the general or average condition of the circulation of the atmosphere, while weather refers to local and temporary atmospheric conditions. The unequal distribution of the sun's heat between the equator and the poles causes a circulation of the atmosphere, which, in turn, is influenced by the rotation of the earth. The climate and the weather are the result of prevailing winds, ocean currents, the relative distribution of land and water, the altitude, and local topography.

The great wind systems of the atmosphere are the result of warm air rising at the equator and cold air flowing down from the poles, together with the effects of the rotation of the earth.

The ratio expressed as a percentage of the amount of water vapor present to the maximum amount possible at the existing temperature is called the relative humidity. The relative humidity increases with a decrease in temperature. The temperature at which the relative humidity is 100 per cent is called the dewpoint. When air is cooled below the dewpoint, condensation takes place in the form of fog, rain, snow, or hail.

Thunderstorms are caused by intense vertical convection, and by fronts.

Violent whirls of small diameter produce tornadoes or waterspouts; similar whirls of larger diameter are hurricanes.

Study Questions

1. DEFINE: stratosphere, troposphere, ionosphere, magnetosphere, climate, weather, front, horse latitude, doldrums, jet stream, dewpoint, relative humidity, tornado, waterspout, hurricane, trade wind, roaring forties, vapor pressure, convection, typhoon.
2. What causes the widespread variations in climate?
3. Where are the extremes of continental climatic conditions found? Explain.
4. Explain the equable climates on the western coast of North America.
5. At what time, day or night, do breezes blow down mountain canyons, and why?
6. How do breezes from the land and sea change from winter to summer?
7. Discuss the factors which are the basis for climate and weather.
8. Differentiate between whirlwinds, tornadoes, and hurricanes.
9. Discuss the causes of rain, snow, fog, and hail.
10. Explain how convection currents are produced.
11. Why do we have less frost in cloudy weather than on clear nights?
12. Discuss the causes of thunderstorms.

Weather Forecasting

The belief that nature is orderly is not yet universal. Savages, we are told, live in a completely capricious universe, and we still find congregations praying for rain although they would hesitate, probably, to pray that the sun might stand still. That is because astronomy is a more developed science than meteorology.

J. W. N. SULLIVAN[1]

INTRODUCTION

It is a common saying that "everybody talks about the weather but nobody does anything about it." The first part of this saying is quite true, but many people do many things about the weather. Thousands of professional meteorologists and amateur weather observers keep track of the weather, and make weather predictions and forecasts.

This chapter deals with scientific weather forecasting, which is an excellent example of the application of the scientific method.

THE WEATHER ELEMENTS

Many observations must be made *for weather forecasting. The kinds of information required* are called the **weather elements.** These elements make up what we call weather. For example, we might associate bad weather with high winds, high humidity, low pressure and considerable rain or snow. The weather elements are: air pressure; direction and velocity of the wind; temperature; relative humidity; amount, kind, and height of the clouds; the amount of rain or snow; the visibility; and the ceiling.

---

[1] *The Limitations of Science*, The Viking Press, New York, 1934, p. 284.

THE MEASUREMENT OF THE WEATHER ELEMENTS

Methods of automatic measurement of the weather elements and of transferring the data to offices where they may be processed have been developed. Measuring devices are sent up into the upper atmosphere by balloons, rockets, or satellites, from which the data are transmitted by radio signals. Automatic weather stations are used in many places, but the Weather Bureau still depends upon the observations of several thousand meteorologists and amateurs, on land, sea, and in airplanes. The basic instruments used to measure the weather elements are described as follows:

The Velocity and Direction of the Wind

The **cup anemometer** *measures the velocity of the wind and records it by means of an electrical-contact system.* Dials geared to the shaft read miles per hour directly, while automatic records are made on a time graph in the station. The wind direction is recorded every minute by an electrical connection to the weather vane, and is registered on the graph.

In order to obtain the direction and velocity of the winds at higher altitudes, pilot balloons are sent up four times a day at more than 150 places in the United States. Their

Figure 20–1. An anemometer and wind vane. (Courtesy, U.S. Department of Commerce, Weather Bureau)

position is observed with a **theodolite,** which shows the direction and velocity of the wind at each level. A **theodolite** *is an instrument to measure horizontal and, usually, vertical angles.*

The Beaufort Scale lists and defines 12 different wind velocities. For example, a fresh breeze represents a velocity of 19 to 24 miles per hour, a gale is between 39 and 46 miles per hour, while velocities of 64 to 75 miles represent a storm. A hurricane velocity is any velocity above 75 miles per hour.

The Amount of Rain and Sunshine

The rain gauge and the sunshine recorder are also provided with electrical devices that make it possible to register the amount of precipitation and sunlight on the same graph. The self-recording **rain gauge** *operates by a tiny bucket that tips each time a hundredth of an inch of rain has fallen into it,* thus making an electrical contact that operates the recording pen.

The Humidity

Relative humidity is measured in a variety of ways. One method is to determine the difference in the temperature shown by a wet- and a dry-bulb thermometer. Inasmuch as the rate of evaporation from a piece of wet muslin, wrapped around the bulb of a thermometer, will be determined by the relative humid-

ity; and inasmuch as heat is used up when evaporation takes place—the lowering in the temperature of the wet thermometer will depend on the relative humidity. In other cases, the two thermometers are whirled: in the sling psychrometer the thermometers are whirled by hand, whereas other psychrometers are whirled by a simple machine. **Psychrometers** *are devices to measure relative humidity.*

Another type of instrument to measure relative humidity is the hair hygrometer. The American Indians had a gruesome proverb: "When the locks turn damp in the scalp house, surely it will rain." As high humidity does favor rain, this proverb was well founded. The **hair hygrometer** *makes use of the high susceptibility of human hair to moisture.* The hair is treated to remove oils, and then a bundle is fastened in such a way that its changes of length under variations of humidity are shown by the movement of an indicator.

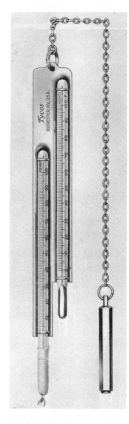

Figure 20–2. A sling psychrometer. (Courtesy, Tycos)

The Temperature

The maximum-temperature thermometer is like the ordinary kind, except that a constriction near the bulb end prevents the mercury from going back to its bulb after it has risen. Just like a clinical thermometer, it must be reset by whirling. The minimum-temperature thermometer contains alcohol instead of mercury, and it is kept in a nearly horizontal position. As the alcohol recedes with a falling temperature, a little dumbbell-shaped index is carried along with it. Since this index is not carried forward when the alcohol expands, the point where the index is located indicates the lowest temperature reached since the time when the thermometer was last set.

Visibility and Ceiling

Visibility and ceiling are important for aviation. **Visibility** *is the greatest distance toward the horizon at which known objects, such as mountains or buildings, can be recognized with the unaided eye.* It is generally expressed in terms of miles or kilometers. **Ceiling** refers to *the height of the base of a cloud above the surface,* at or below an altitude of 9,750 feet. Above 9,750 feet, the ceiling is said to be unlimited. It is expressed to the nearest 100 feet up to 5,000 feet, and above that to the nearest 500 feet. A **ceilometer** has a *photoelectric device to record the height at which a vertical light beam enters a cloud.*

Clouds

Clouds are reported in terms of the numbers of tenths of the sky covered by the clouds. Clouds may be thought of as nature's writing in the sky. Clouds differ in different kinds of weather. *Very high streaks,* called **cirrus clouds,** consist of ice crystals, and generally are far ahead of storms. *Fluffy, white, heaped-up clouds, with rounded tops, and usually having dark bases,* are called **cumulus clouds.** Their bases may lie about a mile or so above the earth, but the clouds may tower as high as 25,000 feet into the upper atmosphere. They are usually daytime, or afternoon hot-weather clouds, but they may become storm clouds, typical of thunderstorms. *Thick*

layers of gray clouds are called **stratus clouds.** Of course, there are many other types of clouds, but those listed above are the more common ones.

The Measurement of Atmospheric Pressure

The measurement of air pressure is very important, because air pressure and the weather are closely related. *The pressure of the atmosphere may be measured with* the mercurial **barometer,** illustrated in Figure 20-3.

Since we live at the bottom of the atmosphere, we have become adjusted to its pressure, and we are not usually aware of the pressure of the atmosphere except when changes in the pressure or altitude produce various effects on the body, such as headaches or aching corns. An interesting experiment to demonstrate the pressure of the atmosphere is that shown in Figure 20-4.

Figure 20-5 shows the principle of a more convenient type of barometer, called the aneroid barometer. **Aneroid** means *without liquid.*

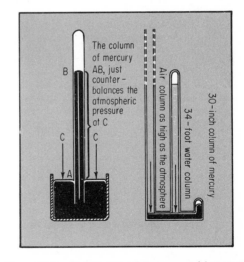

Figure 20–3. The principle of the mercurial barometer.
Left The atmosphere at sea level exerts an average pressure which may be counterbalanced by a column of mercury, 76 centimeters, or about 30 inches high.
Right The pressure exerted by a column of air as high as the atmosphere extends is the same as that exerted by a 34-foot water column or a 30-inch mercury column.
In each case there is no gas above the liquid in the closed tubes.

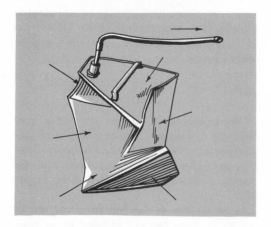

Figure 20–4. A five-gallon can is crushed by the pressure of the atmosphere after most of the air has been removed by means of a vacuum pump. The vacuum may also be produced by boiling water in the can, placing a rubber stopper in the opening and allowing the can to cool in order to condense the steam.

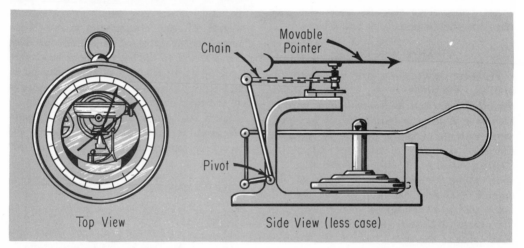

Chain

Movable Pointer

Pivot

Top View

Side View (less case)

Figure 20–5. The essential parts of an aneroid barometer. The mechanism consists of a metal cell covered with a flexible metallic lid which will move up and down in response to changes in atmospheric pressure. The inside of the cell is partially evacuated. A movable pointer is attached to the lid, and the position of the pointer is read on a scale for the type of aneroid barometer illustrated. In a recording barograph a pen attached to the metallic lid makes a record on a chart which is revolved by clockwork. Such a chart usually shows the pressure record for the period of a week. If the scale on the above aneroid barometer is calibrated in terms of the average pressure at different altitudes, the barometer may then serve as an altimeter.

In many cases, it is desirable to have a running record of pressure changes. Such *a record of the atmospheric pressure, over a period of a week, may be obtained with the* aneroid **barograph,** shown in Figure 20-6.

NATURE OF HIGHS AND LOWS

The Coriolis Effect. *The effect of the rotation of the earth on the general circulation of the winds,* discussed in the previous chapter, is known as the **Coriolis Effect,** named after G. G. Coriolis (1792–1843). This law states that *every body, moving north or south on the surface of the earth, is deflected to the right in the northern hemisphere, and to the left in the southern hemisphere, by the earth's rotation.*

Most of the weather in the northern temperate zones is produced by the large masses of air which move up from the equatorial regions, and down from the polar regions. As a result of the Coriolis effect, **Buys Ballots'** law states that *there will be a counterclockwise circulation around the centers of low pressure, called cyclones.* The word, **cy-**

Figure 20–6. An aneroid barograph. (Courtesy, U.S. Department of Commerce, Weather Bureau)

clone, as commonly used, has a variety of meanings. Therefore the word, **low,** is preferred for *low-pressure air masses.* Similarly, *air masses of high pressure,* are called **anticyclones,** or **highs.**

WEATHER FORECASTING

Highs and lows pass over the United States from westerly toward easterly directions, in succession, with speeds varying from about twenty miles per hour in the summer to thirty miles per hour or more in the winter. These highs and lows cover territories ranging up to more than a thousand miles in diameter. Highs generally are accompanied by fair weather, though not always; whereas lows usually represent more or less stormy conditions. In general, a storm is approaching when the barometer indicates falling air pressure. The more rapidly the pressure is falling, the more rapidly is the storm approaching, and the more severe it is likely to be. The indications afforded by the wind and barometer are the best guides now available for determining future weather conditions.

INTERPRETING THE WEATHER

Weather moves at about 30 miles per hour, depending upon the time of year. At the end of 24 hours, it will have moved about 720 miles. Since weather moves, maps are needed to show its probable path. **Weather forecasting** is *based on the facts that weather usually travels in the direction of the prevailing winds, and that weather patterns tend to repeat themselves.* Thus, the meteorologist is able to predict future weather on the basis of present weather over comparatively large areas.

One kind of weather map, called a **synoptic chart,** *gives the synopsis of weather conditions over an extended area at a given time. When lines are drawn to connect points of equal pressure,* one obtains a series of lines, called **isobars,** which show lows and highs. *The atmospheric pressure is expressed in terms* of **millibars.** The average pressure at sea level (standard pressure) is 1,013.2 millibars. Isobars are drawn for every 2, 3, or 4 millibars, according to the scale of the map to be used. See Figure 20-7.

In addition to the pressure data, wind and temperature data are plotted on weather maps. The weather generally follows paths of equal temperature. Areas of rapid change, characteristic of fronts are also shown on the maps.

The weather forecast is then based on this weather map, plus related information concerning wind velocities and direction, the amount of sunlight, humidity, and precipitation.

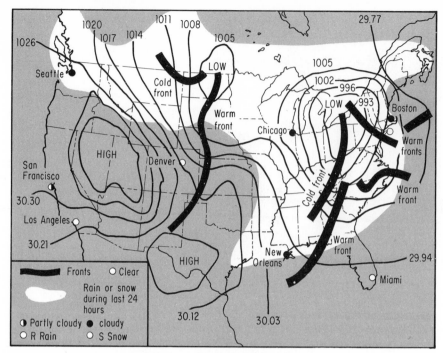

Figure 20–7. A simplified daily weather map.

In the United States, the Weather Bureau, in Washington, D.C., prepares **prognostic** charts *for periods of twelve to thirty hours in advance,* and issues a new chart every six hours. These charts are transmitted by facsimile machines to regional stations, where they serve as the basis for radio and television broadcasts and newspaper reports. Special warnings of storms, frosts, cold waves, floods, winter-sport conditions, and hourly reports for use in aviation are made. Major airports maintain a staff of meteorologists to provide airmen with information concerning the weather.

The meteorologist can predict future weather for the next twenty-four hours, with an accuracy of about 85 per cent. Five-day forecasts are more often right than wrong. Experimental 30-day and 90-day forecasts have been attempted, but these experiments involve almost impossibly complex problems. Perhaps the modern electronic brains now used in the Weather Bureau will help to solve some of these problems, especially now that information is being obtained by weather satellites.

BENEFITS OF WEATHER FORECASTS

Warnings of storms are displayed at more than four hundred points along the coasts and the Great Lakes. Such warnings enable vessels at sea to prepare for a hurricane as far as possible, and to make for the nearest port. Millions of dollars are saved by detaining ships until the danger is over.

Frost warnings are very important to market gardeners, fruit-, tobacco-, and cranberry-growers, for they are thus enabled to prepare to save their crops by the use of smudge pots and other means. Transportation companies are enabled to protect perishable shipments en route, or to refuse to accept such products for shipment until the danger is past.

Warnings of snowstorms enable highway departments and railroads to be ready with snowplows, and to decrease or halt traffic if necessary. Sheep and cattle ranches must prepare to protect their livestock against blizzards and heavy snows. Weekend winter-sport carnivals are planned or called off on the basis of weather forecasts.

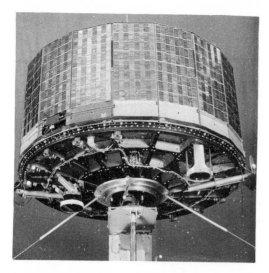

Figure 20-8. The Tiros IV weather satellite prior to launching. Note the large number of solar cells used to power the satellite by sunlight. (Courtesy, National Aeronautics and Space Administration)

Data Required for Weather Prediction	Instrument Used
Maximum and minimum temperatures	Maximum and minimum thermometers
Wind velocity	Anemometer
Wind direction	Weather vane
Precipitation	Rain gauge
Hours of sunshine	Sunshine recorder
Relative humidity	Psychrometer or Hygrometer
Pressure	Barometer or Barograph

One of the most important services of the Weather Bureau is that rendered to aerial transportation. The United States Weather Bureau maintains about fifty airport weather stations, while a great many more airports maintain their own weather service.

THE TIROS METEOROLOGICAL SATELLITES

On February 8, 1962, the Tiros IV satellite was successfully launched. (See Figure 20-8). Tiros V and Tiros VI were launched later during this year. Each of these satellites sent back thousands of cloud-cover photographs for analysis by the weather bureau. Tiros I (1960), Tiros II and Tiros III (1961) had already supplied a wealth of information. Highs, lows, fronts, hurricanes, and even occasional jet streams stood out in clear relief.

SUMMARY

Data for weather predictions are obtained by making the following observations at many widely separated locations; the data are then organized at centrally located stations.

Cyclones, or lows, are low-pressure areas, blowing spirally inward in a counterclockwise direction in the northern hemisphere; they are associated with stormy weather, and move from the west to the east.

Anticyclones are high-pressure areas, or highs, blowing spirally outward in a clockwise direction; they are associated with fair weather. A falling barometric pressure indicates an approaching storm. High cirrus clouds also indicate an approaching low. High pressure areas and low pressure areas follow the paths of equal temperature.

The Coriolis Effect—Every object or air mass, moving north or south on the surface of the earth, is deflected to the right in the northern hemisphere and to the left in the southern hemisphere.

Buys Ballots' Law—Winds in the northern hemisphere blow in an anticlockwise direction around the center of low pressure.

Study Questions

1. DEFINE: weather elements, barometer, barograph, aneroid, cyclone, anticyclone, high, low, isobar, millibar, cup anemometer, Beaufort scale, hygrometer, ceilometer, cirrus cloud, cumulus cloud, stratus cloud, weather forecasting, theodolite, rain gauge, psychrometer, visibility, ceiling, Coriolis effect, synoptic chart, prognostic chart.
2. What data are required for weather prediction?
3. How far ahead may the weather be predicted?
4. What is meant by air-mass analysis?
5. State Buys Ballots' Law.
6. State the Coriolis effect.

The History of the Earth

It is well to stop our star-gazing occasionally and consider the ground under our feet. Maybe this is celestial, too; maybe this brown, sun-tanned, weather-worn old earth is a star also—who knows?

JOHN BURROUGHS

INTRODUCTION

If we should return to our favorite resort near some mountain stream, lake, or seashore in the year 3000, very little change would be noted. We might find that the stream had cut a little deeper channel, that the shores of the lake or ocean had moved a few hundred feet or so, but the general contour of the mountains and the configurations of the coast would be familiar.

But if we should return several million years later, nothing would seem to be the same. Where we had known mountains, plains might exist. New mountain ranges might be observed, and the oceans might now be covering large sections that were formerly high, dry land. Our dams and skyscrapers might long since have been ground to powder under a glacier.

Suppose that we were to excavate a portion of a city dump that had been gradually built up over a period of two hundred years. In the lower layers we might find old knives, spinning-wheel parts, horseshoes, and handmade square nails. In other layers, sewing-machine parts, cylindrical phonograph records, tin cans, machine-made wire nails, aluminum utensils, and radio tubes would appear for the first time. A study of the contents of these different strata in the city dump would enable us to piece together a fairly accurate story of the developments which took place during the

two-hundred-year period. In this same way, archeologists are studying civilizations which existed thousands of years ago by excavating the ruins of ancient cities, many of which were found to rest in turn on six or more layers of previous ruins. The geologist obtains a story of the history of the earth by a similar process.

The geologist's history book consists of the rock strata and the fossils which they contain. The history of the earth, as recorded in this book of strata, extends far back beyond a billion years. Probably, the earth existed for another three billion or more years before it got around to writing its more recent history.

GEOLOGIC PIONEERS

Leonardo da Vinci (1452–1519), the great artist, engineer, and scientist of Florence, Italy, had been employed to dig some canals in stratified rock in northern Italy. He observed fossils in the rocks, and correctly concluded that they were the remains of living organisms, which were deposited when the *rock layers* (**strata**) were formed.

Nicolaus Steno (1638–1687), a Danish churchman and physician, wrote "where shells and other similar deposits of the sea are dug up, these lands are sediments of the turbid sea. . . . When the lower strata were being formed, none of the upper strata existed."

Comte de Buffon (1707–1788), a great French naturalist, reasoned that fossils are the remains of creatures that lived in the oceans and that they were left on land when the oceans receded. He thought that the history of the development of living organisms could be found in the study of fossils.

James Hutton was the first man to observe and demonstrate that the past history of the earth might be understood through the study of processes that are taking place today. It was Hutton's contention that the *"present is a key to the past."*

Baron Georges-Léopold-Chrétien-Frédérick-Dagobert Cuvier (1769–1832), a French scientist and the founder of the sciences of anatomy and paleontology, applied the methods of comparative anatomy to the study of fossil fragments, and was thus able to trace the relationships between the various types of creatures as revealed by the fossils. After a careful study of the fossils in various strata, he concluded that each group of living organisms was the result of a special creation, and that catastrophic changes destroyed nearly all of these organisms before the next special creation.

William Smith (1769–1838), an English quarryman, observed that the same strata in various places in England contained similar fossils. He also noted that the various strata followed one another in the same order, regardless of their location.

Charles Lyell advanced the idea that the present features of the earth resulted from the slow, natural processes of erosion, sedimentation, and volcanism, rather than from a series of catastrophes. His **law of uniform change** is one of the most basic principles of geology. It states that *past changes of the earth's surface may be explained by processes now in operation.*

Charles Darwin (1809–1882) introduced the theory of biologic evolution, which explained the differences between the fossils found in succeeding rock strata.

FOSSILS

Fossils *are traces or impressions of animals or plants of past geological ages that have been preserved in rock strata.* They reveal an orderly progressive change from simple to more complex forms of life.

Relatively few of the countless living organisms have been in a position to form fossils. Living organisms must be buried at death in such media as clay, sand, silt, dust, volcanic ash, or asphalt, in order to form fossils. Otherwise fungi, bacteria, or animals soon destroy them. Only a few fossils have been formed from soft-bodied organisms.

Carcasses of woolly mammoths have been found frozen in Siberia, so well preserved that their flesh was still edible after thousands of years. Fossil remains consist of the shells, skeletons, and other hard parts of living organisms that contain enough mineral matter to enable them to resist decomposition long enough for them to be covered by deposits, which have preserved them in stratified rock until the present time. Often, pseudomorphs are found in the older rocks. A **pseudomorph** *is a fossil that has been preserved by the substitution of the original material by mineral matter, in such a way as to preserve the original shape and features of the specimen.* Petrified trees are pseudomorphs.

Figure 21–1. Uncovering Brontosaurus bones, Bone Cabin Quarry, Wyoming. (Courtesy, American Museum of Natural History)

Frequently, fossil molds or casts are found. A **mold** is *a cavity left in a rock by the complete decay or solution of a dead organism, leaving its form in the sediment. If a mold is later filled with mineral matter that retains the shape of the mold, the fossil is called a* **cast.**

Tracks, trails, and furrows have also been preserved in rocks.

Peat bogs and asphalt pits have proven to be especially good sources of fossils of animals, which have been trapped in them. Coal deposits often show patterns of leaves, while volcanic ash and lava yield fossil remains that have been caught and petrified in these deposits. In the Mojave Desert, there is a stratum of volcanic ash that probably settled in a lake and covered over branches and trunks of trees, which were then petrified as they lay in this sediment at the bottom of the lake.

The fact that the types of fossils in different rock layers vary from simple one-celled organisms, in the lowest rock layers, to the complex mammals in the top layers, indicates that life has not always existed on the earth in

Figure 21–3. Dinosaur tracks in sandstone in Peace River Canyon, British Columbia. (Courtesy, Department of Mines and Resources, Canada)

its present forms, but has passed through an evolutionary process. Repeated observations have shown that rocks of a given period contain fossils peculiar to that period. *Geologists who specialize in the study of fossils are called* **paleontologists;** they are able to date a given stratum by an examination of the microscopic fossils which it contains. This identification of strata is very important in petroleum geology, because it enables the geologist to examine oil-well cores, and tell what stratum is being drilled, and when a stratum that usually contains oil may be expected to be reached.

ESTIMATING THE AGE OF STRATA

All methods of estimating the age of strata are based on a few fundamental assumptions: (1) The same causes that produce present geologic changes are those which produced similar changes in the past. (2) In a series of strata, the lower strata were deposited before the upper strata, and are older. (3) Whenever an igneous intrusion (dike) is found cutting across a sedimentary layer, it must be younger than the layer. (4) Rocks are the same age as the fossils contained in them. (5) Rocks containing similar fossils are of the same age, regardless of their location.

There are several methods of estimating the age of strata, but the most reliable one is based on the study of the radioactive elements contained in them. The rate of decay of radioactive elements has been determined with considerable accuracy, and it is known that the rate is constant. It requires 4.5 billion years for one-half of a sample of uranium to decompose to form a special isotope of lead, having an atomic weight of 206. This isotope of lead can only be formed by the radioactive decay of uranium 238. So, by measuring the relative amounts of uranium 238 and lead 206 in a rock the age of the rock may be calculated. Other radioactive elements also yield similar information. This method is best for the study of igneous rocks, but it may be used for sedimentary rocks if they contain radioactive material.

Radiocarbon dating is used to date the remains of carbon-containing objects such as wood, charcoal, shells, grains, bone, textiles, etc. up to about 40,000 years of age. As a result of cosmic radiation, the radioactive carbon isotope (atomic weight of 14) instead of ordinary carbon (atomic weight of 12) is present in the air in the form of carbon dioxide. The amount of radioactive carbon is very small in comparison to the amount of ordinary carbon 12. However, the relative amounts of carbon 14 have been very uniform throughout the primordial past. Carbon 14 is utilized by plants, and appears in their residues. It has a half-life of 5,568 years. The amount of carbon 14 in a sample furnishes an estimate of its age.

UNCONFORMITIES—LOST INTERVALS OF TIME

Occasionally, railroad and highway cuts expose stratified deposits in which horizontal strata lie on strata which have been tipped and worn off by erosion, thus leaving a line of demarcation where the strata are not parallel or do not conform to the strata below. Such an angular unconformity may separate two periods or even eras, which are typified by great uplifts in the earth's surface.

An **unconformity** is *a record of three important events of importance in geologic history:* (1) *an uplift* produced by diastrophic movement, which results in the exposure of older rocks; (2) *a period of extensive erosion* when the land was above sea level; (3) *a change, such as subsidence,* which resulted in the deposition of new strata on the eroded surface. Unconformities make possible the dating of past diastrophic movements.

Cores obtained from oil wells drilled down to more than 25,000 feet provide some in-

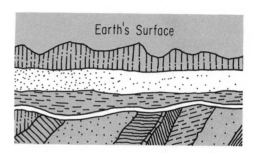

Figure 21–4. An unconformity represents a gap in the historical record which may be world-wide in nature.

formation concerning strata. Then, of course, deep gashes in the earth's surface, such as the Grand Canyon of the Colorado River, have exposed thousands of feet of rock strata. Still lower strata have been pushed upward, bent, eroded, and left exposed, thus making it possible to study them. Four major unconformities divide the strata record into five sections. Each **unconformity** *represents a break in the record of deposition, during which world wide uplifts took place.* Thus, there is a natural basis for dividing the strata into five **eras.** Each era contains a distinct group of fossils.

THE HISTORY OF THE EARTH

Each **era,** *consisting of millions of years, represents a time of widespread mountain-building; each* **period** *represents local disturbances and uplifts of relatively short duration; an* **epoch** *is a subdivision of a period.* Each period begins with increasing submergence of lands, and closes with the retreat of

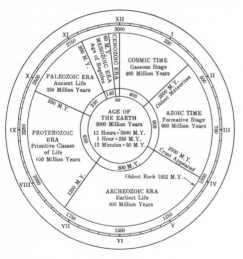

Figure 21–5. Summary of the earth's history in a clock's face. (Courtesy, Chester A. Reeds, the University Society, and the American Museum of Natural History)

the oceans. Recent estimates, it will be recalled, place the age of the earth at about 4,500 million years. Table 21-1 gives a synopsis of the Cenozoic Era, the most recent era in the history of the earth. The Cenozoic Era represents about $\frac{1}{80}$ of the age of the earth.

THE HISTORY OF NORTH AMERICA

In the Archeozoic era, one-celled animals first put in their appearance, and sedimentation and mountain-building were going on as they do today. The locations of the present Appalachian and Rocky Mountains were huge elongated depressions occupied by areas of the ocean, and for the next few periods (extending into the Paleozoic era), North America was flooded by the oceans a number of times. At one time, at least three-fifths of North America was flooded with shallow water. Great beds of limestone, shale, and sandstone were formed. Eventually, a hot dry climate evaporated large bodies of water and formed layers of salt and gypsum several hundred feet thick.

Toward the close of the Paleozoic era, the great Pennsylvania coal fields were formed, and the strata of organic materials from which petroleum was formed were buried under many layers of sedimentary rocks. By the close of the Paleozoic era, the Appalachian trough had filled up with sediment in excess of 40,000 feet in depth, and there were widespread uplifts of the continent. The Appalachian Mountains were formed at this time.

During the fourth, or Mesozoic era, North America was inhabited by huge reptiles, such as the fierce Tyrannosaurus, 50 feet in length, and the 75-foot Brontosaurus. Luxuriant vegetation must have been required to meet the daily needs of the 50-ton herbivorous Brachiosaurus. The great Rocky Mountain Trough remained as an inland sea for millions of years; but it gradually filled up, petroleum deposits and coal beds were formed, and, by the end of this era, the Rocky Mountains were lifted up.

About sixty million years ago, at the beginning of the Cenozoic era, the principal continental features of North America were about as we see them today; but few of the present topographical features, such as the plains, hills, valleys, and canyons that are familiar to us, existed at that time. The Florida peninsula and the western and southwestern portions of the continent were submerged.

Mount Rainier in Washington, and Mount Shasta in California, were active volcanoes, and many lava flows occurred, some 5,000 feet in depth.

Toward the close of the Mesozoic era, the Cascade and Coast Ranges in western North America were uplifted, the whole Rocky Mountain area was elevated, and the Colorado River began cutting the Grand Canyon.

The Pleistocene epoch, of the Quarternary period, of the Cenozoic era includes a very brief time, only one million years, in the history of the world; and yet, it was during this period that horses and elephants approached their modern form, and the Cro-Magnon man developed. During this epoch, there were five great ice ages, in which large sheets of ice, possibly thousands of feet thick, moved down into the part of North America now occupied by the United States, as far as Illinois and Ohio, and receded again. Great ice flows seem to be peculiar to this period, and rank high in importance as terrestrial events. Each of these ice ages lasted for tens of thousands of years, and between each there were warm periods which lasted at least 50,000 years.

About 10,000–20,000 years ago, the last great glacier retreated, leaving behind it the Great Lakes and thousands of smaller lakes in northern United States and in Canada. Niagara Falls is estimated to have taken 20,000 years to cut its way to its present position, from the place where it started as the last glacier receded—hence the conclusion that the last glacier was receding 20,000 years ago. This glacier still covers a large portion of Greenland and regions around the North Pole, to an extent of 6 million square miles. The polish and scratches left on rocks by the glaciers are evidence that these glaciers are of fairly recent date, as geologic time goes.

We are still living in a comparatively cool period of the earth's history.

SUMMARY

Geologic time is divided into eras, periods, and epochs, on the basis of major mountain-building.

The Law of Superposition: The youngest rocks are in the top strata, and the oldest rocks are in the lowest strata.

Lyell's Law of Uniform Change: Forces now in operation are the same ones that were effective in the past.

The Theory of Organic Correlation: Rock formations containing similar fossils were deposited at the same time.

The Theory of Organic Evolution: Living organisms have evolved progressively, in well-recognized stages.

The Theory of Unconformity: An unconformity represents a break in the regular deposition of stratified rocks, in which lower strata were uplifted and eroded before the upper series of strata were deposited.

Study Questions

1. DEFINE: strata, fossil, pseudomorph, mold, cast, paleontologist, unconformity, era, period, epoch.
2. What outstanding events took place in the Cenozoic era?
3. In what regard were Cuvier's conclusions not in line with present thinking?
4. State Lyell's law of uniform change.
5. On what fundamental assumptions are estimates of the ages of strata based?
6. How is radioactivity used in estimating the age of strata?
7. What is meant by an unconformity, and of what value is it to geologists?
8. How is the geologist able to study successive layers of stratified rock?
9. How would you account for the formation of salt beds?
10. What climatic conditions probably existed when the coal beds were laid down?
11. Which of the mountain ranges in the United States is (a) oldest, (b) youngest?
12. If each minute should represent 1,000,000 years, how long has the earth been in existence?
13. What evidence can you give to prove that the earth's surface has undergone many changes?
14. Upon what bases are divisions in geological time made?
15. Of what value is the study of fossils to the scientist?
16. How does the paleontologist identify rock strata?
17. In what respects did Hutton and Lyell agree?
18. What contribution did Darwin make to the study of fossils?

The X-15 Experimental aircraft; an aircraft with some spacecraft characteristics. It has been flown faster than 4,000 miles per hour, and has reached an altitude of about 60 miles above the surface of the earth. (Courtesy, U.S. Air Force)

Harnessing Energy

One machine can do the work of fifty ordinary men. No machine can do the work of one extraordinary man.

ELBERT HUBBARD

EVERY man, woman, and child in the United States has eighty slaves working for him. These slaves are his machines, which are powered by the energy that man has learned to harness. Nearly all of this energy had a common origin, the sun. It has been stored for us in the form of carbon compounds such as are found in coal, petroleum, and natural gas. A small portion of the energy that we use comes from waterpower that we have harnessed by building dams and hydraulic generators, but waterpower also has its source in the sun. A very small fraction of our energy comes from the energy that is locked up inside of the atom, a source that we have barely tapped.

It is through the labor of our mechanical slaves that man is acquiring more and more leisure time, and is producing more and more time-saving devices. These slaves transport him from place to place with ever-increasing speed; they dig his ditches, till his soil, reap his crops, prepare his foods, and make his clothes.

Early civilized man learned that two men could do more work than one man, so they made war, captured their enemies, and put them to work as slaves. Eventually, the horse, ox, buffalo, and donkey were domesticated and put to work. The steam engine was invented, and put to work in pumping the water out of coal mines. Soon it was applied to furnish the power to operate trains, ships, and factories. As time progressed, the steam engine was replaced by the internal combustion engine. Gasoline engines could be made lighter, safer, and more adaptable than steam engines. The present generation has witnessed the slow fading of steam power. Most of the steam locomotives have been dismantled or preserved in museums and parks as mementos. Few members of the present younger generation have seen a puffing, whistling steam engine in operation. They have been denied the romantic thrill of horsedrawn fire engines, belching forth smoke and sparks on their way to a fire at night.

In this unit we will study machines, simple and complex, the mechanical advantage and efficiency of machines, and the way machines are used in order to make our work easier.

Making Work Easier and More Efficient

Another interesting conclusion is, that the animal frame, though destined to fulfil so many ends, is as a machine more perfect than the best contrived steam engine—that is, it is capable of more work with the same expenditure of fuel.

JOULE

INTRODUCTION

A comparison of modern industrial civilizations with such backward civilizations as the Amazon Indians or the Australian aborigines will show that one of the chief differences between them is their tools. Backward people do their work, except for the help which they may obtain from domesticated animals, while industrialized civilizations employ power-driven machines to do their work. The development of power-driven machines will be the topic for the next chapter.

One marvels at the genius of the ancient Egyptian pyramid builders in solving the problems of moving huge stones long distances. Even the quarrying of these stones with the tools available must have been a tremendous undertaking. Undoubtedly, the pyramid builders used hundreds of thousands of slaves, but it would be almost impossible to get enough slaves around one of these stones to lift or carry it. Perhaps levers were used to raise the stones so that long poles could be placed under them, thus making it possible to use more slaves to lift and carry the stones. Probably long inclined planes were used, and perhaps skids or rollers were used to decrease the friction. Perhaps long ropes pulled by hundreds of men furnished the force to move the stones up the inclined planes. In any case, one can be sure that some of the principles of simple machines were known by the pyramid builders.

Ancient civilizations learned how to use such simple machines as the wheel and axle, the inclined plane, and the lever. To these simple machines add the pulley, the wedge (a double inclined plane), and the screw (a spiral inclined plane), and we have the six **simple machines,** which, in one form or another, or in combination, form the basis for devices to *enable man or his animals to do work more advantageously*. These simple machines do not add energy, but they do enable man to apply energy so as to do work with less force on his part.

Modern, power-driven machines use various combinations of simple machines to change the direction or rate of motion.

WHY WERE MACHINES INVENTED?

Laziness is a common human trait. Webster's dictionary defines laziness as the indisposition to action. A lazy person avoids moving anything, even himself, if possible. Supreme laziness is represented by the actions of a person who works very hard to develop a method of doing work with less effort. Human slaves, domesticated animals, and power-driven machines have been used to do work for man. However, the earliest **machines** were simply devices to enable man to do work more advantageously. They *permitted man to exert a push instead of a pull*, or to *gain force at the expense of distance, or vice versa.* Using simple machines, the same amount of work is always done; but these machines may make it possible to do it more rapidly or more slowly. Man himself represents a combination of simple machines, but at times it may be desirable to extend one's arm by use of a long fishing pole, or to use the force supplied by his muscles more advantageously by means of such simple machines as hammers, saws, axes, or shovels.

WORK

It will be recalled that energy is the capacity to perform work and that work is a product of force and distance. If we were to push on a wall with all of the force at our command and no motion was imparted to it, we would be doing no work because work requires that something be moved. Now, if it were possible to have a frictionless machine, it could be set in motion, and once it was set in motion, it would continue to move. Such a machine would represent perpetual motion. Many "perpetual motion" machines have been invented, but none of them work because friction cannot be entirely eliminated. But if we could have a perpetual motion machine, it could do no work because it would be exerting no force.

At times, the force or distance elements of work are not apparent. If one were to jump out of a flying airplane he would fall quickly, that is he would move through a considerable distance without any exertion on his part. However, work would be done, because the force of gravity would be in operation.

Work may be expressed in foot-pounds, gram-centimeters or any other units of weight and distance. Weight is a measure of the force of gravity. Energy may be expressed in the same units as work, because energy is the capacity to perform work.

POWER

Power is often confused with energy, but it differs from energy in that *it represents the rate of doing work, or the rate at which energy is expended.* No time element enters into the definition of work. Power units combine work units with time units; for instance, foot-pounds per second, or gram-centimeters per second. When we buy electric power we would not be satisfied if the electric lights barely glowed, or if the motor of a fan or mixer turned very slowly. We want the motors to turn fast enough to do the work for which they were designed. The rate of doing work is an important consideration. *Any kind of power can be expressed in terms* of **watts** or **kilowatts.**

Now, if we were buying electric power, we would not be satisfied if the power lasted only a few minutes. We want some motors, such as those in electric clocks, to run continuously. So the time element enters in again and we buy electric power in units of kilowatt-hours. In other words, we want the electric power to do work at a given rate for a given length of time. Note that the **horsepower-hour** or the **kilowatt-hour** are *units of work* rather than power.

MECHANICAL ADVANTAGE

Simple machines, as we shall see, often make it possible to trade distance for force. We might use a crowbar (a lever) to pull a nail from a block of wood. The force exerted on the nail is more than we are exerting on the crowbar, but at the same time, our hand moves a greater distance than the nail. *The force multiplication factor of a machine is known as the actual* **mechanical advantage.** *It is equal to the weight or resistance divided by the force that is exerted.*

THE INCLINED PLANE

In order to accomplish a given amount of work, less power is required, if the work is done more slowly.

The use of the inclined plane is one method of decreasing the vertical distance an object is moved per unit of time. Thus, it requires more power but less time to climb a steep stairway than one that is not so steep. An inclined plane is a simple machine that enables one to trade force for distance.

A stairway is an inclined plane, broken

up into steps. A ramp is a simple inclined plane. Inclined planes are often used for unloading or loading trucks, railroad cars, ships, or airplanes. A highway built on a slope is likewise an inclined plane. Less power is required for an automobile to climb a long, gentle slope than a steep grade. Railroad tracks were laid out in such a way as to avoid steep grades, and in many cases the best solution to this problem was to dig tunnels.

A ladder resting against a house is a steep, inclined plane, but if it is mounted vertically it is not a simple machine. It takes less force to climb a flight of stairs than it does to climb a ladder.

THE WEDGE

A wedge is a double inclined plane. An ax head is a wedge. The most common wedge is the wedge used to split logs apart. A nail is a wedge. Nails often cause wood to split apart, although this is not the desired outcome. A crowbar is a wedge, but it may also be used as a lever. A needle, an icepick, a chisel, a knife blade, and a carpenter's plane are examples of wedges. A saw is filed so as to provide a series of wedges.

THE SCREW

A screw is a spiral inclined plane. Thus, spiral stairways or highways that wind around a mountain may be considered to be screws. The object is to trade distance for a gain in force.

The carpenter's bit is a screw. Many jacks employ the principle of the screw. Propellers are screws. Revolving piano stools generally use screws. A meat grinder is an example of a machine that consists of two simple machines, a wheel-and-axle and a screw. Bottle and jar caps are screws. Vises, and many wrenches, operate with screws.

Inclined planes, wedges, and screws have the same purpose, i.e., they trade distance for force.

Some screws are combinations of simple machines. The ordinary screw, for example, may be considered to be a tapered wedge as well as a spiral inclined plane. Ordinary bolts, on the other hand, are not intended to drill holes and are simple screws.

LEVERS

"Give me a place to stand and rest my lever on and I can move the earth," said Archimedes. This great mathematician and inventor was the first man to set forth the principle of levers, which he applied in constructing machines of warfare.

Levers differ as to the relative positions of the fulcrum, the effort (force), and the resistance, as shown in Figure 22-1.

The lever aids man in doing work, for it enables him to exert a force to move an object a short distance, in which his limited force is made to act through a long distance.

If an automobile gets stuck in a ditch, it may be that one or more jacks properly placed would make it possible to move it out of the ditch. But, if a jack were not available, or if it could not be conveniently used, then a resourceful man would start looking for a heavy pole or timber to use as a lever. He might find that he would also need a *support about which the lever pivots,* called a *fulcrum,* such as a block of wood. The fulcrum may be at the end of the lever or at the center, as in the case of the seesaw, or it may be some place between the center and the end of the lever. The force may be applied at one end of the lever, or it can be applied between the fulcrum and the weight. Where one places the fulcrum depends upon whether he wants to exert a force as a push or a pull. The only point to placing a fulcrum in the center of a lever is that an object may be lifted by pushing down on the opposite end of the lever. There is no gain in force or distance, but the advantage of direction is gained.

The distance from the force to the fulcrum is called the **force arm,** and *the distance from the weight (resistance) to the fulcrum* is called the **weight arm.** When the weight arm is longer than the force arm, distance is gained, and when the force arm is longer, force is gained. In a pair of sheet-metal snips, it is desirable to gain force, while distance

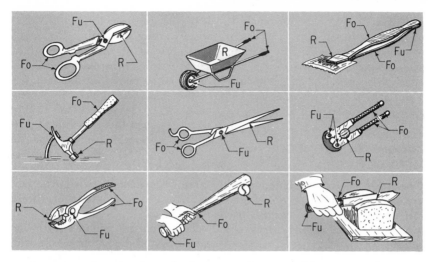

Figure 22–1. Examples of everyday levers. Fo = force, Fu = fulcrum, R = resistance.

rather than force is desired in a pair of paper shears, because the paper is cut with little force.

PULLEYS

Pulleys may be considered to be circular levers. A simple, one-strand pulley is like a lever with the fulcrum at the center. Neither force nor distance is gained, but a change of direction is accomplished. For example, by means of a simple pulley at the top of a flag pole, one can pull down on a rope to raise a flag. Several pulleys may be joined in a variety of ways to enable one to trade distance for force. Very heavy loads may be lifted with pulley systems, such as one finds in a block and tackle. Pulleys have long been used to aid in the lifting of windows. By placing the window at one end of a rope and a heavy weight at the other end, and a pulley between them, a small force may be exerted on the window in order to lift it.

One wheel can be made to turn another wheel by connecting them with a belt or chain. The old-time threshing machine used a belt, while the bicycle uses a chain. One wheel can be made to turn another by fitting them together as gears. A big wheel or gear, turning slowly, will turn a little wheel or gear rapidly. Clocks and watches illustrate this fact.

In an automobile, belts and pulleys are used to transmit the power of the engine to the fan, or perhaps the air conditioner. In the home, ventilating blowers use belt and pulley connections. At one time, belts were used to transmit the power from power-developing machines to the machines to be operated. Sometimes the object was to simply change the direction of the application of the force. At other times, rate of motion was increased or decreased by trading distance for force, or vice versa.

WHEELS AND AXLES

The wheel and axle is a circular lever in principle. An ordinary wheel is merely a device to lessen friction and is not classed as a machine. Wheels turn on axles, but the axles of wheels and axles are fastened to the wheels and turn with them. A typical wheel and axle is the windlass, which may be used to raise water from wells, or to raise and lower ships' anchors. The crank of a windlass is a wheel with just one spoke. The rod, on which the rope winds, is the axle. The wheel and axle are fastened to each other, so that the wheel turns the axle or vice versa. When the axle turns the wheel, as in the case of the automobile, force is gained; and when the wheel turns the axle, distance and speed are gained.

Door knobs are wheels and axles. The knob

is the wheel, and the rod that the knob is fastened to, is the axle. It moves the catch, when it is turned by the knob. The steering wheel of an automobile is likewise a wheel and axle. Each drive wheel of an automobile is a wheel and axle. A fishing reel is another good example of a wheel and axle.

COMBINATIONS OF SIMPLE MACHINES

Most of our machines are combinations of two or more simple machines. A pair of scissors is a combination of two wedges, two levers, and a screw. The cutting edges are the wedges.

A drill is a combination of a wheel and axle and a screw. A pencil sharpener may consist of two screws, two wedges, and a wheel and axle. A scythe is a combination of a wedge and a lever. A bicycle has several wheels and axles, and a pulley.

INCREASING THE EFFICIENCY OF MACHINES

The efficiency of a machine is defined *as the work output divided by the work input.*

The wheel enables one to decrease friction and thus increase efficiency. Whenever wheels, or gears are used to transmit energy, it is desirable to reduce friction as much as possible. The invention of ball bearings, roller bearings, and improved lubricants have represented important advances in this direction.

The rougher the surface, the greater is the amount of friction when it is moved. A **lubricant** *helps to make the moving surfaces smoother.* Perhaps, the pyramid builders used mud for a lubricant, to make it easier to move the huge building stones. Today, the majority of lubricants are made from petroleum, but many different additives are being added to petroleum to impart certain desired properties.

Lubricants must have as low a viscosity as possible and still have sufficient body to keep the moving parts from touching each other. Water has a low viscosity, but it would not be a good lubricant, because it does not have enough body. A lubricant for the automobile crankcrase should have a low viscosity when

it is cold, in order to prevent excessive wear when starting the engine. On the other hand the lubricant should not be of too low a viscosity when it becomes heated. Such a condition is the reverse of the natural properties of lubricating oils. Such oils increase in viscosity when they are cooled and decrease in viscosity when they are heated. What is desired for example, may be an oil with a viscosity of S.A.E. 10 at low temperature and the viscosity of S.A.E. 30 at higher temperatures. This situation calls for an additive that will change the natural properties of the lubricating oil.

Lubricants are required for many different purposes, and the problem of providing a satisfactory lubricant for a given purpose is a highly technical one.

FRICTION

As a result of **friction,** *useful energy is converted into useless heat energy.* Seldom would one want to use friction as a source of heat, although that is exactly what we do when we strike a match. Similarly, the Indians rotated a stick to obtain sufficient heat to ignite readily combustible material to start a fire. Fires sometimes result when brakes get too hot, but it is not the heat that is wanted in this case. Experienced mountain drivers use their brakes as little as possible in order to prevent overheating and loss of braking power.

An important undesirable result of friction is that it causes wear. Many home appliances do not last as long as they should because of a lack of proper lubrication. Children's roller skates, wagons, and bicycles are especially vulnerable.

USEFUL FRICTION

We could not get along without friction. We could not walk, and automobiles and trains could not move without friction. Nails and screws would not hold without friction. We could not pull on a drapery cord or write with a pencil or pen without friction. Shoestrings would not remain tied and bolts would come loose. In the home, we use cleansing powders to provide needed friction for cleaning purposes. For sanding woodwork, we use sandpaper that is especially designed to provide the necessary friction.

Try to think of examples by which friction is reduced. The secret of ice-skating is the small amount of friction between the skates and the smooth ice. It is reduced further by the melting of the ice as a result of the pressure exerted by the weight of the skater. The water so formed serves as a lubricant, but freezes again immediately after the pressure is released. Again, one might call to mind the difficulty of driving an automobile on ice or mud, or the difficulty of walking on an icy pavement. Perhaps you have tried to write on an oily paper without success.

ROTARY MOTION VERSUS RECIPROCATING MOTION

In the **reciprocating steam engine,** the *piston moves back and forth, coming to a dead stop between each change in direction of motion—thus wasting energy, and cutting down speed.* The power-driven, circular saw saws wood much more rapidly than the ordinary reciprocating handsaw of carpenters. Similarly, the steam turbine is more efficient and more speedy than the reciprocating steam engine, and the gas turbine is simpler and more efficient than the reciprocating automobile, airplane, or Diesel engine. Vibrations are cut down in rotary machines. Rotary ma-

chines are much easier to lubricate than are reciprocating engines; compare the ease of lubricating an electric motor with the problem of lubricating an internal-combustion engine.

Many inventions have represented rotary machines which would replace reciprocating machines. Thus, the oar was replaced by the propeller, the paddle by the paddle wheel, the broom by the carpet sweeper, the carpenter's plane by the rotary plane, the sickle or scythe by the lawn mower, and the file by the grinding wheel. A bicycle is an improvement over walking.

The reciprocating motion of the automobile engine pistons *is converted into rotary motion* by *the means* of **cranks.** On the other hand, *rotary motion may be converted back to reciprocating motion by means of* **cams.**

One may use an ordinary food grinder to understand how a crank works. The handle of the food grinder is the crank. It converts the up and down motion of the arm to the rotary motion of the meat grinder.

SUMMARY

Modern machines are combinations of six simple machines: the inclined plane, the lever, the wheel and axle, the pulley, the screw, and the wedge. The two basic simple machines are the inclined plane and the lever. A wedge is a double inclined plane, while a screw is a spiral inclined plane. Wheels and axles and pulleys are circular levers.

A machine enables man to do work more advantageously, by trading distance for force, or vice versa. In the lever, the force times its distance from the fulcrum, equals the resistance times its distance from the fulcrum. It is never possible to gain both force and distance by a simple machine. When there is a gain in mechanical advantage by using a simple machine, there is a loss in speed, and vice versa.

Rotary-motion machines are more efficient, more rapid, more free from vibrations, and easier to lubricate than reciprocating (up-and-down, or back-and-forth) machines. Cranks are used to transfer reciprocating motion to rotary motion, and cams are used to reverse this process.

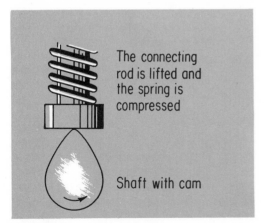

The connecting rod is lifted and the spring is compressed

Shaft with cam

Figure 22–2. A cam as used as a valve lifter in an automobile engine. Rotary motion is thus changed into up-and-down motion.

Efficiency is the ratio of output to input. All machines are inefficient, because part of the energy is transformed into useless heat energy by friction. Friction can be reduced by ball and roller bearings, by wheels, and by lubricants. Friction is frequently useful.

Study Questions

1. DEFINE: machine, mechanical advantage, efficiency, force arm, weight arm, cam, friction, lubricant, reciprocating motion, power, watt, kilowatt-hour, horsepower, fulcrum, crank.
2. What is a horsepower?
3. What becomes of that portion of the energy supplied to a machine that does not do useful work?
4. What simple machines are illustrated by the following: (a) bicycle, (b) can opener, (c) chisel, (d) playground slide, (e) automobile jack, (f) meat grinder, (g) knife, (h) automobile clutch, (i) scissors, (j) saw, (k) lawn mower, (l) windmill?
5. Why is it necessary to push or screw the handle of a jack so many times when jacking up a car to change a tire?
6. Why is it easier to kill a fly with a flyswatter than with the hand?
7. Why does an ax split a log when driven into it?
8. What type of machine is the nut and bolt?
9. All of the marvelous machines of today are combinations of what six simple machines?
10. What is the function of a machine?
11. What advantages do rotary-motion machines possess as compared with reciprocating-motion machines?
12. Give several examples of reciprocating-motion machines that are being displaced by rotary-motion machines.
13. Why are rotary-motion machines more efficient than reciprocating-motion machines?
14. In what units is power measured?
15. Differentiate between energy and power.

Heat

False facts are highly injurious to the progress of science, for they often endure long; but false views, if supported by some evidence, do little harm, for everyone takes a salutary pleasure in proving their falseness; and when this is done, one path towards error is closed and the road to truth is often at the same time opened.

CHARLES DARWIN

INTRODUCTION

Three physical effects of heat are recognized: (1) rise in temperature, (2) expansion, and (3) change in physical state. Two hundred years ago, these effects were known, but there was no theory which would account for them. Heat was observed to "flow" from a hot body to a cooler body. Friction was known to produce heat, but the process was not understood. It was known that some substances would heat up much quicker than others. About 1750, Joseph Black studied the phenomena of heat. He made a clear distinction between heat and temperature, and he defined what we now know as **specific heat** —i.e., *the amount of heat required to raise the temperature of 1 gram of mass 1° C.*

Joseph Black (1728–1799) developed the caloric theory of heat to explain his observations. He envisioned an invisible, weightless substance which he called caloric. The temperature of a substance was a measure of the amount of caloric present, and different substances had different capacities to hold caloric. Caloric would force particles of substances apart, thus accounting for expansion. Chemical changes and stresses caused caloric to be lost. This theory was a beautiful example of a false theory. However, it possessed the value

of any theory in that it led to further experiments designed to test its validity.

LATENT HEAT OF FUSION AND VAPORIZATION

As mentioned above, Black was aware of specific heat. The specific heats of a few substances in calories per gram per 1° C are shown as follows:

TABLE 23-1

Substance	Specific Heat
Brass	0.090
Copper	0.092
Iron	0.108
Aluminum	0.216
Water	1.000

Black also measured the amount of heat required to transform ice into water, and water into steam, and found that a considerable amount of heat was used in each case, without producing a rise in temperature. He originated the word *latent* (from the Latin *latere*, meaning "to hide") to describe this heat that became insensible in the changes of state mentioned above. Black also boiled water, and found that the continued application of heat to boiling water would not raise its temperature. *This heat, used up in the vaporization of a liquid,* came to be known as the **latent heat of vaporization.** The latent heat of vaporization of water, i.e., the amount of heat required to vaporize 1 gram of water, is 540 calories. *The latent heat involved in melting a substance* such as ice is called **the latent heat of fusion.** For ice, it is 80 calories per gram.

THE MECHANICAL EQUIVALENT OF HEAT

Benjamin Thompson (Count Rumford; 1753–1814) realized that there was some correspondence between the work done and the heat produced. As minister of war in Bavaria he became interested in the seemingly endless amount of heat generated in the boring of brass cannon. Thompson distrusted the caloric theory, but he failed to arrive at a satisfactory theory to replace it. Thompson failed largely because he did not obtain quantitative data. It was during his time that Lavoisier introduced the use of the balance, and it is surprising that Thompson did not carry out quantitative measurements.

In 1847, James Prescott Joule (1818–1889) carried out experiments in which a given amount of work was changed into heat. He devoted about forty years of his life to quantitative measurements of the amount of heat produced by a given amount of work. For example, he measured the rise of temperature of water in which paddle wheels were caused to move by means of pulleys and falling weights. He also measured the amount of heat produced by passing an electric current through a resistance wire immersed in water. Ultimately, he proved that a definite amount of work would always produce a definite amount of heat. Furthermore, he proved that all forms of energy (known to him) could be changed into heat without any loss. He called *the ratio between the number of units of work to the number of calories of heat* the **mechanical equivalent of heat.** His most basic contribution was the idea that heat is a form of energy.

THERMODYNAMICS—THE RELATION OF HEAT TO MECHANICAL ENERGY

The First Law of Thermodynamics

Joule originally stated the first law of thermodynamics in terms of mechanical energy. His law stated that mechanical energy could be transformed into heat without gain or loss. Further experiments with other forms of energy led to a broader statement: *In transformations of heat into other forms of energy, or vice versa, no energy is created or destroyed.* Finally, this first law of thermodynamics came to be known as the **law of conservation of energy:** *In all energy transformations there is no gain or loss of energy.* The first law of thermodynamics, stated non-technically, is: *"Something cannot be obtained from nothing."*

The Second Law of Thermodynamics

Joule showed that all forms of energy could be transformed into heat without loss of energy. Would the reverse process be true?

Technically, the **second law of thermodynamics** states that *heat energy tends to flow from a higher to a lower temperature, and will not flow by itself from a lower to a higher temperature.* In other words, heat, just as water, does not flow uphill.

Sadi Carnot (1796–1832) is usually considered to be the founder of the science of **thermodynamics** (from Greek words for *"movement of heat"*). He showed that the 100 per cent conversion of heat into work is impossible. The second law cannot negate the first law, so what happens to the heat that is "lost" in transforming heat into work? The "loss" in heat is really not a disappearance, it represents heat that becomes unusable and is unavoidably wasted. This *unusable heat,* known as **entropy** *represents the heat that is dissipated into the environment as the random motion of molecules.*

The consequences of thermodynamical reasoning, not only have enabled the engineer to design more efficient heat engines, but they have aided progress in many branches of physical science, ranging from atomic structures to weather forecasting.

THE KINETIC THEORY OF HEAT

Daniel Bernoulli (1700–1782) was the first man to devise a theory of gases. In 1738, he explained gas pressure as due to the impact of molecules on the wall of a container. He believed that **heat** *represented the motion of molecules,* but his ideas were too far ahead of the times, and were not accepted. Later, Thompson had the same idea, but it remained for Joule to supply the quantitative basis for the kinetic theory.

James Clerk Maxwell (1831–1879) and Ludwig Boltzmann (1844–1906) developed the mathematical basis for the kinetic theory, which led to its general acceptance. In terms of this theory, **heat** *is the total energy represented by all of the molecular motions in a given quantity of matter.* **Temperature** *represents the average energy of the motion of the molecules in that matter.*

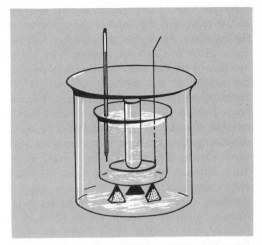

Figure 23–1. A simple calorimeter. The heat liberated by a chemical reaction in the inner tube, raises the temperature of the surrounding water. The weight of the water multiplied by the temperature rise in °C gives the number of calories.

ENERGY IS USUALLY MEASURED IN THE FORM OF HEAT

Other forms of energy are more readily and more completely changed into heat energy than into any other form; for that reason, and because heat can be readily measured, other forms of energy are usually converted into heat for measurement.

HEAT IS MEASURED BY MEANS OF CALORIMETERS

The **calorie** is *the amount of heat required to raise the temperature of one gram of water one degree centigrade.* A **calorimeter** is *a vessel in which we measure the change in the temperature of a given weight of water by heating it, under such conditions that little heat is lost by radiation.* The product of a change in temperature and the number of grams of water undergoing the change, gives the number of small calories. The large **Calorie,** written with a capital *C, is equal to 1,000 small calories.*

The calorie is used in most scientific measurements, but the unit of quantity of heat still used by engineers in the English-speaking countries is the **B.T.U. (British thermal unit),** which is *the amount of heat required to raise the temperature of one pound of water one degree Fahrenheit.*

MEASUREMENT OF TEMPERATURE

Temperatures may be measured with thermometers, which measure the expansion or contraction of a liquid or gas due to temperature changes. The measurement of high temperatures or the measurement of very small temperature changes usually requires mechanical or electrical devices.

Galileo used the expansion of a gas to measure temperature. It is true that a gas will expand more than a liquid but his "thermometer" had the disadvantage that a change in pressure would also change the volume of a gas, and the pressure of the atmosphere would change from day to day. Fahrenheit found that mercury expands much more than glass when heated, and thus devised the mercury-glass thermometer with which we are so familiar.

In order to establish a temperature scale, it is necessary to have two standards readily available. The boiling and freezing points of water serve as these standards. If mercury is introduced into a *tube of quite small diameter,* called a **capillary tube,** there will be a considerable rise in the height of the mercury in the tube, and the smaller the diameter of the capillary, the higher the mercury will rise for a given temperature change. Two marks are placed on the tube, which correspond to the height of the mercury column at the freezing and boiling points of water. The distance between these marks is divided into a number of equal spaces, the number of marks depending upon the kind of temperature scale used. Figure 23-2, on the next page, shows three different temperature scales. The Fahrenheit thermometer is used in the English-speaking world. On the Fahrenheit scale, the freezing point of water is called 32° and its boiling point is called 212°. There are, therefore, 180 degrees between these two marks.

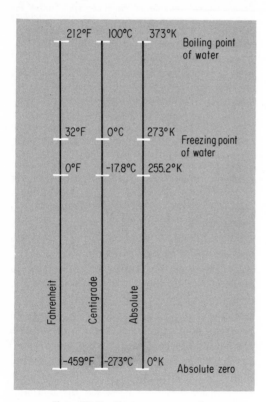

Figure 23–2. The temperature scales.

In the countries which use the metric system of measurement, the freezing point of water is called 0° and the boiling point is marked as 100°, and the distance between these two points is marked off into 100 degrees. Such a thermometer, formerly called a centigrade

thermometer is now, by international agreement, called the Celsius thermometer. The temperature indicated on its scale would be called the Celsius temperature, but the same abbreviation, namely "C" would be used. It is easy to convert temperature readings from one scale to another by a simple mathematical formula which one could derive by considering the differences between the two scales, but the non-scientist is seldom confronted with this problem, so it is omitted from this text.

One might wonder what would be *the lowest possible temperature*. This temperature, called **absolute zero**, is *273° C below 0° C*. By adding 273° to the Celsius temperature the absolute or Kelvin temperature is obtained. Absolute temperature is of great importance to the scientist, and will be referred to from time to time in this text.

For measuring temperatures too high for thermometers, where accuracy is not important, a thermocouple or a thermopile may be employed. A **thermocouple** *consists of two metals joined together*. When the junction is heated, a measurable electric current is produced. Thermocouples may be used from 600° C to 1,600° C. A **thermopile** *consists of several sets of junctions* that give more current. A thermopile may be made so sensitive that it will register a temperature change of one hundred-millionth of a degree. **Bimetallic strips,** such as those shown in Figure 23-3,

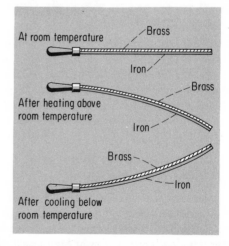

Figure 23–3. Bimetallic strips. The different rates of expansion of two metals in a bimetallic strip cause the strip to bend when exposed to temperature changes.

consist of strips of two metals having different coefficients of expansion, such as brass and steel, fastened together so that the strips will bend when heated.

TABLE 23-2

COEFFICIENTS OF LINEAR EXPANSION

Substance	Change of Length per Unit Length for 1° C Change
Aluminum	0.000025
Brass	0.000018
Iron	0.000011
Glass	0.000003

Bimetallic strips are not only used in **thermostats** to *regulate temperature*, but they are also employed to indicate temperatures. Some oven thermometers are based on the use of bimetallic strips, as shown in Figure 23-4.

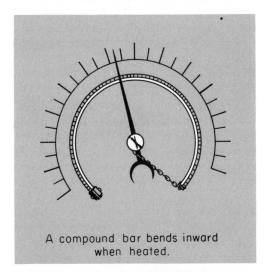

A compound bar bends inward when heated.

Figure 23–4. A bimetallic strip controls the movement of the pointer in this metallic thermometer.

HEAT IS GENERATED BY MANY DIFFERENT METHODS

Heat may be produced by mechanical effects, such as friction, percussion, and compression. Cutting tools often become red hot when they are cutting iron at high speed. An emery wheel produces a shower of red-hot sparks. Railroad rails become heated by the passage of a train over them, while automobile brake bands sometimes catch fire when using brakes on steep mountain roads. Babbitt metal melts out of connecting-rod bearings when friction is increased, due to inadequate lubrication. Heat may also be produced by pounding on a nail. All of these changes represent the transformation of mechanical energy into heat.

Heat may also be produced by changes in the composition of matter. Every chemical reaction is accompanied by a heat change, and certain chemical reactions constitute the chief sources of heat. *When oxygen combines with different elements, heat is evolved. Such a chemical reaction* is called **oxidation.** The oxidation of the foods in our bodies produces body heat and other forms of energy. The oxidation of coal, wood, petroleum, and natural gas produces most of the heat used to run our machinery, and to heat and light our homes.

Heat is produced by electricity. Most electric heating devices produce heat by passing the electric current through wire, which offers high resistance to the passage of the current and therefore becomes hot.

Heat may also be produced by radiant energy. The radiant energy from the sun is, of course, our ultimate source of heat. It is more convenient to change radiant energy into chemical energy in the form of food or fuel, and then burn the substances so formed, than it is to transform light directly into heat.

HEAT TRANSFER

Heat is transferred from one place to another, or from one body to another, by conduction, convection, and radiation.

1. Conduction

It is a common observation that some materials transfer heat better than others. This *transfer of heat* is called **conduction.** Wooden handles are used to handle hot metal utensils, because wood is a *poor conductor* (i.e., good **insulator**) of heat.

All metals are good conductors of heat, although they differ considerably among themselves. Non-metals are poor conductors of heat. The conductivities of some common substances, taking copper as a standard, are listed as follows:

TABLE 23-3
RELATIVE HEAT CONDUCTIVITIES

Silver	1.096
Copper	1.000
Aluminum	0.50
Iron	0.167
Glass	0.002
Water	0.0014
Hair felt	0.00009
Air	0.000057

Heat conductivities are the bases for many practical applications. A study of the above table explains why a steel railroad track will be almost too hot to touch on a hot day, while the wooden ties under the track will feel much cooler, assuming equal absorption coefficients. Wood feels cooler because heat is quickly conducted away from it to the skin at points of contact, which thus come down to the temperature of the skin. Steel, being a much better conductor, requires that a much greater mass be cooled by absorption by the body before the temperature of the point of contact can be reduced to skin temperature. A rug feels warmer to bare feet on a cold morning than hard wood does, because less heat is required to warm up the portion of the rug in contact with the skin, partly because the rug is a poorer conductor of heat, and partly because there are fewer points of contact. The walls of refrigerators, the walls of buildings, hot-water pipes, ovens, etc. must be insulated to keep heat in or out, whichever the need may be. In other cases, such as cooking utensils, good heat conductivity is desired.

Inasmuch as air is a very poor conductor of heat, layers of air between windows (storm windows) and in the walls of buildings act as good insulators. The minute air spaces in woolen textiles account for their warmth.

2. Convection

The *transfer of heat by* **convection** *currents of liquids or gases,* which results from their expansion and consequent decrease in density when heated, is an important consideration in air conditioning; for example, adequate provision should be made for the ventilation of the openings between the roof and the house proper so as to provide for the removal of hot air by convection, during hot weather.

3. Radiation

Most of the heat energy which we receive is *transferred to us in the form of rays* by **radiation.** The warmth of a fire or of the sun is radiated energy. Air is such a poor conductor of heat that conduction would not account for this warmth. Convection currents in the air move upward from the earth and, therefore, could not conduct the heat of the sun down to the earth. Furthermore, there is insufficient material in interstellar space by which heat could be conducted, or in which convection currents could form.

The presence of radiant energy can be recognized only when there is something present to absorb it. The nature of radiant energy will be discussed in Unit VI. It will be sufficient at this point merely to mention that radiant energy can be transformed into heat, and that the heat can be transformed back into radiant energy. A familiar illustration of the latter process is the illumination obtained from an electric light bulb, produced by heating a filament to a high temperature.

When radiant energy reaches our atmosphere, certain molecules in the atmosphere such as those of carbon dioxide, absorb the radiation and change it into heat. The radiant energy which reaches the earth's surface is either absorbed, or it is reflected. Materials differ considerably in their ability to absorb or radiate heat. Good absorbers are also good radiators, while poor absorbers are good reflectors. Radiation is directly proportional to the temperature. Reflecting surfaces, such as aluminum or aluminum paint, are often used on the roofs and walls of buildings to reflect radiant energy.

Rough, black bodies absorb and radiate heat better than white or shiny bodies.

The vacuum bottle, originally designed by Dewar as a liquid-air container, has found its place in nearly every home; it is a thin-walled glass flask with double walls, so constructed that the air can be removed by a vacuum pump, and the glass air outlet can then be sealed off by melting it. The removal of the air produces a partial vacuum, which prevents conduction or convection. The walls are made thin to decrease conduction by the glass, and to prevent it from cracking from unequal expansion or contraction. One of the walls is silvered. The mirror reflects radiant energy, and thus cuts down the transfer of heat by radiation.

SUMMARY

Thermodynamics is the science of the conversion of heat into mechanical energy and vice versa.

The Laws of Thermodynamics

The First Law—(The Law of Conservation of Energy). Energy may be transformed from one form to another without any loss.

The Second Law—Heat energy flows from a higher to a lower temperature and will not flow by itself from a lower to a higher temperature.

The Effects of Heat

The three effects of heat are (1) rise in temperature, (2) expansion, and (3) change in physical state. The measurement of the amount of heat required to raise the temperature of 1 gram of a substance 1° C is its specific heat. The measurement of the amount of linear expansion of a material due to a rise in temperature of 1° C is the coefficient of linear expansion.

The heat involved in changes of physical state is known as latent heat of fusion (solid to liquid), and latent heat of vaporization (liquid to gas).

The 100 per cent conversion of heat into work is impossible. Unusable heat, called entropy, is dissipated into the environment as the random motion of molecules.

All forms of energy are best converted into heat for their measurement. Heat is expressed in terms of calories.

Heat is transferred by conduction, convection, and radiation. Heat is molecular motion.

Study Questions

1. DEFINE: thermodynamics, heat, convection, conduction, insulator, latent heat of fusion, latent heat of vaporization, specific heat, latent, entropy, oxidation, temperature, calorie, Calorie, British thermal unit, thermocouple, thermopile, bimetallic strip, thermostat, coefficient of linear expansion, mechanical equivalent of heat, calorimeter, capillary tube, absolute zero.
2. Name three effects of heat.
3. Name three methods of heat transfer.
4. What was the value of the caloric theory?
5. State the two laws of thermodynamics.
6. State the law of conservation of energy in modern terms.
7. With what does the science of thermodynamics deal?
8. Why is it impossible to convert heat 100 per cent into work?
9. What happens to non-usable heat?
10. Define temperature in terms of molecules.
11. Why is energy generally measured in terms of heat?
12. What is the difference in functions between thermostats and thermocouples?
13. Explain how bimetallic strips regulate temperature.
14. List six different methods of generating heat.
15. Are good heat absorbers good radiators, or good reflectors?
16. What is the difference between heat conduction and heat convection?
17. Explain heat conduction and heat convection, in terms of the kinetic theory.
18. How does radiation convey heat?
19. Explain how a thermos bottle keeps liquids hot or cold.
20. Explain how oven temperature indicators work.

Three Social Revolutions

I was thinking upon the engine at the time (while taking a walk), and had gone as far as the herd's house, when the idea came into my mind that, as steam was an elastic body, it would rush into a vacuum, and if communication were made between the cylinder and an exhausted vessel, it would push into it, and might be there condensed without cooling the cylinder.

JAMES WATT

INTRODUCTION

This chapter might have been entitled "The Steam Engine." Steam engines have almost disappeared from our everyday environment. So one might question the necessity for this chapter on the steam engine. However, it was the invention of the steam engine that ushered in the *industrial revolution*. **This first** revolution made a profound impact on society, and an understanding of its background and its effects should be an important outcome of any study of physical science.

We are living in a time of transition from the *industrial revolution* to a second revolution in the production of goods designed to make possible a more abundant life. This **second revolution** is *automation*, and it is likely to have as profound an impact on society as that which resulted from the industrial revolution. Many of the remaining chapters in this book will provide the background for an understanding of electricity, electronics, and other developments of physical science, which made automation possible.

The **third revolution** may turn out to be an *intellectual revolution*, the most important of the three. The need for it has been accentuated by the industrial revolution and automation.

THE INVENTION OF THE STEAM ENGINE, AND THE INDUSTRIAL REVOLUTION

The steam engine introduced a new concept, i.e., the power-driven machine to do man's work for him rather than to make his work easier, as in the case of simple or even complex machines. *Power-driven machines* are generally called **engines.** An **engine** *is a machine which converts some type of energy into mechanical energy.*

The invention of the steam engine, like many other important inventions, represented the bringing together of a number of different observations and simple devices; no one can be given credit for discovering the principle of the steam engine. Hero (between 100 B.C. and A.D. 200) is credited with inventing the earliest steam engine, in which the recoil of steam issuing from a jet was used to make an arm carrying the jet move about an axis.

Up to the eighteenth century the chief hindrance to industrial development was the lack of power. Men, women, and children did back-breaking work, from twelve to eighteen hours per day. Animals were likewise overworked, and yet the results were comparable to what one would accomplish by attempting to cut a square mile of wheat with a hand

178

sickle. In many mines as many as five hundred horses were used to get the water out of the workings, and the mines were still often abandoned after losing the battle with subterranean water.

Thomas Newcomen (1663–1729) invented a steam engine in which a piston was moved in a cylinder by the introduction of steam. The steam was then turned off, and a spray of cold water condensed the steam in the cylinder, and caused the piston to return to its original position. The operator had to admit steam and cold water, in turn, by manually operated valves. This engine was used to pump water from mines and wells.

James Watt (1736–1819), a mechanic at the University of Glasgow, was one day given the job of putting in order a small model of a Newcomen engine. He was impressed with the very large amount of steam required to operate it. Greater efficiency required that the cylinder be kept as hot as the steam, and yet the cylinder must be cooled as much as possible to obtain a good vacuum. He constructed a steam engine with the condenser separate from the cylinder. The piston was forced up by introducing air into the cylinder and was forced down again by removing the air—pumping it out of the cylinder by means of the steam condenser.

Watt's steam engine became a commercial success, only after it was applied to pump water from the deep coal mines of Cornwall.

The next advance in steam engines was to use the expansive force of the steam on one side of the piston, and the partial vacuum produced by the steam in the condenser on the other side of the piston. By thus avoiding the back pressure of the atmosphere, more power is developed. In reciprocating steam engines, the steam acts alternately on either side of the piston. The piston is fastened by means of a connecting-rod to a wheel or shaft, which is thus caused to rotate as the piston moves back and forth in the cylinder. Attached to the wheel or shaft is an eccentric, which cuts off the steam at the proper time. A large flywheel gives enough inertia to the system to maintain a uniform motion when steam is not pushing on the piston. Figure 24-1 shows the principle of a simple slide-valve steam engine.

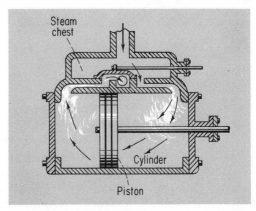

Figure 24–1. The principle of a simple slide-valve steam engine.

Steam engines are **external-combustion engines,** i.e., *combustion does not take place within the cylinder.* On the other hand, **internal-combustion** engines—such as the gasoline engine or the Diesel engine studied in the next chapter—as their name implies, *carry out the combustion of the fuel in the cylinder.* Both engines are heat engines, and they are not very efficient, because only a portion of the kinetic energy of the molecules of gases or steam can be transferred to the motion of the piston and flywheel. Furthermore, most of them have had the disadvantage that they were reciprocating engines.

The Revolution in Transportation

Early developments in highway, railroad, and water transportation were based on the steam engine, and the chief fuel was coal. Now, after about a hundred years, steam engines have been largely replaced by internal-combustion engines, which use petroleum-based fuels. The interurban railroads came and went. In most cities, electrically operated streetcars have disappeared.

We are now living in a period of adjustment to the problems created by the revolution in transportation. Power-driven machines in factories and in transportation have brought about tremendous social changes. The education of many adults now living was of the horse-and-buggy variety, which failed to prepare them to live in the age of the machine. The indications are that we are about due for an intellectual revolution.

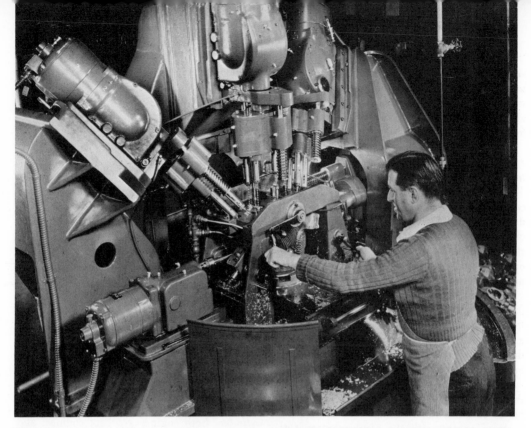

Figure 24–2. Machine tool at Pratt & Whitney Division, United Aircraft Corporation, East Hartford, Connecticut. This machine drills 14 holes simultaneously in aircraft engine cylinders. Drills come in from five different directions. The operation is entirely automatic. This machine and two similar ones for reaming, countersinking, spotfacing and tapping, now do in three minutes what previously required work on seven machines and took one hour. (Courtesy, National Machine Tool Builders' Association)

Machine-Tools

Watchmaker's precision, precision to a ten-thousandth of an inch, has been made possible by modern machine-tools, which represent a major contribution of engineering, metallurgy, and invention to modern civilization. Machine-tools are the reproductive members of the machine world; they are the machines that make machines. Progress in production methods is therefore closely geared to the useful life of machine-tools. A single machine-tool may cost as much as $150,000, and for that reason, it cannot be replaced very often.

A study of present trends points toward fewer machines, the workers being arranged in shifts, and the machines being used day and night. Cheaper electricity facilitates night-shift work, and around-the-clock operation of machines will promote more rapid changes in industrial processes because fewer machines will be required, and therefore less money will

Figure 24–3. An automatic machine operated by directions provided by punched tape. (Courtesy, Pratt & Whitney Aircraft Corporation)

be tied up in them. Furthermore, the machines will wear out more quickly, and will thus require replacement with more modern machines.

Machines have made possible interchangeable parts and mass production technics, such as assembly lines. These technics have made the United States the world's richest nation. They were a natural outcome of the industrial revolution.

Eli Whitney, inventor of the cotton gin, was largely responsible for the evolution of the principle of interchangeable parts. In 1818, he instituted the production of interchangeable parts for firearms. America has made such progress in the development of interchangeable parts that this principle is known in Europe as the American system.

Many of the advances in the realm of power-driven machinery simply represent the development of larger machines which employ more powerful energy sources. For example, coal mining, road building, and the construction of dams is greatly aided by heavy earth-moving equipment.

Technological Advances and Unemployment

Technological advances have been responsible for shifts in employment. The decrease in the use of coal, and the increased mechanization of coal mining resulted in the loss of jobs by many coal miners. However, the decrease in the use of coal was caused by the increase in the use of natural gas and fuel oil, water-power, etc., all of which created new jobs for many workers. Railroad employment has dropped considerably because of the decrease in business resulting from the competition of automobiles, trucks, buses, and airplanes. But these competing modes of transportation have created many times more jobs than were lost in railroad transportation. Actually, technology has created many more jobs than it eliminated. Job opportunities increase the fastest in industries where technological progress has gone forward the fastest.

One of the outstanding causes of unemployment today is the addition of women to the labor forces. Nearly half of the working-age women are now employed. In general, the supply of workers relative to the population has increased more than 50 per cent during the past hundred years. In addition to an increase in the number of women in the labor market, there has been an increase in the number of older people employed, because people are living longer.

One of the results of an increase in the number of adult workers has been a decrease in the number of children employed. It is typical of the present time that many high-school-age young people want to drop out of school and get married, and find employment. However, it is becoming increasingly more difficult for these unskilled, untrained young people to obtain employment.

Other Results of the Industrial Revolution

The introduction of power-driven machinery multiplied productivity and released man from exhausting and repetitious tasks.

Living standards were improved as the result of increases in production and increases in income. During the past 25 years, the work week decreased from about 45 hours per week to less than 40 hours per week, and the trend is toward even less.

AUTOMATION—THE SECOND REVOLUTION

Automation is *the conversion of production systems or methods to automatic operation.* It applies to the fabrication, inspection, testing, and packaging of manufactured articles.

Automation should not be confused with mechanization. Actually it means the application of the principle of feedback or self-correction to machines and processes. Automatic machines make their own decisions. Such a feedback mechanism is illustrated by the home heating system which is turned on and off automatically by the information furnished by the thermoregulator. Modern dishwashers and laundry machines are other examples of automation. Once they receive their instructions, they carry out the entire process of washing, rinsing, and drying without further attention.

Figure 24–4. This machine winds the coil for a transformer in accordance with instructions furnished by an electronic computer. Electronic "brains" are widely used to operate and monitor automatic machines. For a more detailed study of electronic computers see chapter 61. (Courtesy, International Business Machines Corporation)

Automatic Machines

Most of the machines in present-day factories require people to tend them. Machine tenders have to do the same thing day after day, at the pace which the machine sets. Such work is not creative, and such workers are really slaves to the machines which they tend. An important development in industry is the introduction of automatic machines, which require no human labor other than that involved in producing, adjusting, and repairing them. Modern nail-making machines keep up their incessant clatter without the presence of an attendant. Modern automatic bottle machines can turn out 250,000 bottles a day. In automobile

factories, automatic machines are coming to be used on an increasingly large scale. For example, engine blocks are turned out by automatic machines, which perform 530 operations without the aid of human beings.

A survey of industrial operations shows that less than 25 per cent can be automated profitably. Automation lends itself to mass production. It is especially adapted to such factories as chemical plants, petroleum refineries, steel refineries, cigarette manufacture, bottle and container manufacture, electric light bulbs, and plastic forming.

Some of the most interesting automatic machines are those used for packaging and inspection.

An excellent example of automation is the modern telephone with its automatic, dial-operated, long-distance features.

The Automobile—An Example of the Social Impact of Automation

Statistics of automation become out of date so fast that we dare not use them. However, it is safe to say that automobile manufacturers can produce at least 50 per cent more automobiles with fewer workers than they did a decade or two ago. Many automobile workers have lost their jobs. On the other hand, new jobs have been created for many more workers by the automobile industry. Some of these new jobs are listed as follows:

Service stations	Taxis
Automobile sales	Trucks
Repairs	Parking lots
Painting	Highway construction
Washing	Petroleum exploration
Insurance	and refining
Highway patrols	Advertising
Motels	Boating
Resorts	Sports

You could add many items to the above list.

Living Standards and Automation

The industrial revolution, with its power-driven machinery, mass production and interchangeable parts, has gone about as far as it can toward raising the standard of living. Higher salaries to workers no longer result in increased production; and the workers' higher salaries barely balance increases in taxes and the cost of living.

More automation will be required to meet the needs of our increasing population. We look forward to a better life, with yearly increases in income in excess of yearly increases in taxes and the costs of living. We want to achieve this goal by working shorter hours, taking longer vacations, and retiring earlier in life. Automation will help us attain these goals.

THE INTELLECTUAL REVOLUTION

As a result of modern automated technology, many products have been introduced that require servicing. Television sets must be installed and repaired. Radios must be repaired. Typewriters, adding machines, and electronic computers likewise require servicing. The important thing about so many of the servicing operations is that they require highly trained and skilled workers. There is a shortage of skilled automobile mechanics. Competent mechanics to service refrigerators and washing machines are scarce. As Professor Gordon Brown of Massachusetts Institute of Technology says, "I think the human being has to become smarter. This isn't anything to be afraid of—this is what man, intellectually, was destined to become."

Adult Education

Automation may bring about even greater social upheavals than the industrial revolution caused. Many jobs will change in character, and many people will find it necessary to change their vocations two or three times, as a result of changes in employment opportunities. Formal education of the "one shot" variety will no longer suffice, and education will have to be a continuous program.

One of the adjustments of society to this problem of the displacement of workers by machines is the widespread development of adult education. Unemployment insurance will help to provide a living while the worker is preparing for a new job. The majority of adults did not receive as much higher education as the younger generation is now obtaining, and, as a rule, their education was less practical and less general than that which

their children are receiving. The scientific knowledge now being taught in the schools was not known when many present adults were in school, and the scientific attitude and method had not been generally recognized as an essential for every citizen in a democracy. Many adults will find that, when they are displaced from their jobs, they will have to compete with very much better-prepared younger people for new jobs. Furthermore, scientific developments and the progress of technology are taking place at an ever-accelerating pace, which means that our young people now graduating from the colleges will find themselves to be so far behind the times within twenty years—unless they make it their business to continue their education after their formal schooling—that they will be ill fitted for employment in the new industries that do not now exist, and poorly equipped to cope with the new social problems that will arise.

The Revolution in Education

Education is now failing to meet the needs of many young people. This is partly due to the fact that too little money is available for education. There is a shortage of teachers, classrooms are overcrowded, and teachers' salaries are not adequate to compete with other employment opportunities. Still more important is the fact that education is not geared to the needs of many of our young people. There is an appalling dropout of high-school and college students. Lacking useful skills, too many of these young people seek to meet their needs through crime.

Many people expect the next revolution to be an intellectual one.

SUMMARY

Steam engines introduced power-driven machinery. Power-driven machines with the addition of machine-tools made interchangeable parts and mass production possible. Power-driven machines revolutionized not only production, but also transportation. The total impact of these new power-driven machines is called the industrial revolution.

A second revolution, automation, is now under way. It has introduced the idea of automatic machines that will operate with very little human supervision. Automation will help us to make one more step towards a better life, but it will create problems of changes in employment.

A third revolution, an intellectual revolution, must take place in order to enable man to live in this age of the machine.

Unemployment has been due to the fact that there has been an ever-increasing supply of workers relative to the size of the population. In addition, it is due to unemployables, i.e., people who have not been trained to use their minds or their hands.

The industrial revolution and automation have raised living standards. They have provided leisure time, which could be used for intellectual growth.

Study Questions

1. DEFINE: automation, engine, internal-combustion engine, external combustion engine.
2. What three social revolutions are mentioned in this chapter?
3. How did the steam engine contribute to the industrial revolution?
4. What were the desirable outcomes of the industrial revolution?
5. What social problems were created by the industrial revolution?
6. What are the desirable outcomes of automation?
7. What problems, created by the industrial revolution, will be accentuated by automation?
8. Why is an intellectual revolution needed?
9. What would be the nature of an intellectual revolution?
10. Many people have been concerned about an attitude of anti-intellectualism in the United States. Can you cite any examples of this attitude?
11. Is an intellectual attitude popular in modern high schools?
12. Why do students drop out of high schools and colleges?
13. What are the contributions of machine tools to industry?
14. Why are heat engines not very efficient?
15. What is the basic principle of heat engines?

CHAPTER 25

Internal-Combustion Engines

The greatest thing civilization has had thus far is the internal combustion engine. For the first time in the history of the world mankind has had a small, mobile, inanimate power device. The greatest factor that has caused the development of all our civilizing devices has been the use of inanimate power. The internal combustion engine has absolutely changed our whole method of living. The city has developed because of its wonderful system of electrical distribution. Back of this is a great power unit. If the power unit stops, the lights go out and the motors stop. But with the internal combustion engine we carry with us the powerhouse. We move it wherever we please.

C. F. KETTERING

INTRODUCTION[1]

The internal-combustion engine, exemplified by the ordinary automobile engine, is more efficient than the combination of a steam engine and boiler. In this case, the boiler is not necessary, because the combustion of the powdered coal, fuel oil, kerosene, gasoline, natural gas, or other fuel takes place within the cylinder of the engine itself, and thus eliminates the heat losses of the boiler.

The internal-combustion engine is much lighter in weight than the steam engine-boiler combination in comparison with the power developed. Internal-combustion engines also possess the advantages of compactness, ease, and quickness of starting and stopping, along with ease of attachment to machines to be operated.

Since internal-combustion engines are used widely by nearly everybody in the form of automobiles, tractors, airplanes, motor boats, power and light plants, graders, motorcycles,

[1] Most of the material in this section has been selected from the booklets, "How the Wheels Revolve" and "Diesel, the Modern Power," through the courtesy of the General Motors Corporation.

pumps, and scores of other machines, it is important that everyone understands the principles of their operation.

Some of the improvements made in automobiles, such as automatic transmissions, power steering, and power brakes, will be taken up in Chapters 46 and 47 of Part II, where present and future trends, and the impact of the automobile on society will be discussed. This chapter must be restricted to internal-combustion engines as used in automobiles, trucks, railroad engines, ships and stationary power plants.

THE GASOLINE INTERNAL-COMBUSTION ENGINE

The parts and method of operation of the gasoline engine are quite simple in their elementary form. Let us start with the cylinder. It is merely a tube closed at one end, about the same size and proportions as a tall one-pound coffee can. A piece of pipe with one end closed would also make a cylinder. Inside this cylinder, a closely fitting piston slides up and down. This combination gives us a pump similar to the familiar tire pump. Each time the piston moves up and down, air is pumped. This up-and-down movement must be converted into rotary movement; the crankshaft and connecting rod of the automobile engine do this. A crankshaft is familiar in the form of the crank for an emery wheel. The hand crank is the crankshaft; your arm or leg, as the case may be, is the connecting rod. At the maximum speed of the automobile, the crankshaft may be revolving over 4,500 times a minute. Each time the crankshaft makes one revolution, the automobile moves ahead about half a yard.

On the end of the crankshaft, a heavy wheel called a flywheel is mounted. If we turn the emery wheel by hand very rapidly and then let go, the wheel will continue to revolve. This is similar to the flywheel. It keeps the engine turning between power impulses.

By combining the tire pump and emery wheel we obtain a good air pump. Let us take this air pump and add the things necessary to change it into an engine. Additions must be made to the air pump to allow it to pump a mixture of air and gasoline.

The automobile engine takes a mixture of gasoline and air in the correct proportions and burns it in the cylinder. Mixing air properly with liquid gasoline requires a **carburetor.** The carburetor operates much like an atomizer or a flysprayer. *Air, rushing past an open tube of the correct size, picks up the liquid and mixes it with the air.* For every pound of gasoline, about fifteen pounds of air are normally necessary to obtain the correct proportions for a good burnable mixture. The air contained in a room ten feet square and twelve feet high is barely enough for the combustion of each gallon of gasoline. For starting and for accelerating, a richer mixture is necessary. Various devices built into the carburetor make it possible to obtain a mixture containing more pounds of gasoline for each pound of air, on starting.

The engine must have doors which will open and close to allow the mixture of gasoline and air to enter the cylinder and the burned gases

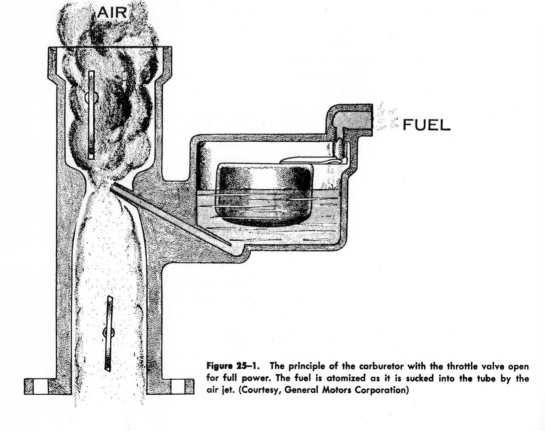

Figure 25–1. The principle of the carburetor with the throttle valve open for full power. The fuel is atomized as it is sucked into the tube by the air jet. (Courtesy, General Motors Corporation)

to pass out again at the proper time. The drafts on your stove or furnace control the intake of air and outlet of burned gases. Likewise, the valves in the engine let in the gases or allow them to be expelled. In the furnace we can take our time about opening and closing the drafts; but in the engine, the valves must open and close in less than one hundredth of a second.

It is necessary to open and close the valve automatically at exactly the right time. The cams and shaft are provided to do this. A cam is a device to convert rotary motion into up-and-down motion of the valves. The camshaft is made up of a series of cams, a cam for each valve. The camshaft is driven by the crankshaft, and rotates at exactly one-half the speed of the crankshaft.

At the top of the cylinder, above the piston, is a space called the "combustion chamber," where the mixture of air and gasoline is burned. It is into this space that the mixture is compressed. If the space is small, the gas is highly compressed. If the space is large, it is not compressed as much. We call an engine with a small space a high-compression engine.

Compression ratio is the fancy term used to describe *the extent of the compression in the combustion chamber*. The volume of the cylinder and combustion chamber is measured in cubic inches, although we could just as easily use quarts or gallons.

To obtain the value for compression ratio, let us take one cylinder of an engine. Turn the crankshaft over until the piston is at the bottom of the cylinder. Now let us measure the volume of the space above the piston, including the combustion chamber. To do this, we can fill the space with oil and then drain the oil out and measure its volume. Suppose we find we have 50 cubic inches of oil. Then let us turn the crankshaft until the piston is at the top of the cylinder. Again we fill the space above the piston with oil and measure its volume. Suppose we find it is 10 cubic inches. The compression ratio is then the volume with the piston at the bottom divided by the volume with the piston at the top. In other words, 50 divided by 10 equals 5. The compression ratio is then 5 to 1. This means that, if the cylinder is full of gas when the piston is at the bottom, the gas will occupy

only one-fifth of the volume when the piston is at the top. That is all there is to compression ratio. The value for compression ratio in automobile engines varies between about 8 to 1 and 11 to 1.

To bring the liquid gasoline to the carburetor from the tank in the rear requires the fuel pump. It operates in a manner similar to the old water pump. Each stroke of the pump pulls gasoline from the tank in the rear and deposits it in the carburetor.

All the above operations must go on in an orderly fashion, each event occurring at the proper time and for the right duration of time. The schedule on which the engine runs to do this is called the four-stroke cycle. A stroke is one movement of the piston from one end of the cylinder to the other; from top to bottom, or from bottom to top. The four-stroke cycle simply means that the schedule each cylinder works on requires four strokes of the piston—first down, then up, again down, and up.

In a four-stroke-cycle engine, the first downstroke of the piston is the intake stroke, which reduces the pressure so that the mixture is forced by the atmospheric pressure into the cylinder. At the bottom of the stroke, when the cylinder is full, the intake valve closes.

The next upstroke of the piston, the compression stroke, compresses the mixture into the small space in the cylinder head. The pressure is increased from approximately that of the atmosphere to 180 pounds per square inch. This is six to eight times the pressure carried in an automobile tire.

Between the second and third strokes firing occurs. An electric spark occurs at exactly the right time, after the gas is compressed. The pressure in the cylinder is raised to about 600 or 700 pounds per square inch in a fraction of a second by the burning of the mixture of air and gasoline.

The next downstroke is the power stroke. The hot gases, expanding against the wall of the enclosed chamber, push the piston (the only movable part) downward.

The last stroke is the exhaust stroke. The gases have now spent their energy in pushing the piston downward, and it is necessary to clear the cylinder to make room for a new charge. The exhaust valve opens, and the

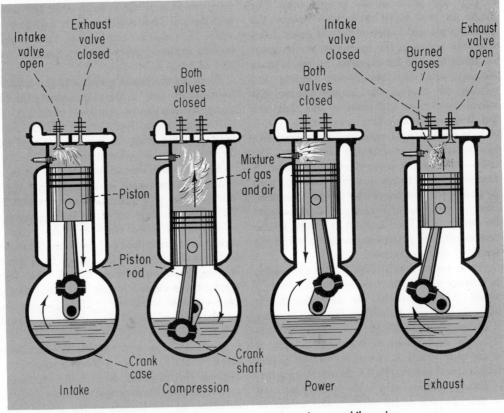

Intake valve open

Exhaust valve closed

Both valves closed

Intake valve closed

Both valves closed

Intake valve closed

Burned gases

Exhaust valve open

Piston

Mixture of gas and air

Piston rod

Crank case

Crank shaft

Intake   Compression   Power   Exhaust

Figure 25–2.   The strokes of a four-stroke cycle automobile engine.

piston, moving upward, forces the burned gases out.

The spark which starts the mixture burning is the electric discharge between the points of the spark plug. The distributor sees to it that each spark plug fires at the correct time.

Let us summarize the information we now have about the engine. A fuel pump brings the gasoline to the carburetor. The carburetor mixes it in the right proportions with air and delivers it to the cylinders through the valves. The mixture is burned in the cylinder, and mechanical power results. The piston moves up and down, causing the crankshaft to rotate. We now have the chemical energy in the gasoline converted into useful work.

AUTOMOBILE ENGINES MUST BE COOLED

Temperatures of 4,000° to 4,500° F, or almost twice the temperature necessary to melt iron, are produced in the cylinder. If cooling were not provided, the pistons, valves, and cylinder head would be only a molten, misshapen piece of metal in a short time. The easiest way to cool the engine is to provide a water jacket around the hottest parts to carry away the heat.

Let us consider the engine, from the cooling standpoint, as a device for producing heat and liberating it to the air. Heat is taken up by the water in the jackets and conveyed to the radiator, where the heat in the water is given up to the air. The action of the hot-water or steam furnace is similar. The furnace boiler is the engine, the steam radiators, the radiator on the automobile.

THE DIESEL ENGINE

In a **Diesel engine**, the *compression ratio is far above that used for even the highest compression-ratio automobile engine. The* greatest difference in the two engines is this difference in compression ratio.

In an internal-combustion engine, either a Diesel or gasoline type, the higher the compression ratio the greater the efficiency. The compression ratio of automobile engines has been increased year by year. Each increase has resulted in more efficient engines and has required better, more expensive fuels. The greater efficiency of the high-compression automobile engine results in greater power for the same cylinder volume, and less fuel consumption. In terms of performance of the automobile on the road, it has meant more miles per gallon, higher speeds, better hill climb, and faster "getaway."

Air Only Is Compressed in the Diesel Engine

When the charge is compressed as much as 16 times, it is heated to about 1,000° F. If we increased the compression ratio in a gasoline engine to 16 to 1, this high temperature would start the mixture of air and gasoline burning in the cylinder long before it should. The mixture would start burning while the piston was on its upstroke and cause a violent "knock," or even force the piston back down the cylinder and cause the engine to start running backwards. Even the best commercial antiknock gasoline would not stop this fuel knock. To prevent this premature burning in the Diesel engine, only air is compressed. This is the first difference between the Diesel engine and the gasoline engine. *Only air is compressed in the Diesel engine,* and a mixture of air and gasoline is compressed in the gasoline engine.

A Fuel Injector Replaces the Carburetor in the Diesel Engine

The carburetor is therefore unnecessary in the Diesel engine, because its only purpose is to mix air and gasoline in the correct proportions before they enter the cylinder. Compressing the air until its temperature reaches 1,000° means that the fuel, which would start burning at 450°, must not enter until the engine is ready to burn it. A fuel-injection system is the device used to blow, or force, the fuel into this superheated air, just before

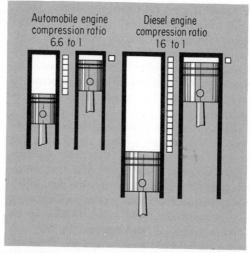

Automobile engine
compression ratio
6.6 to 1

Diesel engine
compression ratio
16 to 1

Figure 25–3. The mixture of a vaporized fuel and air is compressed more in a Diesel engine than in an automobile engine. Modern automobile engines employ higher and higher compression ratios as gasolines with higher antiknock values have become available.

Figure 25–4. Photograph of oil spray from an injector. (Courtesy, General Motors Corporation)

the piston reaches the top of the stroke. There is this difference between the ways the Diesel engine and gasoline engine handle the fuel. The gasoline engine uses a carburetor to mix air and gasoline before it is compressed. The Diesel engine uses an injection system to force the fuel into the cylinder after the air is compressed.

The heart of the Diesel engine is the fuel-injection system. It is often stated that the Diesel engine is simpler than the gasoline engine, because it eliminates the carburetor and ignition system. However, the fuel-injection system in the Diesel engine, which must be substituted for these parts, brings up as many problems as are involved in the carburetor and electric-ignition system. The fuel-injection system is somewhat more costly and difficult to make than the parts which it replaces in the conventional carburetor-electric-ignition system.

Ignition Is Accomplished by Compression in the Diesel Engine

In the gasoline engine, when the mixture is compressed by the upward stroke of the piston, it is necessary to supply a spark to start it burning. The electric-ignition system supplies the spark. In the Diesel engine, compressing the air to $\frac{1}{16}$ of its original volume heats it to such a high temperature that the fuel will start burning by itself as soon as it is injected; it catches fire just like the flashing of grease in a frying pan.

The Two-Stroke-Cycle Engine

Some Diesel engines, and one foreign-manufactured automobile, use two-stroke-cycle engines. The principle of this engine is shown in Figure 25-5.

The Diesel Engine Has a High Part-Load Efficiency

Engines are not always run so as to develop their full power and speed. In the automobile we seldom have the foot accelerator all the way down to the floor boards. The smaller the amount of power and speed at which we run, the lower is the efficiency. In the Diesel engine, the efficiency does not drop off with a decrease in power output; it actually increases.

It is a common experience that the higher the temperature, the easier and faster the heat will flow. The gasoline engine, with a higher temperature in the cylinder, will transfer heat faster to the cooling water and engine parts than the Diesel engine will. Inasmuch as the heat that goes into the cooling water is wasted,

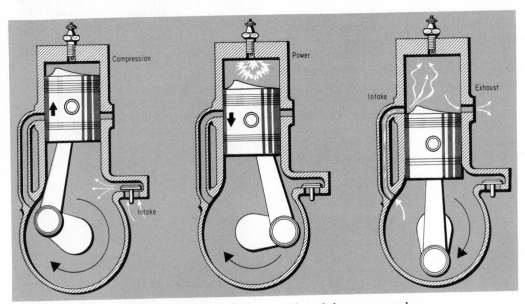

Figure 25–5. The principle of the two-stroke cycle lawn-mower engine.

the Diesel engine wastes less of the heat in the fuel, and more of the heat is used to move the piston because the temperature is lower.

This is one of the fundamental reasons for the higher efficiencies of the Diesel engine. It wastes less heat, at both full and part throttle, because the temperature within the cylinder is lower than in the gasoline engine.

The Diesel engine requires a petroleum fuel oil, which is held to specifications which are comparable to those for the gasoline used in the automobile. First, it must be fluid enough so it can be pumped and injected into the cylinder. Second, it must be clean, or else the closely fitted parts of the fuel system will wear rapidly, and the fine holes and passages will be plugged. Third, it must have the proper ignition properties so it will burn rapidly when it is injected into the hot compressed air in the cylinder and so the engine will start readily. Fourth, it should be reasonable in price.

The real reasons for the lower fuel costs on a Diesel engine are not only that it burns a cheaper fuel, but that it obtains more useful work from the fuel, and the fuel has a higher energy content per gallon.

Diesel Engine Applications

The Diesel engine has long been established on the sea. Yachts, passenger ships, freighters, tugs, trawlers, tankers, and ferries have all been powered by the Diesel engine. In the past several years, more boats have used Diesel engines than any other type of engines.

On land, the Diesel engine has applications in factories, ice plants, oil piplines, electric power plants, and large office buildings.

Diesel engines are now being used in increasingly large numbers to power railroad locomotives, large trucks, buses, and tractors, due to the introduction of the high-speed Diesel.

In their present state of development, the gasoline engine is still superior to the Diesel engine for automobiles, but fuel injection for automobile engines is being investigated.

SUMMARY

In internal-combustion engines, the combustion of the fuel takes place within the cylinder. In the gasoline engine, a mixture of air and gasoline is compressed and ignited with a spark. In Diesel engines, the air is compressed and the fuel is injected into the compressed air. Heat ignites the mixture of air and fuel.

The Diesel engine is more efficient than the gasoline engine, especially when it is operating under its load rating, because it wastes less heat.

Study Questions

1. DEFINE: compression ratio, Diesel engine, carburetor.
2. Why is it not possible to use as high a compression ratio in a gasoline engine as in a Diesel engine?
3. What is the function of the crankshaft?
4. What is the function of the camshaft?
5. What is the function of the carburetor?
6. How does the two-stroke-cycle engine differ from the four-stroke-cycle engine?
7. Why must an automobile engine be cooled?
8. Why is it unnecessary to cool a Diesel engine?
9. What is the purpose of a flywheel in an automobile engine?
10. What are the functions of (a) the valves, (b) the spark plugs, (c) the water, (d) the distributor, in an automobile?
11. What happens when the timing is not right in an automobile?
12. How does the Diesel engine differ from other internal-combustion engines?
13. Why is the Diesel engine more efficient than the ordinary automobile engine?
14. What is the advantage of a high-compression engine?
15. Why is a carburetor unnecessary in a Diesel engine?
16. Why is an automobile engine less efficient at low loads than at moderately high loads?

Turbines and Jet Engines

The whole burden of philosophy seems to consist in this—from the phenomena of motions to investigate the forces of nature, and then from these forces to explain the other phenomena.

ISAAC NEWTON

INTRODUCTION

About two thousand years ago, Hero of Alexandria demonstrated his aeoliphile, shown in Figure 26-1.

Isaac Newton recognized the principle of jet engines, which represent an application of his **third law of motion:** *To every action there is an equal and opposite reaction.* A simple illustration of the principle of the jet engine is shown in Figure 26-2.

Newton pictured an engine in which a fire was built under a boiler to generate steam. The steam would escape through an outlet and impart motion to a vehicle. The principle was correct, but it was not practical because too much water would be required and because the available fuels, wood or coal, would yield too little energy.

The jet engines described in this chapter are reaction engines, i.e., the motion is produced by the rapid expelling of gases in a direction that is opposite to the direction of motion. Reaction engines are direct applications of Newton's third law of motion. Turbines are included in this chapter, because they are often used in combination with jet engines. Turbo-jet engines combine the advantages of internal combustion and the rotary motion of turbines. Pure jet engines, like Newton's engine, are not very practical except for the high speeds of ram-jets. Chapter 28 will take up pure jets in the form of rockets.

JET ENGINES

In a **jet engine,** *combustion of the fuel occurs in a chamber, and the gaseous products together with the unused portion of the air (if air is used to burn the fuel), now increased in volume because of the expansion resulting from the heat of combustion, exit in the rear at high temperatures and high speeds. In the jet, the thrust is the result of a rapidly created gas pressure pushing against the forward end of the combustion chamber in which it is created.* Figure 26-3 shows a typical jet engine used in modern airplanes.

TURBINES

The principle of turbines has been known for a long time. In general, they are more efficient than reciprocating engines, because they produce rotary motion directly. They eliminate the lost motion of the push-and-pull, up-and-down, stop-and-go of the reciprocating engine. The child's pinwheel and the windmill are wind-driven turbines with only a few blades. The old waterwheel was the forerunner of modern high-speed turbines used in hydraulic power plants, in which a high-pressure jet of water is directed against the blades or cups mounted on a wheel.

In 1884, Charles A. Parsons (1854–1931) invented a more efficient steam engine, the steam turbine. Steam turbines are used today

Figure 26–1. The great-grandfather of today's supersonic jets—the aeolipile.

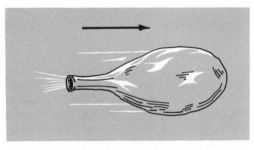

Figure 26–2. Escaping air from this rubber balloon shows the jet principle.

in ocean liners and stationary power plants. In one type of steam turbine, the steam pushes curved blades around on a number of wheels on the same shaft. The steam strikes a row of blades on a wheel, then a row of stationary blades to change its direction, and then a row of blades on a wheel again, until the energy of the steam is about exhausted.

GAS TURBINE ENGINES

Just as the steam turbine is more efficient than the reciprocating steam engine, so the gas turbine engine is more efficient than gasoline or Diesel reciprocating engines. To distinguish gas turbines from the above engines, the term, piston engine, is often used when referring to gasoline or Diesel reciprocating engines. The more general term, internal-combustion engine, does not distinguish between these different kinds of engines, because all of them are internal-combustion engines.

Gas turbines may be used to compress the air for combustion in jet-propulsion power plants, or they may be used to turn propellers, electric generators, or mechanical transmissions. Gas-turbine engines compared with internal-combustion engines, weigh about one-third as much per horsepower delivered. Because of their smaller weight and size they have been used for small boats.

Gas-turbine locomotives, using oil or powdered coal, are less efficient than Diesel electric locomotives, but they cost less to

Figure 26–3. Cutaway shows internal configuration of Boeing 300 horsepower T50 turboshaft engine. (Courtesy, The Boeing Company)

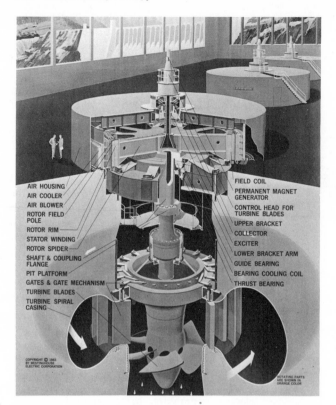

AIR HOUSING
AIR COOLER
AIR BLOWER
ROTOR FIELD POLE
ROTOR RIM
STATOR WINDING
ROTOR SPIDER
SHAFT & COUPLING FLANGE
PIT PLATFORM
GATES & GATE MECHANISM
TURBINE BLADES
TURBINE SPIRAL CASING

FIELD COIL
PERMANENT MAGNET GENERATOR
CONTROL HEAD FOR TURBINE BLADES
UPPER BRACKET
COLLECTOR
EXCITER
LOWER BRACKET ARM
GUIDE BEARING
BEARING COOLING COIL
THRUST BEARING

COPYRIGHT © 1961 BY WESTINGHOUSE ELECTRIC CORPORATION

ROTATING PARTS ARE SHOWN IN ORANGE COLOR

Figure 26–4. The waterwheel generator. (Courtesy, Westinghouse Electric and Manufacturing Corporation)

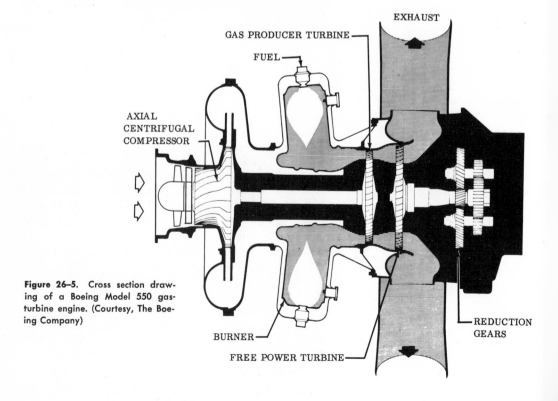

EXHAUST

GAS PRODUCER TURBINE

FUEL

AXIAL CENTRIFUGAL COMPRESSOR

Figure 26–5. Cross section drawing of a Boeing Model 550 gas-turbine engine. (Courtesy, The Boeing Company)

BURNER

FREE POWER TURBINE

REDUCTION GEARS

Figure 26–6. A turbine-electric locomotive. (Courtesy, Union Pacific Railroad)

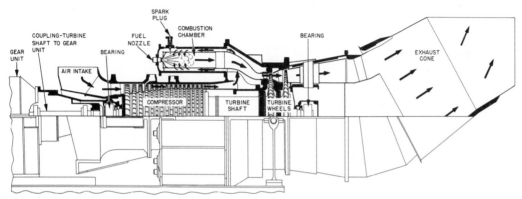

Figure 26–7. Diagram of the Union Pacific locomotive gas-turbine engine. (Courtesy, Union Pacific Railroad)

operate. They can use cheaper fuels, and they have low lubrication and maintenance costs. Furthermore, they produce less smoke and smoother power than Diesel engines. They can reach full operating efficiency within five minutes after they are started. The higher the operating temperatures and the lower the temperature of the air, the more efficient these engines are. High altitudes and arctic regions, or wintry conditions, are best for these engines. If the proper materials can be found that will withstand temperatures of 2,000° F or above, gas turbines may be the most efficient type of engine.

GAS-TURBINE AUTOMOBILE ENGINES

Considerable research has been devoted to the study of gas turbines for automobiles, buses, and trucks. The gas turbine has an appealing simplicity. The basic parts are a compressor and two turbines. One turbine operates the compressor and the other turbine turns the wheels of the vehicle concerned. For railroad locomotives, the gas turbine is used to operate electric generators, and the electricity is then used to operate motors.

The gas turbine is smaller and lighter than a piston engine of equivalent horsepower and has about one-fifth as many parts. It requires no radiator fan or cooling system, no water pumps, no distributors, no timers, no antifreeze and only one spark plug for starting the engine.

Experimental gas turbine engines have been used for boats, trucks, buses, and automobiles for about ten years. Why are they not widely used now? Gas-turbine engines have several inherent shortcomings. The first one is that one has to wait a second or two for them to deliver power. Acceleration is slow. The

195

American public likes the quick getaway and rapid acceleration of the modern automobile. Would they settle for less?

The second problem involved in the use of gas-turbine engines is that of manufacturing turbines out of materials which will withstand the high temperatures. By their very nature, gas turbines are very noisy. To muffle the noise requires an elaborate system of mufflers.

These problems are gradually being whipped. Fairly inexpensive alloys have been developed that make it practical to manufacture gas-turbine engines. Methods have been found to improve acceleration, but the problem of idling at stop lights remains, because considerable fuel must be used to keep the engine running. There is also the problem of wear on the turbine blades, resulting from the high speeds, high temperatures, and dust in the air. Can this problem be solved, so that the inherently lower maintenance costs will not be balanced or outweighed?

The best early applications may be those which demand both speed and power. They are likely to be used in heavy-duty commercial, military, and marine applications.

Gas-turbine engines possess the advantages of smooth, almost vibrationless riding. Furthermore, they do not require expensive fuels. They may even surpass Diesel engines in efficiency.

TURBO-JET ENGINES

The **turbo-jet engine** *uses a gas turbine to compress the air required for the combustion of the fuel. At the front of the engine, there is a turbine which compresses the air entering the engine. At the rear end of the firing chamber is a small gas turbine which uses part of the power to operate the compressing turbine.* About three-fourths of the power generated by the fuel is used by the air compressor. The compressor and turbine are mounted on the same shaft, so there is only one moving part. Of course, accessories are added to provide the heat and electricity required by the aircraft.

THE ADVANTAGES OF TURBO-JET AIRCRAFT ENGINES

Turbo-jet engines present many advantages for use in aircraft. In the first place, they use fuels which are cheaper than aviation gasoline. They are quite efficient, and often give more miles per gallon of fuel than piston aircraft engines do. Turbo-jet engines have only one-tenth as many moving parts as reciprocating internal combustion engines; they require less than one-fifth of the time and labor for maintenance. Turbo-jet engines do not have to be warmed up, and they cool quickly. Aircraft powered with turbo-jet engines are

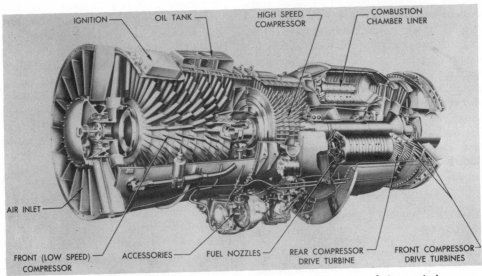

Figure 26–8. A turbojet airplane engine. (Courtesy, Pratt & Whitney Aircraft Corporation)

Figure 26–9. A Boeing twin gas-turbine-powered generator set to be used in a U.S. Navy mine-sweeping boat. (Courtesy, The Boeing Company)

relatively inefficient at low altitudes, but they are the most economical aircraft operating between speeds of 500 and 600 miles per hour.

DISADVANTAGES OF TURBO-JET ENGINES

Turbo-jet aircraft engines are very noisy. Once in the air, the noise does not constitute a problem, because the pressurized cabins are well insulated against sound, and also because the airplane may be traveling faster than sound. Since turbo-jet aircraft operate best at high altitudes, the cabins must be pressurized.

Turbo-jet engines produce a great deal of heat. Therefore, the placing of the engines is important. Since turbo-jet engines do not operate so well at lower altitudes it is more difficult to get turbo-jet aircraft off the ground than it is for propeller-driven aircraft.

TURBO-PROP ENGINES

Turbo-prop engines combine the advantages of propeller-driven aircraft and turbo-jet aircraft. In **turbo-prop engines,** a *larger gas turbine is used at the rear in order to provide sufficient power to operate a propeller as well as the compressor.* An aircraft using the turbo-prop engine gets about one-half of its push from the propeller. Turbo-prop engines permit easier takeoffs and landings. Aircraft powered with turbo-prop engines travel faster than those powered with piston engines. Turbo-prop aircraft are most efficient for heavy loads, lower altitudes, and speeds below 500 miles per hour.

RAM-JET ENGINES

The **ram-jet,** i.e., the "flying stovepipe," *consists of a cylinder into which air enters at one end and from which the products of combustion exist at the other end.* The air is compressed as a result of a reduction in its velocity as it enters the tapering entrance to the cylinder. Ram-jets are limited to supersonic speeds, but they are the most efficient engines at such speeds, especially at high altitudes and low temperatures. The pulse-jet is similar to the ram-jet, with the exception that it involves intermittent combustion, and the speed is less. The German V-1 missile employed the pulse-jet. Concerning the ram-jet, there is a saying that "The faster it goes, the faster it goes."

One of the problems presented by a turbo-jet engine is that it gets too hot. One way to solve this problem is to deliver more air to the combustion chamber than is necessary to burn the fuel. The extra air lowers the temperature. It may then be used in an afterburner, which consists of a ram-jet placed behind the turbo-jet engine. Fuel is sprayed into the ram-jet to utilize the extra air. Airplanes employing this principle are used for speeds in excess of 700 miles per hour.

The ram-jet cannot start itself. It must be traveling at least 300 miles per hour before it can function. So airplanes that use ram-jet engines only must be carried by "mother" airplanes, to be released when they attain sufficient speeds to operate.

SUMMARY

Reaction engines are applications of Newton's third law of motion.

Reaction engines include (1) jet engines, (2) turbo-jet engines, (3) turbo-prop engines, and (4) ram-jet engines. Rockets, to be taken up in the next chapter, are also jet engines.

Turbines are used to generate rotary motion from high-pressure streams of water or steam. Gas turbines combine the advantages of rotary motion and an internal-combustion engine.

Gas-turbine engines are much simpler than piston-type internal-combustion engines.

Gas-turbine engines are used at higher altitudes to compress the air. At high altitudes the air is too rarefied for satisfactory operation of jet engines.

Study Questions

1. DEFINE: jet engine, turbo-jet engine, turbo-prop engine, ram-jet engine.
2. What is the law which is applied in jet engines?
3. What characteristics of gas turbines recommend them for land, water, or air transportation?
4. Why are turbo-jet engines preferred to simple jet engines for high altitudes?
5. How is the principle of the ram-jet engine used in combination with turbo-jet engines?
6. What types of airplane engines are used for modern high-speed airplanes?
7. What are the advantages and disadvantages of jet airplanes?
8. What would be the advantages of gas-turbine engines for automobiles?
9. Why is it unlikely that gas-turbine engines will displace piston-type, internal-combustion engines for automobiles in the near future?
10. Why are turbines more efficient than reciprocating engines?
11. Under what conditions are gas turbines most advantageous for trucks?
12. What are the advantages of turbo-jet engines for use in aircraft?

Rockets and Satellites

We have stepped into a new, high road from which there can be no turning back. As we probe farther into the area beyond our sensible atmosphere, man will learn more about his environment; he will understand better the order and beauty of creation. He may then come to realize that war, as we know it, will avail him nothing but catastrophe. He may grasp the truth there is something much bigger than his one little world. Before the majesty of what he will find out there, he must stand in reverential awe.

WERNHER VON BRAUN

INTRODUCTION

Some of the outstanding scientific work of the 1960's was devoted to the development of rockets and artificial satellites by countries throughout the world. In the United States, it has become a multibillion-dollar industry, involving many private companies and taxing our scientific man-power resources.

A SHORT HISTORY OF ROCKETS

Rockets were first used in China, in 1232. In 1807, the Danish fleet was sunk at Copenhagen by a barrage of 25,000 British rockets. Again, British rockets were used to bombard Fort McHenry in Baltimore harbor in 1814, as referred to in our national anthem.

By 1900, military rockets had become unpopular because most of them exploded before reaching their target, and few of them could reach a target anyway, because of lack of means of steering them.

During World War II, the United States used rocket ships to launch as many as 1,000 short-range rockets a minute as a prelude to invasion landings. The most famous American rocket was the bazooka, which was powerful enough to penetrate the armor of tanks.

Two men could hold the bazooka, which weighed only a few pounds. It was open at the rear so there was no kickback or recoil.

Germany used its "buzz" bombs and V-2 rockets to frighten the Allies. German V-2 rockets traveled at the speed of 3,400 miles per hour, or about five times faster than sound. They were 46 feet long, weighed about 15 tons, and were controlled by gyro and radio. They carried 2,200 pounds of explosive, had a range of about 170 miles, and a peak altitude of about 60 miles. They used ethyl alcohol and liquid oxygen as a propellant. At the conclusion of World War II, the United States experimented with about fifty V-2 rockets captured from the Germans.

ROCKETS

A jet can operate only in the atmosphere, because it obtains its oxygen from the atmosphere to burn its fuel. The **rocket,** on the other hand, can penetrate space, because it *carries its own supply of oxidizer,* i.e., source of oxygen to burn the fuel.

Rocket engines are the hottest, fastest, and farthest-ranging of all power plants. They attain speeds of 5,000 miles per hour. Tem-

Figure 27–1. Up from the depths, fired from a nuclear submarine, the U.S. Navy's Polaris Ballistic Missile breaks the ocean's surface on its way to a distant target. Powered by solid-propellant motors, Polaris is the Navy's greatest deterrent force, giving submarines global power. (Courtesy, Aerojet-General Corporation)

peratures inside of a rocket engine may exceed 5,000° F.

Rockets work best where other engines lose thrust; they attain maximum thrust when the outside pressure is zero. They take off of the ground at slow speeds, but as they lose weight due to the burning of the propellants, their speed increases.

Rockets may be used to propel missiles, and to place satellites into orbit. Placing satellites into orbits requires rockets of a tremendous amount of power. The first-stage rocket of America's 1964 super-rocket, the Saturn I, developed 34 million horsepower. Rockets are regular blast furnaces, which develop more power than the entire output of Hoover Dam during the short period of time that they are in operation.

Rocket Propulsion

A rocket engine is a reaction engine. A rocket propellant consists of an oxidizer and a fuel to be oxidized. The thrust depends upon the production of a large volume of gas with a high velocity produced by the heat of the reaction. More thrust from chemical fuels can be obtained only by increasing the amount or efficiency of the propellant and the size of the vehicle. Of course, increasing the size of the vehicle increases the amount of propellant required, so research is directed toward more efficient propellants.

The flight of rockets is a direct application of Newton's third law of motion: For every action there is an equal and opposite reaction. As the combustion of the fuel takes place in the combustion chamber, tremendous pressures are developed. Because of the construction of the combustion chamber, the gases are driven by the pressure through a specially designed nozzle or orifice at the rear of the rocket. The gas molecules attain a very high velocity as they leave the orifice. The velocity of the gas molecules multiplied by their mass constitute the "action" of Newton's third law. As a consequence, the rocket will move in the opposite direction, its mass times its velocity being the "reaction" of Newton's law.

It is important to note that a rocket does not need a material medium to push against. In fact, a rocket performs more efficiently in the absence of air because the presence of air creates friction with the skin of the rocket.

Liquid Propellants—Various types of liquid fuels have been tried out, such as hydrazine, aniline, kerosene, and hydrogen. An ideal propellant should be stable and storeable. It should be nontoxic and noncorrosive, and it should produce lightweight molecules such as water, the oxides of nitrogen, or carbon dioxide, which have high kinetic energy. No propellant meets all of these requirements; however, liquid hydrogen is nearest to an ideal rocket fuel. Hydrogen has the disadvantage of a low density, and therefore requires a relatively large container. Furthermore, it liquefies at −424° F, causing important technical problems in transporting and handling it.

Liquid oxygen has been the most common liquid oxidizer. The addition of up to 25 per cent of liquid ozone has increased its power. Another powerful oxidizer is liquid nitrogen tetroxide, which requires no refrigeration. Liquid fluorine is at the top of the list of

oxidizers, and a more difficult oxidizer to prepare or handle could not be found. It is very
toxic and corrosive, but it furnishes the most
thrust per weight unit of oxidizer. It boils at
−306° F. The hydrogen-fluorine reaction is
the ultimate in chemical fuels, and the
hydrogen-oxygen reaction is a close runner-up.
Liquid propellants act as a team, and on a
weight basis usually two to three times as
much oxidizer as fuel is required.

One of the major problems of liquid-fuel
rockets is the pumping of the fuel and oxidizer
from the rocket's storage tanks to the combustion chamber. One of the methods by
which this problem has been solved is the use
of another liquid which will volatilize readily
to create the necessary pressure to force the
fuel and oxidizer to the combustion chamber.
Another method makes use of a steam-driven
turbine pump, which is powered by hydrogen
peroxide. Hydrogen peroxide will decompose
to form steam in the presence of a perman-
ganate, which acts as a catalyst. This reaction
can also be used to produce sidewise thrust to
steer rockets or satellites.

The combustion chamber would soon melt
if a way could not be found to cool it. It was
found that the propellant could be circulated
around the chamber to cool it, and thus pick
up added energy for the reaction. Another
approach has been to introduce small amounts
of propellant through small holes in the combustion chamber, to form a cooling film.

The nozzle must be designed and constructed
just right. If the orifice is too large, thrust
falls off. If it is too small, the gases cannot
escape fast enough, and the engine explodes.

Solid Propellants—Rockets powered by
liquid propellants are more complex than
rockets powered by solid propellants, but they
are also more powerful and more efficient. For
some purposes, solid propellants are preferred:
as in the Polaris rocket, which is launched
from submarines; or the Minuteman, which
is stored in underground silos ready for use at
any time. In such cases, the immediate readiness of the rocket far outweighs its decreased
efficiency.

There is no problem of cooling a combustion chamber for solid rockets, because the
container is filled with the propellant and
burns from the inside to the outside. Am-

Figure 27–2. Saturn SA-5 lifts off on January 29, 1964.
The total weight was 562 tons, and it was as high as a
16-story building and had 1.5 million pounds of thrust.
(Courtesy, National Aeronautics and Space Administration)

monium perchlorate often serves as the solid oxidizer. Various solid hydro-carbons such as tar, rubber, or plastics may serve as the fuel. Sometimes magnesium or aluminum powder is mixed in. Rubber may serve as the binder for the ingredients. A compound such as nitrocellulose or nitroglycerine has its own built-in oxidizer.

MISSILES

A **missile** is *any object propelled toward a target. If a missile follows a predetermined path, like a bullet without any guidance from the ground, it is called* a **ballistic missile.** A missile may be propelled by jets or rockets.

Military missiles have many functions. The United States has seen fit to develop a wide variety of rocket-propelled missiles.

1. Ground-to-Ground Missiles

The effective distance of ground-to-ground missiles varies from 100 miles or less to a distance of 5,000 to 6,000 miles or more for ICBM (Intercontinental Ballistic Missiles) designed to carry a nuclear bomb payload.

The *Thor* and *Jupiter* missiles are liquid fueled and are of the surface-to-surface type.

The *Subroc* missile is launched under water by submarines, travels through the atmosphere for 50 miles or so, and then re-enters the water to track down an enemy submarine or surface vessel, being guided by its own self-contained sonar system.

The **IRBM Missiles** (*Intermediate Range Ballistic Missiles*), having a range of 100 to 1,500 miles, include the *Jupiter, Thor,* and *Polaris.* The Polaris missile uses a solid propellant, carries atomic warheads, and can be launched from submarines at depths of a hundred feet or more.

The Minuteman missile, the first solid-propellant *Intercontinental Ballistic Missile* (**ICBM**) was launched on February 1, 1961. It was an outstanding success. These missiles have replaced the larger Atlas and Titan missiles, but like them they are placed in underground silos in many strategic locations.

2. Ground-to-Air Missiles

Ground-to-air missiles, such as the Terrier and the Nike, are designed to intercept air-planes or missiles while in flight. The *Nike* was the first combat-ready anti-aircraft missile. It is controlled from the ground by a complex electronic system, composed of 1½ million individual parts. It is liquid-fueled. It has a diameter of about 1 foot, and it is 20 feet long. The Nike missiles have been installed near most metropolitan centers.

3. Air-to-Air Missiles

The *Sidewinder* is an air-to-air missile, directed by infrared homing devices.

SATELLITES

The first satellite, the Russian Sputnik I, was placed into orbit on October 4, 1957.

Prior to 1957, there were only 31 known satellites, and these were the natural satellites (moons) revolving about the planets. Four years later there were 31 additional satellites in orbit, placed there by the United States and Russia. By the end of 1962, the United States had 100 satellites in orbit, as compared with 27 for the Soviet Union.

Types of Satellites

Satellites which circle about the earth are called **artificial satellites,** but *those which go into orbit around the sun* are called **artificial planets.**

Anything written about satellites will be out of date before this book is published. The best that we can do is to outline the situation as it was in the spring of 1964. The United States' satellites at that time could be grouped as follows:

1. Communication Satellites. (a) *Passive Communication Satellites*—Echo-1 and *Echo-2* satellites were large aluminum-covered balloons from which radio signals could be reflected. Echo-2, launched in January, 1964 had a diameter of 135 feet. Its orbit was around the poles of the earth. Such satellites require international cooperation to avoid jamming with too many radio signals.

(b) *Relay Satellites*—Relay satellites are powered with solar batteries to operate electrical relay equipment to receive and rebroadcast radio and television signals. Such satellites were the *Telestar-1 and -2,* and the *Syncom-2.*

Figure 27-3. The Nike Ajax missile. (Courtesy, Douglas Aircraft Company)

Figure 27-4. Photographic conception of the Syncom spacecraft in simulated space environment. (Courtesy, National Aeronautics and Space Administration)

Figure 27-5. The MINUTEMAN solid-fueled intercontinental missile. (Courtesy, Aerojet General Corporation)

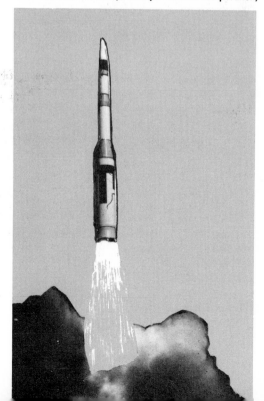

(c) *Courier Satellites*—These satellites pick up a message at one place and rebroadcast it at another place.

2. Space-Spy Satellites—Space-spy satellites are designed to maintain photographic surveillance over the whole globe. The *Midas* satellite (*Missile Defense Alarm System*) has an infrared eye which can detect an enemy ICBM attack. It weighs about 5,000 pounds.

3. Weather Satellites—Weather satellites, such as the *Tiros I* and *Tiros II*, are furnishing weather information that should result in improvements in weather prediction.

4. Transit Satellites—Transit satellites will make it possible to navigate by satellite from any place on the earth.

5. Other Types of Satellites—There have been many *Discoverer* and *Explorer rockets* or satellites, which carried instruments to obtain

Figure 27–6. Echo II satellite undergoing tensile-strength tests. (Courtesy, National Aeronautics and Space Administration)

Figure 27–7. Artist's conception of the Orbiting Geophysical Observatory. (Courtesy, National Aeronautics and Space Administration)

Figure 27-8. The Mariner spacecraft. Artist's conception of the craft as it flies by the planet Venus. (Courtesy, National Aeronautics and Space Administration)

such scientific data as the measurement of radiation, the effects of micrometeorites, biological experimentation, solar X rays, cosmic rays, radiation belts, testing of guidance control and stabilization systems, and communication.

PILOTED SPACECRAFT

The *Mercury* satellites have all made successful orbits around the earth, and have been returned to the earth by their pilots. The X-15, an experimental, manned spacecraft has already been flown at a speed in excess of six times the speed of sound and to heights of almost 100 miles. It is propelled by a rocket engine.

PLACING A SATELLITE IN ORBIT

At a speed of 4.9 miles per second, a satellite could be put into orbit at a height of one mile, but at this altitude, the friction of the atmosphere would soon slow it down to speeds of less than 4.9 miles per second, and it would fall to the surface of the earth. The problem is to provide enough thrust to enable the satellite to reach an altitude where the friction of the atmosphere would be negligible. It would not be possible to give the satellite sufficient speed at the start, but this can be

Figure 27-9. The Gemini spacecraft. (Courtesy, National Aeronautics and Space Administration)

done with a rocket consisting of several stages, each of which provides an additional boost as it climbs.

It is best to launch a rocket vertically, because it thus travels through the minimum amount of atmosphere. However, it would continue out into space and be lost, unless it could be directed to a horizontal position. This is accomplished by employing a small rocket engine to direct a blast from one side of the satellite, or by altering the direction of the main blast.

A satellite with a very high orbit will remain in orbit longer than a satellite with a lower orbit, but it requires more thrust to get it into the higher orbit. On the other hand, less velocity is required to keep it in orbit, because there is less gravitational force to be overcome. For example, a satellite at a distance of 4,000 miles would require a velocity of 4.89 miles per second in order to remain in orbit, while a satellite intended to orbit the moon at a distance of 239,000 miles would require a velocity of only 0.63 miles per second.

SUMMARY

Missiles may be propelled by jets or rockets, but rockets are necessary to place satellites into orbit, and to propel and steer them while in orbit. If a satellite encounters even rarefied air it will slow down and gradually be drawn to the earth, unless it can be given an additional thrust.

Missiles and satellites have been developed largely to provide defensive weapons and offensive deterrents.

Military missiles include, short range, intermediate range (IRBM), and long range (ICBM) missiles. They have the following functions:

(1) ground-to-ground for offensive purposes.

(2) ground-to-air for defense against enemy planes or missiles.

(3) air-to-air for defense against enemy planes or missiles.

(4) variations of the above include missiles launched by submarines and ships, which can be used for both offensive and defensive purposes.

Rocket propellants may be either liquid or solid. Solid propellants are the most stable and ready-for-use propellants, preferred for missiles. Liquid propellants are the most powerful and most efficient ones, and are used for multistage rockets to place satellites in orbit.

Satellites have been used to obtain scientific data, and to provide practical applications in communication, weather, and navigation. For military purposes they are used to photograph enemy military installations, and to detect possible enemy missiles or airplanes.

Study Questions

1. DEFINE: rocket, missile, IRBM, ICBM, ballistic, missile, artificial satellite, artificial planet.
2. What speed would be required to enable a spacecraft to escape from the earth's pull?
3. Differentiate between the two kinds of communication satellites.
4. What are the military functions of satellites?
5. What are the nonmilitary functions of satellites?
6. What is meant by the statement that a rocket is a reaction engine?
7. Which law or laws of motion apply to rockets?
8. List some of the problems involved in placing a man on the moon.
9. What are the different kinds and functions of military rockets?
10. What is the fundamental difference between jets and rockets?
11. Why are rockets the only type of engines that can place satellites in orbit?
12. What are the relative advantages of liquid and solid propellants for rockets?
13. Why are rockets fired in a vertical direction?

Principles of Flight—
Aerodynamics

I have brought to a close the portion of the work which seemed to be specially mine—the demonstration of the practicability of mechanical flight—and for the next stage, which is the commercial and practical development of this idea, it is probable that the world may look to others. The world, indeed, will be supine if it does not realize that a new possibility has come to it, and that the great universal highway overhead is now soon to be opened.

S. P. LANGLEY

INTRODUCTION

Airships and balloons depend upon the buoyancy of lightweight molecules to keep them floating in the atmosphere, while airplanes owe their lift to *the forces resulting from the motion of the airplane relative to the molecules in the atmosphere,* the study of which is called **aerodynamics.** Both airships and airplanes obtain their forward motion and their ability to change direction as a result of the motion of the propellers and airfoils (surfaces) relative to the molecules of the atmosphere. An **airplane** is *a mechanically driven heavier-than-air craft, fitted with wings which support it in flight by the dynamic action of the air which results from the forward motion of the airplane relative to the air. The forward motion of the airplane is the result of a force,* called the **thrust,** *which is produced by the airplane propeller.*

The dynamic action of the air resulting from the forward motion of the airplane may be resolved into two forces, the lift and the drag. The force of gravity is a static force, i.e., it acts without any motion of the airplane.

It is the purpose of this chapter to show how the forces of thrust, drag, lift, and gravity are controlled so that an airplane is enabled to fly.

THE THRUST

Birds use their wings to attain forward motion in the air as well as to maintain their position in the air. In the airplane, these functions are separated, and the propeller—which is really a specialized wing—is used to maintain forward motion. In the helicopter, however, the propeller has the dual action of the wings of a bird.

The propeller produces the force, called the thrust, in accordance with **Newton's third law** of motion, which states that *to every action there is always an equal and opposite reaction.* The faster the propeller pushes back the air, the faster the airplane will move forward. The backward force of a propeller against the air is what forces it forward. The *propeller may be placed in front of the engine or behind it.* In the first case the airplane is called a **tractor,** and in the second case it is called a **pusher.**

The denser the air is, the greater will be the forward motion produced by a revolution of the propeller, because a greater mass of material has to be moved by the propeller and therefore a greater force is exerted.

Takeoffs require longer runs, and the rate of climbing is lower on damp days than on dry days, because the density of damp air is less than that of dry air.

The **pitch,** i.e., **the angle of attack or the "bite"** of a propeller, determines *the distance which the propeller advances per revolution.* When taking off and climbing, the pitch of the propeller should be least, thus obtaining maximum power by allowing the number of revolutions per minute of the engine to increase; but when flying at a cruising altitude, the propeller pitch should be increased in order to permit it to take the maximum "bites" out of the air. The maximum amount of power is required when taking off and climbing. When flying at a level, the highest efficiency is obtained by maintaining the manufacturer's recommended number of revolutions per minute and increasing the pitch of the propeller. Large, high-speed airplanes have devices by which the propeller pitch may be varied automatically, so as to keep the number of revolutions per minute constant. This is of special importance in multi-engined aircraft, as it is a means of keeping the engines accurately synchronized.

THE FORCE OF GRAVITY

The performance of an airplane depends upon the power and the weight of the airplane. The speed of an airplane is not greatly increased by increasing the power of the engine, because the horsepower varies as the cube of the speed—doubling the speed requires eight times as much horsepower.

Weight, i.e., *a measure of the force of gravity* has a pronounced effect on the performance of an airplane, as would be expected; and designers go to great lengths to obtain light materials of great strength, and to design structures of great strength for the weight of materials used.

THE DRAG

The **drag** is *the resistance of the motion of the airplane relative to the air.* The drag is the result of the displacing of air masses, surface friction, and turbulence. Surface friction is reduced by keeping down the surface area, and by making the surface smooth. **Turbulence** is the *irregular motion of the atmosphere produced when air flows over an uneven surface.* By placing many holes in the wings and drawing air through them, turbulence is considerably reduced.

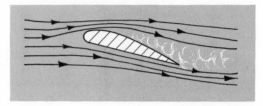

Figure 28–1. When the angle of attack is too great, the air no longer flows smoothly over the wing and turbulence results.

The drag is decreased by streamlining. Landing gears are made retractable in large planes so as to reduce the drag. The earlier airplanes had most of their struts and braces exposed, but modern airplanes enclose these within the airfoils in order to decrease the drag.

An important principle to keep in mind is that the drag increases with increased speeds just as the lift does, and for that reason streamlining is very important for high-speed airplanes. The greater the area of the airfoil is, the greater will be the drag. *The portion of the aircraft, such as the wing, rudder, etc.,* called the **airfoil,** *is the part which produces lift or change of direction.* Inasmuch as the lifting power of an airfoil is increased by increasing the speed of an airplane, the tendency in modern airplane design is to decrease the wing area so as to decrease the drag, and to use more powerful engines so as to increase the speed, especially to give the airplane performance or climbing ability.

The same results are obtained by moving the air relative to the airplane that are accomplished when the airplane moves relative to the air. Wind tunnels enable engineers to test small-scale models and even full-scale airplanes. Lift and drag measurements made in wind tunnels enable engineers to calculate the number of feet of wing area required to

Figure 28–2. A N.A.C.A. full-scale wind tunnel, Langley Field, Virginia. (Courtesy, National Advisory Committee for Aeronautics)

support an airplane of a given weight carrying a maximum load at a given speed.

The drag increases with increases in the angle of attack, until at the **burble point** (*the angle of attack at which the air no longer flows smoothly over the airfoil*) the airplane **stalls,** i.e., *it ceases to maintain altitude because the lift has been destroyed.*

The greater the **camber** (i.e., *curvature*), the greater will be the drag. Inasmuch as the lifting power is also increased by increasing the camber, the airplane designer is forced to compromise, depending on whether he wishes high speed or high lift characteristics.

BERNOULLI'S PRINCIPLE

A **venturi tube** is a *short tube of small diameter, with large openings in the front and the rear. The flow of air through the venturi tube causes the pressure to drop in the tube in proportion to the velocity of the flow of air.* The venturi tube is an application of **Bernoulli's principle,** *which states that when the rate of flow of gases or liquids is increased the pressure decreases.* A **pitot tube** in an airspeed indicator is a *venturi tube.* The pressure in the tube is reduced as the speed of the air is increased.

A "cut" tennis ball, a "sliced" golf ball, or a "curved" baseball, given a spin when pitched, will follow a curved path because the rotation of the ball piles up air on one side and reduces the pressure on the other side. The path of the ball is therefore deflected toward the direction of least pressure.

In the automobile carburetor, a stream of air flows through a narrow passage and thus sucks in gasoline through small jets. The steam injector used in forcing water into boilers at high pressure is based on the same principle.

Two ships at anchor near each other in a river current or tide, or two ships moving through the water side by side, may be drawn together because of the reduced pressure created between them by the flow of water relative to the motion of the ships.

THE LIFT OF AN AIRPLANE

Figure 28-3 shows how the streamlining of the wing causes the air above the wing to travel faster than the air below the wing. The increase in the velocity of the air above the wing thus decreases the pressure above the wing, and the decrease in the velocity of the air below the wing increases the pressure below the wing. This *combination of low and high pressures produces an upward push on*

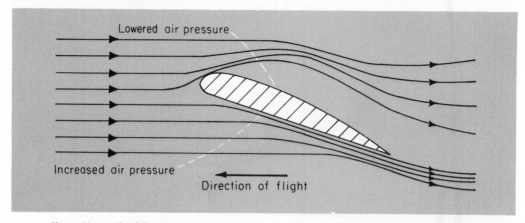

Figure 28–3. The difference between the air pressure above and below the wing produces lift.

the wing, which is called the **lift.** From 65 to 100 per cent of the lift is due to the low pressure above the airfoil, depending upon the angle of attack.

The force which lifts the airplane from the earth and sustains it while in flight, is called the **lift.** The main airfoils, which produce the lift, are the wings. The lift of an airfoil depends upon four factors: (1) **the angle of attack,** i.e., *the angle at which the wing meets the air;* (2) the density of the air; (3) the speed of the airplane relative to the air; and (4) the design or shape of the airfoil.

Lift increases as the angle of attack increases, up to a certain point. Lift also increases with an increase in the density of the air, and as the square of the speed of the

airplane. If the speed is doubled, the lift is increased four times.

In taking off from the ground, the airplane has to attain a certain speed before the lift is sufficient to overcome the force of gravity.

For an airplane of a given weight, the greater the wing area, the slower the airplane can fly without stalling. Wings are given a camber (curvature) to increase the lift, but in so doing, the drag is increased and the speed is decreased.

FLAPS AND SLOTS

In order to obtain a relatively low landing speed, a relatively large wing area is required, but such a large wing area causes too much

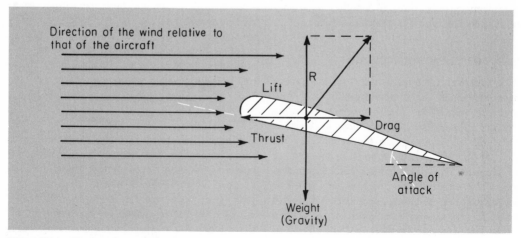

Figure 28–4. The four forces acting on the wing of an airplane are lift, thrust, drag, and weight (gravity). *R* is the resultant force of the wind and lift.

drag at high speeds. Flaps on the trailing (rear) edge of a wing airfoil change the camber of an airfoil and thus give it the greater lifting power and slower speed required for landing.

Sometimes slots are provided in the leading edge of the wing airfoil. These slots make it possible to increase the angle of attack from 2° up to 30° or more without going into a stall, and thus increase the lifting power of an airplane at slow speeds. When the airplane is nosed up into a high angle of attack, the air, instead of flowing over the leading edge, flows up through the slot and over the thick part of the wing, which gives the airfoil a high lift characteristic. Fixed slots, i.e., those which remain open at all times, work automatically to prevent stalls. Modern small airplanes are usually stallproof.

THE CONTROL OF THE DIRECTION OF FLIGHT OF AN AIRPLANE

The direction of flight of an airplane is controlled by such airfoils as the rudder, the elevators, and the ailerons.

There are three axes of motion of an aircraft—the vertical, the longitudinal, and the lateral—about which the airplane may be rotated, one, two, or all three at a time.

1. The Vertical Axis

Rotation about the vertical axis, called the **yaw,** changes the direction in which the nose is pointing from left to right and vice versa. Deflection of the tail rudder causes the airplane to turn just as that of the rudder on a boat turns the boat.

2. The Longitudinal Axis

Rotation about the longitudinal axis causes one wing to lift as the other wing is lowered, and the airplane is said to **roll.** The rolling does for an airplane what banking a turn on a highway does for an automobile. The rolling of an airplane is controlled by the ailerons. The **ailerons** are *identical to flaps in their action, except that as one aileron moves down the one on the opposite wing moves up.*

3. The Lateral or Transverse Axis

Rotation about this axis produces what is called **pitch,** i.e., *the motion in which the nose goes up or down.*

THE VERTICAL AND HORIZONTAL STABILIZERS

The loading of an airplane may be such that it changes its center of gravity; the consumption of gasoline decreases the weight of the fuel, and the amount of freight and number of passengers also change the center of gravity. If the airplane flys nose-heavy, the pilot adjusts the horizontal stabilizer to a position where the nose will neither be up nor down.

The action of the propeller on the air not

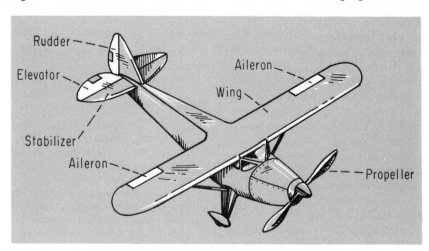

Figure 28–5. The principal control parts of an airplane.

only creates a backward thrust, but also causes the swirling motion in the air which tends to yaw the plane by its action on the vertical tail surfaces. The vertical stabilizer is adjusted to overcome this force, by adjusting the trimming tab or offsetting the vertical fin.

THE STABILITY OF MODERN AIRPLANES

The ability of an airplane to return to its original normal position, without effort on the part of the pilot, or with the controls released, is called positive **stability.** Many modern airplanes will practically fly themselves; they will recover from a dive or climb, a bank or a turn, with the controls released. The stability of an airplane is accomplished by proper design features.

When a wing dips downward, it automatically comes back up again because there is an additional lift on the lower wing.

When the airplane is disturbed longitudinally, i.e., when the nose is pulled up, the airplane loses speed, and the tail comes up, thus placing the airplane again in level-flight attitude.

When the airplane is disturbed directionally, it will assume the new course but not continue to turn. This is due to the fact that there is a greater amount of fin area back of the center of gravity than in front of it.

AN AIRPLANE PRACTICALLY FLIES ITSELF

It is said that a well-trained pilot is four times as safe flying in an airplane as he would be in driving an automobile, but that a poorly trained pilot is four times as safe in an automobile as he would be in an airplane. The student pilot has a tendency to use brute strength and violent manipulation of the controls when an airplane goes into an unexpected motion, and in his excitement, he may do the wrong thing. A safe rule is to leave the controls alone and let the airplane return to its normal position by itself, provided that there is sufficient altitude. The majority of airplane accidents not caused by drunkenness are caused by flying so close to the ground that there is not time for the air-

plane to return to a normal position if something unexpected happens.

An airplane will not fall just because the engine fails. Gliders often remain in the air for many hours, and the heavier airplanes can glide for some time in search of a landing field, provided that the original altitude above the ground is high enough.

SUMMARY

Aerodynamics is the study of the forces produced by the relative motion between the air and an object. The forces acting on an airplane are thrust, lift, drag, and gravity. Lift is imparted to the wings as a result of the thrust produced by the propeller in accordance with Newton's third law of motion. The drag is the resistance to motion through the air. It is decreased by streamlining, cutting down the wing area, and decreasing the camber of the wings. The lift is partly due to the reduction of the pressure over the upper surface of the wings. The lift is increased by increasing the angle of attack, the density of the air, the speed of the airplane, and the camber of the wings. Flaps and slots make it possible to increase camber for landings.

CONTROL OF THE AIRPLANE

Axis of Motion	Direction	Airfoil Controlled
Vertical	Left or right (yaw)	Tail rudder
Longitudinal	Banking (roll)	Ailerons
Lateral	Up or down (pitch)	Rear elevator

Modern airplanes are so stable that they practically fly themselves.

Study Questions

1. DEFINE: aerodynamics, lift, drag, thrust, turbulence, stability, burble point, stall, airfoil, angle of attack, pitch, camber, venturi tube, pitot tube, yaw, roll, aileron, rudder, airplane, tractor, pusher weight.
2. State Bernoulli's principle, and show how it applies to aerodynamics.
3. Give several common examples of the application of Bernoulli's principle.
4. What causes the dynamic action of the air upon an airplane?

5. List the airfoils of an airplane and mention the useful purpose of each.
6. What are the four forces which act on an airfoil?
7. In flying out of a small field, which would be preferred: a small pitch or a large pitch for the propeller?
8. What causes an airplane to stall?
9. What factors most affect the speed of an airplane?
10. Explain the thrust produced by the propeller.
11. Explain the lift of an airplane.
12. Name the three axes of an airplane and describe the controls which the pilot uses to determine the rotation about each axis.
13. What are the advantages of cambered wings over flat wings? What factors determine the maximum amount of camber that can be used?

Caustic evaporation plant, Geismar, Louisiana. (Courtesy, Wyandotte Chemicals Corporation)

The Realm of Chemistry— Changes in the Composition of Matter

The chymists are a strange class of mortals, impelled by an almost insane impulse to seek their pleasure among smoke and vapor, soot and flame, poisons and poverty; yet among all of these evils I seem to live so sweetly that may I die if I would change places with the Persian King.

from Physica Subterranea, *a medieval treatise on the physical sciences*

SINCE MEDIEVAL TIMES, when this paragraph was written, this "strange class of mortals" has provided us with a world of luxury and convenience. Today's laboratories are not necessarily "among smoke and vapor, soot and flame, poisons and poverty," but may be rather clean, pleasant, and orderly, depending upon the working habits of the chemists. They are often smelly, but the true chemist does not mind a few unpleasant smells. Any time that he wants to he can prepare some sweet-smelling perfumes. Here in these laboratories the chemist's ideas are formulated, tested, and passed on to the production engineers, and eventually result in many "better things for better living." Keep in mind that the chemist is concerned with changes in matter. His laboratories are simply places where he can carry out various changes in matter on a small scale.

Some of man's greatest achievements in mastering his material world may be found in the transformations of matter. The elegance of synthetic fibers, the versatility of plastics, the beauty of synthetic dyes, the durability of metal alloys, and the effectiveness of disease-fighting drugs are the products of man's mastery of the science of materials.

This unit is not designed to tell about the products of chemistry such as are mentioned above. The study of these products has been saved for Units 10, 11, and 12. The purpose of this unit is to present an overview of the science of chemistry, the nature of chemical units, and how they react with each other.

Atoms—The Chemical Units of Matter

With accurate experiment and observation to work upon, imagination becomes the architect of physical theory. . . . Out of the facts of chemistry the constructive imagination of Dalton formed the atomic theory.

JOHN TYNDALL

INTRODUCTION

Chemistry is a quantitative science, and the balance, used to weigh quantities of materials, is the chief tool of the chemist. Atoms have been defined as the chemical units of matter. Atoms have definite weights but they are much too small to see or weigh. This chapter will explain how the chemist gets around this problem.

Chemical reactions consist of the reactions of atoms and their compounds. Atoms of some elements have a great affinity for each other, while atoms of other elements will not react under any circumstances. What is the nature of this affinity? This chapter suggests that it is electrical in nature.

Another characteristic of the atoms of many of the elements is that they may combine with each other in several different ratios. Valence, taken up in this chapter, is an expression of this idea, and it is also found to be electrical in nature.

THE NATURE OF COMBUSTION

Joseph Priestley (1733–1804) discovered oxygen by heating mercuric oxide with sunlight focused by a reading glass, as illustrated in Figure 29-1. Priestley did not know that air contains oxygen, so he was not in a position to discover the true nature of combustion. It was Antoine Lavoisier who proved that air contains oxygen, by his experiment illustrated in Figure 29-2.

Lavoisier recognized the true nature of combustion as the combining of the oxygen of the air with a material such as wood, coal, paper, or candle wax. Figure 29-3 shows how he used a balance to show that the weight of the products of the combustion of a candle equaled the weight of the original candle plus the amount of oxygen consumed. It will be recalled that this experiment laid the foundation for the law of conservation of mass. However, his most important contribution was the introduction of the balance. The balance is the most important tool of the chemist, because he is chiefly concerned with how much of a given material will react with how much of another material.

THE LAW OF DEFINITE PROPORTIONS

The balance was soon used to settle an argument between Joseph Louis Proust and Claude Louis Berthollet (1776–1856) as to whether or not a compound is composed of elements in definite proportions. Proust won out, giving us the **law of definite proportions,** which states *that the elements which make up a chemical compound are combined*

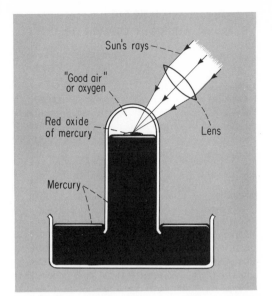

Figure 29–1. Priestley prepared oxygen by heating mercuric oxide with sunlight focused on the oxide with a burning glass (lens).

in definite proportions by weight. An outcome of his work was a distinction between compounds and solutions. Both compounds and solutions are homogeneous, but they differ in that the composition of a compound is always definite, while the composition of solutions may be varied over fairly wide limits. For example, ordinary sugar always has the same relative amounts of the elements, hydrogen, oxygen, and carbon. It makes no difference

whether it came from sugar cane or sugar beets, the composition is always the same. On the other hand, the composition of a sugar solution may be varied considerably.

DALTON'S ATOMIC THEORY

The English school teacher, John Dalton, made one of the great contributions to chemistry with his atomic theory, which he advanced in 1803. The early Greeks, and Democritus, in particular, believed that all matter could be reduced to indivisible particles which he called atoms (meaning nondivisible), and that various materials could be obtained by the interactions of these atoms. Aristotle rejected this idea and because of his great influence, the atomic theory had

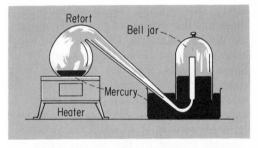

Figure 29–2. Lavoisier's proof that air contains oxygen. Lavoisier heated mercury in contact with air for twelve days. Mercuric oxide was formed in the retort, while the volume of air in the bell jar was decreased by one-fifth.

Figure 29–3. Lavoisier's experiment which overthrew the phlogiston theory. A candle seems to lose weight when burned in the air (left), but when the gaseous products of combustion are absorbed by a mixture of sodium hydroxide and calcium chloride, the candle side of the balance increases in weight, the increase being due to the weight of the oxygen removed from the air.

not been revived until Dalton resurrected it more than two thousand years later. The fact that he used the term *atom*, showed that he was familiar with the ideas of Democritus, which he combined with the idea of weights, as expressed by the law of definite proportions, in the form of his **atomic theory**: *"If elements consist of tiny, indestructible particles, called atoms, and if all atoms of a given element are alike in properties and have the same weights, but atoms of different elements have different properties and different weights, then a compound is formed by the combining of atoms of elements in definite ratios expressed by small, whole numbers."*

ATOMIC WEIGHTS

It was a natural outcome of Dalton's atomic theory that chemists began experiments to determine the relative weights of the atoms of the different elements. Of course, the simple approach would be to weigh atoms of different elements. But how could one weigh something that he could not even see? The solution to this problem was to weigh the amounts of elements which would combine to form compounds, or to weigh the amounts of elements formed by the decomposition of a given weight of a compound. In every case, these weights would yield the relative weights of atoms. It is understood that **atomic weights** are not weights, but that they *are merely numbers (ratios) which express the relative weights of atoms.* The Swedish chemist, Jöns Jacob Berzelius (1779–1848), credited with the discovery of five elements, was the first man to make an organized study of the relative weights of the atoms. In 1828, he published a list of atomic weights based on two standards. In one case, he used oxygen as a standard, with an arbitrary value of 100. In the other case, he used hydrogen as a standard, with an arbitrary value of 1. Since his time, atomic weights have been calculated on the basis of oxygen as a standard, with an arbitrary value of exactly 16, which would give a value of 1.008 to hydrogen. So Berzelius' ideas persisted down to 1961.

In 1961, the International Union of Pure and Applied Chemistry, following a similar action by the physicists in the previous year, accepted a particular isotope of carbon as a

TABLE 29-1

ATOMIC WEIGHTS OF COMMON ELEMENTS

	Symbol	Atomic No.	Atomic Weight
Aluminum	Al	13	26.9815
Antimony	Sb	51	121.75
Argon	Ar	18	39.948
Arsenic	As	33	74.9216
Barium	Ba	56	137.34
Beryllium	Be	4	9.0122
Bismuth	Bi	83	208.980
Boron	B	5	10.811
Bromine	Br	35	79.909
Cadmium	Cd	48	112.40
Calcium	Ca	20	40.08
Carbon	C	6	12.01115
Chlorine	Cl	17	35.453
Chromium	Cr	24	51.996
Cobalt	Co	27	58.9332
Copper	Cu	29	63.54
Fluorine	F	9	18.9984
Germanium	Ge	32	72.59
Gold	Au	79	196.967
Helium	He	2	4.0026
Hydrogen	H	1	1.00797
Iodine	I	53	126.9044
Iron	Fe	26	55.847
Lead	Pb	82	207.19
Lithium	Li	3	6.939
Magnesium	Mg	12	24.312
Mercury	Hg	80	200.59
Neon	Ne	10	20.183
Nickel	Ni	28	58.71
Nitrogen	N	7	14.0067
Oxygen	O	8	15.9994
Phosphorus	P	15	30.9738
Platinum	Pt	78	195.09
Plutonium	Pu	94	
Potassium	K	19	39.102
Radium	Ra	88	
Radon	Rn	86	
Silicon	Si	14	28.086
Silver	Ag	47	107.870
Sodium	Na	11	22.9898
Sulfur	S	16	32.064
Tin	Sn	50	118.69
Titanium	Ti	22	47.90
Tungsten	W	74	183.85
Uranium	U	92	238.03
Zinc	Zn	30	65.37

1961
(Based on Carbon-12)

standard, with an arbitrary value of 12.00000. Table 29-1 lists the weights of the more common elements based on this standard, but they vary only slightly from the previous atomic weights.

The reason for abandoning oxygen as the standard for atomic weights was that the oxygen used to obtain these weights was a mixture of isotopes, i.e., atoms of oxygen of different atomic weights but similar chemical properties.

THE LAW OF MULTIPLE PROPORTIONS

John Dalton predicted the law of **multiple proportions,** which states that *when two elements unite to form two or more different compounds, the ratios of the mass of one element to the masses of the other element will be small whole numbers.* Dalton was able to furnish experimental proof of this law, which represented the final triumph of the atomic theory.

For example, it was found that hydrogen and oxygen would combine with each other to form two different compounds having different compositions. In one case, water may be formed. In this case, two atoms of hydrogen combine with one atom of oxygen to form one molecule of water. Under different conditions, hydrogen peroxide may be formed. In this case, two atoms of hydrogen combine with two atoms of oxygen. The amounts of oxygen which combine with a given weight of hydrogen would thus be in the ratio of 1 to 2.

Since some elements may have several different **combining weights** (equivalent weights, i.e., *the weight of the element which will combine with, replace, or be equivalent to an atomic weight—1.00797—of hydrogen in a chemical reaction*), the chief problem for the early atomic-weight workers was to decide which multiple of the combining weight would be the atomic weight. There were various approaches to this problem. One approach was the law of **Dulong and Petit,** which states that *the product of the atomic weight and the specific heat is approximately equal to 6.3,* served in some cases to tell which combining weights were atomic weights. Another approach was to determine the molecular weights of many compounds of an element, and then to analyze them to determine the combining weights. *The number of equivalent weights in an atomic weight* is the **valence** of an element. **Valence** is generally defined as *the combining capacity of an element.* Many of the elements have two or more valences; the highest valence that an element could have is seven.

The idea of metallic and nonmetallic valences came into use for the metals and nonmetals. The metallic valence was designated as positive ($+1$, $+2$, etc.) while the nonmetallic valence was designated as negative (-1, -2, etc.). This fortunate designation of positive and negative valences later fitted into the electronic theory of valence, but at the time that this designation was first proposed there was no idea that valence might be electrical in nature. The plus and minus signs were used only to represent opposite combining capacities. The terms, male and female could have been used just as well. *Minus* did **not** mean *negative,* because an element could not have a negative combining capacity. Actually, an element, according to the electronic theory, is said to have lost one or more electrons if it has a positive valence. An electron is designated by a *minus* sign to *represent a negative charge of electricity,* but in the field of electricity, the terms plus and minus have no meaning beyond the idea that they are opposite electrical charges.

Valence might be considered to represent the quantity factor of chemical energy just as calories represent the quantity factor of heat energy.

Since the *atomic weight, divided by the valence,* gives the **equivalent weight,** valence tells the chemist how much of one element will combine with a given weight of another element. When the chemist writes a formula for a compound, the subscript numbers tell how many atoms of one element are combined with one or more atoms of another element. For example, the formula, CO_2, states that two atoms of oxygen are combined with one atom of carbon. Since O_2 represents four equivalent weights of oxygen, the valence of carbon in CO_2 is 4.

CHEMICAL AFFINITY

Chemical changes represent rearrangements of atoms within molecules, or the decomposition or combination of molecules to form smaller or larger molecules, containing fewer or more atoms. What force holds atoms together within molecules? Are these forces the same for all atoms? By what means may these forces be overcome to bring about new arrangements of atoms within molecules? These are the questions which have puzzled chemists for many years. Some of them can now be answered, although the answers are still very incomplete.

In the thirteenth century, the Dominican monk Albertus Magnus used the word "affinitas," which expressed the idea that only atoms having a similarity or kinship would unite to form molecules. The Greek philosopher Hippocrates expressed the same idea when he maintained that "like unites only with like." In the eighteenth century, Boerhaave and others arrived at the opposite conclusion, namely, that dissimilar atoms show the greatest tendency to combine.

Before the knowledge of electricity developed, the nature of this force of affinity was not known. The terms "love" and "hate" were often used for want of anything better. It was known, however, that the affinity between the various atoms differed, and many attempts were made to arrange the elements in the order of their affinity for other elements. Today it is believed that **chemical affinity** is *a force, electrical in nature, which acts between the different kinds of atoms to bring about chemical changes.* In carrying out reactions between the elements it soon becomes evident that some elements are much more active than other elements. For example, iron combines with oxygen in the air at ordinary temperatures rather slowly, while other metals, such as sodium or potassium, react very rapidly with oxygen. Still other metals, such as gold, show no activity with oxygen. Why is this true? One might suggest as an answer that elements differ in chemical affinity, but this answer simply substitutes affinity for activity. What, then, is chemical affinity? Can it be measured? Chemical affinity might be considered to be the intensity factor of chemical energy, similar to temperature as the intensity factor of heat energy. It can be expressed quantitatively in terms of E.M.F. (electromotive force) measurements as shown in Table 29-2. Using these figures, the chemist

is able to predict the relative affinities of the different elements. Such a table is sometimes called an electromotive series or a displacement series. Such a series was constructed, long before the idea of electromotive force was known, by listing the elements in the order in which they would displace each other from their compounds.

The electromotive force measurements in this table simply indicate the relative attractions of the different elements for electrons. The meaning of electromotive force will be given in a later chapter.

TABLE 29-2

ELECTROMOTIVE (DISPLACEMENT) SERIES OF COMMON METALS

Element	Electromotive Force
Potassium	+2.92
Sodium	+2.71
Zinc	+0.76
Chromium	+0.56
Iron	+0.44
Nickel	+0.23
Tin	+0.14
Lead	+0.12
Hydrogen	0.00
Copper	−0.34
Silver	−0.80
Mercury	−0.85

(This displacement series lists only a few of the common metals. A similar series may be constructed for the nonmetals. This series is often called the electrochemical or electromotive series because the relative attraction of the elements for electrons may be measured electrically and be expressed as electromotive force.)

VALENCE IN TERMS OF ELECTRONS

Valence is now believed to represent *the number of electrons gained or lost, or the number of pairs of electrons shared in chemical reactions.* Knowledge of the structure of atoms made possible the electron theory of valence. According to this theory, the reactions between atoms are governed by the number of electrons in the outermost levels

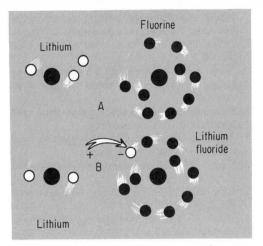

Figure 29–4. The ionic bond as shown by lithium fluoride. (A) Before bonding; (B) after bonding.

or orbits of the atoms. In certain types of reactions, the atoms of metals give up all of their outside electrons to the atoms of non-metals, and the nonmetals annex enough electrons to make the sum of eight in their outermost orbits. As the result of this *loss of electrons by the metals to become positively charged*, and *the gain of electrons by the nonmetals to become negatively charged, the metals and nonmetals are attracted to each other to form compounds*. Such changes are called **electrovalent reactions,** the *compounds produced* are called **electrovalent compounds,** and the *valence, represented by the gain or loss of electrons* is called **electrovalence.**

Some atoms exhibit two, three, or more

valences. This is explained by the Bohr theory by assuming that the number of electrons in the outside orbit differs in each case, as the result of one or more of the electrons moving from the outside orbit to an inner orbit, or vice versa. Obviously, energy is used up in changing the orbits of these electrons.

Various factors influence the tendency of elements to gain or lose electrons. *Elements that have fewer than four electrons in the outer orbit tend to lose their electrons, and thus become positvely charged. Such elements are said to have a metallic or* **positive valence.** Elements that have four electrons in the outer orbit tend either to lose or to gain these electrons, and may thus act as metals or nonmetals. *Elements, having more than four electrons in the outer orbit, tend to gain electrons,* and are said to exhibit a *nonmetallic,* or **negative valence.**

The larger atoms show a greater tendency to lose electrons, inasmuch as the outer electrons are held less firmly, because of the greater distance that separates them from the nucleus. Atoms of light nonmetals tend to gain electrons more readily because the distance from the nucleus to the outer electrons is less, and, therefore, the nucleus exerts a greater attraction for the electrons.

In many chemical reactions, there is *no gain or loss, but rather a sharing of electrons.* The compounds thus produced are called **covalent compounds,** and the valence represented is called **covalence.** Molecules of elements, for example, are covalent in nature.

SUMMARY

The Laws

Law of Definite Composition—The composition of a chemical compound is definite in nature, i.e., it is always composed of the same elements in the same proportions by weight.

Law of Multiple Proportions—When two elements unite to form two or more different compounds, the ratios of the mass of one element to the masses of the other element will be small whole numbers.

Law of Dulong and Petit—The product of the atomic weight and the specific heat is approximately 6.3.

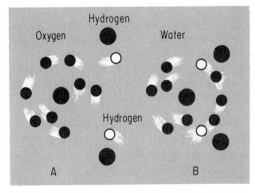

Figure 29–5. The covalent bond as shown in the water molecule. (A) Before bonding; (B) after bonding.

The Atomic Theory

The smallest division of an element is an atom. Atoms do not change in ordinary chemical reactions. Atoms of different elements differ in mass and other properties, while atoms of a given element have the same average mass and similar chemical properties. Compounds are formed by combining definite whole numbers of atoms.

Atomic Weights are Relative Weights

$$\frac{\text{Atomic weight}}{\text{valence}} = \frac{\text{equivalent weight}}{\text{(combining weight)}}$$

Valence

Valence is equal to the number of electrons gained, lost, or shared in a chemical reaction. Chemical affinity represents the relative attractions of elements for electrons.

Study Questions

1. DEFINE: combining weight, atomic weight, valence, chemical affinity, equivalent weight, electrovalent reaction, electrovalent compound, electrovalence, positive valence, negative valence, covalent compound, covalence.
2. Differentiate between a solution and a compound.
3. What is the relationship between the combining weight and the atomic weight of an element?
4. State the law of multiple proportions, and illustrate it with an example.
5. State the law of definite composition, and illustrate it with an example.
6. What information does an electromotive force table give?
7. How may chemical affinity be expressed? What is it?
8. What is the combining capacity of an element called?
9. Give the main points of Dalton's atomic theory.
10. What was the outstanding contribution of Lavoisier?
11. If one knew the combining weight of an element, what other information would be required to obtain the atomic weight?
12. How did the law of Dulong and Petit help in the determination of atomic weights?
13. What do the plus and minus signs mean when referring to valence?
14. Give the electronic theory of valence.

Atomic Complexity

The classification of the elements has not only a pedagogical importance, as a means for more readily learning assorted facts that are systematically arranged and correlated, but it has also a scientific importance, since it discloses new analogies and hence opens up new routes for the exploration of the elements.

MENDELÉEFF

INTRODUCTION

William Prout, having observed that many atomic weights are whole numbers, and having assumed that all atomic weights would prove to be whole numbers, advanced the hypothesis that the atoms of all elements are simple multiples of the atoms of smallest mass, those of hydrogen. Prout was on the track of a great idea, but it was not until some of the information presented in this chapter became available that his idea that atoms are complex in nature received confirmation.

Two lines of evidence pointing to the complex nature of atoms, periodicity and discharge tube phenomena, are described in this chapter. Additional evidence is presented in the next chapter.

PROUT'S HYPOTHESIS

Since hydrogen is the lightest element, and since the atomic weights of many elements are nearly whole-number multiples of the atomic weight of hydrogen, would it not be reasonable to assume that the hydrogen atom is the building stone from which all of the elements are made?

William Prout (1785–1850), the chemist, suggested that all elements were made of hydrogen atoms. At first it was thought that atomic weights which were not whole numbers

were the results of inaccurate analyses, but very careful work showed that such atomic weights as 35.46, the atomic weight of chlorine, were very accurate. Later, it was found that these non-whole-number atomic weights represented mixtures of isotopes, all of which have whole numbers for their atomic weights. Prout's idea was not accepted, but today we know that the hydrogen nucleus, the proton, is one of the building blocks of atoms, but not the only one.

DOBEREINER'S TRIADS

As early as 1817, Johann Wolfgang Dobereiner (1780–1849) noticed regularities in the atomic weights of chemically similar groups of elements. *In groups of three, the atomic weight of the middle element is approximately the average value of the atomic weights of the extreme elements,* which is a statement of the **law of triads.** For example, chlorine, bromine, and iodine, members of the halogen family of nonmetals, constitute a triad. Chlorine is a gas, iodine is a solid, while bromine between the other two is a liquid. The atomic weight of bromine is approximately equal to the average of the atomic weights of chlorine and iodine. The fact that one triad exists might be due to chance, but the existence of at least six sets of triads in-

223

dicates that there must be some unknown relationship between the elements that are members of triads.

NEWLANDS' LAW OF OCTAVES

As a result of a great deal of very careful work, the atomic weights of most of the elements were obtained, and it thus became possible to construct an atomic weight table. Table 29-1 lists the atomic weights of the more common elements, most of which are already known to you by name, and some of which, such as aluminum, iron, lead, or mercury, are known to you by their physical properties.

Once a table of the atomic weights of the elements became available, chemists speculated as to the possibility of any relationships that might exist among the elements.

In 1865, John Newlands observed that the elements seem to exist as families. Today, for example, we recognize that the inert gases of the atmosphere—helium, neon, argon, krypton, and xenon—are so much alike chemically that it is difficult to separate them. These elements had not been discovered in Newlands' time, but he observed other families. For example, the alkali-metals group consists of lithium, sodium, potassium, rubidium, and cesium, all very active metals with a combining power of one. Another such family is the alkaline-earth group, consisting of magnesium, calcium, strontium, and barium; these metals occur in similar types of compounds, and exhibit a combining power of two. The halogens are a group of very active nonmetals with a combining power of one. This group consists of fluorine, chlorine, bromine, and iodine. Newlands arranged the elements in the increasing order of their atomic weights, and observed that every eighth element seemed to belong to the same family. As Newlands expressed it, "*the eighth element starting from a given one is a kind of repetition of the first, like the eighth note of an octave of music.*"

THE PERIODIC LAW AND TABLE

Independently of each other, and in ignorance of Newlands' work, Lothar Meyer, in Germany, and Dmitri Ivanovitch Mendeléeff, in Russia, made a thorough study of the properties of the elements and noted a similar relationship. They proposed the law, known as the periodic law, which states that the *properties of the elements are periodic functions of their atomic weights.*

Periodicity (*regular recurrence*) is very common in nature. The growth of trees, periods of large sunspots, the tides, and the full moon all occur periodically. A flattened wheel on a railroad car produces a periodic clatter, which is a function of the distance traveled, because every full turn of the wheel brings the flattened portion of the wheel into contact with the track.

Mendeléeff prepared a table of the elements based upon their periodicity in properties. He left a number of gaps in this table in places where the progression in properties seemed to demand it, arguing that there must be elements which had not yet been discovered. The known character of the elements above and below these gaps made it possible to predict the properties of the missing elements. Mendeléeff made these predictions in 1870 for three elements, calling them eka-boron, eka-aluminum, and eka-silicon. These elements, discovered in 1879, 1875, and 1886, and named scandium, gallium, and germanium, showed properties that checked remarkably closely with those predicted by Mendeléeff. This strong support of the periodic law was strengthened later by the discovery of all of the remaining missing elements, partly through the aid furnished by the periodic table.

Table 30-1 is an abbreviated periodic table. The atomic weights and atomic numbers of the elements have been deliberately omitted. This table of elements was prepared by placing families of elements having similar properties in separate groups. If you will refer to Table 29-1, page 218, you will be able to obtain the atomic weights and atomic numbers of most of the elements in this periodic table. If you will fill in the table by placing the atomic numbers of the elements above their names and the atomic weights below their names, you will discover that the elements in each family were listed in the order of their increasing atomic weights and atomic numbers. Were there any cases in which the

TABLE 30-1

AN ABBREVIATED PERIODIC TABLE SHOWING ONLY EIGHT MAIN GROUPS

The Alkali Metals	The Alkaline Earth Metals					The Halogens	The Inert Gases
Group I	Group II	Group III	Group IV	Group V	Group VI	Group VII	Group VIII
Hydrogen							Helium
Lithium	Beryllium	Boron	Carbon	Nitrogen	Oxygen	Fluorine	Neon
Sodium	Magnesium	Aluminum	Silicon	Phosphorus	Sulfur	Chlorine	Argon
Potassium	Calcium	Gallium	Germanium	Arsenic	Selenium	Bromine	Krypton
Rubidium	Strontium	Indium	Tin	Antimony	Tellurium	Iodine	Xenon
Cesium	Barium	Thallium	Lead	Bismuth	Polonium	Astatine	Radon
Francium	Radium						

order of the elements listed by atomic weights was not the same as the order obtained by listing them by their atomic numbers? Are there any elements in the abbreviated atomic weight table for which there were no places in this periodic table?

Table 30-2 is one form of a periodic table which lists all of the elements. Many different

TABLE 30–2

The Periodic Table of Meyer and Mendeléeff

The transition elements are those that occur between Groups II and III in the periodic table. The lanthanides and actinides (shown in white spaces) are placed as footnotes in this form of the periodic table.

Group I	Group II											Group III	Group IV	Group V	Group VI	Group VII	Group VIII
H		THE TRANSITION ELEMENTS															He
Li	Be											B	C	N	O	F	Ne
Na	Mg											Al	Si	P	S	Cl	A
K	Ca	Sc	Ti	V	Cr	Mn	Fe	Co	Ni	Cu	Zn	Ga	Ge	As	Se	Br	Kr
Rb	Sr	Y	Zr	Nb	Mo	Tc	Ru	Rh	Pd	Ag	Cd	In	Sn	Sb	Te	I	Xe
Cs	Ba	*	Hf	Ta	W	Re	Os	Ir	Pt	Au	Hg	Tl	Pb	Bi	Po	At	Rn
Fr	Ra	**															

* The Lanthanides
** The Actinides

*	La	Ce	Pr	Nd	Pm	Sm	Eu	Gd	Tb	Dy	Ho	Er	Tm	Yb	Lu	
**	Ac	Th	Pa	U	Np	Pu	Am	Cm	Bk	Cf	E	Fm	Mv			

kinds of periodic tables have been devised to show a logical place for the transition elements and the lanthanides and the actinides. Any theory dealing with the complex structure of atoms must be able to explain these apparent inconsistencies.

The periodic table of Meyer and Mendeléeff was imperfect. For example, several elements, when listed according to the order of increasing atomic weights, would not fit into the group of families to which they obviously belonged because of the similarities of their properties. Mendeléeff placed these elements where they belonged in terms of their properties, and later knowledge showed that he had made a wise decision. It was the discovery of isotopes that explained this discrepancy. Meyer and Mendeléeff's table made it possible to correct many erroneous atomic weights, and also was of great value in deciding which combining weight should be selected as the atomic weight.

The periodic table is one of the most useful generalizations in chemistry, because it is of great value in predicting the properties of elements and in classifying chemical information.

How shall one explain the periodic law? One generally expects to find a common origin or a common building material for people, houses, or materials which are similar in properties. It is the fact that houses are made of smaller units, such as bricks, that makes possible such a wide variety of patterns. This complexity of structure also makes it possible to build large or small houses of the same design, using different numbers of bricks. If the atoms of the elements are ultimate, no relationships should exist. The chief significance of the periodic law is that it suggests the existence of atoms of similar, and therefore complex structure.

THE IONIZATION POTENTIALS OF THE ELEMENTS

Many charts or graphs could be used to show how such properties as physical state, melting point, and boiling point are periodic in nature. We have selected one interesting property of the elements, the ionization potential, to illustrate periodicity in properties.

The **ionization potential** is a measure of the *tightness with which atoms hold on to their electrons*. It can be measured by determining the energy required to pull an electron off of an atom of an element placed between two plates in a gas discharge tube. The voltage between the plates is increased until it is high enough to rip the electrons away from the atoms, at which point an electric current passes between the plates. Table 30-3 shows the ionization potentials of the elements in the abbreviated form of the periodic table.

DISCHARGE TUBE EXPERIMENTS

Heinrich Geissler (1814–1879), a German glass blower, became famous for his *vacuum tubes of various shapes, which produced beautiful displays when an electric current was passed through them.* By using different kinds of glass, he obtained fluorescent effects of different colors. Such tubes are still called **Geissler tubes.**

About 1878, William Crookes (1832–1919) became interested in Geissler tubes. He made some *tubes in which he produced a very high vacuum.* Tubes similar to those shown in Figure 30-1 are called **Crookes' tubes.** The tube contains a side tube which may be connected to a vacuum pump. When filled with air at atmospheric pressure the tube will not conduct an appreciable amount of electric current, but as air is evacuated from the tube the current begins to flow. When the pressure is reduced to about 10 millimeters of mercury, bluish ribbons of light will pass between the electrodes, if the voltage between the plates exceeds the ionization potential. This is assured

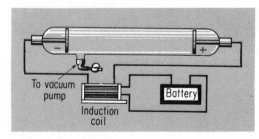

Figure 30–1. A simple vacuum discharge tube. The high voltage produced by the induction coil excites the small amount of gas left in the evacuated tube.

TABLE 30–3

The Ionization Potentials of the Elements. Progressing across the table from Group I through Group VIII, the number of electrons in the outside layer increases, as do the ionization potentials. The ionization potentials (expressed in Electron Volts) decrease with increasing atomic weights.

Group I	Group II	Group III	Group IV	Group V	Group VI	Group VII	Group VIII
Hydrogen 13.6							Helium 24.6
Lithium 5.4	Beryllium 9.3	Boron 8.3	Carbon 11.3	Nitrogen 14.5	Oxygen 13.6	Fluorine 17.4	Neon 21.6
Sodium 5.1	Magnesium 7.6	Aluminum 6.0	Silicon 8.1	Phosphorus 11.0	Sulfur 10.4	Chlorine 13.0	Argon 15.8
Potassium 4.3	Calcium 6.1	Gallium 6.0	Germanium 8.1	Arsenic 10	Selenium 9.8	Bromine 11.8	Krypton 14
Rubidium 4.2	Strontium 5.7	Indium 5.8	Tin 7.3	Antimony 8.6	Tellurium 9.0	Iodine 10.4	Xenon 12.1
Cesium 3.9	Barium 5.2	Thallium 6.1	Lead 7.4	Bismuth 8	Polonium •••	Astatine •••	Radon 10.7
Francium •••	Radium 5.3						

Adapted from *Chemistry* by Sienko and Plane. 2nd. Ed., Copyright, 1961. McGraw-Hill Book Company. Used by permission.

by using a source of high voltage. Crookes observed flickering streams of light shooting from the negative electrode to the positive electrode, which he found would cause diamonds, rubies, and other substances to become fluorescent or phosphorescent. The rays would not penetrate mica or relatively thick layers of certain metals, but cast a shadow of the pattern in which they were cut. He found that these rays would heat a target placed in their path or cause a paddle wheel to revolve, and therefore concluded that the rays consisted of particles having mass. He also found that a beam of these rays, passed through a slit in a shutter placed in front of the negative electrode (cathode) and made visible by a fluorescent screen placed in its path, was deflected by a magnet. These discoveries aroused the interest of the whole scientific world as few others have ever done. Later experiments in which the **cathode rays** were deflected by both electric and magnetic fields proved that

they were negatively charged. H. R. Hertz (1857–1894) demonstrated that these rays, which would not penetrate mica or certain other substances, would pass through thin sheets of certain metals, such as aluminum.

In 1894, P. Lenard (1862–1947) showed that these cathode rays would affect a photographic plate. He was able to obtain the rays by passing them through an aluminum window at the end of the tube. In 1895, C. W. Roentgen (1856–1923) studied these rays that had been passed through the aluminum window and found that rays of another kind were emitted by the Crookes tube itself and *were produced whenever the cathode rays struck an obstacle, such as a metal or glass target, placed in their path.* These were **X rays,** or **Roentgen rays,** as they are often called in honor of their discoverer. We will come back to this important discovery later. Let us turn to still other observations.

In 1897, J. J. Thomson (1856–1940) at-

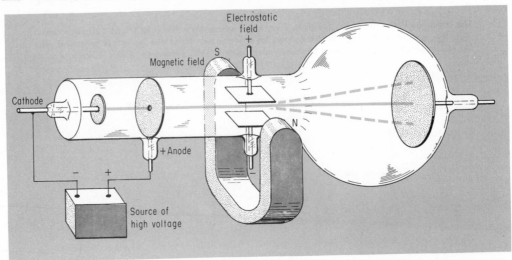

Figure 30-2. Sir J. J. Thomson's apparatus by which the velocity and the ratio of the charge to the mass of the electron was determined.

tempted to measure the speed with which these cathode particles moved, and the ratio of their electric charges to their masses. In October, 1897, he made a historic experiment in which he found that the cathode rays could be deflected by a magnetic field. With his apparatus, shown in Figure 30-2, he could measure the deflection of the cathode rays by an electromagnet when they passed between oppositely charged plates. The whole apparatus was placed between the poles of a powerful electromagnet. With this apparatus, Thomson was able to show that the ratio of the charge on each particle to its mass was constant, regardless of the nature of the electrodes or of the gas in the tube. It was suspected that the mass of these particles was very small, but so far, neither the mass nor the charge had been actually measured.

ELECTRONS AND PROTONS

Thomson checked his value for the ratio of the mass to the charge of an electron, using the cloud chamber invented by C. T. R. Wilson (1869–1959). The principle of Wilson's cloud chamber is shown in a homemade model in Figure 30-3. He showed that the mass of the electron was only 1/1836 of the mass of the hydrogen atom. He also showed that the charge on a hydrogen atom which had lost an electron was exactly equal but opposite to, the

Figure 30-3. A simple cloud chamber. A cake of dry ice is placed under the glass jar. In the bottom of the jar there is a black cloth. The jar is covered with a thin layer of porous material which is moistened with ethyl alcohol. A hot iron placed on top of the cover causes the alcohol vapor to enter the jar. Fog tracks will form in the alcohol vapor when charged particles pass into the jar. Wilson's cloud chamber used water vapor instead of alcohol vapor.

charge of an electron. This *charged nucleus of a hydrogen atom* was called a **proton.**

Wilson's cloud chamber experiment was further improved by Robert Millikan (1868–1953), who substituted oil droplets for water droplets. Millikan imparted negative charges

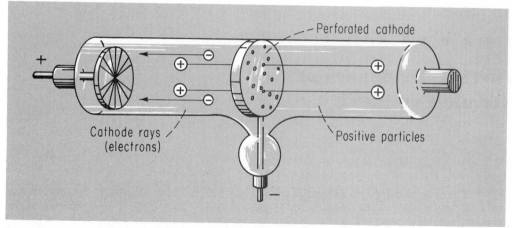

Figure 30-4. A canal-ray tube. The positively charged "canal rays" are not rays but they consist of a stream of positively charged atomic nuclei called ions. These positive ions pass through the perforated cathode towards which they are attracted.

to oil drops; the amount of the upward acceleration of the oil drop in an electric field was a measure of its electric charge. Millikan's experiments gave a value for the mass of the electron which was about 1/1850 of the mass of a hydrogen atom, not far different from Thomson's value.

CANAL RAYS

It was found that discharge tubes would also produce *a stream of positively charged particles,* by using a discharge tube such as is shown in Figure 30-4. It turned out that these positively charged particles *were formed by the bombardment of the atoms of the gases in the tubes by the cathode rays.* These rays have little practical significance, although they have furnished evidence that atoms possess positively charged nuclei as well as electrons. These positively charged rays were called **canal rays.**

SUMMARY

The Periodic Law

The properties of the elements are periodic functions of their atomic weights (and atomic numbers).

Atomic Complexity

1. Similarities in properties indicate similarities in structure. Similarities in structure imply simpler structural units.

> Dobereiner's Triads
> Periodic Law and Table

2. Two structural units were discovered.

Discharge tubes showed two types of particles, the cathode rays, negatively charged, and the canal rays, positively charged. Conclusion: atoms are complex; they consist of positively charged nuclei and electrons.

Study Questions

1. DEFINE: cathode ray, canal ray, periodicity, ionization potential, Geissler tube, Crookes' tube, X ray (Roentgen ray), proton.
2. Show how the periodicity in the properties of the elements suggests atomic complexity.
3. What evidence do discharge-tube experiments give to support the idea of atomic complexity?
4. List some of the properties of cathode rays.
5. Give an example of Dobereiner's triads.
6. In what regards does the periodic table show discrepancies?
7. State the periodic law.
8. What were Prout's ideas? Why did they not work out for an element such as chlorine?
9. Name several different families of elements found in the periodic table. In what regards do these families differ from each other?

Further Evidences of Atomic Complexity

There is probably no subject in all science which better illustrates the importance to the entire world of research in pure science, than does X-rays. Within three months after Roentgen's fortuitous discovery, X-rays were being put to material use in a hospital in Vienna in connection with surgical operations. Had Roentgen deliberately set about to discover some means of assisting surgeons in reducing fractures, it is almost certain that he would never have been working with evacuated tubes, induction coils, and the like, which led to his famous discovery.

F. K. RICHTMYER

INTRODUCTION

In 1895, C. W. Roentgen first observed the evidence of X rays when he found that rays from a Crookes' tube which ordinarily caused phosphorescent material on a piece of paper to glow, still caused the material to glow even though he had shielded the Crookes' tube with a piece of paper. This experiment has been described as a fortunate accident, but such a combination of circumstances would not occur for many men. A similar fortunate accident led to the discovery of radioactivity by Becquerel as described in this chapter.

X RAYS

From the above experiment, Roentgen concluded that there were rays produced by the Crookes' tube that would pass through opaque substances. He found that they would pass through a thousand-page book, two packs of cards, and thick blocks of wood. Thin sheets of metal also permitted the rays to pass, but thick layers prevented their passage. When the hand was held between the Crookes' tube and the fluorescent screen, shadows of the bones were seen. He then tried taking pictures

with X rays, and was delighted to find that it could be done. On Christmas Eve, 1895, Roentgen showed his first X-ray pictures to an astonished group of German physicists. Among these pictures were photographs of the bones of his hand and of keys contained in a purse.

These rays were unlike any previously studied, and their relation to cathode rays was for some time unknown, so they were called **X rays,** *X standing for the unknown.*

Early X-ray tubes were devised by Sir Herbert Jackson, of King's College, London, who refused to patent them, and thus permitted a fortune to slip through his hands for the sake of Science. Such sacrifice of personal benefit to the development of Science is not uncommon; true scientists are more interested in the development of knowledge than they are in personal gain. In fact, a scientist can usually do his best work only when his mind is completely free from financial worries.

X rays are widely employed in photographing the bones and organs of the body. Considerable detail of the soft tissues of the body is also revealed, so that X rays can be used in diagnosis. Tuberculosis of the lungs, abscessed

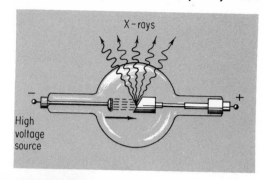

Figure 31-1. X-ray tube. Cathode rays, i.e., a stream of electrons from the cathode strike the metallic target, from which X rays are radiated.

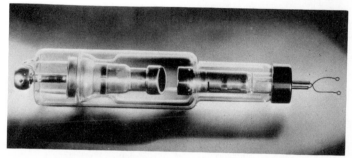

Figure 31-2. A shockproof 200,-000-volt X-ray tube used for cancer treatment. (Courtesy, Westinghouse Electric and Manufacturing Corporation)

or abnormal teeth, fractures, calculi (stones) in the kidneys, and many other abnormal conditions can be detected by X rays. The whole length of the digestive canal can be studied by giving the patient a harmless dose of bismuth carbonate or barium sulfate, which are opaque to X rays and thus show the digestive organs in outline. X rays should be used with caution, because they may cause severe burns that are difficult to heal. There were many martyrs to X rays before their harmful properties were recognized, and effective means of protection from them were devised.

Besides their use in medicine, X-ray machines have been used in detecting flaws in metals and welds; for example, every weld in the huge pipes used in the Hoover Dam project was X-rayed by a 300,000-volt X-ray machine, and twenty-nine miles of film were used in taking these X-ray photographs. X-ray machines have also been used to solve paint problems, to determine the cause of differences in physical properties of different samples of graphite, and in the examination of porcelains, papers, electrolytic deposits, patent leather, rayon, asbestos, grease, rubbers, soaps, resins, ice cream, and many other materials.

Instead of using photographs, the fluoroscope may be used with X rays in observing the body. The fluoroscope depends on the fact that X rays cause a fluorescence in certain substances.

A recent development is the use of 35-millimeter miniature films for X-ray photographs, which greatly reduces the cost of X-ray examinations. X rays cannot be bent by optical lenses in the same manner as light waves are bent, and for that reason small pictures cannot be taken by the direct use of X rays. In this new development, the subject to be examined is placed between the X-ray machine and a fluorescent screen, and a photograph is made of the resulting image produced on the screen. The camera and film holder are made of lead to keep out X rays.

THE NATURE OF X RAYS

The nature of X rays remained a mystery for several years after their discovery. They are not deflected by electric or magnetic fields and are therefore different from cathode rays in that they have no charge. Since they cannot be reflected or diffracted by ordinary optical means, it appeared at first that they

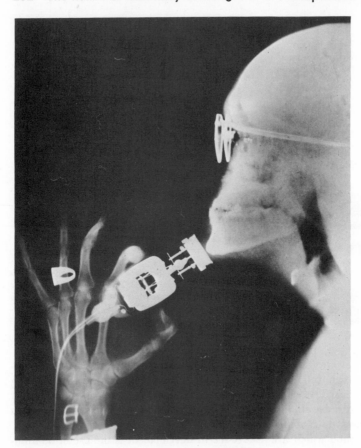

Figure 31–3. X-ray radiograph of a man using an electric shaver. (Courtesy, Westinghouse Electric and Manufacturing Corporation)

were not electromagnetic radiations similar to light waves. However, it was later concluded that X rays must be electromagnetic radiations of very small wavelength—so small, in fact, that no diffraction gratings or prisms would diffract them. It had been observed that X rays were formed when cathode rays (electrons) hit another object, especially a metal target. Did the rays come from the target material or were they produced from the electrons? It is now known that X rays are formed from the electrons, as a result of being stopped suddenly, in accordance with Clerk Maxwell's electromagnetic theory of light. They are *electromagnetic rays*.

RADIOACTIVITY—THE NEXT MAJOR EVIDENCE OF THE COMPLEXITY OF ATOMS

The discovery of radioactivity was made, in 1896, by Antoine Henri Becquerel while he was engaged in the study of the phosphorescence of certain substances. Becquerel selected certain compounds of uranium for the experiments because they are very phosphorescent. The thought occurred to him that uranium compounds might emit X rays, so he exposed a uranium compound to sunlight and placed it above a metal cross which rested on a photographic plate wrapped in a piece of heavy black paper. With the development of the plate the image of the cross became visible, thus showing that a penetrating radiation had been emitted by the uranium.

Becquerel continued his study of this interesting phenomenon and, by a lucky accident, made one of the most momentous discoveries of physical science. He had placed his photographic plate in a dark cupboard with some uranium salt until he could find time on a sunny day to carry out some more experiments. Nearly a month went by before he got around to further work on this problem. It occurred to him to develop the plate and see if it had been affected by the unexposed uranium. This he did, and the plate had been affected; here was a substance that emitted penetrating rays without any excitation.

Pierre Curie (1859–1906) and his Polish wife, Madame Marie Curie (1867–1934), became interested in these Becquerel rays, and started an investigation to learn whether or not there were other substances besides uranium salts that would emit these rays. They discovered that uranium ore, pitchblende, showed this property of emitting rays even more than the uranium extracted from it. After laboriously working over about a ton of the rock, they extracted about 0.1 gram of a material that gave radiations several thousand times as intense as those emitted by uranium salts. After the death of her husband, Madame Curie obtained, in 1910, a metallic element from their material, and gave the new element the appropriate name, radium. *The property of emitting radiations shown by uranium, radium, and various other elements is called* **radioactivity.**

In addition to uranium and radium, Madame Marie Curie discovered another radioactive element, polonium. Other radioactive elements were later discovered, but the most important discovery concerning radioactivity was the fact that radioactive elements disintegrate to form other radioactive elements, with different intensities of radioactivity and with half-lives varying from fractions of seconds to millions of years. The **half-life** *of a radioactive element is the time required for one half of the element to undergo radioactive disintegration.* In 1903, Ernest Rutherford (1871–1937) and a co-worker, Frederick Soddy (1877–1956), proposed their **disintegration hypothesis.** This hypothesis stated that *radioactive elements disintegrate, ejecting high-energy* **alpha** *or* **beta** *particles* (discussed in the next paragraph), and forming a new element, which may also be radioactive. They found three series of elements which underwent radioactive disintegration. One series started with uranium, which disintegrated to form radium—which, in turn, formed lead as the end product of the series. Lead is also the end product of two other series of radioactive elements called the ac-

tinium and thorium series. Still another series, the neptunium series, is known.

THE NATURE OF RADIOACTIVE RAYS

It was found that the alpha rays were not radiant energy, but consisted of a *stream of helium nuclei* which were named **alpha particles.** The **beta rays** likewise turned out to be *a stream of negatively charged particles.* The only true *radiations from a radioactive element* are the **gamma rays.** The interesting thing about these gamma rays is that they are *very similar to X rays,* and may be used instead of X rays for most purposes. The alpha rays correspond to the canal rays of a vacuum discharge tube containing helium, while the **beta rays** and cathode rays in each case consist of a *stream of electrons.* However, the electrons of beta rays have much higher speeds than those in cathode rays.

ALPHA PARTICLES

Alpha rays are not like true electromagnetic rays, such as X rays or other electromagnetic radiations, but consist rather of positively charged particles of matter, as is shown by their deflection by magnetic and electrical fields. These alpha particles, as they are called, ionize gases by dislodging electrons from the molecules with which they collide. The formation of these ions can be demonstrated by causing the alpha particles to pass through a space that is saturated with water vapor. When the moist air is expanded under suitable conditions, the ions produced act as nuclei for the condensation of small droplets of water, which may then be photographed. *When alpha particles strike a screen painted with zinc sulfide, tiny flashes of light are produced.* This furnishes a method of counting alpha particles. By means of such a device called a **spinthariscope,** and by means of alpha-particle tracks in a cloud chamber, we become witnesses of the effects produced by single individual atoms, and our belief in the atomic theory is thereby strengthened. The total charge of a number of alpha particles may be determined, and this charge, divided by the number of alpha particles present, proves that they have two positive charges. The mass of an alpha particle is four times that of a hydrogen ion. Rutherford showed that **alpha particles** are *charged helium atoms.*

The Geiger counter became a very well-known instrument for prospecting for radioactive minerals containing uranium. The fundamental principle of the **Geiger counter** is that *alpha particles, when passed through a gas, will ionize the gas, making it a better conductor. A current of electricity can then flow between the electrodes. The current may be amplified to produce an audible noise or to move a needle on a dial.*

THE POSITIVE CHARGES IN THE NUCLEI OF ATOMS

Electrons and alpha particles may be shot through thin sheets of glass or metal containing thousands of layers of atoms very close together. The only way we can account for this fact is by assuming that atoms have an open structure similar to that of our solar system. Each atom is therefore considered to consist almost entirely of unoccupied space, which electrons or alpha particles could pass through without hitting anything, just as the stars move rapidly through space for millions of years without meeting another star.

Ernest Rutherford found that the majority of alpha particles would pass through very thin metal foils without changing their direction, but that some alpha particles would be more or less deflected, while others would rebound from the foil. A relatively heavy mass, positively charged, must have caused these deflections in direction. Rutherford calculated that all of the positive charges in a gold atom must be concentrated into a space having a diameter of about one hundred-thousandth that of the whole atom in order to produce the deflection which he observed. He therefore concluded that atoms are composed of a very small, positively charged nucleus surrounded by electrons, distributed at intervals throughout the rest of the space within the atom. The atom is, therefore, not a solid unit of matter but a portion of space in which the nucleus maintains its attraction for a *number of electrons equal to the charge on the*

nucleus. This number is the **atomic number** of an element.

Rutherford and his co-worker, Chadwick, bombarded nitrogen atoms with high-speed alpha particles obtained from radium. The nitrogen atoms were disrupted, hydrogen was produced, energy was evolved, and an isotope of oxygen was obtained. Similar results were obtained with other elements. Aluminum yielded hydrogen and magnesium, and sodium yielded hydrogen and neon. The significance of these results was that hydrogen was found to be a building stone of elements.

ISOTOPES

Chemical analyses turned up some forty different elements obtained by the radioactive disintegration of the three series of naturally occurring radioactive elements. As previously mentioned, these series started with such heavy elements as uranium, thorium, or actinium and ended up with the same stable element, lead. Now there are only ten atomic numbers in the periodic table between uranium (92) and lead (82), so how could forty different elements fit into these ten spaces?

In 1913, Soddy showed that the loss of alpha particles and electrons by a given element could give rise to several elements of *identical chemical properties and atomic numbers, but with different atomic weights. Such elements, representing different varieties of a given element,* were called **isotopes.** With the mass spectrograph, Aston was able to separate and determine the atomic weights of the various radioactive isotopes. He found that many nonradioactive elements also consist of mixtures of isotopes. Isotopes were shown to have whole-number atomic weights. Soddy showed that elements such as chlorine, with an atomic weight of 35.46, actually consist of a mixture of isotopes, which thus accounts for their fractional atomic weights.

In 1932, an isotope of hydrogen with the atomic weight of 2 was discovered by Harold C. Urey and his co-workers by examining spectroscopically the least volatile portion of some liquid hydrogen which had been subjected to fractional distillation. This new hydrogen is called deuterium, and its oxide, deuterium oxide, is called heavy water. Later, another isotope of hydrogen, tritium, with an atomic weight of 3, was discovered.

THE ATOMIC NUCLEUS

Vacuum discharge tubes, and the discovery of electrons, protons, X rays, and radioactivity *furnished clues as to the complex structure of atoms.*

The hydrogen nucleus, i.e., the **proton,** had been discovered, and it seemed possible that the two positive charges on the helium nucleus might be due to two protons, and that the balance of the mass of the helium nucleus might be contributed by a *neutral particle having the mass of two hydrogen atoms.* Although no such neutral particle had been discovered, Rutherford concluded that such a particle must exist, and he called it the **neutron.** He concluded that the alpha particle consists of two protons plus two neutrons, and that each neutron consists of one proton and one electron in close association. It was not until 1932 that the existence of the neutron was actually confirmed. In 1932, Chadwick produced neutrons by bombarding beryllium with alpha particles. Neutrons have the mass of protons, but have no charge. Later it was found that more neutrons were produced when deuterons (heavy hydrogen nuclei) were used as bullets.

NUCLEAR BOMBARDMENT WITH HIGH-SPEED PARTICLES

The nuclei of atoms, when bombarded with high-speed particles, emit particles, and the protons and neutrons remaining in the nucleus are rearranged to form the nuclei of new elements. Such changes in the nuclei of atoms are called **nuclear reactions.** The first nuclear reaction was carried out by Ernest Rutherford in 1919. He bombarded nitrogen atoms with alpha particles, and obtained protons. Other workers have used protons, deuterons (deuterium nuclei), and neutrons as atomic bullets. In order to impart the required velocities to these bullets, various atom-smashing machines such as the cyclotron, the synchroton, the betatron, and the linear accelerator have been developed. Using various particles such as protons and neutrons as bul-

lets in atom-smashing machines, nearly all of the elements have been transmuted. Nuclear reactions have shown that the nuclei of all elements except hydrogen contain neutrons as well as protons. *The number of protons in the nucleus is equal to the* **atomic number.**

ARTIFICIAL RADIOACTIVITY

In 1934, Madame Irene Curie-Joliot, the daughter of Madame Marie Curie, and her husband, F. Joliot, discovered that ordinary inactive elements, such as aluminum, boron, and magnesium, when bombarded with alpha particles, became radioactive. Since that time about five hundred artificially radioactive isotopes have been prepared.

SUMMARY

The Picture of the Complex Atom as of 1933

Periodicity, discharge tube experiments, X rays, radioactivity, and bombardment experiments gave the following picture of an atom by 1933: the atom consists of a very small, compact, positively charged nucleus, composed of neutrons and hydrogen atoms, surrounded by a number of electrons equal to the charge on the nucleus.

The charge on the nucleus = the number of protons in the nucleus = the number of electrons outside of the nucleus = the atomic number. The atomic weight is equal to the weights of the protons and neutrons in the nucleus. The difference between the atomic number and the atomic weight is equal to the number of neutrons in the nucleus.

An alpha particle consists of two protons and two neutrons.

Electrons obtained from the radioactive decompositions of elements come from disrupted neutrons. The loss of an electron thus leaves an extra positive charge on the nucleus, and therefore increases the atomic number by one.

The ejection of an alpha particle reduces the charge on the nucleus by two positive charges, thus producing a new element with a lower atomic number.

The loss of a neutron would not change the

atomic number, but it would produce an element with a lower atomic weight. Such elements, having the same atomic number but different atomic weights are called isotopes.

Study Questions

1. DEFINE: X ray, proton, neutron, radioactivity, half-life, alpha particle, atomic number, isotope, beta ray, gamma ray, spinthariscope, Geiger counter, nuclear reaction.
2. Explain how Becquerel discovered radioactivity. What was the significance of this discovery?
3. List the main lines of evidence which led to the electron theory.
4. What are X rays? How are they produced, and for what are they used?
5. Describe Roentgen's discovery of X rays.
6. Describe the various phenomena of vacuum discharge tubes that led to the electron theory.
7. How were the mass and charge on an electron measured?
8. What are isotopes? How may they be identified without separating them?
9. Why is it difficult to separate the isotopes of a given element?
10. In what respect did the discoveries related in this chapter verify Prout's hypothesis?
11. What was the concept of the atomic nucleus in 1933?
12. How did J. J. Thomson discover the electron?
13. How does the mass of an electron compare with the mass of a proton?
14. Explain how Becquerel discovered radioactivity. What was the significance of this discovery?
15. How were atomic numbers determined experimentally?
16. In what regard are X rays and gamma rays similar?
17. How do cathode rays differ from beta rays?
18. Describe the work that led to the discovery of radioactivity.
19. How are X rays produced?
20. List the applications of X rays.
21. Give the principle of the fluoroscope.
22. How was it shown that X rays are electromagnetic waves?
23. How has it been made possible to take miniature X-ray photographs?

Ions

Although we know nothing of what an atom is, yet we cannot resist forming some idea of a small particle, which represents it to the mind; and though we are in equal, if not greater, ignorance of electricity . . . yet there is—an immensity of facts which justify us in believing that the atoms of matter are in some way endowed or associated with electrical powers, to which they owe their most striking properties, and amongst them their mutual chemical affinity.

MICHAEL FARADAY

INTRODUCTION

There are two kinds of molecules, (1) *those in which the atoms are held together by the sharing of pairs of electrons,* and (2) *those which are held together because of the attraction between oppositely charged atoms.* The *former* are called covalent compounds or **nonelectrolytes,** while the latter are called electrovalent compounds or **electrolytes.** Electrolytes are discussed in this chapter. Covalent compounds will be the topic for Chapter 35.

The two theories of ionization presented in this chapter present two basic ideas, (1) that electrolytes dissociate, and (2) that these dissociation products carry electrical charges. These *electrically charged atoms or groups of atoms are called* **ions.** This chapter presents examples of the basic facts which led to these conclusions.

THE DISSOCIATION OF ELECTROLYTES

There are several properties of solutions that depend upon the *number* of particles present *rather than the chemical nature of* these particles. These properties include the lowering of the freezing point, the lowering of the vapor pressure, the elevation of the boiling point, and the osmotic pressure of solutions. Solutions of covalent compounds all exhibit the same effects on these properties, when the same number of molecules of the compounds are dissolved in a given volume of water. However, when the same number of molecules of electrolytes are dissolved in the same volume of water, the effects on the above properties are all higher than attained by the covalent solutions.

The above principle may be illustrated by reference to just one of these properties of solutions, the lowering of the freezing point. The use of antifreeze for the water in the cooling system of automobiles is an example of the lowering of the freezing point by adding a solute to water. The amount of antifreeze to be added to a given amount of water depends upon how much one desires to lower the freezing point. Such covalent compounds as denatured alcohol or glycerine have been used as antifreezes. The choice of an antifreeze depends upon the volatility and the cost of the substance to be used. Alcohol is relatively cheap, but it is volatilized at the temperature of the water in a radiator, and hence must be replaced from time to time. The time for this replacement cannot be readily ascertained by the average person. Glycerine is more expensive but it is not volatile. Various covalent compounds have been used as antifreezes, but regardless of their nature, the lowering of the freezing point is always the same when they are used in the same molecular concentrations. Furthermore, the amount of the lowering of the freezing point is in direct proportion to the number of molecules of the antifreeze solute present in a given volume of water.

Why not add a salt to the radiator water? Any acid, base, or salt would lower the freezing point of water, but unfortunately such compounds would act on the metals in contact with them. Otherwise, such compounds would be excellent for use as an antifreeze, because they lower the freezing point of water more than would such compounds as alcohol or glycerine. Common salt is often used to lower the freezing point of water for other purposes, such as melting ice or snow on walks, or the lowering of the freezing point of water for freezing ice cream. Common salt would lower the freezing point of a given amount of water twice as much as would the same number of molecules of alcohol or glycerine. Other salts, such as calcium chloride, would lower the freezing point of water three times as much as would be expected. Aluminum chloride would lower the freezing point four times as much as covalent compounds would, molecule for molecule. In fact, all electrolytes produce similar irregularities in solutions.

The explanation of the above irregularities of solutions of electrolytes was not at once apparent to early workers. To you, who have already been introduced to the theory of ionization, the explanation is obvious. Since the regularities of solutions depend upon the number of particles present, the irregularities, i.e., the abnormally large effects, must be due to the presence of more particles which behave like molecules in their effects on the properties of solutions. The additional particles could only have been produced by the *splitting* (**dissociation**) *of the molecules of electrovalent compounds into two or more particles, consisting of either atoms or groups of atoms.*

THE CHEMICAL PROPERTIES OF ELECTROLYTES

Many chemical properties of electrolytes indicate that they dissociate in water solution.

For example, solutions of all sodium salts, when placed on a platinum wire and held in a flame, impart a yellow color to the flame. Again, solutions of all soluble chlorides of the metals, such as sodium chloride or calcium chloride, form a white precipitate of silver chloride when a silver nitrate solution is added. In each of the above examples it must be that the salts dissociate to produce particles having identical properties.

All solutions of acids exhibit such similar properties as a sour taste or the ability to dissolve certain metals, which indicate the presence of a common constituent. An examination of the composition of acids shows that only one element, hydrogen, is common to all of them. It must be that acids dissociate to form particles or ions of hydrogen.

Bases likewise show similarities in properties, such as a slippery feeling or a bitter taste. An examination of the composition of bases shows that hydroxyl radicals are the only common constituents. A **radical** is a *group of elements which act as a unit.* It has an excess or deficiency of electrons which thus give it a negative or positive charge. A hydroxyl radical is composed of one hydrogen atom and one oxygen atom, with one extra electron, giving the hydroxyl radical or ion one negative charge. It must be that bases dissociate to form hydroxyl radicals.

THE SPEEDS OF CHEMICAL REACTIONS BETWEEN SOLUTIONS OF ELECTROLYTES

Reactions involving covalent compounds are quite slow as a rule. For example, the chemical reactions involved in the cooking of foods and in their digestion are quite slow because they involve organic, covalent compounds such as sugars, starches, fats, and proteins.

It is a characteristic of the chemical reactions between solutions of acids, bases, and salts that they take place almost instantaneously. For example, the addition of washing soda to hard water forms a white precipitate at once. Again, the addition of vinegar to ammonia water will neutralize both of them in an instant.

The explanation of these differences in the speeds of chemical reactions for covalent and electrovalent compounds is that the slow steps in chemical reactions are the disruptions of the chemical bonds typical of covalent compounds. Ionic compounds, on the other hand, dissociate when dissolved in water so that the only reactions involved are the joining of these dissociation products to form ionic compounds.

THE HEAT OF NEUTRALIZATION

Every chemical reaction involves an energy change, which may be expressed in terms of the amount of heat which is gained or lost in the reaction. *When equivalent amounts of acids and bases react with each other, the amount of heat,* called the **heat of neutralization,** *is always the same.* This fact is explained by the assumption that the reaction in each case is identical, and that it is the reaction of the hydrogen of an acid with the hydroxyl radical of a base to form water.

VOLTA'S CHEMICAL CELL

Alessandro Volta (1745–1827), professor of physics at the University of Paris, was a distinguished investigator. Volta discovered that when two metals, similar to those used by Galvani, made contact between his mouth and his eye, he experienced the sensation of light. He noticed the formation of a bitter taste when a copper coin and a gold coin were placed on opposite sides of his tongue and were connected with a wire. From these results, he arrived at the conclusion that these effects were produced by the two metals. He showed that a frog's leg would twitch when touched with two wires heated unequally, and thus laid the foundation for the thermocouple. In 1800, Volta invented the Voltaic pile, which consisted of a series of little disks of zinc, copper, and paper moistened with water or brine, and placed upon each other in the order named. He also produced the "crown of cups," which consisted of a series of vessels filled with brine or dilute acid, each of which contained a strip of zinc and copper. Thus, Volta provided the first source of continuous electric current, the chemical cell.

CELL ACTION

Volta's chemical cell led to a great deal of research to produce better and longer-lasting cells and batteries. Two different metals in contact with an acid, base, or salt in solution will produce an electric current if the metals are connected by a conductor. The electromotive force of the cell, expressed in volts, depends upon the differences between the electrode potentials as shown in Table 29-2.

To produce an electric current, some form of energy must be converted into electrical energy, in order to maintain the current. In the cell, the source of the current is chemical energy. The stream of electrons flows between two metals when they are placed in a solution that conducts the electric current, if they are connected with a conductor outside of the cell, because the metals differ in their affinity for electrons. One metal gives up electrons and, in the process, goes into solution, while another metal in solution accepts electrons and goes out of solution. It is this chemical change that supplies the energy for the production of the electric current. A cell can continue to furnish an electric current as long as the necessary chemical reactants are present, unless *a non-conducting layer of gas or other reaction product causes a decrease in current. This non-conducting layer is said to polarize the electrode.*

The common dry cell, shown in Figure 32-1, consists of zinc and carbon electrodes in contact with moist ammonium chloride. **Polariza-**

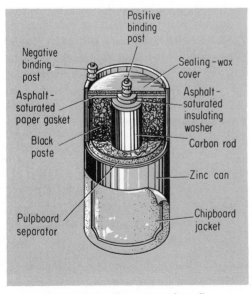

Figure 32-1. The common dry cell.

Positive binding post

Negative binding post

Sealing-wax cover

Asphalt-saturated paper gasket

Asphalt-saturated insulating washer

Black paste

Carbon rod

Zinc can

Pulpboard separator

Chipboard jacket

tion of the carbon electrode is prevented by surrounding the electrode with manganese dioxide, which oxidizes the hydrogen gas as fast as it is formed, and thus prevents it from forming a polarizing layer on the carbon.

ELECTRICAL CONDUCTIVITY

From the time of the original discovery of the production of current electricity by chemical cells, many workers observed that solutions of acids, bases, and salts would conduct an electric current, while solutions of covalent compounds such as sugar or alcohol would not conduct an electric current. A simple experiment to demonstrate the electrical conductivity of solutions of acids, bases, and salts is shown in Figure 32-2. If the light bulb glows the solution is a conductor. The intensity of the light is a measure of the relative conductivities of the solutions. It will be found that water solutions of all strong acids and bases, and salts, with a few rare exceptions, will conduct the electric current, but that solutions of weak acids and weak bases are poor conductors. Solutions of salts are good conductors.

FARADAY'S EXPERIMENTS WITH ELECTROLYSIS

Michael Faraday, around 1835, conducted a series of experiments on the electrical conductivity of solutions of acids, bases, and salts.

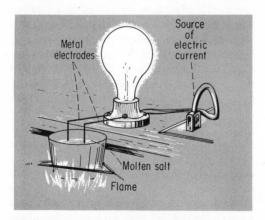

Figure 32–2. The glowing lamp indicates that a molten salt is a good electrical conductor. If the molten salt is replaced with a solution of an acid, base, or salt, the light will also glow.

He also experimented with the conductivity of molten salts, and found that they were good conductors. It thus became apparent that water need not be present to cause a salt to conduct an electric current. In fact, melting a salt seems to have the same effect as dissolving a salt in water.

Faraday observed that the passage of an electric current in a solution, unlike the conduction of an electric current by a metallic conductor, always resulted in a chemical reaction in the solution, in which the solute compound was decomposed.

Faraday introduced the term, **electrolyte,** *for acids, bases, and salts because their solutions in water were electrical conductors.* He called *the decomposition of the electrolyte due to the passage of an electric current,* **electrolysis.** Electrolysis is *the opposite of cell action.* Cells produce an electric current by the chemical reaction of electrolytes with electrodes, whereas in *electrolysis an electric current is used to produce a chemical reaction at the electrodes.* For example, when a direct current is passed through a solution of hydrogen iodide, hydrogen will be liberated at the negative electrode and iodine will be liberated at the positive electrode. Faraday found that water could be decomposed into hydrogen and oxygen by passing an electric current through a weak solution of sulfuric acid in water. He also found that the passage of an electric current through the solutions of salts of certain metals would cause the metal in question to deposit as a bright plate on one electrode. The same electric current will carry out all three of the above examples of electrolysis if the cells are connected in series, as shown in Figure 32-3.

FARADAY'S LAWS

Michael Faraday formulated the laws named in his honor to express the facts of electrolysis as follows: *(1) the quantity of a substance set free at the electrodes is proportional to the amount of electricity passed, and (2) the same amount of electricity liberates chemically equivalent weights of different substances.* These laws thus express a quantitative relationship between electricity and chemical change.

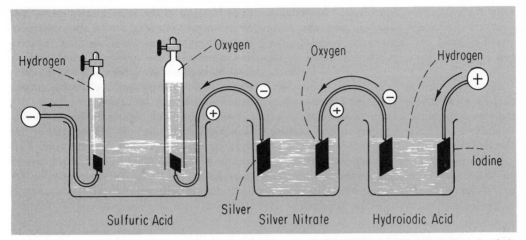

Figure 32–3. An illustration of Faraday's law. A definite quantity of electricity passing through each of the solutions liberates chemically equivalent amounts of iodine, hydrogen, oxygen, and silver at the different electrodes.

During electrolysis, positive ions migrate to the *negative pole* (**cathode**); the negative ions migrate to the *positive pole* (**anode**).

A storage battery is an example of both cell action and electrolysis. Cell action furnishes the electric current, and the battery is charged by electrolysis. The lead-acid storage battery, one cell of which is shown in Figure 32-4, contains an anode of lead and a cathode of lead dioxide, which react with sulfuric acid when producing an electric current to yield lead sulfate at each electrode, using up sul-

furic acid in the process. When the battery is charged the process is reversed.

ARRHENIUS' THEORY OF ELECTROLYTIC DISSOCIATION

In 1887, Svante Arrhenius proposed what is known as **the theory of ionization, or electrolytic dissociation.** According to his theory, *molecules of electrolytes dissociate in water solution to form atoms or groups of atoms, which are electrically charged and*

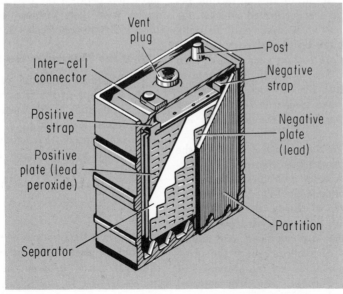

Figure 32–4. A typical storage cell. If several cells are connected together the result is a storage battery.

carry the current in electrolysis. The metallic ions are positively charged, and the non-metallic ions are negatively charged, the charge on the ion being proportional to its valence.

Electrolytes whose solutions are poor conductors of electricity are called **weak electrolytes,** and *those whose solutions are good conductors of electricity* are called **strong electrolytes.**

Arrhenius considered that weak electrolytes are dissociated to a small extent and that an equilibrium existed between the undissociated molecules and the dissociation products.

THE DEBYE-HÜCKEL THEORY

Peter Joseph Wilhelm Debye and E. Hückel, in 1923, proposed their interionic attraction theory of electrolytic dissociation. Because of the electrical charges carried by ions in solution, there is an attraction between them, despite the fact that water acts as an insulator and is quite effective in minimizing this attraction. As one would expect, the attraction between the ions in a solution decreases rapidly with increasing distance between them. In quite dilute solutions the distance between the ions is so great that there is very little attraction between them. However, in concentrated solutions, this attraction is considerable. As a result of this attraction between the ions in a concentrated solution, the solute behaves as if it were only partially ionized. The **Debye-Hückel theory** *proposes that electrolytes are 100 per cent ionized, even in solids, and that interionic attraction in solutions accounts for the fact that concentrated solutions and weak electrolytes behave as if only a portion of the molecules are dissociated.*

In addition to the attraction between the ions of strong electrolytes there is an attraction between the water molecules and the ions which has a pronounced effect in concentrated solutions. There is reason to believe that nearly all positive ions are **hydrated** in solution, i.e., *that they are combined with one or more molecules of water.* Perhaps the properties of ions in solution are the properties of hydrated ions. Perhaps, also, concentrated solutions do not have sufficient water present

to hydrate all of the ions. In any event, both concentrated solutions and weak electrolytes are not well understood. When more information concerning the nature of electrolytes in solution becomes available a more satisfactory theory of ionization may replace the present theories. All salts are considered to be 100 per cent dissociated even in the form of solids. However, acids are not dissociated within their molecules. It must be that they form ions in a water solution by a different process than in the case of the ionization of salts. The next chapter will explain this peculiarity of acids.

SUMMARY

The Theories of Ionization

1. Arrhenius' Theory—(1) molecules of electrolytes dissociate in water solution. (2) The dissociation products are electrically charged ions. (3) The *metallic ions* (**cations**) *are positively charged and travel to the cathode; the nonmetallic ions* (**anions**) *are negatively charged and travel to the anode in electrolysis.* (4) The number of positive charges on the cations is just equal to the number of negative charges on the anions. (5) The charge on an ion is proportional to the valence of the ion.

2. The Debye-Hückel Theory—There is an attraction between the ions in solution which varies with their distance apart. Ions combine with water molecules in solution.

What the Theories of Ionization Explain

1. Abnormal properties of solutions, such as the lowering of the freezing point.
2. Similarities in the chemical properties of acids, bases, and salts.
3. Rapid speeds of reaction for electrolytes.
4. Heat of neutralization—always the same.
5. Electrical properties of solutions.
    (1) Electrical conductivity
    (2) Cell action
    (3) Electrolysis

Cell action is the opposite of electrolysis. Cells produce an electric current as a result of the chemical action between the electrodes and the electrolyte. In electrolysis, a chemical reaction is produced at the electrodes due to the passage of an electric current between them.

Faraday's Laws

1. The quantity of a substance set free at the electrodes is proportional to the amount of electricity passed.

2. The same amount of electricity liberates chemically equivalent weights of different substances.

Study Questions

1. DEFINE: electrolyte, hydrated ion, strong electrolyte, radical, electrolysis, polarization, dissociation, ionization, cathode, anode, cation, anion, non-electrolyte, weak electrolyte.
2. What two types of phenomena does the theory of electrolytic dissociation explain?
3. What types of compounds are electrolytes?
4. Outline briefly the main points of Arrhenius' theory of electrolytic dissociation.
5. How did Arrhenius explain the fact that solutions of some electrolytes conduct the current better than solutions of other electrolytes?
6. What do solutions of all acids have in common?
7. What are the characteristic ions of bases?
8. Differentiate between strong and weak electrolytes.
9. What are the irregularities of solutions of electrolytes?
10. What determines the charge on an ion?
11. How do covalent compounds differ from electrolytes?
12. In what regards does the Debye-Hückel theory differ from Arrhenius' theory?
13. Explain the action of a dry cell.
14. Explain the action of a lead-acid storage battery.
15. Why may electrolysis be considered to be the opposite of cell action?
16. What is required to make an electric cell?
17. How can one predict the voltage of a given cell?
18. Outline the evidence for the dissociation of electrolytes.
19. Outline the evidence for the charges carried by ions.
20. State Faraday's laws.

Water and Its Ions—
Proton Chemistry

When you call a thing mysterious, all that it means is that you don't understand it.

LORD KELVIN

INTRODUCTION

This chapter deals with a special kind of chemistry which depends upon the unique properties of the hydrogen atom and of water. It deals with acids and bases, neutralization, and hydrolysis, which have many applications in everyday life. Fundamentally, acids and bases owe their properties to the transfer of protons.

HYDRONIUM IONS

Before the discovery of the electrical nature of matter, the class of substances known as acids was recognized by the properties common to all acids. Thus an **acid** is *a substance whose water solution (1) has a sour taste, (2) changes certain substances called indicators to develop a color different from that shown with bases, (3) neutralizes bases (i.e., reacts with bases in such a way that the properties of both the acid and base disappear), (4) reacts with the more active metals, such as sodium and calcium, to produce hydrogen gas.*

Acids are familiar in everyday life. Citrus fruits taste sour, because of the presence of citric acid; tartaric acid imparts tartness to grapes; acetic acid is the acid in vinegar; muriatic acid (hydrochloric acid) is used to clean metal surfaces for soldering and to dissolve cement and mortar spots on brick and tile; hydrochloric acid is present in the

gastric juice, and accounts for the sour taste of regurgitated stomach content. It has been noted that ionized hydrogen is the one substance that is common to all acids, so it is only natural to attribute the acid properties to ionized hydrogen.

According to the theory of ionization, an **acid** is *a solution containing hydronium ions.* The properties of acids were formerly ascribed to the presence of hydrogen ions in their solutions. The modern theory, presented in this text, differs from the above theory, in that it ascribes the properties of acids to **hydronium ions,** *which,* as already pointed out, *are considered to be formed by the combining of hydrogen ions with water molecules.* The hydrogen compounds which react with water to form hydronium ions are also termed acids, although they might better be called acid formers. Hydrogen chloride is an acid former. It will react with water to form hydrochloric acid, because it furnishes protons which combine with water to form hydronium ions.

AN ACID IS A PROTON DONOR

Acids react with the active metals, such as sodium, which are above hydrogen in the electromotive force series. In such reactions, the metal gives up an electron to the hydronium ion, which thus forms hydrogen gas and water. Acids will react with ammonia to form an ammonium salt. This reaction is one in which the hydronium ion has contributed a proton to the ammonia molecule.

Acids react with bases to form salts. For example, when hydrochloric acid reacts with sodium hydroxide, the salt, sodium chloride, is formed; but this represents no change insofar as the salt is concerned because its sodium and chloride ions were already present in the acid and base. The reason the acid reacted with the base was that the hydronium ion of the acid gave up a proton to the hydroxyl ion of the base to produce water. Inasmuch as this property of giving up protons to other substances is characteristic of acids only, **acids** are called *proton donors.*

BASES ARE PROTON ACCEPTORS

Bases *have a bitter taste and a slippery feeling. The most characteristic property of bases is that they will neutralize acids.* As mentioned above, *the basic chemical reaction involved in* **neutralization** *is the donation of protons by hydronium ions to hydroxyl ions to form water.* In this reaction the base accepts protons, and *any substance which will accept protons* is called a **base.** In the above reactions, ammonia and hydroxyl ions accepted protons. However, common usage restricts the term, base, to one kind of proton accepter only—the hydroxyl ion.

NEUTRALIZATION

A study of all reactions in which acids neutralize bases and vice versa indicates that the same reaction takes place in each case regardless of the chemical composition of the acids and bases. This reaction is the one mentioned above in which hydronium ions donate protons to hydroxyl ions to form water.

HYDROLYSIS

Whenever a substance reacts with water otherwise than by simple addition, the process is called **hydrolysis.** One type of hydrolysis, restricted to covalent compounds, is the action of water with such substances as proteins or starches to form simpler substances, such as amino acids or sugars.

In electrovalent chemistry, **hydrolysis** *is the action of water with salts of weak acids and/or bases to form acids and bases. The process is the reverse of neutralization,* and the only reason that it can take place is that either the hydroxyl ions of the ionized water combine with metallic ions to form a slightly ionized base, or the hydronium ions of the ionized water combine with the nonmetallic ions to form a slightly ionized acid.

Applications of Hydrolysis

Baking powders are mixtures of sodium bicarbonate with a salt which will hydrolyze to produce an acid solution. The newly formed acid then reacts with the sodium bicarbonate to form carbon dioxide. Starch may be added to keep the mixture dry in order to prevent the desired reaction from taking place before it is required. The carbon dioxide produced in this reaction raises the *biscuit.* Baking soda is often added to sour milk in making biscuit. In this case, the lactic acid in the sour milk replaces the acid-forming salt in a baking powder. Pancakes are often made with this sour milk-baking soda reaction.

Soap, and such detergents as borax, trisodium phosphate, and sodium carbonate (washing soda) owe their detergent action in part to the basic properties of their water solutions. These substances are salts of strong bases and weak acids and therefore hydrolyze to form basic solutions.

Certain substances, called **buffers,** are very important in *maintaining a nearly constant hydronium ion concentration in the human body.* An excess of hydronium ions in the body results in disorders which are generally described as acidosis or hyperacidity. A deficiency of hydronium ions, or an excess of hydroxyl ions, may result in alkalosis or hypoacidity. *Buffer substances must be able to neutralize both acids and bases.* Disodium phosphate is a good buffer substance: inasmuch as it is an acid salt, it will neutralize bases, and inasmuch as it will accept protons, it will neutralize acids.

Baking soda is an excellent buffer substance; it will react with acids and is therefore often taken internally to relieve acid indigestion. Baking soda acts as an acid because it is an acid salt; and it acts as a base because it accepts protons to form a weak acid, carbonic acid. Because carbonic acid is a very unstable compound, it rapidly breaks down to form water and carbon dioxide.

Proteins are capable of reacting with either acids or bases and thus act as buffers, but inasmuch as they are altered somewhat in these reactions and also because they are the substances from which living tissue is made, it is obvious that this reserve should not be overworked.

THE PECULIAR PROPERTIES OF HYDROGEN

Hydrogen does not fit well into the periodic table. In some respects it behaves like a metal, but it will combine with metals. When combined with nonmetals, the resulting compounds are not salts and they are not electrovalent.

The peculiar properties of hydrogen are due to its structure. In the first place, ordinary hydrogen with an atomic weight of 1 is the only element that does not have a neutron in its nucleus. Its nucleus consists of a proton only. The hydrogen atom has only one positive charge on its nucleus and therefore it has a very limited ability to attract and hold electrons, although that is what takes place when it combines with metals. Unlike the metals, hydrogen does not usually give up electrons in chemical reactions, but, instead, it shares pairs of electrons and it is therefore covalent.

The hydrogen molecule consists of two protons and two electrons. The two atoms of hydrogen are held together by the sharing of electrons and, as a result, hydrogen gas is covalent in nature. It appears that the electrons in the hydrogen molecule are readily shared with other atoms.

WATER, A REMARKABLE COMPOUND

The water molecule is composed of one oxygen atom in combination with two hydrogen atoms. The hydrogen atoms share electrons with the oxygen atom and there is no reason why one hydrogen atom should differ from another in this regard. Nevertheless, some hydrogen atoms do give up their electrons to the oxygen and combine with water molecules to form hydronium ions. For every hydronium ion thus produced one hydroxyl ion is also produced.

The water molecule appears to be polar in nature. In other words, the two hydrogen nuclei are partially exposed at one end of the molecule and give this end a partial positive charge, while the oxygen at the other end is surrounded by an excess of electrons which give this end of the molecule a partial negative charge. It is the polarity of the water molecule that enables it to combine with protons to form hydronium ions. There is always an equilibrium between the water, the hydronium ions, and the hydroxyl ions. If the hydronium ion concentration is decreased the hydroxyl ion concentration automatically increases. At the neutral point, the concentrations of the hydronium and hydroxyl ions are equal. An acid solution has an excess of hydronium ions, and a basic solution has an excess of hydroxyl ions.

The concentration of the hydronium ions is expressed in pH. pH 7 is neutral; any value higher than pH 7 is alkaline, and any value lower than pH 7 is acid.

The measurement of hydronium ion concentration, and the maintenance of its concentration within fixed limits, are of importance in many industries. For example, water purification by coagulation and filtration, certain types of sewage disposal methods, the corrosion of boilers, the bleaching, laundering, and dyeing of textiles, the manufacture of gelatine, and the preparation of certain drugs are only a few cases in which success depends on careful regulation of the hydronium-ion concentration. Certain plants grow best in basic soils, others grow best in acid soils, and bacterial cultures must have just the right hydronium-ion concentration for growth.

INDICATORS

Certain dyes are proton donors. If there are already many hydronium ions in a solution, the dye will not give up its protons, but, as the hydronium-ion concentration decreases, the dye gives up more and more protons and its color becomes changed as a result. *Such dyes are called* **indicators,** *because they in-*

dicate changes in the concentration of hydronium ions in solution. Thus the color of methyl orange is pink in an acid solution but yellow in a basic solution. The neutral point is taken as that point just before the production of the basic color. Many of the dyes in nature are weak proton donors. Thus the color of tea is changed when acid (lemon juice) is added. Grape juice is purple in color but changes to a green color when the acid is neutralized. The compounds which are responsible for the colors in wines, vinegar, purple cabbage, and many flowers are indicators. The colors in your clothes may be changed by adding acids, and if the acid is neutralized quickly enough, the original colors may often be restored.

DETERGENTS

Detergents are *substances that have cleansing properties similar to those of soaps.* Any detergent owes its properties to its ability to form films on the surfaces of certain materials which cause them to remain in suspension in water. Today, soaps are manufactured by a process in which strong bases, such as sodium or potassium hydroxide, react with animal or vegetable fats and oils. The fat or oil is a compound of glycerine with an organic fatty acid. In the soap-making reaction, sodium or potassium atoms replace the glycerine, which is therefore a by-product of soap making. One end of the long soap molecule is virtually insoluble in water, but it is attracted by fats and oils. The other end of the molecule exhibits a strong tendency to dissolve in water. It is because of this fact that soap is a good detergent. The dirt most common in our experience is largely composed of particles of dark-colored solids mixed with oils or fats. When soap is used as a cleaning agent, its double-ended molecules get into action, the fatty acid ends of the soap molecules attaching themselves to the dirt-bearing oils, leaving the water-soluble ends exposed to the water, as shown in Figure 33-1.

Soaps have the disadvantages that they hydrolyze in water to form basic solutions, and that the negative fatty acid ions form insoluble compounds in hard water that contains positive calcium, magnesium, and iron ions. Detergents do not have these disadvantages. They do not form insoluble compounds with the

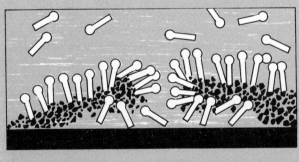

The detergent molecules line up on the surface of the dirt particles, with their water-repelling ends projecting into the water. The dirt may be dislodged by mechanical action.

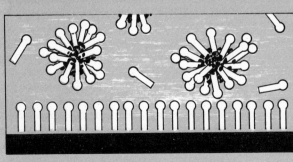

The dirt is held suspended in the solution because the detergent molecules surround them. The detergent molecules also form a protective layer on the surface of the material from which the dirt was removed.

Figure 33–1.   The function of a detergent in removing dirt.

ions which cause hardness in water. Some detergents have a foaming action, but they do not owe their cleansing action to the foams, which cause problems in sewage disposal plants, so there is a trend toward the use of non-foaming detergents. Some detergents resist decomposition by bacteria and go through the usual sewage treatment without being decomposed. They may seep through the soil and contaminate water supplies, or their presence in effluents from sewage treatment plants may cause difficulties. A great deal of research has been devoted to the development of detergents that will be decomposed by bacteria.

HARDNESS OF WATER

Hardness of water *refers to the formation of insoluble curds with soap, due to the presence of certain soluble salts.* With hard water, soap has no cleansing action until enough soap has been added to precipitate all of these objectionable salts. There are two objections to the use of soap to soften water; (1) soap is more expensive than other water softeners, and (2) the curds formed get into the hair and are difficult to rinse out; they form rings on bathtubs; and they get into the clothing and gradually cause it to have a dirty appearance.

There are two kinds of hardness, temporary and permanent. **Temporary hardness** is *removed from water by boiling* it, while **permanent hardness** *cannot be removed by boiling.* Boiling is not a satisfactory method of removing temporary hardness, because the precipitates deposited form a scale that clings tightly to a teakettle, boiler tube, or hot water tank. This scale acts as an insulator and thus causes an increase in fuel bills. Eventually, the scale may become so thick that pipes may become clogged and boiler explosions may be caused.

Temporary hardness *is caused by the presence of bicarbonates of calcium and magnesium in water.* Carbon dioxide will dissolve in water, and the resulting solution will react with limestone, which contains carbonates of calcium or magnesium, forming the soluble bicarbonates.

Permanent hardness *is caused by soluble compounds of calcium, magnesium, iron, and manganese, other than the bicarbonates which cause temporary hardness.* These salts are usually chlorides or sulfates. Wherever water is evaporated, as in boilers, these salts deposit and cause the formation of scale.

In regions where underground or surface water is in contact with limestone the water may be very hard. Large manufacturing plants usually require soft water for their boilers and for other purposes, and frequently a supply of relatively soft water may determine the location of a plant.

WATER SOFTENING

Water may be softened by removing the soluble compounds of calcium, magnesium, and iron by various methods as follows:

1. *Distillation*—Salts which cause hardness may be removed by distillation.

2. *Precipitation* with Such Compounds as Washing Soda (Sodium Carbonate)—Washing soda has been the traditional water softener for home use. It has been used as such or it has been added to soaps and soap powders. It has the disadvantages that it reacts with water to form a fairly alkaline solution and it forms precipitates which are objectionable.

3. The Use of *Sequestering Agents.* Several compounds such as borax, or one of the complex polyphosphates, combine with the objectionable salts in hard water to **sequester** them, i.e., *to react with the salts to form complex compounds which will not react with soap.* Such compounds are mild cleaning agents themselves. More than a billion pounds of these polyphosphate compounds are used annually in the United States in making common industrial and household detergent mixtures.

4. The Use of *Ion Exchangers*—For many homes, the installation of water softeners that soften all of the water used in the home seems to be the best solution to the hard-water problem. Such water softeners employ the same principle as that used in many large-scale industrial installations, i.e., the use of **ion exchangers. An ion-exchanging material** *is a compound, such as a mineral called zeolite, or a modern plastic, which will remove the objectionable ions from water and replace* *them with sodium ions which are not objectionable.* For home use, such an ion exchanger may consist of two tanks, one to hold the ion-exchanging material and the other to hold a solution of salt water. When an ion exchanger has been exhausted, i.e., when it has exchanged all of its sodium ions for objectionable ions, the ion-exchanging material may be renewed by passing salt water through it. Because of the high concentration of the sodium ions in the salt water, they displace the ions of calcium, magnesium, iron, and manganese, which are flushed down the sewer.

5. *The Use of Deionizers*—Deionizers *are plastics which will adsorb either positive or negative ions.* By using a mixture of plastics all of the ions may be removed. Deionizers differ from ion exchangers in that they do not return any metallic ions to the water.

WATER PURIFICATION

Many cities depend upon fresh-water lakes or rivers for their water supply. Smaller communities may obtain their water from deep wells, but the supply of ground water is not adequate for large cities. This well water is generally used without any treatment, except the addition of chlorine to kill any bacteria that may have resulted from the possible contamination of the ground water by sewage.

River and lake water generally contains suspended impurities such as mud, organic impurities which may cause objectionable odors or taste, bacteria, and algae. A typical water purification plant would start out by pumping the water into large settling tanks. At this point, chemicals such as aluminum sulfate and lime may be added to produce flocs, i.e., jelly-like precipitates that remove most of the suspended matter as they settle out. The water may now be passed through beds of sand, which filter out any remaining suspended impurities, including most of the bacteria. Chlorine is generally added to the final product to kill any remaining harmful bacteria.

SEWAGE TREATMENT

Sewage treatment is somewhat similar to water purification. In fact, where water sup-

plies such as rivers or lakes have been contaminated with sewage, their treatment amounts to the same thing as the treatment of dilute sewage. Sewage can be purified so well that the water obtained could be used for human consumption. Increasing demands for water may make it desirable to recover the large amounts of water that are lost in the form of sewage.

There are many methods of treating sewage. Most of them depend upon bacterial action to decompose the organic matter present. The resulting product may be settled and filtered to remove suspended matter. The effluent is then treated with chlorine to kill any harmful bacteria present. Further treatment with activated carbon would remove any remaining objectionable color, odor, or taste.

Dumping sewage into rivers, lakes or oceans, should no longer be tolerated by modern civilized society. One of the noteworthy differences between backward peoples and modern civilizations is the way in which they handle the disposal of sewage.

SUMMARY

Water ionizes to a very small extent to form hydronium ions and hydroxyl ions. There is an equilibrium between water and its ions. The hydronium ion concentration may be expressed as pH. The pH of a solution may be shown by indicators, which change color at a given pH.

Acids owe their properties to hydronium ions; they are proton donors. Bases owe their properties to hydroxyl ions; they are proton accepters.

Neutralization is the reaction of an acid with a base to produce a salt and water. Hydrolysis is the opposite of neutralization.

There are two kinds of hardness of water, temporary and permanent hardness. Temporary hardness may be removed by boiling. Permanent hardness may be removed by distillation, precipitation, complexion formation, ion exchangers, and deionizers.

Study Questions

1. DEFINE: acid, base, neutralization, hydrolysis, indicator, ion exchanger, deionizer, deter-

gent, temporary hardness permanent hardness, hydronium ion, buffer, sequester.

2. What are the differences between the two kinds of hardness in water? How is each type removed?

3. Explain the action of detergents.

4. What is the objection to the use of hard water in the home? How may it be softened for home use?

5. Why is sewage treatment important in modern civilizations?

6. How may the concentration of hydronium ions be measured and expressed?

7. What types of salts hydrolyze, and why?

8. Explain the action of baking powders.

9. Why do all soaps produce a basic reaction when they are dissolved in water?

10. What is a buffer substance? Give an example.

11. Explain the action of indicators.

12. Give two chemical properties of acids.

13. Give two chemical properties of bases.

Electrons in Chemical Changes

The greatest part of the affections (properties) of matter—seems to depend on the motion and the contrivance of the small parts of bodies.

ROBERT BOYLE

INTRODUCTION

It is now known that the elements differ in their tendency to release and accept electrons. A very important type of chemical reaction is based on the transfer of electrons from one substance to another. The electrochemical industry, battery action and cell action, the smelting of ores, the corrosion of metals, and many other important types of chemical changes are examples of the transfer of electrons.

This chapter deals with the chemical reactions which involve the transfer of electrons.

The electrons in atoms revolve about the nucleus in different shells depending upon their numbers and energies.

The simplest atom is the hydrogen atom in which an electron revolves about a proton. In the next shell the maximum number of electrons is eight. The majority of chemical reactions involving electrons depend upon the transfer of electrons or the sharing of pairs of electrons in such a way as to complete the possible number of electrons (eight) in the outer shell of an atom.

THE COMBINING CAPACITIES OF THE ELEMENTS

Valence *represents the number of atoms of a standard univalent element (hydrogen) that will combine with or are equivalent to one atom of a given element.* Thus the valence of

oxygen is 2 because it combines with two atoms of hydrogen to form water. The valence of aluminum is 3 because two atoms of aluminum combine with three atoms of oxygen, each of which has a valence of 2, to form aluminum oxide.

It has been found that the maximum valence exhibited by any element is 7. It was also observed early in the history of modern chemistry that metals have a greater tendency to react with nonmetals than with other metals. It was only natural for the expressions, metallic valence and nonmetallic valence, to come into general use. Later, these expressions were changed to positive $(+)$ and negative $(-)$ valence, respectively. The general conclusion was thus reached that molecules are formed by the combination of atoms of positive valence with atoms of negative valence and that the valence of each atom must be completely satisfied in each reaction.

THE ELECTRON THEORY OF VALENCE

The electron theory of valence was outlined in Chapter 29. It is reviewed again in this chapter to emphasize the role of electrons in chemical changes.

According to the electron theory of valence, the reactions between atoms are governed by the number of electrons in the outermost shells of the atoms. In certain types of reactions, the atoms of metals give up all of their outermost electrons to the atoms of nonmetals, and the nonmetals annex enough electrons to make the sum of eight in their outermost shells. As the result of this loss of electrons by the metals to become positively charged and the gain of electrons by the nonmetals to become negatively charged, the metals and nonmetals are attracted to each other to form compounds.

Elements which have fewer than four electrons in the outer shell tend to lose their electrons and thus become positively charged. Elements which have four electrons in the outer shell tend either to lose or gain these electrons. Elements having more than four electrons in the outer shell tend to gain electrons.

In many chemical reactions, there is no gain or loss, but rather a sharing of electrons. The compounds thus produced are called covalent compounds. Such compounds are the topic of the next chapter.

THE PROPERTIES OF THE ELEMENTS AND THEIR ELECTRONIC STRUCTURES

Some metals are good conductors of electricity; others are not. Some metals may be pulled out to form fibers smaller in diameter than that of spider-web filaments; other metals crumble readily. What causes these differences in the properties of the elements? According to the present theory of atomic structure, the

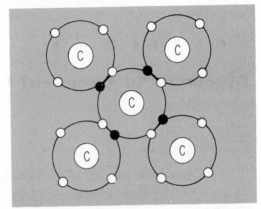

Figure 34–2. Carbon atoms share pairs of electrons.

differences in the properties of the elements are explained in terms of the differences in the number of electrons in the outermost shells of the atoms.

When there are eight electrons in the outermost shell, the atoms show no attraction for each other and will not combine with other atoms of the same kind or with atoms of different elements. The rare gases, helium, neon, argon, krypton, xenon, and radon, have eight electrons in their outside shells. Even the very heavy element, radon, is a gas. These gases consist of molecules which have only one atom to the molecule.

In contrast with the rare gases, carbon and silicon form by far the largest number of the known compounds of the elements with the exception of hydrogen. These atoms are assumed to have four electrons in the outer shell, and because of this fact they are the most gregarious of all of the elements. Four carbon atoms may cooperate, each sharing one of its outside electrons with one carbon atom, to produce an arrangement somewhat similar to the one shown in Figure 34-3. By cooperating, each atom is given a stable configuration. In the diamond, which is pure carbon, we see how well the carbon atoms have joined each other to form a very hard, compact, inert substance.

Silicon has an outside structure similar to that of carbon, and likewise forms hard crystals. Silicon will also combine with carbon to form the beautiful, very hard crystals of carborundum.

Silver has only one electron in the outer-

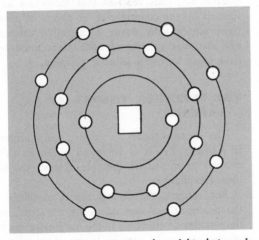

Figure 34–1. The argon atom has eight electrons in the outer layer. It does not react with other elements.

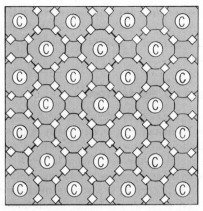

Figure 34–3. The carbon atoms in the diamond are arranged very compactly.

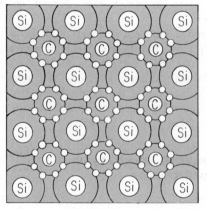

Figure 34–4. Each silicon atom is surrounded by four carbon atoms in carborundum. This is a stable arrangement.

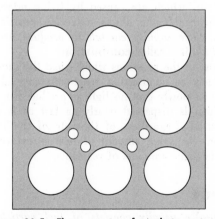

Figure 34–5. There are too few electrons to keep these metallic atoms in a rigid position. The electrons are mobile.

most shell. Seven other silver atoms would have to share their electrons to enable one silver atom to fill its level with eight electrons, but in the meantime each of these seven other atoms would require seven other atoms to complete their outer shells. It is thus apparent that there are not sufficient electrons to form a stable arrangement. Each atom has an attraction for other atoms, but there are fewer electrons to hold them together. Therefore, such elements as sodium, copper, and silver are quite soft, and conduct electricity readily because electrons are free to pass from one atom to another. Such metals can be pounded into very thin sheets and will combine readily with any element which has a greater affinity for electrons. A piece of hot copper foil, when placed in chlorine gas, bursts into flame because of the greediness of chlorine for electrons; inasmuch as each chlorine atom has seven electrons in its outer shell, it needs and takes an electron from a copper atom in order to obtain the stable arrangement of eight electrons in the outer shell.

Metals like magnesium, which have two outer electrons, and aluminum and iron, which have three outer electrons, show increasing hardness and decreasing electrical conductivity.

Nonmetals like nitrogen, oxygen, and chlorine—which have five, six, and seven electrons, respectively, in their outer shells—have too many electrons to form large stable groupings and exist as gases, containing only two atoms to the molecule.

TYPES OF ELECTRON TRANSFER REACTIONS

There are four important types of electron transfer reactions: decomposition, direct union, displacement, and oxidation-reduction.

(1) Decomposition

In general, **decomposition** refers to *the breaking down of one compound to form two or more simpler compounds or elements;* for example, mercuric oxide, when heated, gives mercury and oxygen. In this reaction mercury receives two electrons from oxygen.

(2) Direct Union

Direct union *is the opposite of decomposition;* for example, iron combines with oxygen in the presence of water to form iron oxide (rust). In this reaction iron gives up electrons to oxygen.

(3) Displacement

In **displacement** reactions, *one element displaces another element in a compound;* for example, iron will displace copper from a solution of an iron salt. In this reaction, iron gives up electrons to copper ions. It was observed early in the history of modern chemistry that the elements could be listed in the order in which they would displace each other from their compounds. Such a series of elements is shown in Table 29-2, page 220.

(4) Oxidation-Reduction

Oxidation-reduction *refers to a reaction in which there is a change in valence but no decomposition, direct union, or displacement.* All of these types of reactions involve a change in valence and are therefore oxidation-reduction reactions, but common usage limits the term oxidation-reduction to the type of reaction mentioned above.

When oxygen combines with any substance, the process is called **oxidation,** and *when oxygen is removed from a compound,* the process is called **reduction.** Thus the rusting of iron is oxidation because this process involves the combining of iron with oxygen to form iron oxide; oxygen is an example of an **oxidizing agent,** i.e., *a substance which gains electrons.* On the other hand, when iron ore is treated with coke in a blast furnace, the process is reduction, because the iron oxide is reduced to iron. Carbon (coke) is an example of a **reducing agent,** i.e., *a substance which furnishes electrons.* According to the **electron theory,** *changes in valence are the result of a loss or gain of electrons;* thus oxidation and reduction fundamentally involve a loss or gain of electrons by atoms or ions. Inasmuch as an increase in positive valence is oxidation and inasmuch as this change is accomplished by the loss of electrons, **oxidation** is the *loss of electrons* or **de-electronization,** as the process is sometimes called. **Reduction** must therefore be *a gain of electrons,* or **electronization.**

REDUCING REACTIONS

The separation of metals from their compounds in metallurgy is essentially a process of reduction, because electrons must be added to the metal in the compound to set it free. Hydrogen is an important reducing agent.

An electric current is a stream of electrons, and it may serve as a reducing agent. Sodium, aluminum, magnesium, and other metals which have a relatively poor attraction for electrons are best separated from their compounds by electrolysis, in which they deposit on the cathode.

Nonmetals have a relatively high attraction for electrons, but these elements may be separated from their compounds at the anode by electrolysis, because electrons are removed from substances at the anode. In electrolysis, reduction takes place at the cathode and oxidation takes place at the anode.

OXIDIZING REACTIONS— COMBUSTION

A log of wood will gradually decay as it lies on the ground in the forest, and it is eventually consumed, giving the same products and the same amount of heat as if it had been burned. All forms of decay are oxidation reactions which are caused by living microorganisms. *If the* above *oxidation reaction takes place rapidly enough to produce heat and light* it is called **combustion.**

Most of the reactions which yield the same products as combustion reactions may take place so slowly that no light is produced and the heat is dispersed nearly as fast as it is produced. Regardless of the rate of the reaction, the same amount of heat is evolved for the same amounts of reactants.

SMOKE

Smoke *usually consists of fuel particles which have not been oxidized.* When burning natural gas, gasoline, or coal, if the amount of air (oxygen) is not sufficient to completely oxidize the fuel, smoke will result. By decreasing the amount of air admitted to a gas burner a yellow flame and smoke will be produced. The yellow flame is due to luminous particles of unburned carbon.

SPONTANEOUS COMBUSTION

Sometimes the heat produced by decay accumulates *until a temperature is reached at which combustion takes place;* this temperature is called the **kindling temperature.** For example, a rag containing some oil such as linseed oil, which is easily oxidized, may start a fire. Linseed oil is used in paints because it will slowly combine with oxygen to form a tough, resistant coating. Such paints dry best when plenty of oxygen is available. If an oily rag is placed in a closet or some other place where *the heat produced by the oxidation* of the oil *will not diffuse away as rapidly as it is produced, the kindling temperature may be reached and a fire started;* such a process is called **spontaneous combustion.** Many fires are started by the spontaneous combustion of damp hay, paper, coal, and other organic materials.

An important factor in spontaneous combustion is that the speed of a chemical reaction *is roughly doubled or trebled for each ten-degree rise in the Celsius temperature.*

Thus, as the temperature rises, heat is given off more and more rapidly until the slow oxidation becomes rapid combustion.

Some substances are so active with oxygen that spontaneous combustion takes place in even the most exposed places. Thus, a lump of white phosphorus left on the table will start burning spontaneously. Certain other substances, having a higher kindling temperature, will ignite spontaneously only on unusually hot days. A hot piece of iron placed in the vapor of carbon disulfide will cause it to ignite. When grease is spilled on a hot stove lid, it ignites because its kindling temperature has been reached. The purpose of a match, used in lighting a fire, is to raise the temperature of a portion of a combustible material above the kindling temperature.

THE COMBUSTION OF GASES— FLAMES

Has it ever occurred to you as you watched the flames play over a burning log that the **flames** are merely *the result of the combustion of gases driven from the log by the heat of the fire?* A candle flame is produced by the burning of the vaporized wax after it has been melted and drawn up the wick.

EXPLOSIONS

Combustible gases or very finely divided dusts of combustible substances such as coal, cotton, flour, etc., when mixed with the proper amounts of air or oxygen, will explode violently if ignited. In such cases, the activation of a few molecules is quickly propagated throughout all the gas present by the increasing temperature due to combustion, the whole mass of material being oxidized almost instantaneously with the evolution of large volumes of gases.

FIRE EXTINGUISHERS

Water extinguishes fires by lowering the temperature of the burning material below its kindling temperature, and by shutting off the oxygen supply. The various types of more efficient fire extinguishers are based on the principle of smothering the fire by preventing an access of air (oxygen), just as a blanket wrapped around a person whose clothes are on fire will smother the flame.

The majority of fire extinguishers use carbon dioxide. One type of fire extinguisher, called the soda-acid type, consists of a fairly large cylinder containing a solution of sodium bicarbonate and a bottle of sulfuric acid. The acid pours into the baking soda solution when the cylinder is inverted, thus generating carbon dioxide. The carbon dioxide liberated in the above reaction produces a pressure that causes relatively large amounts of the carbon dioxide to dissolve in the solution and forces the resulting solution out through a nozzle to extinguish the fire. In the foam type of extinguisher, a licorice extract is added to the carbonate solution to produce

Sulfuric acid

Baking soda solution

Figure 34–6. The soda-acid fire extinguisher. When this fire extinguisher is tipped upside down, the acid runs out of the bottle and reacts with the baking soda to liberate carbon dioxide.

a foam, and alum replaces the sulfuric acid of the soda-acid type. The alum hydrolyzes, i.e., reacts with water, to produce sulfuric acid, which reacts with sodium bicarbonate to produce carbon dioxide. The carbon dioxide forms a foam which issues from the nozzle of the fire extinguisher and spreads over such burning materials as gasoline and liquid fuels to smother them.

Some very efficient fire extinguishers use liquid carbon dioxide, which produces carbon dioxide snow as it is sprayed on a fire and serves to smother (not cool) the fire by diluting the inflammable mixture of air and fuel. In another type of fire extinguisher, finely divided particles of magnesium carbonate, or sodium bicarbonate, are forced onto the fire with the pressure produced by liquid carbon dioxide or compressed nitrogen.

The vaporizing-liquid type of extinguisher contains carbon tetrachloride, which is forced onto the fire by a pump in the cylinder. Carbon tetrachloride forms a heavy vapor that smothers certain types of fires, such as oil and gasoline fires, quite efficiently if the vapors are confined over the surface of the fuel. However, the vapor is toxic and if used in a room where natural gas is burning it may form phosgene, a more poisonous gas.

SUMMARY

Electrovalent compounds are formed by chemical reactions in which there is a transfer of electrons. Such reactions include decomposition, direct union, displacement, and oxidation-reduction reactions.

Metals have less attraction for electrons than nonmetals. The fewer the number of electrons in the outside shell the greater is the tendency to give up electrons. The reverse is true of the nonmetals. The farther the outside electrons are from the nucleus the less tightly they are held.

Figure 34–7. The principle of the foam-type fire extinguisher. Note how the foam floats over the burning liquid and extinguishes the fire. (Courtesy, American La France and Foamite Industries)

TABLE 34-1

SUMMARY OF REDUCTION AND OXIDATION

Reduction	Oxidation
Loss of oxygen	Gain of oxygen
Gain of hydrogen	Loss of hydrogen
Decrease in positive valence	Increase in positive valence
Increase in negative valence	Decrease in negative valence
Addition of electrons (Electronization)	Loss of electrons (De-electronization)

Study Questions

1. DEFINE: oxidation, reduction, valence, electronization, de-electronization, reducing agent, oxidizing agent, combustion, spontaneous combustion, kindling temperature, flame, oxidation-reduction, decomposition, direct union, displacement, smoke.
2. What is the principle of fire extinguishers?
3. Explain why the maximum valence of an element is seven.
4. Differentiate between metallic and nonmetallic valence.
5. Explain why metals and nonmetals are attracted to each other in electrovalent compounds.
6. How can the fact that some elements exhibit more than one valence be explained?
7. Do metals tend to gain or lose electrons in chemical reactions?
8. Organic compounds are usually covalent compounds. What is meant by the term covalent?
9. Why are the rare gases so inactive?
10. Why are some metals more active than other metals?
11. What is the name of a series of metals listed in the order of their tendency to give up electrons?
12. Why do carbon and silicon form so many compounds?
13. Why are some metals better conductors of heat or electricity than other metals?
14. List the four types of electron-transfer reactions.
15. What is the fundamental nature of all oxidation-reduction reactions?
16. What is the cause of smoke?
17. How should a smoky gas burner be adjusted so as to eliminate the smoke?
18. What would be the result of adjusting an automobile carburetor so that the air-fuel mixture is richer in fuel?
19. What is combustion? Give two or three examples. How would you demonstrate it?

The Covalent Bond

It is no paradox to say that in our most theoretical moods we may be nearest to our most practical applications.

A. N. WHITEHEAD

INTRODUCTION

The two main fields of chemistry are inorganic and organic. At one time, it was considered that the compounds found in plants and animals could only be produced by living matter. In 1807, Jöns Jakob Berzelius called these compounds organic. *All compounds not produced by living organisms* he called **inorganic.** The first important milestone in the history of organic chemistry was the preparation of urea, a compound produced by animals, from an inorganic compound, ammonium cyanate, by F. Wöhler (1800–1882) in 1828. Soon other organic compounds were prepared in laboratories. The term **organic** continued, but it came to be used to *refer to the compounds of carbon because most of the compounds found in living matter are compounds of carbon.*

This chapter deals with carbon and the covalent bond that distinguishes carbon compounds from electrovalent compounds. It also describes the covalent nature of hydrogen, and the compounds consisting of carbon and hydrogen, the hydrocarbons, the basic structures on which organic compounds are built.

THE CHEMICAL BOND AND COVALENCE

In earlier days, the attraction between atoms which caused them to unite to form molecules was called chemical affinity. Today, this idea is now expressed by the chemical bond. The **chemical bond** is defined *as the attraction between atoms in a molecule.* This attraction may be in part electrical and in part magnetic. With the exception of the electrovalent acids, bases, and salts, all molecules are held together by the sharing of one or more pairs of electrons. **Covalence** refers to the *sharing of electron pairs between atoms.*

THE ELECTRONEGATIVITIES OF THE ELEMENTS

Table 35-1 lists the electronegativities of some of the more common elements. The **electronegativity** *of an element is a measure of its power of attraction, or "greediness," for electrons.* It may be measured by determining the amount of energy required to break a bond. An examination of this table will show that electronegativity is a periodic property of the elements.

The electronegativity increases from left to right in this table, and it decreases as one moves down in a given group. Actually, the table of electronegativities is similar to the table of ionization potentials shown on page 227 in that it indicates the relative attractions of the atoms for electrons. Atoms which have the greatest tendency to gain electrons are those which hold their electrons most firmly.

The greater the difference in electronegativity between two elements, the greater their attractions for each other will be and there-

TABLE 35-1

THE ELECTRONEGATIVITIES OF THE ELEMENTS
The numbers below the names are electronegativities

Group I	Group II	Group III	Group IV	Group V	Group VI	Group VII	Group VIII
Hydrogen							Helium
2.1							0
Lithium	Beryllium	Boron	Carbon	Nitrogen	Oxygen	Fluorine	Neon
1.0	1.5	2.0	2.5	3.0	3.5	4.0	0
Sodium	Magnesium	Aluminum	Silicon	Phosphorus	Silicon	Chlorine	Argon
0.9	1.2	1.5	1.8	2.1	2.5	3.0	0
Potassium	Calcium	Gallium	Germanium	Arsenic	Selenium	Bromine	Krypton
0.8	1.0	...	1.7	2.0	2.4	2.8	0
Rubidium	Strontium	Indium	Tin	Antimony	Tellurium	Iodine	Xenon
0.8	1.0	...	1.7	1.8	2.1	2.4	0
Cesium	Barium						
0.7	0.9						

Adapted from *Chemistry* by Sienko and Plane. 2nd. Ed., Copyright, 1961. McGraw-Hill Book Company. Used by permission.

fore the more likely they will be to react with each other to form ionic compounds. Elements far apart in the electronegativity table tend to form ionic compounds. For example, a compound of sodium and chlorine would be electrovalent. Elements with small differences in electronegativities will form covalent compounds.

POLAR AND NON-POLAR COVALENCE

As one goes across the table of electronegativities, it is evident that there is no sharp break, but there is a gradual transition from the tendency to form electrovalent bonds to the tendency to form covalent bonds. The terms polar and non-polar refer to the distribution of the charges within the molecule. **Non-polar compounds** *are strictly covalent compounds*, while **polar covalent compounds** *are in that no-man's-land between electrovalent and covalent compounds*.

When two or more atoms join to form molecules there is a redistribution of charges. *If the centers of charge distribution of each of the two kinds of charges coincide the molecule is said to be* **non-polar.** The **non-polar molecule** *is electrically neutral,* and it is not affected by an electric field. On the other hand, *if there is no common center, the molecule is said to be* **polar.** In **polar molecules,**

there will be centers of positive charge and centers of negative charge in different parts of the molecule.

Figure 35-1 shows the distributions of electrons in different kinds of solids. The clouds of fine lines represent the various paths of the electrons. The figure in the upper right hand corner depicts polar molecules, which are held together in solids by the weak forces between their centers of positive and negative charges.

The polar, covalent molecule does not dissociate into ions as does an electrovalent molecule, but it does show electrical properties when placed in an electric field. The farther the positive and negative centers are from each other within the molecule, the more polar they are.

WATER, A STRONGLY POLAR COMPOUND

When oxygen bonds to the other atoms in a covalent compound, an angle of slightly over 100 degrees is formed, as shown in Figure 35-2. The reason for this angle lies in the nature of the electronic structure of the oxygen atom; a further discussion of this reason is well beyond the scope of this text. The electrons shared between the two hydrogen atoms and the oxygen atom are not shared equally, i.e., the electrons spend a greater proportion of their time in the region of the

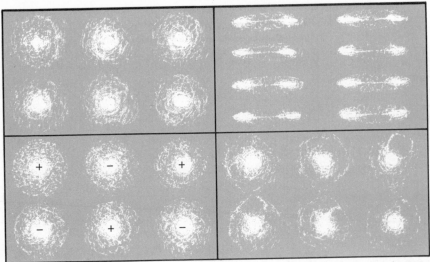

Figure 35–1. The arrangement of the atoms and their electrons in different kinds of solids. Upper Left—A metallic crystal in which the electrons are free to move through the crystal. Upper Right—A molecular crystal composed of molecules held together by weak forces. Lower Left—An ionic crystal in which the atoms are held together by opposite electric charges. Lower Right—A covalent crystal in which atoms share their outer electrons.

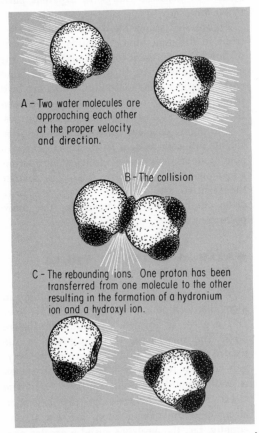

A – Two water molecules are approaching each other at the proper velocity and direction.

B – The collision

C – The rebounding ions. One proton has been transferred from one molecule to the other resulting in the formation of a hydronium ion and a hydroxyl ion.

Figure 35–2. The ionization of water molecules caused by the collision of the molecules.

oxygen atom than in the region of the hydrogen atoms. For this reason, there is a separation of the center of positive charge and the center of negative charge. The water molecule, therefore, is a highly polar covalent molecule. This feature of the water molecule accounts for many of its remarkable properties, such as its unusual ability to dissolve ionic compounds. If water were not polar, the boiling point of water would be about 100 degrees below 0° C rather than 100 degrees above 0° C.

THE ELECTRICAL CONDUCTANCE OF WATER

Since water is a covalent compound, how can we account for the fact that it has a small, but definite electrical conductivity? The answer is that a proton may be removed from a water molecule and share a pair of electrons with another water molecule, thus forming a positively charged hydronium ion and a negatively charged hydroxyl ion. See Figure 35-3. This new hydronium ion is not as stable as the original water molecule and, as a result, protons will be continually shifting back to the hydroxyl ions to form water. At any one time, only about two molecules per billion are ionized in this way. However, there is a definite equilibrium between the non-ionized water molecules and their ions, which accounts for the fact that water will react with salts of weak acids or bases to contribute hydronium ions or hydroxyl ions to form weak acids or bases.

THE UNIQUE NATURE OF THE HYDROGEN ATOM

The hydrogen atom does not fit into the periodic table satisfactorily because it exhibits both metallic and nonmetallic properties. It exhibits negative valence when it combines with metals, and a positive valence when it combines with nonmetals. In other words, it has a great attraction for electrons. Hydrogen has the electronic configuration of a metal, i.e., one electron in its outside orbit.

THE COVALENT HYDROGEN MOLECULE

A comparison of the electronegativities of hydrogen, carbon, and silicon indicates that, like carbon and silicon, hydrogen should form

covalent bonds. It is because two hydrogen atoms are joined by the sharing of a pair of electrons that the molecule of hydrogen contains two atoms. The covalent nature of hydrogen explains why it is not a conductor of electricity, and does not exhibit other properties of metals.

DOUBLE AND TRIPLE BONDS

When two carbon atoms are joined by only one pair of electrons, the compounds formed are said to be **saturated,** *because no more atoms can be added.* See Figure 35-3. *If two neighboring carbon atoms are joined by a* **double bond,** *i.e., if they share two pairs of electrons, the double bond may be broken by* **adding** *two atoms,* each of which will share a pair of electrons with the original carbon atoms. *Compounds which may be formed by* **addition** *are said to be* **unsaturated.** A further degree of unsaturation is exhibited by compounds which have **triple bonds,** *i.e., compounds in which neighboring carbon atoms are joined by sharing three pairs of electrons.* Unsaturated compounds

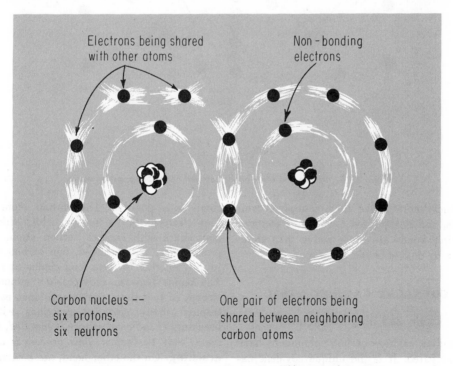

Figure 35–3. Single covalent bond between neighboring carbon atoms.

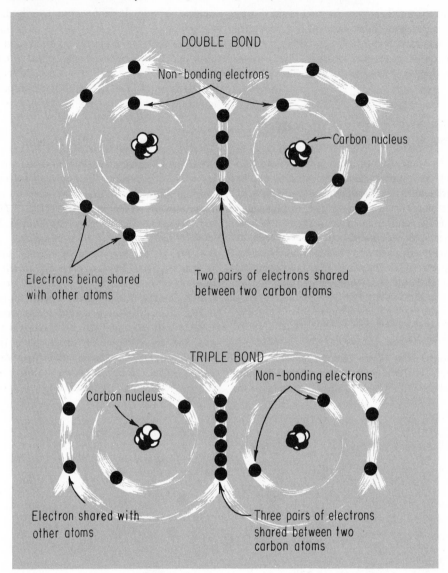

DOUBLE BOND

Non-bonding electrons

Carbon nucleus

Electrons being shared
with other atoms

Two pairs of electrons shared
between two carbon atoms

TRIPLE BOND

Non-bonding electrons

Carbon nucleus

Electron shared with
other atoms

Three pairs of electrons
shared between two
carbon atoms

Figure 35–4. Double and triple bonds between neighboring carbon atoms.

are much more active than saturated compounds, and unsaturated compounds containing triple bonds are more active than those containing double bonds. See Figure 35-4.

THE COVALENT CARBON ATOM

Chain and Ring Compounds

A million or more carbon compounds have been prepared. It is the unique covalent nature of the carbon atom that makes so many compounds possible. The carbon atom has four electrons in its outside orbit, which it may share with another carbon atom. This process may be continued, one carbon atom joining another to form long chains or rings. The bonds between these carbon atoms are strong, so that these chains and rings can go through many chemical reactions without breaking. *If sufficient energy is supplied, these bonds may be broken. This process is called* **cracking.** On the other hand, *these chains of carbon atoms may be increased in length by* *the process called* **polymerization,** which may be defined as *the combining of small molecules to form larger ones.* In Chapters 76 and 77, the production of rubbers, plastics, and fibers by polymerization is described.

Hydrocarbons

Because of the covalent nature of the carbon atoms, large numbers of carbon compounds are made possible. It is often stated that the number of carbon compounds exceeds the number of the compounds of all of the other elements taken together. This statement is not true, because carbon has a rival which, as a result of its unique covalent nature, forms an even greater number of compounds than carbon forms. This rival is hydrogen, the champion covalent compound former. Nearly all carbon compounds contain hydrogen. In addition, hydrogen forms covalent compounds with many other elements, and it is present in all acids and bases. Now, *if* the champion, *hydrogen, is combined with* the runner-up, *carbon,* **hydrocarbons** result. These hydrocarbons are the basic building blocks from which nearly all of the other carbon compounds are derived.

Hydrocarbons—There are two main classes of hydrocarbons: (1) *the chain hydrocarbons,* or **aliphatic compounds,** of which there are three types depending upon the presence of single, double, or triple bonds between carbon atoms; and (2) the *ring hydrocarbons.* The ring hydrocarbons and their derivatives are called **cyclic compounds.** The two main branches of organic chemistry are **aliphatic** and **aromatic** although the distinction between them is rapidly breaking down. *The term* **aliphatic** *was based on the fact that the fats are found to be chain compounds.* The term **aromatic** *was based on the fact that some of the benzene-ring compounds had odors that are pleasant,* as in the case of perfumes.

As an illustration of saturated and unsaturated chain hydrocarbons we might start with ethane, a saturated hydrocarbon composed of two carbon atoms and six hydrogen atoms. It is relatively inactive. But another carbon compound, ethylene, which is composed of two carbon atoms and four hydrogen atoms, contains a double bond. It is very active; so

active, in fact, that molecules of ethylene will join with each other, i.e., polymerize, to form polyethylene. Millions of pounds of polyethylene plastics are manufactured by this reaction. The hydrocarbon containing two carbon atoms with a triple bond (two carbon atoms and two hydrogen atoms) is acetylene. Acetylene is used as the starting point for many carbon compounds because of its great activity.

The Ring Hydrocarbons—The most common ring hydrocarbon is benzene, which is composed of six carbon atoms and six hydrogen atoms. The ratio between the carbon and hydrogen atoms is 1 to 1, the same as in the case of acetylene. For a long time the structure of the benzene molecule was a puzzle, but eventually the German chemist, F. A. Kekule (1829–1896), thought of writing the formula in the form of a hexagonal ring in which three double bonds were equally spaced between the six carbon atoms. This hexagonal ring resembles one segment of ordinary hexagonal chicken wire, and the chemistry of the ring compounds has sometimes been referred to as "chicken-wire chemistry." This designation is especially apt because there are ring compounds in which two, three, and more rings are joined to each other to form a pattern that looks much like chicken wire when their structural formulas are laid out on paper in one plane.

ISOMERISM

One reason why there are so many carbon compounds is isomerism. Many hydrocarbons having the same **molecular formula** (i.e., *the same number of carbon and hydrogen atoms*) exist in the forms of *compounds having different properties because they differ in structure.* There may be only a few such compounds, called **isomers,** in the case of hydrocarbons containing only a few carbon atoms, but the number of possible isomers increases tremendously as the number of carbon atoms increases. For example, heptane, a hydrocarbon containing seven carbon atoms, forms nine different compounds having exactly the same number of atoms of the same elements. On the other hand a hydrocarbon containing 40 carbon atoms could exist in 62.5 trillion different isomeric forms. Compounds having this many or more carbon atoms are not at all uncommon.

STRUCTURAL FORMULAS

Structural formulas are very important in organic chemistry because *they show how the elements are joined together in a molecule.* They are like an architect's plan for a building. Once the structural formula for a new synthetic vitamin, hormone, or antibiotic has been derived, small changes in the structure may be made to determine whether or not new compounds may have properties superior to those of the original substance. In this way, many new drugs with greater potency and fewer undesirable side effects have been produced.

The names of organic compounds are designed to tell their structural formulas. Some of these names are quite long, and most of them are unintelligible tongue twisters for the average person. For this reason, common names, such as rayon, nylon, fat, soap, sugar, and alcohol, are used instead of chemical names for nontechnical purposes.

SUMMARY

Covalence is the kind of chemical bond which involves the sharing of pairs of electrons.

The table of electronegativities enables one to predict which elements will form covalent compounds.

Hydrogen and carbon are covalent compound formers. These two elements form more compounds than all of the other elements put together, and these compounds are mostly covalent in nature. Carbon and hydrogen together compose the hydrocarbons, which are the basic foundations for most of the organic compounds.

Hydrocarbons are found in chains containing saturated covalent bonds. There are also chains of hydrocarbons containing double and triple bonds. The chain hydrocarbons and their derivatives are called aliphatic compounds. Aromatic compounds consist of ring hydrocarbons and their derivatives.

Hydrocarbons may be cracked or polymerized to decrease or increase the size of the molecules.

Saturated hydrocarbons form derivatives only by substitution, while unsaturated hydrocarbons may form derivatives by either substitution or addition.

Isomerism is one of the reasons why so many organic compounds exist.

Study Questions

1. DEFINE: chemical bond, covalence, aliphatic, aromatic, hydrocarbon, double bond, triple bond, electronegativity, polar covalence, nonpolar covalence, cracking, polymerization, addition, saturated, unsaturated, structural formula, organic, inorganic, isomerism, molecular formula.
2. Account for three types of chain hydrocarbons.
3. How may the table of electronegativities be used to predict which elements are covalent?
4. Outline the unique nature of the hydrogen atom and molecule.
5. Contrast polar and non-polar covalence.
6. Account for the fact that water is a highly polar covalent molecule.
7. Explain the electrical conductivity of pure water.
8. What are the two main branches of organic chemistry?
9. What was the original basis for the term, organic chemistry? What is its present meaning?
10. How do saturated compounds differ from unsaturated compounds?
11. What is the nature of the benzene ring?
12. Why is it possible for so many organic compounds to exist?
13. Why are the chemical names of many organic compounds so long?
14. Why are simple names, like rayon or lye, used instead of chemical names in the nontechnical world?

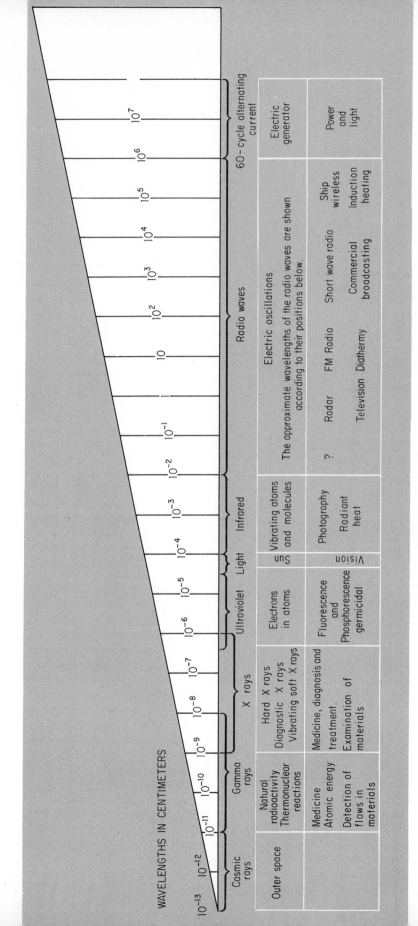

6

Waves in Space and Matter

If there is no other use discovered of electricity, this, however, is something considerable, that it may make a vain man humble.

BENJAMIN FRANKLIN

ELECTROMAGNETIC and sound waves have very little in common except that they are waves. Electromagnetic waves travel through space and even to a limited extent through matter, as in the case of light passing through glass. On the other hand, sound waves cannot travel through space, but they do travel through matter in the form of vibrations. Electricity, introduced in this unit, serves as a sort of link between matter and energy. Electromagnetic waves may be changed into sound waves by using electricity as an intermediary. On the other hand, sound waves may be changed into electromagnetic waves by the use of electricity and vacuum tubes. Electricity, electromagnetic waves, and sound waves are so intertwined in modern telephone, telegraph, motion picture, radio, and television that it seems appropriate to consider them together in this unit.

No better illustration of the impact of physical science on the activities of mankind can be found than in the case of magnetism and electricity. Suppose that all of the sources of electrical power were to be suddenly and permanently cut off; the results would be similar to those experienced in a large city in one of those very rare occurrences when the power is shut off for a few hours, due to damage to the power lines by an electrical storm. Streetcars would be stalled, motion picture theaters would be darkened, stores and offices would be forced to close, and elevators, ventilating fans, and air-conditioning would cease to function. In general, man would find himself reduced to the life of a backwoods farm, except that he would not be equipped with candles or kerosene lamps, and he would not have his own private spring or well to furnish him with water.

Modern civilization is built around electricity. Without electricity, modern factories could not run; the radio, telephone, television would be useless. Can you imagine the modern all-electric home without electricity?

CHAPTER 36

The Electromagnetic Spectrum

I have a new electromagnetic theory of light, which until I am convinced to the contrary I hold to be great guns.

CLERK MAXWELL

INTRODUCTION

In this chapter we shall examine the background for the different theories concerning the nature of radiant energy. Because Science has different theories regarding the nature of radiant energy, it is evident that we do not know as much as we would like to concerning it. This chapter also describes the various experiments designed to determine the speed of light, a very important quantity in modern physics.

THEORIES CONCERNING THE NATURE OF RADIANT ENERGY

Two Conflicting Theories

The Greek philosophers were familiar with only a tiny portion of the electromagnetic spectrum, in the form of visible radiation, i.e., light. They knew that light travels in straight lines, casts sharp shadows, and decreases in intensity in direct proportion to the square of the distance from the source to the observer. They believed that light traveled from the heavenly bodies in the form of particles. In 1678, Christian Huygens (1629–1695) developed the wave theory of light, first suggested by Leonardo Da Vinci. A few years later, Sir Isaac Newton proposed a particle (corpuscular) theory of light, because he could not account for sharp shadows in terms of wave motion.

For about one hundred years Newton's particle theory was the most popular one, but in 1801, Thomas Young (1773–1829) demonstrated the wavelike nature of light by interference experiments.

In 1800, Thomas Young (*Young's Works I,* page 202) wrote,

Suppose a number of equal waves of water to move upon the surface of a stagnant lake, with a certain constant velocity, and to enter a narrow channel leading out of the lake; suppose then another similar cause to have excited another equal series of waves, which arrive at the same channel, with the same velocity, and at the same time with the first. Neither series of waves will destroy the other, but their effects will be combined; if they enter the channel in such a manner that the elevations of one series coincide with those of the other, they must together produce a series of greater elevations; but if the elevations of one series are so situated as to correspond to the depressions of the other, they must exactly fill up those depressions, and the surface of the water must remain smooth. Now I maintain that similar effects take place whenever two portions of light are thus mixed; and this I call the general law of the interference of light. Thus whenever two portions of the same light arrive to the eye by different routes either exactly or very nearly in the same direction, the light becomes most intense when the difference of the routes is any multiple of a certain length, and least intense in the intermediate state of the interfering portions; and this length is different for light of different colors.

One of Thomas Young's critics denounced the principle of interference, in an article in the Edinburgh Review, Vol. 5 (1805), p. 103, as follows:

We now dismiss, for the present, the feeble lucubrations of this author in which we have searched without success for some trace of learning, acuteness, and ingenuity, that might compensate his evident deficiency in the powers of solid thinking, calm and patient investigation, and successful development of the laws of nature by steady and modest observation of her operations.

New theories often lead to controversies, which, in turn, lead to additional experiments.

The great tragedy of science—the slaying of a beautiful hypothesis by an ugly fact.
Thomas Huxley

Thomas Young passed a beam of light through two closely spaced holes onto a screen. A series of bands of light, separated by dark bands, was obtained on the screen. It has been shown that sound waves and water waves may show interference in which they cancel and reinforce each other. Light should behave similarly if it is wavelike in nature. In terms of the wave theory, Young's bright bands were the result of the reinforcement of the waves from one beam by waves from the other beam. The dark bands represented places where the waves were out of phase and canceled each other.

From the width of the bands and the distance between the holes, Young was able to calculate the wavelength of the light, which turned out to be very short. This was a significant fact, because it explained why light waves travel in straight lines, cast sharp shadows, and will not curve around obstructions. These properties of light had been one of the chief stumbling blocks for the wave theory.

In 1818, Augustin Jean Fresnel (1788–1827) showed that light would bend around an object if the object was small enough. The light produces a diffraction pattern as a result. Diffraction should not be confused with **refraction** which is *the bending of light as it passes from one medium to another.* **Diffraction** refers to *the bending of light as it passes through very small openings or around corners.* A diffraction grating, which is a piece of glass with many parallel, uniformly spaced scratches on it, diffracts light, and at the same time produces a spectrum similar to that produced by a prism. The reason why the different colors of the spectrum are produced is because the amount of diffraction depends upon the different wavelengths of the different colors of light. A phonograph record, if held at the proper angle, will also show the colors of the rainbow. Fresnel's work supported the Young's theory so well that Newton's corpuscular theory was retired in favor of the wave theory.

The Ether Theory

One of the difficulties of Huyghen's wave theory was that it could not account for waves in space. Since electromagnetic waves are **transverse waves,** *undulating at right angles to the direction of travel,* and since transverse waves are conveyed only in solids, it was difficult to explain how these waves could travel through space. The **hypothetical ether** was invented as the medium in which electromagnetic waves travel. This ether must have properties which are difficult to imagine. For example, it must fill all space, even that in atoms and molecules; it must have no mass; it must offer no resistance to the motion of objects in it; and finally it must possess the rigidity of a solid.

The ether theory met its downfall strangely enough as a result of a classical experiment that failed. Albert Michelson invented an interferometer to measure "absolute motion." He reasoned that if the ether was motionless, a beam of light projected from the earth in the direction of its motion and reflected back would travel a shorter distance than a beam sent out at right angles. In 1887, Michelson failed to find any difference in the distance that the light traveled in different directions. The conclusion was that either the ether moved with the earth or that there was no such thing as the ether. The first conclusion was untenable, so it was concluded that ether does not exist. Therefore the ether theory was placed on Science's scrap heap of discarded theories.

The Quantum Theory

In 1879, Joseph Stefan demonstrated that the total energy radiated by a body depends on its temperature and is independent of the nature of the body. As the temperature is increased, the wavelength of the radiation emitted is decreased. It was found that existing theories could not explain the various facts of this radiation by hot bodies.

Max Karl Ernst Ludwig Planck, in 1901, cleared up the connection between temperature and the wavelengths of emitted radiation with his introduction of the idea that electromagnetic radiation consists of small packets, which he called quanta. He argued that radiation could be absorbed only in whole numbers of quanta and that the amount of energy in a quantum depends only upon the wavelength of the radiation. Thus, a **quantum** appeared to be *a packet of waves*. Later, his ideas formed the basis for quantum mechanics, which is beyond the scope of this text.

Philip Lenard discovered the photoelectric effect, i.e., the fact that certain metals will emit electrons when light strikes them. It was found that an increase in the intensity of the light has no effect on the amount of energy of the electrons emitted, but merely increases their number. However, by changing the wavelength of the light a considerable difference in the energy of the electrons is observed. The photoelectric effect cannot be explained in terms of waves. Albert Einstein explained the photoelectric effect in terms of *quanta,* often called **photons.** These bundles of radiant energy contain an amount of energy determined by the wavelength of the radiant waves to which they correspond.

Later, Einstein, in his special theory of relativity, suggested that light travels through space in the form of quanta. Einstein's theory finished off the ether theory because the idea that radiant energy travels in the form of quanta no longer required any kind of a medium for the propagation of waves.

The confusion between the wave theory and the quantum theory may be avoided by regarding radiant energy as wavelike when one wants to know where it will go, and as a stream of particles when one wants to know what it will do after it arrives. Transmission phenomena, such as diffraction and interference, are best explained in terms of the wave theory. For absorption and emission phenomena, the quantum theory is best. Obviously, the opposing theories concerning the nature of light constitute a basic problem for research.

THE ELECTROMAGNETIC ORIGIN OF RADIANT ENERGY

In 1864, James Clerk Maxwell proposed a mathematical theory of radiant energy in terms of electromagnetic waves, or vibrations set up by alternating currents.

If a stream of electrons, shot out from the sun during periods of large sunspots, passes through the earth's magnetic fields at the poles, the *Aurora Borealis* is produced.

The production of radio waves by oscillating electrons likewise indicates that radiant energy is electromagnetic in origin.

The Electromagnetic Spectrum

About 1800, William Herschel (1738–1822) held a thermometer in the beam of sunlight transmitted through a prism, beyond the red portion of the visible spectrum, and found that the temperature was raised more than at any portion of the visible spectrum. In this way the existence of one type of invisible radiant energy, now called infrared radiation, was discovered.

In another simple experiment, Johann Wilhelm Ritter found that silver nitrate was darkened by radiation beyond the violet end of the visible spectrum. This type of invisible radiation is now known as ultraviolet.

In 1887, Heinrich Rudolf Hertz produced what are now known as radio waves by the spark of an induction coil. A similar result is the static produced in radio reception by the ignition system of an automobile.

Then, in 1895, Wilhelm Konrad Roentgen discovered X rays, and thus opened up the shorter wavelength end of the spectrum. Finally, the gamma rays of radioactivity were found to have even smaller wavelengths than X rays.

Figure 36-1 shows the wide range of wavelengths of radiant energy. These different types of energy differ considerably in some of their properties because of the differences in their wavelengths. In many regards the different types of electromagnetic waves are similar, as one would expect, because of their same fundamental nature. This figure shows

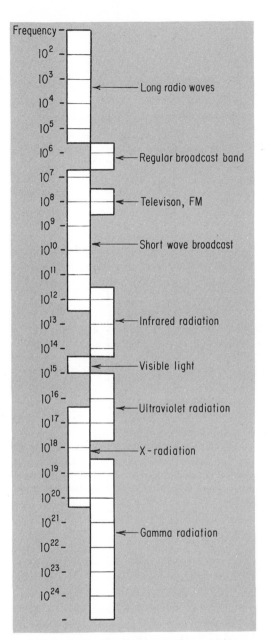

Frequency

10² – Long radio waves

10³ –

10⁴ –

10⁵ –

10⁶ – Regular broadcast band

10⁷ –

10⁸ – Televison, FM

10⁹ –

10¹⁰ – Short wave broadcast

10¹¹ –

10¹² –

10¹³ – Infrared radiation

10¹⁴ –

10¹⁵ – Visible light

10¹⁶ –

10¹⁷ – Ultraviolet radiation

10¹⁸ – X-radiation

10¹⁹ –

10²⁰ –

10²¹ –

10²² – Gamma radiation

10²³ –

10²⁴ –

Figure 36–1. The electromagnetic spectrum.

that the long wavelengths are grouped under the title of radio waves. Radio waves may be subdivided into long, short, ultrashort, and micro waves, based on their wavelengths. Long radio waves may be more than a mile long, while the shortest radio waves may be no longer than 0.1 millimeter.

Infrared radiation consists of wavelengths longer than those of light. Light represents a very small portion of the electromagnetic spectrum. Beyond light waves, the wavelengths become shorter as one progresses through ultraviolet radiation, X rays, and gamma rays. Refer to the electromagnetic spectrum on page 266.

THE SPEED OF LIGHT

During the Middle Ages, there were two schools of thought concerning the speed of light. One school considered that it was instantaneous, and the other school believed that the speed of light was finite and that it could be measured.

Galileo experimented with flashing lanterns, but the speed of light was too great to be measured with such crude equipment.

Rene Descartes (1596–1650) and Johann Kepler concluded that the speed of light was instantaneous. Kepler argued that since light is not material in nature, nothing could offer it resistance.

In 1676, Ole Roemer (1644–1710) proved that light travels at a measurable speed. He showed that the light from a moon of Jupiter at the time of its eclipse varied with the distance of Jupiter from the earth. As Figure 36-2 shows, at one time the distance is farther than it is another time by 186 million miles, the diameter of the earth's orbit around the sun. By checking the time of the eclipse in each position he could determine the amount of time that is required for light to travel 186 million miles. Roemer obtained a figure of 140,000 miles per second, which was fairly close to the figure of about 186,282 miles per second accepted today, considering that he had no way to determine the diameter of the earth's orbit about the sun accurately.

In 1849, Armand Hippolyte Louis Fizeau (1819–1896) directed a narrow beam of light over a distance of 8,633 meters and reflected it back again with a mirror. He used a toothed wheel which he rotated in front of the light source to produce flashes of light. The speed of the wheel was so adjusted that the reflected beam would hit the center of the next tooth on the wheel. The number of turns of the wheel per minute and the number of teeth and spaces in the wheel furnished the necessary data to calculate the speed of light. His result

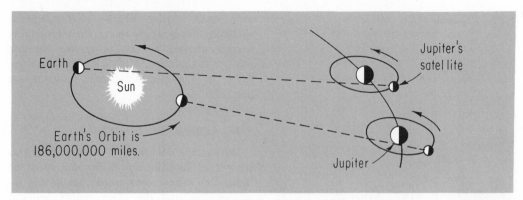

Figure 36–2. Roemer's measurement of the speed of light. Light takes 1000 seconds to travel across the diameter of the earth's orbit.

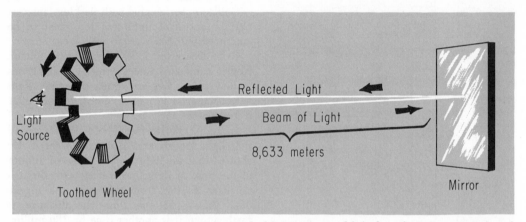

Figure 36–3. Fizeau's method for measuring the speed of light. A beam of light from the source passes through a gap between two teeth of the rapidly spinning toothed wheel. It is reflected back to the wheel by the distant mirror to the next tooth or gap depending upon the speed of the wheel. If it passes through the next gap it then continues to the observer.

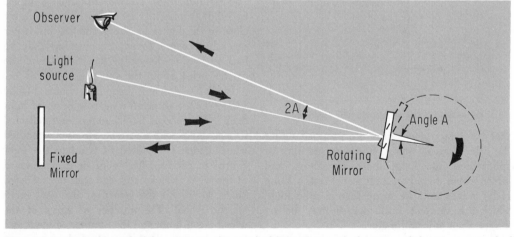

Figure 36–4. Foucault's method for measuring the speed of light. The speed of rotation of the mirror, instead of the speed of rotation of the toothed wheel in Fizeau's method, made possible the calculation of the speed of light.

was 194,675 miles per second. See Figure 36-3.

In 1862, Leon Foucault modified Fizeau's method by using a rotating mirror instead of a toothed wheel, as shown in Figure 36-4. His result was 185,177 miles per second.

The above experiments measured the speed of light in air. Since light travels through matter at varying speeds, depending upon the nature of the matter and the wavelength of the light, it seemed to be desirable to obtain the speed of light in space.

Albert Abraham Michelson (1852–1931) worked for fifty years on a method to measure the speed of light in a vacuum. After his death, his co-workers continued his work. At last, in 1932, they completed a steel pipe, three feet in diameter and one mile long, in which they reduced the pressure to 0.01 pound per square inch by means of vacuum pumps. They used a rotating mirror method to measure the speed of light in this tunnel. It came out to be 186,270 miles per second, a figure very close to the best figure obtained with electronic vacuum tubes of today, which is about 186,282 miles per second.

SOME PROPERTIES OF RADIANT ENERGY

Penetration of Matter

The longer waves in the infrared radio range can penetrate matter to a certain extent. For example, when the visible portion of sunlight is removed by a canvas tent, infrared rays penetrate it. Infrared radiation will pass through ordinary window glass, which is transparent to light, but not to ultraviolet radiation. However, ultraviolet radiation can penetrate quartz glass. Radio waves can be received inside of a building, but they cannot penetrate dense, massive solids such as stone or metal. Visible light can penetrate some liquids and solids which are therefore said to be transparent; but the majority of solids are **opaque,** i.e., *they will not transmit light.* Ultraviolet radiation behaves much like light. It will kill bacteria, but it cannot be used to sterilize foods because it will not penetrate them. X rays will penetrate matter to a limited extent, but the denser a material is the

less it is penetrated by X rays. Gamma rays, emitted from radioactive substances, have far greater penetrating power than X rays. They can be stopped by a few centimeters of lead, but cosmic rays will pass through 75 feet of lead. If cosmic rays consist of naked atoms (atoms which have lost their electrons), theory holds that they, like beta rays, should be classed as particles of matter rather than radiant energy.

Absorption by Matter

On striking atoms and molecules, radiant energy is either reflected, transmitted, or absorbed. *When radiant energy is* **absorbed** *it loses its wavelike nature and its energy produces an increased motion of molecules, atoms, or electrons within the atoms.* This increased motion may result in an increased temperature. When radiant energy strikes a metal conductor, a high-frequency alternating current is set up in the conductor. If there is a high resistance to the flow of electrons, most of the radiation is changed into heat. The heating of the earth's surface by the sun's rays is an example of this change of radiant energy into heat. Ultraviolet radiation, as described later, may result in fluorescence or phosphorescence. X rays and gamma rays may produce the same results.

Emission of Energy

If one heats a metallic object, it will begin to radiate long invisible, infrared waves. As it grows hotter the wavelengths become shorter. Soon the metal becomes red hot, which means that the radiation has now moved into the red portion of the visible spectrum. Further heating will result in the shorter wavelengths of yellow light. Still higher temperatures will produce a mixture of wavelengths characteristic of white light.

The nature of the surface of an object determines how much energy will be absorbed or radiated. An object that absorbs energy also has good radiating efficiency.

The **emission** of radiant energy from atoms *is explained in terms of the vibration of the electrons within the atoms.* The wavelengths of the radiation emitted will be determined by the frequency of vibration of the electrons. The maximum amount of radiation emitted is at right angles to the direction of vibration. Since the different electrons in mixtures of many different kinds of atoms may vibrate in all possible directions, the waves emitted will also vibrate in all directions.

When electromagnetic waves impinge on an object, the electrons in the atoms will be caused to vibrate in tune with the waves received and radiation will be emitted in random directions. This *reradiation of energy is called* **scattering.** The particles of the atmosphere scatter light; otherwise the sky would be dark. Most of the light by which we see is scattered light. Another source of scattered light is a rough surface which scatters light by multiple reflection, as in the case of the frosting on a light bulb.

Biological Effects

Various types of radiation produce biological effects on tissue to varying degrees. The amount of tissue exposed to radiation is important. Thus the permissible limit of exposure of ones hands, head, feet, and ankles is perhaps five times that permissible for the whole body.

Starting with the long-wavelength end of the electromagnetic spectrum, we will briefly consider the biological effects of the different kinds of radiation. The longer radio waves do not seem to have biological effects, but *high-frequency short radio waves can produce heat deep within the tissues of the body without harming the surface tissues. This type of therapy is* called **diathermy.**

Infrared radiation heats the surface tissues. It is a common experience to have to back away from a hot fire to avoid being burned.

It is difficult to distinguish between the effects of light and ultraviolet radiation. Sunlight, for example, is rich in ultraviolet radiation, and it is likely that most of the effects of sunlight on the tissues of the body are caused by the ultraviolet radiation in sunlight. Sunlight, or the ultraviolet radiation from a sunlamp, has certain beneficial effects. It produces Vitamin D, and causes a drop in blood pressure and serum cholesterol. It may serve in other unknown ways to stimulate normal functions of some of the body tissues. However, it can cause a severe sunburn which may be very serious. Overexposure to ultraviolet radiation causes skin aging and even cancer. It may do permanent damage to the eyes.

X rays are sometimes used instead of surgery in ridding the body of diseased tissue. X-ray therapy must be used with caution because it may result in severe burns.

Gamma radiations from radioactive materials are similar to X rays in their effects on the body. The difficulty with this type of radiation is that the body has no way of recognizing it, and because its effects are cumulative; not only must one avoid a short exposure to a high concentration of radiation but he must avoid less powerful radiation over a longer time.

SUMMARY

Radiant energy is electromagnetic in nature. It appears to be both wavelike and corpuscular in nature. Its wavelike nature explains such transmission phenomena as interference and diffraction. Its corpuscular nature explains such absorption phenomena as radiation by hot bodies, the photoelectric effect, and the fact that light travels through space, where there is no medium present to propagate waves.

The electromagnetic spectrum, arranged in the order of increasing wavelengths; is as follows:

Gamma rays	The shorter wavelengths have
X rays	the greatest biological effects
Ultraviolet	and penetrating ability.
Light	
Infrared	
Radio waves	

The speed of radiant energy is about 186,282 miles per second.

Study Questions

1. DEFINE: quantum, transverse waves, diffraction, absorption of radiant energy, emission of radiant energy, scattering, refraction, photon, opaque, diathermy.
2. What objections to the wave theory were removed by Thomas Young? What phenomena of light were used to do this?
3. What experiments led to the downfall of the ether theory?
4. What is the significance of two different theories of radiant energy?

5. Why is radiant energy often called electromagnetic radiation?

6. How does the quantum theory explain the absorption and emission of radiation by matter?

7. What are some of the results when radiant energy strikes matter?

8. Why was the ether theory for the propagation of radiation developed?

9. What property of the various types of electromagnetic radiation causes them to vary in penetrating ability?

10. List the various types of electromagnetic radiation starting with the short wavelength-end of the spectrum.

11. Compare the biological effects of the different types of radiation.

12. Strictly speaking, would it be correct to speak of ultraviolet or infrared radiation as light?

13. What is the speed of light? Describe a method for measuring the speed of light.

14. Give the evidence that radiant energy is wavelike in nature.

15. In what two ways may light be scattered?

16. How may light be diffracted?

17. Account for the fact that the sky appears to be light during the daytime, but that high-altitude observations show that the sky is dark and that the stars may be seen during the daytime.

Light

Nature and Nature's laws
lay hid in the night;
God said, Let Newton be!
and all was light.

ALEXANDER POPE

INTRODUCTION

Sometimes the term "light" is used to refer to radiant energy, regardless of the wavelength. Frequently, the terms "black light" or "ultraviolet light" are used when referring to the invisible radiation having wavelengths a little longer and a little shorter than the wavelengths of visible radiation. While it is true that the different wavelengths of radiant energy are similar in that they may be reflected, absorbed, and refracted, this is no reason to speak of all wavelengths of radiant energy as light. It is preferable to restrict the term **"light"** to *the small band of wavelengths, called the visible spectrum, to which the cells of the eye are sensitive.* The general term for radiant energy is electromagnetic radiation, because all of the wavelengths of radiant energy have an electromagnetic origin.

TERMS USED IN CONNECTION WITH THE PROPAGATION OF LIGHT

Light travels through space without loss of energy, but when it travels through matter, such as water or glass, *a small amount of energy is absorbed;* such materials are said to be **transparent.** Some materials, like frosted glass, which *scatter most of the incident light,* are said to be **translucent.** Other materials, like wood or stone, which *transmit no light,* are said to be **opaque.**

When light is thrown back upon striking a surface, it is said to be **reflected.** *The ray striking the surface* is called the **incident ray,** and *the ray leaving the surface* is called the **reflected ray.** *That portion of light which is lost when a beam of light passes through a transparent medium, or when it is reflected from a medium,* is said to be **absorbed.** Light that is absorbed is changed into some other form of energy, such as chemical energy, electrical energy, or heat energy. *When light changes its direction as it passes from one medium to another,* it is said to be **refracted.** *When light strikes the edge of a body or passes through a small aperture,* the light does not cast a sharp shadow, because *a portion of the light deviates from its course, i.e., it spreads out. This spreading out of light is* called **diffraction.** The **diffusion,** or *scattering, of light is different from diffraction in that it is the result of multiple reflections from rough surfaces.*

REFRACTION OF LIGHT BY WATER

Light may be bent, or in technical language, **refracted,** *as it passes from one transparent medium to another of different density.* Figure 37-1 is an interesting example of the re-

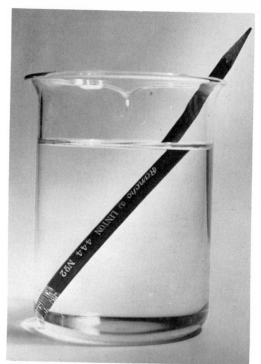

Figure 37-1. A straight pencil appears broken when seen at an angle. On emerging from water the light is bent.

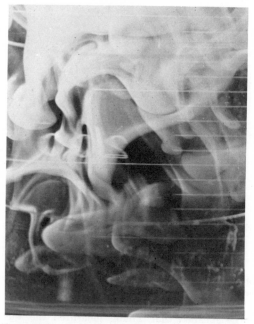

Figure 37-2. Convection currents in water. A cold solution of fluorescein is poured into a cylinder of hot water. The convection currents show up when the solution is radiated with an ultraviolet light.

fraction of light as it passes from water to the air.

If a coin is placed at the bottom of a crystallizing dish slightly below the line of vision, it will be invisible to the audience until water is poured into the dish.

When one looks into the clear water of a mountain lake it appears to be shallower than it really is, but the fish seen in the water seem to be much larger than they really are.

CONVECTION CURRENTS

Convection currents *in the atmosphere,* which may be seen on a hot day, and which account for the twinkling of the stars, *are visible because light is refracted as it passes from a cooler, more dense atmosphere to a warmer, less dense atmosphere or vice versa.* Convection currents in water are shown in Figure 37-2.

MIRAGES

Mirages *are refraction phenomena.* There are two types of mirages; (1) *the ocean mirage* and (2) *the desert mirage,* as shown in Figures 37-3 and 37-4.

Light is refracted as it passes from chilled surface layers of air into warmer air above. Such a mirage would enable one to see an object over water which is really below the horizon. In the case of the desert mirage, light is bent as it passes from the hot, less dense air near the surface, through cooler, more dense air at higher levels. The hot air is less refracting than the cool air. Thus the light from a distant object appears to be reflected in much the same way that light striking a hot pavement is reflected, making it appear wet.

THE REFRACTION OF LIGHT BY PRISMS

Figures 9-5 and 9-6, page 66, show how light is refracted as it passes through a prism. Newton observed that white light was again obtained by passing the light from the first prism through a second prism. The same effect can be produced by causing the component colors of white light to be reflected by small mirrors back to one point. Newton explained

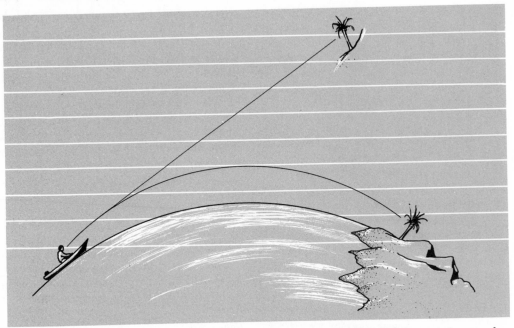

Figure 37–3. A mirage over water. This type of mirage is the result of refraction of light rays as they pass from the chilled surface layers of air into the warmer layers of air above. In this case the image is not inverted.

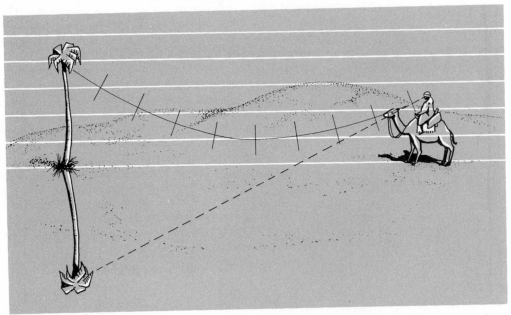

Figure 37–4. The desert mirage. The light from a distant object is bent as it passes from the cooler upper layers of air to the hot surface layers of air. The image is reflected as from a mirror.

the formation of the spectrum by saying that white light is composed of light of various colors, which the prism can sort out and disperse or recombine to form white light. It will be recalled that Young measured the wavelengths of different colors. It is now accepted that white light is a mixture of light waves of different wavelengths and hence of different frequencies. The frequency of the light waves increases from the red toward the violet end of the spectrum. The reason that a prism **disperses** (*i.e., separates*) the white light is that waves of different frequencies are refracted differently, the waves of higher frequency being refracted the most.

THE REFRACTION OF LIGHT BY LENSES

Lenses are devices to bend light in a desired direction. Their applications in such important aids to the human eye as telescopes, microscopes, projectors, cameras, spectacles and cameras will be discussed in Chapter 53.

Parallel rays of light may be focused by a convex lens and may be diverged by a concave lens as shown in Figure 37-5.

THE ABSORPTION AND REFLECTION OF LIGHT

When light rays strike an object they may be transmitted, absorbed or reflected. Dark, rough, and unpolished surfaces favor absorption. When light strikes a rough, black surface all of it may be absorbed. On the other hand, if only certain wavelengths are absorbed and the remaining wavelengths are reflected, the sensation of color is the result. When light strikes an object which absorbs it, a shadow is cast. This shadow would be perfectly black if it were not for the scattering of light by molecules and dust particles in the atmosphere.

White paper reflects all of the wavelengths of white light, but it does not reflect light like a mirror does because of its porous or rough surface. If the paper is coated, the amount of light that is reflected is increased and the glare is increased. The glare from a mirror that is reflecting sunlight can be almost blinding. Smoothness increases reflection. See Figure 37-6, page 280.

LAW OF REFLECTION

The basic **law of reflection** is that *the angle of incidence is equal to the angle of reflection* as shown in Figure 37-7. **The angle of incidence** *is the angle which a ray of light falling on any surface makes with a perpendicular to that surface.* Similarly, **the angle of reflection** *is the angle between the reflected ray of light and the perpendicular.*

MIRROR REFLECTIONS

The outstanding application of reflection is the mirror, which is designed to reflect a high percentage of the incident light rays.

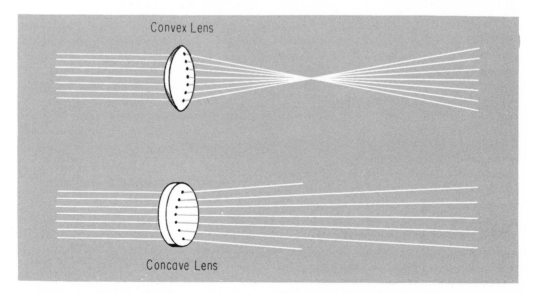

Figure 37–5. Parallel rays of light may be focused by a convex lens, and may be diverged by a concave lens.

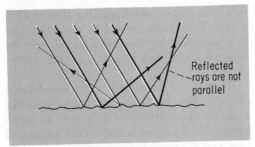

Figure 37–6. Irregular reflection from rough surfaces diffuses or scatters light.

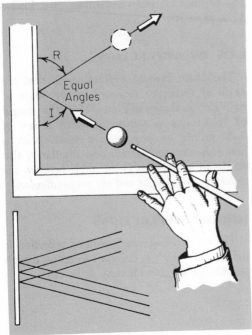

Figure 37–7. The angle of incidence *I* equals the angle of reflection *R*.

A perfect mirror would reflect all of the light falling upon it and would in itself not be visible, while a rough surface reflects some of the light and absorbs some of the light which falls upon it. The reflected light is reflected from the rough surface in many directions and is thus diffused. Under such conditions, the surface becomes visible. If two mirrors are placed at right angles to each other, the rays will be reflected in a line parallel to that in which they came, regardless of the angle at which the incident rays reach the first mirror.

If three mirrors are placed perpendicular to each other, all light rays will be reflected back in the direction from which they came, regardless of how the combination of mirrors is held. The success of signal buoys at sea and the red and white reflectors now used so widely on bicycles, signs, guard rails, and house numbers depends upon this principle.

The images of objects in flat mirrors differ from the original only in that they are reversed. Mirror-writing is a common example of this effect.

Concave and convex mirrors are used like lenses to focus or diverge light. Mirrors of concave shape are used in automobile headlights and flashlights. Concave mirrors can produce three kinds of images depending upon the position of the object: (1) if the object is very close to the mirror, the image will be upright but larger than the object—dentists' exploratory mirrors use this principle; (2) if the object is placed somewhat farther from the mirror, the image will be inverted and larger than the object; (3) if the object is placed still farther away, the image will be inverted, but it will be smaller than the object.

Typical examples of convex mirrors are the chrome-finished back of a spotlight, the bowl of a spoon, or the side-rear-view mirror of some trucks; the image is always smaller than the object.

REFLEX REFLECTORS

There are two taillights on modern automobiles, which enable one to judge how far ahead a car is at night. If the lights appear to be close together, the car is far ahead, but if they spread apart rapidly, you are rapidly approaching the car ahead.

Modern taillights have sections (reflex reflectors) which will reflect the light from a car behind if the taillight bulb burns out.

DIFFUSION OF LIGHT BY THE ATMOSPHERE

The sky would appear black if it were not for the fact that the molecules and dust of the atmosphere diffuse the light of the sun and moon by reflecting a portion of the light. It can be shown that it is the dust particles that are responsible for this diffusion of the light of the sun, which causes the changing colors at sunrise and sunset, because, when light is passed through a dust-free box, it is invisible, although it can be seen before it enters and after it leaves the box; light cannot be seen unless it is coming toward one. Thus a powerful beam of light from a searchlight could be passed through a dust-free room and leave it in complete darkness. The room would be illuminated at once, however, by placing a white object in the path of the light. A useful application of this idea is the placing of a white object in front of an automobile to reflect the light from the headlights, when one is caught with tire trouble at night without a flashlight.

THE RAINBOW

The rainbow, one of nature's most magnificent spectacles, is due to the optical properties of the numerous spherical drops of water in the presence of sunlight. It is visible to an observer only when the sun is not more than 42° above the horizon, and it will always be on the same side as his shadow.

The rainbow is produced by the refraction of light rays internally reflected within the raindrops, as shown in Figure 37-8.

When parallel rays of light fall on a spherical drop of water, some of the light is refracted and passes into the drop. Here it is totally reflected by the opposite surface and is refracted again as it passes into the air. Only those raindrops that are located along an arch forming a particular angle around a point directly opposite to the sun will reflect the sunlight back to the observer. This explains the circular shape of the rainbow, but what causes the colors?

Each color is strongly reflected at a particular angle. All drops which lie on a circle at an angle of 42° with the observer will reflect red light strongly, while all drops in a circle at an angle of 40° will reflect violet light strongly. Drops lying in circles between these two angles will reflect colors between the red and violet ends of the visible spectrum.

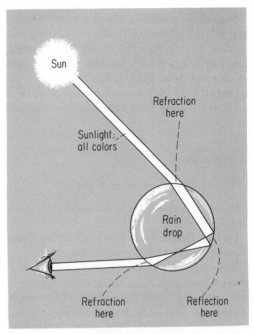

Figure 37-8. A rainbow is produced by refraction, total reflection, and dispersion of light.

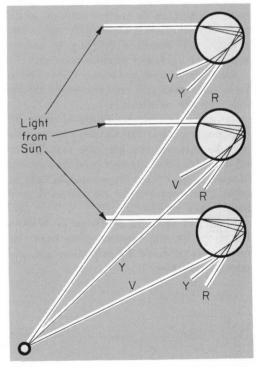

Figure 37-9. How a rainbow is produced. V = violet; Y = yellow; R = red.

Secondary rainbows are the result of two internal reflections within the raindrops, and because of this fact the colors are reversed. The angles are 50.5° for the red light and 54° for the violet light in this case; hence the appearance of the secondary rainbow in a circle is different from the one where the primary rainbow occurs.

SUMMARY

Reflection of Light

Polished, smooth, light-colored surfaces reflect light best.

Law of Reflection: The angle of incidence is equal to the angle of reflection.

Reflection by Concave and Convex Mirrors: Concave mirrors focus or diverge light rays depending upon the position of the object relative to the focal length of the mirror. Convex mirrors focus light rays.

Refraction of Light

Light is refracted (bent) when it passes from one medium to another medium of different density. Layers of air, differing in temperature and therefore differing in density, will refract light, and produce mirages.

Refraction of Light by Lenses—Convex lenses focus light rays and concave lenses diverge light rays by refraction.

Refraction of Light by Prisms—Prisms will disperse (separate) the wavelengths of white light so that the eye may see the different colors which taken together give the sensation of white light. Prisms disperse white light because short wavelengths are refracted more than longer wavelengths.

Refraction of Light by Drops of Water— Raindrops likewise disperse white light. The rainbow is produced by refraction and total internal reflection.

Absorption of Light

Light which is absorbed is changed to other forms of energy. Colors are the result of the absorption of certain wavelengths and the reflection of other wavelengths. The wavelengths that are reflected cause the color sensation in the eye.

Study Questions

1. DEFINE: light, transparent, translucent, opaque, reflection, absorption, refraction, dispersion, diffusion, mirage, diffraction, angle of incidence, angle of reflection, reflected ray, incident ray.
2. Why does the sky appear light on the earth's surface in the day, while it is very dark at higher altitudes?
3. Why does a pencil in a glass of water appear to be bent at the surface of the water?
4. What happens to light as it passes through one transparent medium into another of different density?
5. How may light rays of different colors be combined?
6. What kinds of surfaces favor absorption of light rays?
7. Give some common examples of convex mirrors.
8. Give an example of a concave mirror.
9. What causes the stars to twinkle?
10. Explain the desert mirage.
11. Explain the hot-pavement mirage.
12. Why is it that one can see the sun rise in the morning before it has really risen above the horizon?
13. Why is one likely to be deceived as to the depth of a pool of clear water?
14. How can one judge how far ahead a car is at night?
15. How is a rainbow produced? Account for a double rainbow.
16. Give the fundamental law of reflection.
17. How may one account for the colors of objects?
18. How do prisms disperse light?

CHAPTER 38

Waves in Matter—Sound

There are three voices in Nature. She joins hands with us and says Struggle, Endeavor. She comes close to us, we can hear her heart beating, she says, Wonder, Enjoy, Revere. She whispers secrets to us, we cannot always catch her words, she says Search, Inquire. These, then, are the three voices of Nature, appealing to Hand, and Heart, and Head, to the Trinity of our Being.

J. ARTHUR THOMPSON

INTRODUCTION

Energy has been defined *as that which makes one aware that something exists outside of himself.* Most of this energy arrives in the form of waves. The human body has several different kinds of receptors for waves, such as the heat receptors in the skin, the light receptors in the eyes, and the sound receptors in the ears. In this chapter we shall study, among other things, how the human body can receive sound waves by his ears and generate sound waves by his voice.

This chapter deals with the waves in matter. There are two kinds of waves in matter, transverse waves illustrated by water waves, and longitudinal waves illustrated by sound waves. There is a wide range of longitudinal waves, but only those waves having frequencies between 20 and 40,000 cycles per second are classified as sound waves, because the human ear cannot receive higher frequencies. Most people cannot hear frequencies above 20,000 cycles per second. **Sound** is *the response of the brain to sensations transferred to it from the ear.* Sound is a biological phenomenon, but the generation and propagation of the waves which cause the sensation of sound is definitely physical in nature.

WAVE MOTION IN MATTER

Waves in matter result in the transfer of energy rather than of matter. An earthquake wave transmits considerable energy and yet the position of the surface of the earth is usually not changed by the passage of the earthquake wave. Waves move in water but the water is not transferred, except near the shore, where the energy that the waves carry tends to make them pile up. Even in this case, there is a back and forth motion which is entirely different from the ebb and flow of a tide. A strong wind may cause transverse waves on the surface of bodies of water which do cause water to move, but longitudinal waves in water do not cause the water to move along with the energy.

TRANSVERSE WAVES IN MATTER

Transverse waves may well be understood by studying the motion of ocean waves. One outstanding characteristic of such waves is that they *consist of crests and troughs* which may be illustrated diagrammatically as in Figure 38-1.

The height of transverse waves is expressed as amplitude. The **amplitude** of a wave is

283

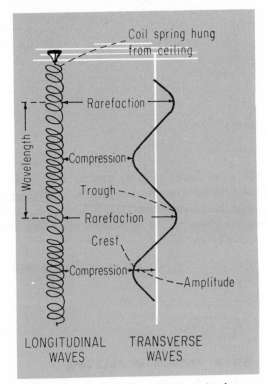

Figure 38–1. A comparison of compressional waves and transverse waves.

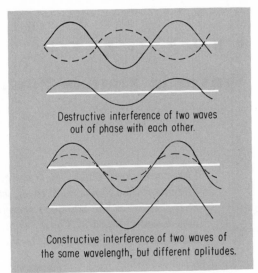

Figure 38–2. The interference of sound waves.

one-half of the difference in height between a crest and a trough. Waves may be close together, as in a pool of water into which a pebble has been dropped, or they may be relatively far apart, as in the case of ocean waves. *The distance between crests* is called the **wavelength.** To increase the amount of energy transmitted, one must increase either the amplitude or frequency or both. *The number of crests that pass through a given position in a given time* is the **frequency** of the waves. The rate of travel of the wave motion is proportional to the product of the wavelength and the frequency. Therefore, the speed divided by the frequency is a measure of the wavelength.

Interference

When two waves arrive at a given point at the same time their interaction is called **interference.** As shown in Figure 38-2, when crests meet crests and troughs meet troughs the waves reinforce each other and the net result is one wave with a higher crest and

deeper trough which is greater than that of the component waves. But, if the crests and troughs arrive out of phase, i.e., a crest of one wave arrives at the same time that the trough of the other wave arrives, the waves will destroy each other, at least, to a certain extent, depending upon their relative amplitudes.

Reflection

It can easily be demonstrated that the direction of water waves may be changed as they strike an object or large surface. Often one can see the reflected waves travel back through the original waves.

Refraction

Refraction *refers to the bending of the direction of wave motion.* If one were to observe ocean waves in a curved bay, he would find that the waves usually arrive parallel to the shore regardless of their angle relative to the shore in the deep water. This bending of the wave direction is the result of the slowing down of the lower portion of the wave in contact with the sloping shore.

Diffraction

When a water wave passes through a narrow opening, new waves will be produced which proceed in the form of a semicircle. It

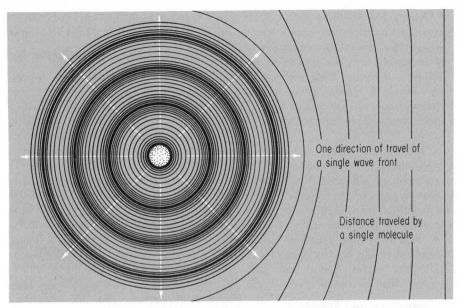

Figure 38–3. An expanding sound wave, showing regions of compression and rarefaction. As the circular wave fronts become larger they eventually become almost parallel to each other.

is a characteristic of waves that they travel in a straight line unless they are reflected or refracted. However, **diffraction** *represents the situation in which waves are bent around corners.* It does not take place unless the waves pass through an opening which is small relative to their wavelength.

LONGITUDINAL WAVES IN MATTER

Longitudinal waves *are transmitted through matter by a back-and-forth motion rather than by an up-and-down motion.* Figure 38-3 shows the nature of longitudinal waves. As previously mentioned, longitudinal waves to which the ear responds are called sound waves. *Longitudinal waves of higher frequencies than sound waves* are called **supersonic** or **ultrasonic waves.** These high-frequency, longitudinal waves will be discussed in Chapter 54.

BEHAVIOR OF SOUND WAVES

Propagation

Sound waves cannot travel in a vacuum. Figure 38-4 illustrates this fact. Sound waves

are usually produced in musical instruments by vibrating objects such as strings, reeds, drums, or air columns. The production of sound waves by musical instruments is dis-

Figure 38–4. A ringing alarm clock can be heard through a bell jar containing air, but if the air is removed with a vacuum pump the sound will no longer be heard.

cussed in Chapter 55. Anything that will set up compressions in matter may cause sound waves. For example, the sudden expansion of the air by an explosion or the expansion due to the heat of a lightning flash will set up longitudinal waves. A similar effect is produced by an airplane when it passes through air at a speed greater than the speed of sound in air.

Most of the sounds with which we are familiar travel through the atmosphere to our ears, but any medium will serve. For example, one may hear an approaching train by placing his ear on a railroad track. Again, a swimmer may hear sound waves transmitted by the water even better than he can hear sound waves transmitted by air, because water transmits longitudinal waves faster and with greater intensity than is true of waves in air.

Frequency and Speed

All sound waves travel in a given medium at the same speed, but they travel in different media with different speeds. The *length of a sound wave (wavelength)* is the *distance between succeeding condensations or rarefactions,* and it depends upon the frequency and the speed of the sound.

The velocity of sound in dry air is 1,085 feet per second at 0° C and it increases at the rate of 2 feet per second per degree C rise in temperature. Corrections for both the temperature and moisture content of air must be made in calculating the speed of sound in air, because the velocity imparted to molecules depends upon their masses rather than their number. Slight changes in barometric pressure do not affect the speed of sound because they merely determine the number of molecules present. Temperature affects the speed of sound in air because it changes the natural speed of the molecules. The velocity of sound in water is more than four times as great as that in air, and in steel, it is nearly fifteen times as great as that in air. The velocity of sound at sea level is 761 m.p.h. (miles per hour), but it is only 663 m.p.h. at an altitude of 40,000 feet. The velocities of aircraft and rockets are now often expressed in **mach numbers,** which *refer to the velocity of an object relative to the velocity of sound at sea level.* Thus, a velocity of an airplane flying at 200 m.p.h. is 0.26 mach, while the velocity of a rocket at 10,000 m.p.h. is 13.14 mach.

Intensity—The Inverse Square Law

The intensity of longitudinal waves, like the intensity of any kind of energy or force spreading out from a central point, is inversely proportional to the square of the distance from a source, because the area of a sphere carrying a given amount of energy increases as the square of the radius. Thus if the distance from the source, i.e., the radius, is tripled, the area of the sphere will be increased nine times, and the amount of energy in the same area of the wave would be only one-ninth as much as at the start, because the original energy has been distributed over nine times as much area.

The sensation which we call the **loudness** of a sound *depends upon the intensity of the longitudinal waves, and it therefore also depends upon the amplitude of the vibrations in the generator which causes these waves.*

Diffraction

It is common knowledge that sound waves originating on one side of a building may be heard on another side even when there is nothing present to reflect or bend them. Sound waves, like transverse waves, travel in a straight line and will cast shadows, but because of their relatively high diffraction, the shadows are not sharp. Most sound waves may be diffracted, but this is not true of longitudinal waves of very high frequencies.

Refraction

Inasmuch as sound travels at different speeds in layers of air of different temperature and relative humidity, sound waves may be bent as they pass from one medium to another, as shown in Figure 38-5. The sound thus appears to travel farther under these conditions. The sound of a guitar played on a boat on a lake, on a hot summer night, will travel long distances with remarkable clearness because of the refraction of the sound waves by the warm air over the cooler water.

The conditions are reversed on a hot day. The sound waves are refracted upward and therefore the sound does not seem to travel so far.

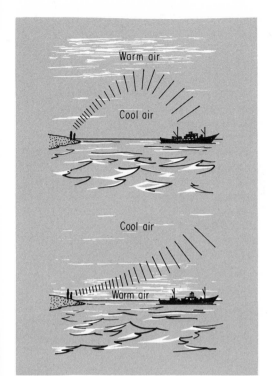

Figure 38–5. Since sound waves travel faster in warm air than in cool air, they are refracted as they pass from warm air to cool air and vice versa.

Reflection

Echoes or **reverberations** are *reflected sound waves,* and may be used to measure the distance between the sound source and the reflecting object. Reverberations constitute one of the major problems of acoustics, to be studied in Chapter 54. The rumbles of thunder are caused by reflections by a number of distant objects at different distances.

Concave or parabolic surfaces may be used to reflect and focus sound waves. Such surfaces are often used back of bandstands to reflect the band music. Speaking tubes and the tubes of one type of stethoscope prevent the sound waves from spreading out and thus transmit the sound with little decrease in intensity. Long corridors are similar to speaking tubes in their transmission of sound with little loss of intensity. Ear trumpets concentrate the energy of large areas of incoming sound waves into a small area, and thus increase the intensity.

As in the case of light waves, sound waves are best reflected by smooth, polished surfaces. Rough, porous surfaces absorb sound waves. The use of sound-deadening materials in acoustics is discussed in Chapter 54.

THE HUMAN EAR

The human ear can detect sharp sounds that occur at intervals as close as a twentieth of a second. It can discriminate between tones or musical notes whose frequency differs by less than 1 per cent. It can analyze and sort out the components of a mixture of sounds, concentrating on one at a time. At least a part of this action, of course, must occur in the brain. The other part of it may be due to the fact that we have two ears, which enable us to determine the direction from which a sound comes. A sound coming from the left will reach the left ear before it reaches the right ear, and vice versa.

The human ear is less sensitive to low frequencies than to high frequencies. On the high-frequency side of the sound spectrum, some children's ears can hear up to 40,000 cycles per second, but as one grows older the acuteness of hearing in the high-frequency range steadily falls at the rate of about 80 cycles every six months.

The human ear is divided into three chambers, as shown in Figure 38-6. The first chamber, the outer ear, consists of a short narrow tube, which, connecting with the visible portion of the ear, acts on the principle of the stethoscope to concentrate sound in one direction by means of reflection. This short, narrow tube of the outer ear is closed at its inner end by an elastic diaphragm, the eardrum. The middle ear consists of a system of three little bones, one end of which is attached to the eardrum and the other to another diaphragm, the oval window. The middle ear acts as a sort of lever to transmit vibrations to the inner ear. The vibrations are thus transmitted with decreased amplitude and increased force.

The inner ear is filled with liquid, and contains a coiled spiral enclosure with bony walls, in the shape of a snail's shell. The length of it, except at the tip, is divided by the basilar membrane, where the auditory nerve endings are to be found.

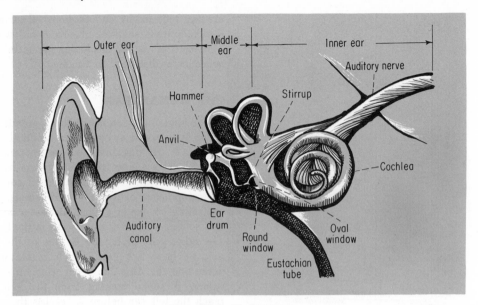

Figure 38–6.   The human ear.

There is another flexible window between the middle ear and the inner ear. Its purpose seems to be to provide for the vibrations in the fluid of the inner ear. Something has to give way as the oval window vibrates, and the liquid in the inner ear is practically incompressible, while the walls are rigid. The vibrations are thus transmitted up one side of the basilar membrane from the oval window and down the other side to the round window. The higher-frequency vibrations appear to be transmitted directly through the lower part of the basilar membrane. Low-frequency vibrations are transmitted by the liquid around the top of the membrane, while vibrations of intermediate frequency are transmitted by both methods.

Figure 38-7 shows the spiral of the inner ear straightened and much simplified. The frequencies to which given portions of this membrane are believed to respond are indicated.

THE HUMAN VOICE IS THE MOST VERSATILE OF MUSICAL INSTRUMENTS

The human voice is a reed type of instrument. The vocal cords act as the generator; and their tension, length, and thickness can

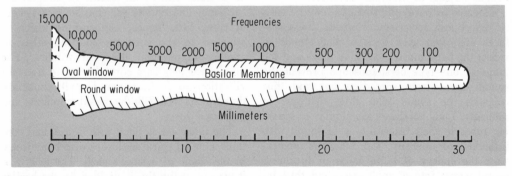

Figure 38–7.   The inner ear straightened out and much simplified (after Fletcher). The millimeter scale shows the approximate dimensions of the adult ear. The frequencies are placed opposite to the portions of the basilar membrane most sensitive to them.

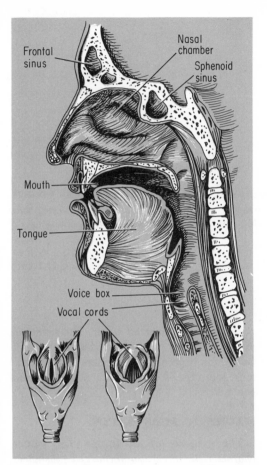

Figure 38–8. This diagram shows the location of the voice box and the various chambers in the head which control the quality of the voice. The smaller diagrams show the vocal cords enlarged. The position of the vocal cords when speaking is shown on the left. On the right, their position when breathing is indicated. The vibration of the vocal cords produces sound.

be controlled by the muscles. The vibrations are produced by the flow of air past the vocal cords, and they are modulated by changing the size and shape of the throat cavities, and by closing and opening the lips. The amplifier consists of head cavities whose shapes markedly affect the quality of the tones produced.

SUMMARY

Waves in Matter

Transverse waves, example: water waves.
Longitudinal waves, example: sound waves.

Sound Waves

Propagation in dry air at 0° C is 1,085 feet per second.

Sound waves may be refracted, diffracted, and reflected. Echoes are reflected sound waves. Sound waves are refracted as they pass from one medium to another having a different density.

Interference—Sound waves may unite in opposite phase to cancel each other, or in like phase, to reinforce each other.

The Ear

Many different sounds may be heard and recognized simultaneously because of the large number of nerve endings which are sensitive to a considerable range of frequencies of sound waves (20 to 20,000, and in some cases up to 40,000).

The Voice

The generator consists of the vocal cords, which resemble a reed type of musical instrument. The cavities in the head serve as the amplifier and modifier of the sounds.

Study Questions

1. DEFINE: longitudinal wave, transverse wave, amplitude, wavelength, frequency, interference, diffraction, echo, reverberation, supersonic, ultrasonic, mach number, loudness, energy, sound, refraction.
2. How is sound propagated through matter?
3. What is the relationship between the speed, the wavelength, and the frequency of a wave?
4. How could one prove that sound does not travel in a vacuum?
5. What is the effect of temperature on the velocity of sound in air? Work out an explanation of this effect.
6. Why does sound not travel through a vacuum?
7. What is the velocity of sound in air?
8. Suppose that one sees the steam of a whistle one minute before he hears the sound; how far away is the whistle?
9. What is meant by the frequency of sound waves?
10. Compare sound waves with electromagnetic waves as to the medium in which they travel, and as to their rate of motion and sources.

Magnetism

In the discovery of secrets, and in the investigation of the hidden causes of things, clear proofs are afforded by trustworthy experiments. . . . To you alone, who seek knowledge, not from books only, but also from things themselves, do I address these magnetic principles. . . .

WILLIAM GILBERT

INTRODUCTION

Magnetism has been known since the time of the early Greeks, but it was not until the past century that it was studied and put to useful application, except in the mariner's compass.

The ancient Greeks knew of the peculiar property of attracting bits of iron possessed by certain lustrous black stones brought from Magnesia in Asia Minor. They were named "magnets" because of their source. These stones were really pieces of an iron ore, now called "magnetite." The Chinese have known the magnetic properties of lodestone since early times. They called it "the stone that loves iron."

Later, the miners on the island of Samothrace came to know that certain types of iron would become imbued with this property of magnetism when rubbed with magnetite.

It was discovered that a piece of magnetite, suspended so as to turn freely about a vertical axis, would always come to rest with the same part of the stone pointing in a northerly direction. This was the first magnetic compass, and the stone thus came to be known as "lodestone," or "leading stone." The origin of the compass is unknown, but it is certain that crude ones were in use during the latter part of the thirteenth century. These early compasses consisted of a magnetic needle sup-

ported so as to float on water. The invention of the compass was of outstanding significance, for it permitted mariners to undertake long journeys of exploration, adventure, and commerce.

MAGNETIC SUBSTANCES

The property of attracting other matter, characteristic of certain uncharged substances, is called **magnetism.** Such objects are described as being magnetic. The only substances which exhibit magnetism to any considerable extent are iron, cobalt, and nickel. Iron is by far the most magnetic of all the elements, although certain alloys far surpass its magnetism: *permalloy,* an alloy of nickel and iron, and *perminvar,* an alloy of nickel, iron, and cobalt, are typical examples. A recent iron alloy, containing aluminum, nickel, and cobalt, hence called *"alnico,"* is so powerfully magnetic when magnetized that it lifts 500 times its own weight. An alnico magnet constructed with many air gaps has supported 4,450 times its own weight. An alloy of cobalt and platinum has 24 times the lifting power of an alnico magnet. Some of the newer, more powerful magnets are made from alloys of bismuth and manganese; iron and aluminum; iron, cobalt, and molybdenum; and iron, cobalt, and vanadium. A whole range of alloys of iron, nickel, chromium, and silicon can be prepared in such proportions that they will lose or regain their magnetism at certain definite temperatures from 150° C to 1,100° C thus providing a new method of producing automatic temperature controls.

The first serious study of magnetism seems to have been made by the physician, Sir William Gilbert (1540–1603), personal physician to Queen Elizabeth, at the end of the sixteenth century. A unit of magnetism, the "gilbert," has been named after him. He noted that in England the needle of the mariner's compass dipped with its north pole downwards through an angle depending on the latitude, and he inferred from these experiments that the earth itself acts as a huge magnet, with its poles considerably distant from the geographical poles. Gilbert's observations concerning magnetism were published in a book entitled *De Magnete* in 1600. Gilbert observed that the attraction of a magnet appears to be concentrated at two points which are called poles. In the case of bar magnets the poles are generally near the ends, as can be proved by dipping them in iron filings. William Gilbert is considered to have been the founder of the sciences of magnetism and electricity. Francis Bacon repeatedly referred to him as one of the first men to practice the experimental method.

THE LAW OF MAGNETIC ATTRACTION AND REPULSION

Gilbert made a small globe out of lodestone and found that it behaved much like the earth toward compasses. He found that what we call the north magnetic pole of the earth corresponds to the south pole of a magnet; north-seeking poles of magnets repel each other, while there is attraction between unlike poles. This is a very important **law of magnetism,** namely, *that like poles repel and unlike poles attract each other.* The amount of their attraction or repulsion varies with the product of the strength of the poles and inversely with the square of the distance between them—another example of the inverse square law. The **north pole of a magnet** is *the end of the magnet that points toward the north pole of the earth.*

A compass supported so that it can swing vertically is called a **dipping needle.** The dipping needle shows the direction of the lines of force in the earth. Large deposits of magnetic minerals alter the direction of these lines of force somewhat in certain localities.

A compass points north because the earth is a magnet with poles near the North and South Poles. The **magnetic north pole** *lies north of Hudson Bay about 1,400 miles from the geographic North Pole.* The fact that a magnetic needle will always set itself with the same pole pointing to the north indicates that the two poles are different. No magnet has been found with only one pole. Long thin bars of steel when magnetized may show more than two poles. A steel ring may be magnetized, but it shows no poles. Small doughnut-shaped magnets, called toroids, have extremely high magnetic permeability. They are used for the storage of facts (memories) in some types of computers.

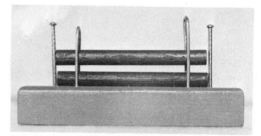

Figure 39–1. A floating magnet. One magnet floats in air above the other because of the repulsion of like poles.

MAGNETIC FIELDS

The fact that it is not necessary for magnets to touch each other for their attractive or repulsive force to act is accounted for by the hypothesis that *the space around a magnet must be in a state of strain. The region subject to this strain* is called the magnet's field, or simply the **magnetic field.** A very good map of such a field can be obtained by placing a piece of paper over a magnet and then sprinkling iron filings over the paper. It will be noted that the complete lines of force (used to represent a magnetic field) extend from the north pole to the south pole or vice versa, and this would be found true of every line **if**

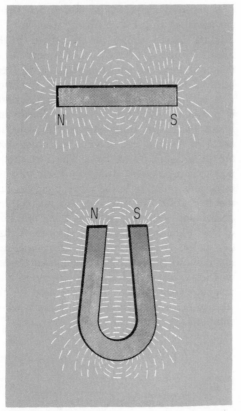

Figure 39–2. Diagrammatic representation of the lines of force of typical magnets.

tions because of the attraction of large deposits of magnetite for the compass needle.

The magnetic field in the gap of a broken ring is very intense. This fact is applied advantageously in the use of horseshoe magnets.

The field concept is very general, and is applicable to electrical phenomena and gravitation as well as magnetism. It should be kept in mind that fields of force are not understood. There is not even a satisfactory theory to explain them. Lines of force are imaginary lines drawn in such a way that the direction of the line indicates the direction of the force. Actually there are no lines of force. The field is continuous. The lines shown when iron filings are sprinkled in a magnetic field appear to be real enough, but they are not definite or unchanging. About all that we know about a magnetic field is that it can exist in a vacuum, i.e., it does not require the presence of matter. Furthermore it can penetrate nonmagnetic materials such as paper, thin sheets of copper, wood, and glass.

THE GYROCOMPASS

When the first iron ships were built, it was found that compasses were so affected by the iron that they were useless. Sir George Airy (1801–1892), in 1838, worked out a method of using compensating magnets which made iron ships practical. Modern iron ships use gyrocompasses which are not affected by the iron. Leon Foucault, who coined the word *gyroscope* in 1851, predicted that the gyroscope would one day be used as a compass. Elmer A. Sperry invented the first practical gyrocompass. At his death, in 1930, a total of 380 patents stood in his name. Speaking about his inventions he once said, "Ninety per cent of any invention is the statement of the problem." It will be recalled that the definition of a problem is an important step in all problem solving. The principle of the gyroscope is that once its axis has been oriented towards the north pole, it will resist any change from this direction.

THE CARE OF MAGNETS

When a magnet is used to induce magnetism in another magnet it does not seem to lose

one could follow it far enough. It may be noted that the magnetic field is stronger at the poles.

Michael Faraday (1791–1867), the experimenter who did more than any other man to place the science of magnetism and electricity upon a firm basis, found that these lines of force behave like stretched rubber bands, trying to shorten in the direction of their length and to widen in the direction of their width.

A magnetic field can freely penetrate nonmagnetic substances such as paper, wood, or glass. Some substances are more readily penetrated by magnetic fields than others. Thus, iron has a **permeability** (*attraction for lines of force*) several hundred times that of air. This is shown by the bending of the earth's lines of force as they pass over a deposit of iron ore. In some parts of the world the compass is rendered useless for telling direc-

magnetism in the process. Permanent magnets do gradually lose their magnetism, but this loss can be decreased by the use of keepers. A **keeper** is *a piece of iron that is put across the poles of a horseshoe or U-magnet.* In the case of bar magnets, a pair of magnets should be placed side by side with opposite poles next to each other, and a keeper should be placed at the two ends of the magnets.

THE MOLECULAR THEORY OF MAGNETISM

A few easily performed experiments suggest that magnetism is molecular in its nature and origin. If we cut a magnetized steel wire showing pronounced poles at the ends into short pieces, each one of these pieces will be a magnet with north and south poles. This subdivision into separate small magnets can be continued until the pieces are too small to be further subdivided by physical methods. Such experiments form the basis for the molecular theory of magnetism. According to this theory, each of the particles (atoms or molecules, or groups of these, as the case may be) of which the iron wire is composed is a tiny magnet having a north and a south pole. In an unmagnetized piece of iron these small magnets point in various directions with no resultant magnetic effect. *Magnetizing of iron consists of turning some of these miniature magnets so that their poles point in the same direction* and therefore unite to make the whole bar show magnetic properties. The above *process of aligning the particles* is called **orientation.** The molecular theory seems to be quite logical when we consider how a bar of iron is magnetized. One way of magnetizing a body is to stroke it with a magnet, always drawing the magnet the same way on the bar. Another way is to hold the bar so that the earth's lines of force pass through it, and to tap it several times. On the other hand, a magnet may be demagnetized by tapping it while it is held in such a position that the earth's lines of force do not pass through it lengthwise. Still another method of destroying the magnetism of an iron bar is to heat it to redness.

All of these phenomena can be explained by the molecular theory. Stroking with a magnet tends to orient the molecules. Tapping temporarily disturbs the forces which hold the molecules together within the solid, thus leaving them free to rearrange themselves in accordance with the forces acting on them. Heating agitates the molecules so much that all previous orderly arrangements are broken up and thus destroys the magnetism. The molecular theory can be demonstrated very nicely by stroking a test tube full of iron filings with the pole of a magnet. The iron filings are found to line up end to end, but this orderly arrangement may be disturbed by shaking the tube.

The molecular theory may also be demonstrated by suspending a large number of small magnets on pivots on a board and submitting them to magnetic fields. The small magnets will spin around as a large magnet is moved over them, or they will become oriented when one pole of the magnet is placed at one end of the board. See Figure 39-3.

The methods described above for magnetizing a piece of iron are examples of what is known as **magnetic induction.** The molecules of soft iron are easily oriented according to the above theory, inasmuch as soft iron acts as a magnet only when it is in a magnetic field. For example, a piece of soft iron held near a magnet acquires the property of picking up iron objects, but loses it at once when the magnet is removed. A whole chain of tacks can be picked up by a magnet because each tack temporarily becomes a small magnet by induction. Steel is more difficult to magnetize, but retains its magnetism for a long time once it is magnetized. According to the

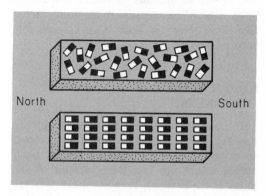

Figure 39–3. Molecular theory of magnetism. The molecules are thought to be aligned in regular order.

molecular theory, the molecules in steel are held together more rigidly than are the molecules in soft iron.

A magnet is said to be **saturated** when *it can acquire no more magnetism,* or, in other words, when the maximum number of the molecules has been oriented.

The molecular theory does not explain magnetism but merely indicates that magnetism is a molecular phenomenon.

THE ELECTRON THEORY OF MAGNETISM

Undoubtedly you have already wondered what iron has that copper or lead do not have as far as magnetism is concerned. According to the Bohr theory of atomic structure, the atom is a miniature solar system in which electrons (negative charges of electricity) revolve about a positively charged nucleus. (The meaning of negative and positive charges will be discussed in the next chapter.) The electrons also spin about their own axes. Later we shall learn that electrons in motion are surrounded by magnetic fields, i.e., that electrons in motion behave like magnets. The electrons in an atom create two magnetic fields, one for their orbital motion and one for their spin. It is the spin that causes each electron to behave like a small bar magnet. In many atoms the electrons spinning in a clockwise direction cancel the magnetic effects of the electrons spinning in a counterclockwise direction. In iron and other magnetic substances, the electrons spinning in one direction exceed the number of electrons spinning in the other direction, and magnetism results. The above theory is based upon considerable experimental evidence.

APPLICATIONS OF PERMANENT MAGNETS

If screwdrivers are magnetized, they may thus hold screws. Hammers may be magnetized so as to hold tacks or nails, but their magnetism would not last long because of the blows of the hammer. Permanent magnets are used in loudspeakers, headphones and hearing aids.

Watches that have steel parts may become magnetized in a powerful magnetic field. However, nonmagnetic watches made from nonmagnetic materials are available.

As we shall learn in the next chapter, a compass may be used to determine whether or not an electric current is flowing through a wire. A compass may be used to locate studs in a wall by the attraction of the nails in the studs. Perhaps the most common application of all is the use of a compass to determine direction.

Wire recorders became very popular for use in the office or home. The piano wire in them was magnetized in the recorder, as sounds were changed to electromagnetic fields in the wire while it ran through the machine. The sounds could be reproduced by running the wire through the machine. The magnetism could be removed as desired, so that the wires could be used over and over again. Soon, however, it was discovered that a thin film of iron oxide could be coated on a thin, strong film, such as Mylar film, and that tape prepared in this way could be used to make magnetic records of sounds and pictures, even color pictures. Magnetic tapes have replaced wire recorders for most purposes. Nearly all original recordings are made on tape for the phonograph industry. Magnetic tape is also widely used in computers and various types of automatic machines.

One large company processes a payroll of 30,000 employees on tape in a computer, and then mails the tape to the Social Security office to be processed on its computer, thus eliminating the necessity of a 900-page report. An insurance company prepared premium notices for 33 million policy holders from data on 300 rolls of tape, which replaced 13 million punch cards. In the television industry, *magnetic tapes, used to record both sound and picture,* are called **video tapes.** They cost about one-half as much as motion picture film, and have the advantage that they can be played back immediately, since there is no problem of developing, as in the case of photographic film. Sound motion picture cameras and projectors, using video tape, represent the next advance in home "movies." Magnetic tape is ideal for stereophonic recording.

Magnetic door catches have become very popular. A magnetic plastic tape has been made. The poles of this tape run along opposite edges rather than being located at the ends. Such tape is used for sealing refrigerators. A magnetic fluid clutch can be changed from a liquid to a near solid by the flick of a switch.

As new, stronger magnets become available, new uses are found for them, and many improvements can be made in electric motors, transformers, and other devices because of the new magnets.

SUMMARY

Some magnets retain their magnetism; these are called **permanent magnets.** *Other magnets lose their magnetism when removed from a magnetic field;* these magnets are called **temporary magnets.** Magnetism may be induced in magnetic materials.

Magnets vary in their strength, depending upon their shape, size, and the nature of the material from which they are made.

Magnets attract iron and steel.

A magnetic field can go through matter such as wood, paper, and glass. It may also go through a vacuum.

All magnets (except ring magnets) have a north and south pole. Unlike poles attract each other and like poles repel each other.

Magnetic fields are strongest at the poles.

A compass needle is a magnet.

The earth is a giant magnet.

Magnetism may be the result of the orientation of molecules or the unequal spin of electrons in atoms of magnetic elements.

The attraction or repulsion between magnetic poles is directly proportional to the product of the strength of the magnetic fields and inversely proportional to the square of the distance between them.

Study Questions

1. DEFINE: magnetism, permanent magnet, magnet, magnetic north pole, dipping needle, magnetic field, temporary magnet, keeper, orientation, magnetic induction, video tape, permeability, saturation.
2. Describe the circumstances that seem to have led to the discovery of magnetism.
3. Describe a simple compass.
4. How can the magnetism of a magnet be destroyed?
5. Why can the magnetic compass not be used in some regions of the earth?
6. What makes a freely moving magnet point north and south?
7. How may an iron bar be magnetized?
8. If an iron bar is easy to magnetize, will it retain its magnetism for a long time?
9. Explain the magnetizing and demagnetizing of an iron bar in terms of the molecular theory.
10. Why does a dipping needle not dip to the same degree at different points on the earth's surface?
11. What is the difference between an unmagnetized and a magnetized iron bar according to the molecular theory?
12. Explain how magnetism may be increased by rhythmical pounding.
13. Give the facts of magnetism, and show how the molecular theory explains each fact.
14. Give the laws of magnetism.
15. How can you prove that the earth is a magnet, i.e., (a) that it has two poles, and (b) that it is surrounded by a magnetic field?
16. Try to explain the laws of magnetism in terms of the molecular theory.
17. What metals compose the alloys which are used to make powerful permanent magnets?
18. Give an example of induced magnetism and explain it.
19. Give the facts that support the molecular theory of magnetism.
20. Distinguish between a magnet and a magnetic substance.
21. What are the advantages of video tape?

Electricity

Like charges repel, and unlike charges attract each other, with a force that varies inversely with the square of the distance between them . . . in all of atomic and molecular physics, in all solids, liquids and gases, and in all things that involve our relationship with our environment, the only force law, besides gravity, is some manifestation of this simple law. Frictional forces, wind forces, chemical bonds, viscosity, magnetism, the forces that make the wheels of industry go round —all these are nothing but Coulomb's law. . . .

J. R. ZACHARAIS

INTRODUCTION

The chief sources of electricity are chemical cells, generators, and friction. Electric generators will be a topic in the next chapter. Chemical cells were studied in Chapter 32. Chemical cells produce direct current electricity, which is discussed briefly in this chapter. The production of static electricity, the main topic of this chapter, forms a foundation for the understanding of current electricity.

STATIC ELECTRICITY—EARLY EXPERIMENTS

Thales of Miletus (640–560 B.C.) rubbed amber with fur and observed that sparks were produced, and that the rubbed amber would attract small objects such as feathers. At the beginning of the seventeenth century, William Gilbert repeated Thales' experiments and found that other materials would behave like amber. Glass and sealing wax were found to acquire the property of attracting certain objects when they were rubbed. Gilbert could not explain the phenomenon, but he did name this new form of energy *"electric,"* after the

Greek word for *amber*. From this term our modern word "electricity" was derived.

In 1733, Charles Francis de Cisternay Du Fay (1678–1739) discovered that charged amber rods would repel each other, and that charged glass rods did likewise. These charged amber rods lost their charges when they were touched to charged glass rods.

Benjamin Franklin (1706–1790) surmised that lightning is the discharge of static electricity. It was he who coined the terms, positive and negative charges. He defined the **negative charge** *as one which is similar to the charge produced by stroking hard rubber with fur,* and a **positive charge** *as one similar to that produced by stroking glass with silk.* He found that like charges repel each other and that unlike charges attract each other, thus explaining du Fay's experiments.

J. T. Desaguliers, in 1740, suggested the term, **conductor,** *for materials along which electricity flows freely. For materials such as* amber or glass, *along which electricity does not flow* he suggested the term **insulator.** All metals are good conductors, although some are better conductors than others. Silver, copper, gold, and aluminum, in the order given, are the best conductors.

Figure 40–1. A comb, when rubbed with silk or wool, will attract pieces of tissue paper.

apart when they become charged. By bringing a negatively charged rod near the top metal ball, which is connected to the gold leaves, negative charges are repelled down to the leaves, which thus fly apart because of their charges. If one touches the metal ball, the negative charges will flow through the body to the earth and the leaves will collapse. If the charged rod is now removed the leaves of the electroscope will fly apart again because they have become positively charged. The electroscope is very useful in detecting static charges.

THE DISTRIBUTION OF STATIC CHARGES

Static electric charges distribute themselves on the surfaces of objects as far apart from each other as possible. They tend to concentrate on pointed objects, and when a sufficient charge is built up, they will produce a faint violet "corona" discharge known as "St. Elmo's Fire." Similar discharges along high-voltage electrical transmission lines are called "corona" discharges. The ions repelled from a charged body may create a wind which is capable of blowing a candle flame out of shape.

STATIC ELECTRICITY MACHINES

Static electricity may be produced by means of various electrostatic machines, such as the Wimshurst machine, which consists of many strips of tin foil mounted on a nonconducting disk. These disks are rotated and produce

INDUCED STATIC ELECTRICITY— THE ELECTROSCOPE

Figure 40-2 shows how an electroscope may be charged by induction. The **electroscope** contains two thin gold leaves that will fly

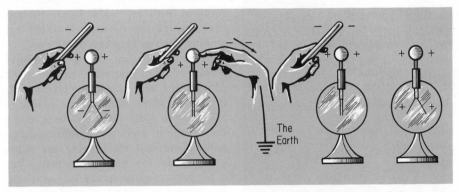

Figure 40–2. Charging an electroscope by induction. The electrons induced on the leaves of the electroscope are conducted by the body to the ground.

Figure 40-3. This spinning phonograph record produces static charges when it rubs against a silk cloth.

charges by induction. The charges are collected by metallic brushes and carried to a Leyden jar, where they are stored. The principle of the Leyden jar will be discussed in the following description of condensers.

The production of static electricity by induction has been carried out on a large scale by Van de Graaff of the Massachusetts Institute of Technology. The 10 million-volt generator conveys electric charges, induced by a transformer-rectifier on a silk belt, to large hollow aluminum spheres where the electric charges accumulate on their surfaces. When the charges have been built up sufficiently, miniature lightning bolts can be produced, as shown in Figure 40-4.

STORING STATIC ELECTRICITY—CONDENSERS

Condensers are merely *pairs of conductors separated by nonconductors*. If a charge is now induced on one plate, an opposite charge is induced on the other plate. These charges become larger than would otherwise be possible because the charge on the one plate partially overcomes the repulsion between the opposite charges on the other plate; the charges thus become condensed. If too large a charge is placed in a condenser, the air will become ionized and a spark will occur. A much larger charge may be placed in a condenser if the conductors are separated by some medium such as oil or glass, rather than air. A "Leyden jar" is simply a glass bottle which separate the two conductors of the condenser. The jar is usually coated on each side with tin foil. The Leyden jar was invented by Pieter van Musschenbroek, a professor at the University of Leyden, in 1746. Charged Leyden jars can produce tremendous shocks, and must be handled carefully. Van Musschenbroek's discovery was based on a shock which he received when he touched with one hand a bottle of water connected to one terminal of an electric machine and touched the other terminal with his other hand. He received such a shock that he said, "I would not take another for the kingdom of France."

Condensers, often called **capacitors** *because of their capacity to store electric charges*, are used in a wide variety of electric circuits. Without them, there would not be television or radio sets. Capacitors smooth out the voltage in a circuit by storing charges on their plates and discharging the stored up voltage into the line at intervals. Variable capacitors, used as tuners in radio sets, can be changed by moving a set of plates relative to each other.

Figure 40-4. Artificial lightning produced by a Van de Graaf generator. (Courtesy, High Voltage Engineering Corporation and Massachusetts Institute of Technology)

LIGHTNING, A STATIC PHENOMENON

In 1872, Benjamin Franklin devised an experiment to prove that a lightning flash is similar to a discharge from a Leyden jar. He flew a kite into a thunderstorm, with a silk thread as a conductor leading to the ground. He found that sparks would fly from a key attached to the thread. Lightning is the discharge between a cloud and the earth. The source of the charges is not thoroughly understood, although it is generally believed that it is produced by the intense friction and splitting of large raindrops brought about by the rapidly rising currents of air so characteristic of thunderstorms.

Figure 40–5. Lightning striking the Empire State Building, New York City. (Courtesy, General Electric Company)

Negative charges concentrate on the bottoms of clouds, leaving the tops positively charged. Discharges may take place between the top and bottom surfaces of adjoining clouds. A charged cloud may induce an opposite charge on the nearest portion of the earth. This induced charge will concentrate on trees, flagpoles, or buildings which rise above the surface of the ground, and thus act as pointed surfaces. Eventually, this charge may become so great that the resistance of the air is overcome and a lightning flash occurs. It was Franklin's suggestion that lightning rods with sharp points be used for the protection of buildings. Such lightning rods must be well grounded in the earth, and it is generally recommended that they be connected with some object such as a copper kettle buried deep in damp earth.

If a house could be enclosed in a **Faraday cage** *of ironwork,* the cage could be struck with lightning repeatedly without producing any observable effect. Modern steel-framed skyscrapers are often struck by lightning, but there is no record of anyone ever having been harmed in the process. See Figure 40-5.

An automobile behaves like a Faraday cage. The lightning discharge is conducted on the outside surface of the automobile body and jumps to the ground. A person seated in the automobile would not be hurt if the automobile were to be struck by lightning, if laboratory lightning experiments produce the same results that lightning in nature produces.

THE ELECTRON THEORY AND STATIC ELECTRICITY

According to the electron theory, a neutral body possesses the same number of positive charges (protons) and negative charges (electrons). A negatively charged body possesses an excess of electrons, whereas a positively charged body possesses an excess of protons. It is a fundamental concept of our modern electrical theory of matter that *opposite charges attract each other, whereas like charges repel each other.*

It is easy to explain by the modern electron theory the phenomena just observed. According to this theory, glass, when rubbed by silk, loses electrons, and therefore becomes

Figure 40–6. Simulated lightning. Three-million volt discharge in the high-voltage laboratory of the Ohio Brass Company. (Courtesy, Ohio Brass Company)

positively charged. On the other hand, hard rubber, when rubbed by wool, gains electrons from the wool, and therefore becomes negatively charged. The pith ball, when touched by the glass rod, is repelled because it gives up some of its electrons to the glass rod; and, thus becoming positively charged, the ball is repelled by the glass rod, which still possesses an excess of positive charges. The electrons in the atoms of nonconductors are thought to be held too tightly within the atoms to move freely, while the electrons in conductors are relatively free to move. The concept that electrostatic fields surround all electric charges is very useful in explaining many phenomena. The imaginary lines of force radiate in all

directions from a single electric charge, either positive or negative, and terminate on other opposite charges.

Charles Augustin **Coulomb** (1736–1806) discovered **the law** named after him, stated as follows: *The force between the electric fields of two charges is directly proportional to the product of the magnitudes of the charges, and is inversely proportional to the square of the distance between them.*

APPLICATIONS OF STATIC ELECTRICITY

Perhaps you have noticed that gasoline trucks drag chains along the ground to prevent the accumulation of static charges that might produce a spark and ignite the gasoline.

The electrostatic filter, used to remove dust and pollens from the air in air-conditioning systems, consists of a plastic material which develops an electrostatic charge due to the friction caused by the air as it passes over it. This charged surface then attracts small electrically charged particles from the air as it passes over it.

An economical copying device deposits static charges which then pick up finely divided carbon to form the printed copies.

CURRENT ELECTRICITY

Galvani's Discovery of Current Electricity

Luigi Galvani (1737–1789), an Italian professor of anatomy and obstetrics at the University of Bologna, in about 1768 noticed that the severed leg of a frog contracted under the influence of a nearby electrostatic machine. This observation aroused his curiosity, and he determined to see whether or not atmospheric electricity would have the same effect. Electricity, carried down a lightning rod specially erected for this experiment, produced the same twitching when a storm approached. He also found that this twitching was produced when a nerve and a muscle were connected with two dissimilar metals placed in contact with each other. Galvani concluded from this experiment that the source of the current was in the frog itself. How was he to know that these two metals in contact with the saline juices in the frog's leg constituted the world's first observed chemical electric cell? Galvani's work was of importance because it stimulated a great deal of investigation. For this service alone it is quite fitting that he be honored by having electric currents and instruments named after him respectively as "galvanic" currents and the "galvanoscope" and "galvanometer."

Volta's Electric Pile

The production of current electricity was discussed in Chapter 32. It will be recalled that Volta invented the voltaic pile, consisting of a series of copper and zinc disks separated from each other by paper moistened with brine. He believed that the contact between the two metals caused the current and that the brine merely served as a conductor. It remained for Sir Humphry Davy (1778–1829) to show that the source of the electric current in a cell is the chemical reaction between the electrodes and the substance in the solution in which they are placed.

THE WATER ANALOGY OF AN ELECTRIC CURRENT

In order that water shall flow in a pipe, the pipe must be of sufficient size to carry the desired quantity of water, and there must be a pressure to maintain the flow of water. The pressure may be supplied by a tank filled with water at a higher level than the water outlet.

If the water outlet is opened, the water will run out of the tank, and the flow of water will stop. This corresponds to the discharge of an electrical charge through a conductor.

If the water level is maintained in the tank, then the water will continue to flow through the pipe at the same rate. This level may be maintained by a pump, which thus supplies the energy contained by the flowing water. Instead of a difference in water levels, there is *a difference in electric charges in the electric circuit,* called a **potential difference,** which is maintained by the electric battery or the generator that supplies the energy to maintain a steady flow of electrons through the wire. The valve in the water pipe corresponds to the switch in the circuit. The requirements for an electric current are, therefore, a sustained difference of potential and a conductor. Pipes offer resistance, which cuts down the flow of water. Electrical conductors also offer resistance to flow. A wire of small diameter will not conduct as much current as a wire of large diameter for equal differences in potential.

The **resistance** *of a circuit determines the amount of current that will flow under a given difference of potential.* This is a simple statement of Ohm's law. It is expressed mathematically as follows:

$$\text{current } (I) = \frac{\text{Difference in potential } (E)}{\text{Resistance } (R)}$$

The electric current, the difference of potential, and the resistance may all be expressed in familiar units:

Quantity Measured	Unit	Named in Honor of	Usual Symbols
Current	Amperes	(Ampere)	(I)
Resistance	Ohms	(Ohm)	(R)
Difference of potential (Electromotive force)	Volts	(Volta)	(E)

Difference of potential is also *called* **voltage.** An instrument that measures voltages is a voltmeter. It corresponds to the pressure gauge on a water line. The ammeter is the instrument designed to measure amperes, and corresponds to a water meter (flow-meter type) that measures the flow of water in gallons per unit of time. Water meters, which measure the total amount of water flowing, correspond to coulometers, which measure coulombs. *The unit of electric current*, the **ampere,** corresponds to the flow of one coulomb per second. The *unit of resistance*, the **ohm,** is the resistance offered by a conductor that conducts one ampere under a potential difference of one volt.

Electricity always follows the easiest path. When it leaves its intended circuit and cuts across to a shorter one offering less resistance, a "short circuit" results.

All materials offer some resistance to the flow of an electric current, and that part of the electrical energy used in overcoming this resistance is transformed into heat. The resistance of a metallic conductor depends on the kind of material from which the conductor is made, and varies directly with the length and inversely with the cross-sectional area. It increases as the temperature increases.

SUMMARY

Static electricity is produced by friction. Charges build up best on dry days. Static charges may be induced by a charged body. Charges on a conductor tend to stay on the outside surface and to be greatest on sharp edges and points.

Every complete electric circuit must have a source of electrical energy, a device to use the electricity (commonly called the load), and connecting wires. If the circuit is broken the electric current will not flow. Switches and fuses are used to break the circuit.

Electric charges may be stored by condensers (capacitors).

Ohm's Law.

$$(I) \text{ (Amperes) Current} = \frac{(E) \text{ (Volts) Voltage}}{(R) \text{ (Ohms) Resistance}}$$

Laws of Static Electricity

(1) Like charges repel each other.

(2) Unlike charges attract each other.

(3) Coulomb's Law—The force between the electric fields of two charges is directly proportional to the product of the magnitude of the charges, and is inversely proportional to the square of the distance between them.

Study Questions

1. DEFINE: condenser, conductor, insulator, electroscope, Faraday cage, potential difference, ampere, ohm, negative charge, positive charge, capacitor, resistance, voltage.
2. What is the nature of an electric current?
3. Use the water analogy in explaining the flow of an electric current through a conductor.
4. Describe the original observations that led to the first chemical cell.
5. State Ohm's law. Give an application of this law.
6. Name the electrical unit of measurement for each term in Ohm's law.
7. Is resistance a property of electricity or of a conductor?
8. Why is it that electricity will not flow to an object but has to flow through the object if the current is to flow at all?
9. What change took place (a) on the hard rubber, and (b) on the glass rod when it was electrified?
10. Discuss the theory of the production of lightning.
11. How does the electrostatic filter work?
12. Explain the action of the electroscope.
13. Give a short description of the Wimshurst static machine.
14. Name five conductors and five insulators.

15. What is the fundamental difference between an insulator and a conductor?
16. What is the value of a lightning rod?
17. List the requirements of a good lightning rod.
18. Describe two methods of producing static charges.
19. Why is static electricity most noticeable on dry days?
20. Explain the charges on bodies in terms of the electron theory.
21. Describe a simple condenser. For what is a condenser used?
22. How may a positive charge be produced? Explain in terms of the electron theory.
23. State the laws of static electricity.
24. Describe Franklin's kite experiment. What did it prove?
25. Explain why the whole electric charge is on the surface of a conductor.
26. Suggest a method of charging an electroscope negatively.

Electromagnetism

The most original experimenter the world has ever seen is lecturing before a distinguished audience at the Royal Institution in London. He shows that when a magnet is brought suddenly near a coil of wire a slight current of electricity is produced in the wire. The experiment is not very impressive; and a lady probably voiced the feelings of most of the audience when she asked afterwards, "But, Professor Faraday, even if the effect you explained is obtained, what is the use of it?" The memorable reply was "Madam, will you tell me the use of a new-born child?"

SIR RICHARD GREGORY

INTRODUCTION

Two discoveries of fundamental importance in putting electricity to work were made in the nineteenth century. The first discovery, made in 1820, that of H. C. Oersted, was that an electric current produces a magnetic field in its vicinity. The second discovery, in 1831, was made by Michael Faraday, who found that under certain conditions a magnetic field can be made to produce an electric current. These two discoveries laid the foundations for the harnessing of electrical energy.

OERSTED'S DISCOVERY

Once the chemical cell had been invented, thus furnishing a convenient source of current electricity, investigators began to study the possible relationship between electricity and magnetism. Hans Christian Oersted (1777–1851) had been trying to find out whether there was any effect when a wire carrying a current was held above a compass at right angles to it. No effect was noted. According to one story, he accidentally placed the wire parallel to the needle during the course of a lecture and was much surprised to see the

needle turn aside. Oersted then tried placing the wire below the needle, and the needle was deflected in the opposite direction.

A. M. Ampere (1775–1836), a French investigator after whom the unit of electric current was named, worked out the principle of this relationship between the electric current and the magnetic field, and suggested that it could be used in communication. By sending an electric current through a wire, a compass needle can be deflected and can thus be made to transmit messages. The first electromagnetic telegraph was built in Gottingen in 1833, by Karl Friedrich Gauss and Wilhelm Weber.

It is now known that when an electric current flows through a straight wire a magnetic field is set up encircling the wire at all points. The direction of this field can be determined with a compass, which shows that the magnetic field is at right angles to the direction of the current. When the direction of the current is reversed, the direction of the magnetic field is reversed. The strength of the magnetic field is proportional to the amount of current being carried.

The magnetic field surrounding a wire can be nicely demonstrated by placing iron filings on a card through which a wire, carrying a

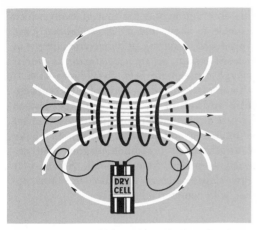

Figure 41–1. A coil of wire carrying an electric current behaves like a bar magnet.

current, passes. Upon tapping the card, the filings will line themselves up in such a way as to show the direction of the lines of force.

THE ELECTROMAGNET

When a wire carrying a current is bent into the shape of a loop, all of the lines of force outside the loop are pointing in one direction, and the same is true of those inside the loop. There is thus a strong magnetic field within the loop. If many loops or turns are added, the magnetic field becomes still stronger. Such a coil of wire carrying a current behaves like a bar magnet. See Figure 41-1.

Joseph Henry (1797–1878) constructed the first electromagnet, a piece of iron wrapped with an insulated wire. The magnetic field through a coil of wire can be very greatly strengthened by placing a core of soft iron in the center. Because of its high permeability to the magnetic lines of force, a great number of lines of force pass through the iron core and make it a powerful magnet. Such an electromagnet, as it is called, acts as a permanent magnet, but only so long as electricity is flowing through the coil; its polarity depends on the direction of the current. The strength of the electromagnet is proportional to the amount of electricity flowing through the wire, and also to the number of turns in the coil.

A coil of wire carrying an electric current is called a **solenoid.** Solenoids are used in industry to operate many automatic devices. If a coil of wire is placed in a vertical position, an iron core, which is held within the coil by the magnetic field as long as the coil is carrying an electric current, will drop through the coil when the circuit is broken. Such a device can be used to lock and unlock doors.

The ordinary electric doorbell consists of a clapper that strikes the bell when the iron strip to which it is attached is attracted to an electromagnet. A spring draws the iron piece back when the current is broken. The vibratory motion of the clapper is produced by an ingenious make-and-break device that breaks the circuit when the iron strip is drawn to the magnet, and closes the circuit when the strip is drawn back by the spring. Electromagnets have many applications; telegraph sounders, magnetic brakes, sensitive relays,

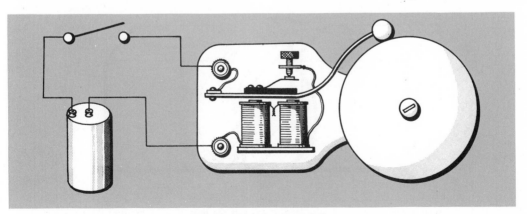

Figure 41–2. An electric bell.

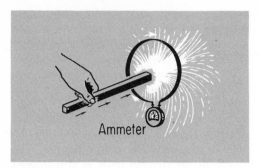

Figure 41–3. Faraday's experiment. An electric current is induced in the loop of wire by the motion of the magnet.

lifting magnets and many other devices are operated by electromagnets.

THE ELECTRIC GENERATOR

Michael Faraday (1791–1867) was the first man to visualize and name the magnetic lines of force. His studies led him to wonder why magnetism should not produce electricity, inasmuch as electricity produces magnetism. The induction of electrical charges by other static charges of electricity suggested the possibility of inducing a current of electricity by use of the current from chemical cells. Faraday wound two coils of insulated wire on the same iron ring and passed a steady current through one coil, and observed that no deflection was produced in a galvanometer attached to the other coil. He observed, however, that a slight deflection of the galvanometer needle occurred when the current started and stopped.

This observation was the first of many which he made to show that *an electromotive force is produced, resulting in an electric current in a closed circuit, when a conductor is moved through a magnetic field.* See Figure 41-4.

Soon ofter his discovery of **electromagnetic induction** in 1831, Faraday devised the first electric generator. In this experiment he rotated a coil of wire between the poles of a permanent horseshoe magnet, and obtained a current from the coil. Nearly fifty years elapsed before this discovery was applied with commercial success.

The Magneto

Magnetos *are devices arranged so as to move a coil of wire through a field between permanent horseshoe magnets.* They are called "magnetos" because permanent magnets are employed. The simplest generator is a magneto in which the loop of wire is attached to a shaft provided with two collars, to each of which one end of the loop is attached. Electricity is taken from these collars, as they revolve with the shaft, by means of carbon or copper contacts, called brushes. Little work is required to turn a magneto when the terminals of the moving coil are not connected by a switch through a lamp resistance; but when the switch is closed, it becomes difficult to turn the magneto. This resistance to motion results from the fact that the current produced in the coil sets up a magnetic field of its own, which opposes the motion.

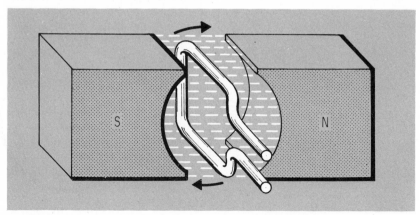

Figure 41–4. Principle of the generator. A wire loop or coil cuts the lines of force between the north and south poles of a magnet.

The current produced by a magneto is an **alternating current;** that is, *the current in the coil twice reverses its direction in each revolution.* Figure 41-4 shows why the magneto gives an alternating current. In the vertical position no lines of force will be cut, while in the horizontal position the maximum number of lines of force will be cut. Thus the current starts from zero, increases to a maximum, and again falls to zero for each half-turn. As the loop passes from one half-turn to the next, it cuts the field in an opposite direction and thus causes the direction of the current to be reversed.

The old style of telephone, in which the user turned a crank in order to ring a bell, depended upon the magneto. Magnetos may also be used where electricity is not otherwise available for furnishing the spark to ignite gaseous mixtures or a charge of powder in blasting operations. Many of the earlier automobiles used magnetos to furnish the spark to ignite the explosive gases in the cylinders and to light the headlights. Such automobiles had to be started by cranking, for there was no spark until the magneto was turned as the automobile was cranked. The introduction of the storage battery and the induction coil permitted the use of the self-starter and electric lights, thus eliminating the need for a magneto. However, some motorized lawnmowers and many motorboat engines must be started with magnetos.

The Dynamo

If powerful electromagnets are used to replace the permanent magnet of a magneto, a greater electromotive force is generated, thus producing a larger current. The strength of the current may be further increased by greatly increasing the number of magnetic lines of force (by use of four, six, or even more electromagnets), by increasing the number of turns in the loop of wire, or by increasing the strength of the electromagnetic field.

The number of times the current reverses in direction depends upon the number of electromagnets in the stator and the speed with which the rotor rotates. Most alternators are built so as to give a current of 60 cycles (or

120 alternations) per second. Inasmuch as the direct-current generator produces direct current, a portion or all of this current, depending on the type of generator, may be used to excite the electromagnets. Direct-current generators differ from alternating-current generators in that they have commutators and do not need auxiliary exciting motors. Alternating-current generators require auxiliary direct-current generators to maintain a constant electromagnetic field. The rotor and stator of an alternating-current generator correspond to the armature and field of the direct-current generator.

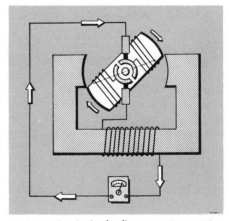

Figure 41–5. A simple direct-current generator.

If direct current is desired from a generator, the *collars or sliprings are split,* forming a **commutator,** *so that when the current reverses in the coil, the connections to the external circuit are also reversed.* Automobile generators are the direct-current type.

DIRECT-CURRENT GENERATORS VERSUS ALTERNATING CURRENT GENERATORS

Thomas Alva Edison (1847–1931) preferred direct-current generators, but Nikala Tesla (1856–1943) thought that an alternating current would be better for electrical transmission. For some time there was a controversy between the advocates of direct- and alternating-current generators. The perfection of alternating-current generators by George Westinghouse (1846–1914) and Charles Proteus

Steinmetz (1865–1923) resulted in their almost universal use. (In 1965, some of the newer super-voltage transmission lines were using direct current advantageously.)

MOTORS—THE REVERSE OF GENERATORS

Faraday made the first motor in 1821, and Joseph Henry paralleled his discovery of the motor. In 1873, Z. T. Gramme (1826–1901) observed that when a direct current was impinged upon a direct-current generator the rotor moved. *Any direct-current generator will operate as a* **motor** *if direct current is applied through the brushes.* The reason for this is that a mechanical force is exerted by a magnetic field on a conductor carrying a current. Whenever a conductor carrying a current is placed in a magnetic field in such a direction that the current flows at right angles to the field, the conductor experiences a force at right angles to both the direction of the current and the magnetic field. **Lenz's law** states this as follows: *an induced current is always in such a direction that its magnetic effect opposes the change by which it is produced.* In the motor, the electricity passes through the coils of the rotor, causing the core to be magnetized. If this core is pointed in such a direction that the north and south poles are opposite the north and south poles of the permanent magnets, it will be repelled, because like poles repel each other. As it makes half a turn as a result of this repulsion, the direction of the current through the commutator is reversed, and the south pole becomes the north pole, which is repelled again; thus the motor is kept running.

The **armature** (*rotating loops of wire*) is called the **rotor,** while *the stationary electromagnets* are spoken of as the **stator,** or **field.**

INDUCTION COILS

Figure 41-6 shows Michael Faraday's accidental discovery of the principle of induction coils. An **induction coil** *is used to increase or decrease voltage.* In Faraday's experiment there was no change in voltage, but merely the production of an electric current in one coil when the electric current in the other coil was stopped or started. An **induction coil** *consists of two coils of wire, the primary and the secondary, differing in numbers of turns.* If the secondary has more turns than the primary, the voltage will be increased in proportion to the ratio of the number of turns to each other. The induction coil operates only when a current starts, stops, or reverses its direction. Direct-current induction coils require automatic interrupters to start and stop the flow of the electric current.

TRANSFORMERS

Transformers are *induction coils used to change the voltage when employing alternating current.* Inasmuch as the direction of the

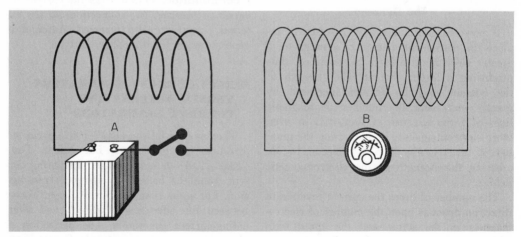

Figure 41–6. An electric current is induced in the secondary coil B when making or breaking the current in the primary coil A.

alternating current changes many times per second, no interrupters are required in transformers. For many purposes, direct current is required, but alternating current can frequently be used and has supplanted the direct type in most communities because electric power can be transmitted more economically by alternating current. The reason for this is that the voltage in the case of an alternating current can be raised by a transformer to a point where the loss in transmission due to resistance is reduced to a minimum; the high voltage can be lowered by another transformer at the place where the current is to be used. Thus the transformer has permitted the commercial use of alternating current. *A transformer that increases the voltage is called a* **step-up transformer.**

Transformers in which the number of turns in the primary is greater than that in the secondary decrease the voltage and are called **step-down transformers.** In the case of large transformers, the insulated coils are usually surrounded by oil to prevent short circuits, and to keep the transformers cool. (The oil is cooled by radiators.) The coils in smaller transformers are frequently packed in pitch or tar for the same reason.

SERIES AND PARALLEL CIRCUITS

Two or more conductors may be connected in series or parallel, as shown in Figures 41-7 and 41-8.

The combined resistance of all conductors

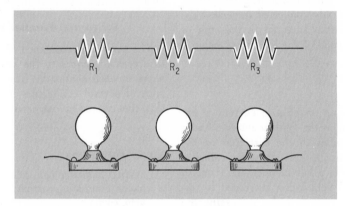

Figure 41–7. Series wiring.

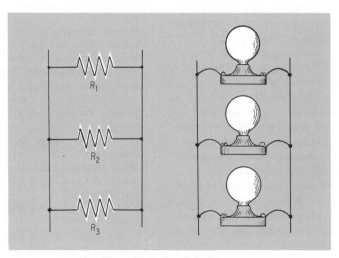

Figure 41–8. Parallel wiring.

is equal to the sum of the resistances of each conductor in a **series,** *while the effective resistance to the flow of current by the same number of conductors in* **parallel** *is less than that offered by any one conductor.* Cheap Christmas-tree lights are often strung together in series. If the current of an ordinary house-lighting circuit passes through one of these lights, it will be burned out at once because it was designed to carry much less current. This would not have been so had the current passed through all of the lights in the string, because less current flows as a result of their combined resistance. In such a string, all the lights go out when one light goes out, because the current is broken at this point.

Lights in ordinary house-lighting circuits are wired in parallel, thus enabling one light to be turned off without affecting the others.

Cells are generally connected in series; the voltage of the series is equal to the sum of the voltages of each of the individual cells.

SUMMARY

A wire carrying an electric current is encircled by a magnetic field counterclockwise and at right angles to the direction of the flow of electrons. A coil of wire, called a solenoid, acts like a bar magnet, the strength of the magnetic field being increased by introducing a soft-iron core, by increasing the number of turns of the wire, and by increasing the amount of current. The direction of a magnetic field is reversed when the direction of the electric current is reversed. This is the principle of the electromagnet. An electromagnet is a temporary magnet; it works only when the electric current is flowing.

Faraday discovered that the motion of a magnet relative to a coil of wire produced an electric current, but that the current was produced only when this motion started, stopped or fluctuated, i.e., whenever there is a change in the number of lines of magnetic force passing across the conductor. The number of turns in the coil of wire determines the voltage, while the speed of motion of the magnet relative to the coil determines the amperage of such an induced current.

The voltage may be increased by an induc-

tion coil that employs a make-and-break device, when using direct current. When using alternating current, the voltage may be increased or decreased by means of transformers, by controlling the number of turns in the primary and secondary coils.

Electric generators produce a direct current or an alternating current by the relative motion of a conductor through a magnetic field. Direct current generators use commutators to obtain the direct current. Motors are the reverse of generators. Generators change mechanical energy into electrical energy and motors reverse this process.

Lenz's Law

An induced current is always in such a direction that its magnetic effect opposes the change by which it is produced.

Series and Parallel Wiring

The combined resistance of each conductor in a series is equal to the sum of the resistances of each conductor. The effective resistance of several conductors in parallel is less than that offered by one conductor.

Study Questions

1. DEFINE: induction coil, solenoid, transformer, motor, alternating current, rotor, stator, magneto, commutator, series wiring, parallel wiring, step-up transformer, step-down transformer, field, armature, electromagnetic induction.
2. How would you proceed to transform a direct current of low voltage to one of high voltage?
3. Why do not alternating-current transformers have a make-and-break device?
4. How would you make a transformer (a) step up voltage, (b) step down a voltage?
5. Discuss Faraday's contribution to electromagnetism.
6. How may a voltage be induced in a conductor?
7. What determines the strength of the voltage produced by moving a coil of wire through a magnetic field?
8. How do transformers differ from induction coils?
9. If the speed of the loop of wire in the generator is increased, what is the effect on the current?

10. Name and give the purpose of the various parts of an alternating-current generator.
11. Describe and explain the action of a magneto.
12. Of what does the simplest motor consist?
13. Upon what does the strength of the current produced by a generator depend?
14. What happens when the direction of the current through a direct-current generator is reversed?
15. What factors determine the electromotive force of a generator?
16. Name two discoveries of fundamental importance in putting electricity to work. Who made these discoveries?

Electrical Communication

If we could only chain the lightning to carry our messages, that would be something!

SAMUEL F. B. MORSE

The real credit for everything that has been done in the field of wireless belongs, as far as such fundamental credit can be definitely assigned to anyone, to Professor Clerk Maxwell, who in 1864 carried out certain abstruse and remote calculations in the field of magnetism and electricity.

ABRAHAM FLEXNER

INTRODUCTION

This chapter presents the historic development of the telegraph, the telephone, the radio, and television. Their transmission technics are similar in that sound or light variations are carried by electromagnetic waves over wires or space and then changed back to light or sound as the case may be. The original telegraph and telephone depended upon the use of electromagnets. Radio and television are applications of the **thermionic effect,** i.e., *the emission of electrons by heated metals.* Television is an application of **the photoelectric** effect, i.e., *the emission of electrons by certain metals when they are irradiated by light.*

All of the above methods of electrical communication have been vastly changed and improved by **electronics,** i.e., *the use of vacuum tubes and semiconductors,* such as transistors, which will be presented in Chapter 59.

THE TELEGRAPH

In 1832, Samuel Morse (1791–1872), an artist, fell into a conversation with Dr. Jack-son, a fellow passenger on the ship in which he was returning to America from Europe. During this conversation, which had turned to the wonders of the recently perfected electromagnet, Morse conceived the idea of sending signals by means of an electric current. He gave up his profession as an artist, and after five years filed a patent caveat for his telegraph. After seven more years of patient, persistent work, poverty, and discouragement, the commercial importance of the telegraph was demonstrated when he was able to send the famous message, "What hath God wrought?" from Washington, D.C., to Baltimore.

The earliest form of the telegraph consisted of a key at one end of the telegraph wire for opening and closing the electric circuit and an electromagnet at the other end. When the sending key was closed, the current passed through an electromagnet and caused it to attract a piece of soft iron to its core. When the current stopped, the iron was pulled away from the core by means of a spring. A code of dots and dashes was used by Morse in sending messages, and was at first recorded on paper tape, but later was read by the operator directly from the sounds of the bar

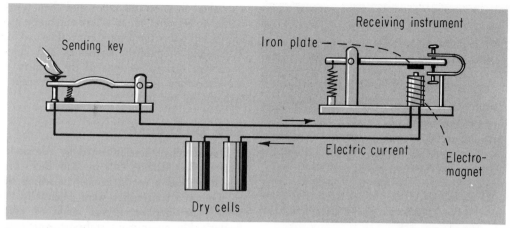

Figure 42–1. A one-way telegraph circuit. Pressing the key closes the circuit and causes the electromagnet in the receiver to pull down the iron plate, with a resulting sound. Actually only one wire would be needed because the ground would replace the wire between the dry cells and the electromagnet.

as it clicked against the electromagnet. Figure 42-1 shows the basic parts of a one-way telegraph system.

By 1872, when Morse died a rich and famous man, there had been many improvements over his original telegraph system, and many more have been made from year to year up to the present time. Modern telegraph systems use devices by which messages may be sent over a wire in both directions at the same time; and today the capacity of a telegraph system has been increased still more by sending a number of messages over a single transmission medium at the same time. In actual practice, many messages are sent simultaneously over a carrier system, or over a microwave radio-beam system. Automatic typewriters, operated directly by the telegraph signals and based on the use of a group of electromagnets, form the basis of the modern teletype used in newspaper and police work, as well as for many commercial and military installations. One linotype machine could operate all of the other linotype machines in the United States by means of the telegraph.

Modern electronic devices have revolutionized the telegraph. For example, the Desk-Fax, facsimile machine, shown in Figure 42-2 is used to send and receive more than 50 million telegrams daily in 40 thousand business offices. The copy to be transmitted is wrapped around a drum, which whirls at a speed of 180 revolutions per minute. An electric eye

scans the material and transmits it to the receiver, where it is reproduced on sensitized paper. Intrafax is a similar system used to link various offices of manufacturing plants. Weatherfax transmits United States Weather Bureau maps every fifteen minutes to 600 stations in the United States.

Figure 42-3 shows a Telex automatic machine for sending and receiving data and messages.

Figure 42–2. Sending a telegram by push-button. More than 40,000 compact, facsimile, "Desk-Fax" machines send and receive messages at the mere push of a button. (Courtesy, Western Union Telegraph Company)

Figure 42-3. An automatic machine for sending and receiving data and messages. The Telex system used by many large companies, consists of a typewriter-like keyboard which produces punched tape. The tape automatically transmits messages which are received without an attendant being present. (Courtesy, Western Union Telegraph Company)

The Autodin, automatic digital network, leased to the Department of Defense by Western Union, is capable of handling every form of electronic communications known. It is the world's largest, fastest, and most advanced communications system. It links more than 360 military installations throughout the world. This system was originally designed for the United States Air Force, but it proved to be so valuable that it is now used by the entire Department of Defense.

An automatic bomb alarm system has been set up with 300 optical "sensor" devices installed around 99 target areas. The sensors would respond only to the blast of a nuclear explosion and some one of the sensors would send its message even if the explosion was nearby. All of the above developments now operated by the Western Union Telegraph Company show how far the telegraph has developed in this age of electronics.

Several magazines and newspapers are now published in a central office and then transmitted to regional offices where automatic machines reproduce the printed copy, thus making it possible to publish magazines and newspapers in various sections of the country at the same time, and saving much in transportation costs and time.

THE TELEPHONE

The telephone was invented by Alexander Graham Bell (1847–1922) in 1876. Bell's first telephone was a crude device, in which the receiver and transmitter were essentially the same. The diaphragm was made of gold-beater's skin, an animal membrane, which was attached to a permanent bar magnet by a kind of lever. This magnet was surrounded by a coil of wire, in which a current was induced when the magnet was moved by the vibrations of the diaphragm. In a later telephone, in which the transmitter and receiver were the same, a horseshoe magnet in the transmitter had two coils wound on its ends, from which wires were connected to similar coils in the receiver. A battery maintained the flow of current through the coils. Sounds caused the iron diaphragm in front of the magnet in the transmitter to vibrate. This caused a fluctuation in the current flowing through the coils, which was transferred to the diaphragm at the receiver end.

Since 1877, there have been more than ninety types of transmitters and more than sixty types of receivers designed and used. In 1877, Thomas Edison patented the carbon transmitter, which was so arranged that vibrations in the diaphragm produced fluctuations in the current. Behind the mouthpiece of the transmitter is a metal box containing two insulated disks between which are packed fine carbon granules. The current passes through these granules and varies with the changes in pressure on the carbon resulting from motion of the diaphragm. Thus the current passing through the wire is not induced as in the earlier type of transmitter but is modulated in intensity. Figure 42-4 shows the basic principles of the telephone. The telephone receiver contains a permanent horseshoe magnet with coils about each pole, through which the incoming current passes, causing

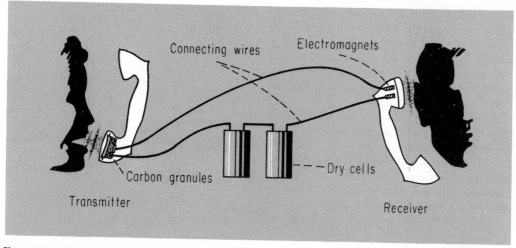

Figure 42–4. The telephone circuit. Sound waves cause spurts of electricity in the transmitter as the diaphragm moves back and forth thus varying the distance between the carbon particles and, hence, varying their electrical conductivity. In the receiver the spurts of electricity cause the electromagnet to attract and bend the receiving diaphragm.

the magnetic field of the magnet to fluctuate and thus altering its pull upon a thin sheet, or diaphragm, of iron nearby. The resulting oscillation of the diaphragm transmits vibrations to the air outside, and in this way produces sound.

Recent telephone advances include automatic telephones and direct, transcontinental dialing. Soon direct dialing to Europe will be a reality. A new signaling system has been developed which may do away with the dial telephone entirely. This new electronic system would be much faster than the dial system; one could obtain a number simply by punching buttons.

THE RADIO

In 1864, Clerk Maxwell, the great English mathematical physicist, reached the conclusion from his calculations that all forms of radiant energy are nothing more or less than electromagnetic waves.

When electrons are in no regular position with relation to each other, as is true in non-magnetized matter, electric fields surrounding the electron neutralize, rather than reinforce, each other. When electrons move in one direction, as in a current of electricity, there is a motion of these fields of influence. Now, what would happen to the field of influence

if the electrons were to oscillate back and forth? According to Maxwell's theory, waves would be set up that would travel out in all directions from the vibrating electron.

The German physicist, H. Helmholtz (1821–1894) suggested to one of his brilliant students, Heinrich Hertz (1857–1894), that he attempt to obtain experimental proof of Maxwell's theory. Hertz accepted the challenge. His first problem was to determine whether or not electromagnetic waves would travel through space without a conductor. While working on this problem, he observed a tiny discharge between the extremities of a flat coil when a nearby Leyden jar was producing an electric discharge between two knob-like terminals. This gave him the clue to the knowledge he was seeking. He produced an oscillating charge by connecting the terminals of an induction coil to two metal plates, which acted as a condenser. By the simple process of charging and discharging this condenser, he produced electric oscillations. That these oscillations really produced electromagnetic waves he then proceeded to prove by use of a loop of wire, with a small spark gap. He found that when it was properly oriented, sparks jumped across this gap in the loop of wire at the same instant that they jumped between the terminals of the induction coil across the room. The confirmation of Maxwell's electromagnetic theory of radiation was one of the greatest advances ever made in the realm of physical science, because it not only presented a principle by which knowledge of radiant energy could be coordinated, but also paved the way for wireless telegraphy and the radio.

Hertz considered the possibility of using these "wireless" waves for communication and devised a method to detect waves at a distance. Discoveries by other men furnished the basis for improvement in wireless wave reception, and Marconi worked out the first long distance radio communication system.

Guglielmo Marconi (1874–1937) improved the sending apparatus so as to give waves of greater intensity. The plates of the condenser had to be enlarged and Marconi conceived the idea of using *a system of wires* (or **antennas**) *supported high in the air* as one plate of the condenser and the ground as the other plate. A high-frequency induction coil, operated by a battery, produced the current, and the signals were produced by making and breaking the current with a telegraph key. The spark was produced between two wires, one leading from the ground and the other leading from the antennas. The spark produced the electromagnetic waves that were detected by the receiving set.

The oscillations in the receiving circuit were very feeble, but their effective reception has been greatly increased by the use of antennas. Marconi used a **coherer tube** as a detector. The principle of the coherer had been worked out by other investigators, but they did not realize its possibilities. The principle is simple; *a tube of nonconducting material, such as glass, is filled with metal particles. When the particles are subjected to electromagnetic waves, they cohere* and thus increase the ability of the particles to conduct a current. Marconi used an electric tapper to cause the particles to decohere after each impulse. A current was thus caused to operate a telegraphic sounder so that Morse signals could be received.

An early form of detector consisted of a crystal of galena in contact with a piece of copper wire. Such a crystal permitted the current to pass more readily in one direction than in the opposite direction, and thus converted the oscillations into impulses in one direction which could be detected by a telephone receiver. Perhaps some of the readers of this book have made their own crystal-detector radio receiving sets.

In his earlier experiments, Marconi succeeded in transmitting messages over a distance of two miles. In 1898, he sent messages from Poole to Alum Bay, Isle of Wight, a distance of eighteen miles. By 1910, Marconi had succeeded in perfecting his apparatus to the point where messages could be transmitted six thousand miles.

In 1900, Marconi produced a much improved wireless apparatus. In the first place, he added tuning coils, thus removing the interference caused by the increasing number of stations. The **tuning coil** *is a device that controls the wavelength of the waves sent out so that the waves of only those lengths desired are sent out.*

Today each transmitting station is required by law to use certain wavelengths in order to avoid the confusion of competing messages on the same wavelength.

The crystal detectors were replaced by vacuum tubes. Later, vacuum tubes were introduced for sending radio waves. The principles of vacuum tubes will be presented in Chapter 59.

Vacuum tubes function like the galena crystal, *as valves which permit the electrons to flow in only one direction.* They are an application of the thermionic effect, i.e., the emission of electrons by heated metallic surfaces, discovered by Thomas Edison.

TELEVISION

Hertz noticed that when two electrically charged metallic conductors were separated by a short air gap, electric sparks would jump across the gap more readily if light happened to be falling on it. It is now known that polished metals emit electrons when light of sufficiently high frequency falls on them. Certain metals, particularly the alkali metals (lithium, sodium, potassium, rubidium, and cesium), lose electrons, even under the influence of light of relatively low frequency. The heavy metals, such as iron and zinc, need to be illuminated with radiant energy of higher frequency than visible radiation, namely, ultraviolet radiation, before they will emit electrons. This action is the photoelectric effect, and it is very similar to the thermionic effect utilized in vacuum tubes. In fact, the very metals that show the photoelectric effect are those which emit electrons most readily when they are heated.

Inasmuch as variations in the intensity of light produce variations in the intensity of the electric current that flows between the electrodes, many fascinating applications can be worked out. This photoemissive type of photoelectric cell is simply a *vacuum tube*, called a **phototube**, *containing two electrodes, one of which is coated with a light-sensitive material and serves as the negative electrode of a circuit on which the light falls, and the other of which is connected with the positive terminal of a battery.*

The television camera contains an **Orthicon**, or **Iconoscope tube**, *containing a plate on which are thousands of tiny silver globules, each of which is coated with cesium and thus constitutes a photoelectric cell.* The picture is focused on the plate, driving off electrons where the light strikes it, and causing the plate to become positive at such spots. These spots attract electrons from an electron beam, thus producing electric currents that are drawn off, amplified, and transmitted. The beam of electrons sweeps across the picture in horizontal lines, 525 lines every $\frac{1}{30}$ of a second. The spot of electrons makes 15,750 complete trips every second. The *receiver*, a **Kinescope tube**, *directs a stream of electrons against a fluorescent screen in the order in which they are picked up.* The brightness of the spot is controlled by the intensity of the electron beam.

The ultrahigh frequencies required for television behave like light rays and will not bend with the curvature of the earth; consequently, television cannot be transmitted more than 50 to 125 miles. Again, television high-frequency signals cannot be transmitted very far by a wire because they fly off into space, but this problem has been solved by the coaxial cable.

The **coaxial cable** was not developed especially to carry television signals, but rather to replace wires for telephone, telegraph, and teletype messages. It can carry more than 1,300 telephone messages and 10,000 telegraph messages simultaneously. Alternately, it can transmit three television programs each direction at the same time. The cable is filled with nitrogen gas under pressure. It *consists of six or eight copper tubes, each about the diameter of a pencil. Each tube contains a wire held in place by insulating disks.* The capacity of a coaxial cable system may be multiplied three or four times by transmitting on pairs of coaxial tubes in a single cable. Coaxial cables are now supplemented by coast-to-coast, microwave, radio relay systems. Three colors are transmitted by using separate video signals for each color. In one type of color receiver, three electron guns, one for each color, focus their beams of electrons through screens having 250,000 perforations onto the face of a tube covered with 250,000 triads of red, green, and blue phosphors, in such a way that the three electron beams are registered on the correct phosphors.

SUMMARY

Telegraph

Electric impulses are controlled by the sender, which is essentially a switch. These impulses actuate an electromagnet in the receiver, which changes them into sound. Relays, which also may be actuated by electromagnets, make it possible to control additional power for telegraph signals as needed.

Telephone

The transmitter acts like a valve to modulate the electric current when it is actuated by sound waves. The receiver uses an electromagnet and diaphragm to change the electric impulses back into sound waves.

Radio

Variations in electromagnetic waves are caused by devices such as the telegraph key or the telephone transmitter. These electromagnetic waves are changed into electric impulses, which, in turn, are changed back into sound waves. Both the receiver and the transmitter usually employ vacuum tubes that serve as electron valves. They are based on the thermionic effect.

Television

In television, light variations are changed into electric impulses by photoelectric camera tubes. The electric impulses produced by both the sound and the light are carried over wires, or are changed into electromagnetic waves for transmission by radio, to the receiver. If the television signals are carried by electromagnetic waves they are first converted into electric impulses by the receiver. These electric impulses actuate an electron gun that produces a stream of electrons of varying intensity. The stream of electrons then activates phosphors on a fluorescent screen in accordance with a scanning device.

Color television sends additional electric impulses by electromagnetic waves of different frequency, one for each of three colors: blue, green, and red. In the receiver, these color signals actuate an electron gun for each color, which activates corresponding color phosphors on the fluorescent screen. Television is, therefore, an application of photoelectric effect.

Maxwell's Theory—All forms of radiant energy are electromagnetic waves. These waves may be caused by oscillating (vibrating) electrons.

Study Questions

1. DEFINE: thermionic effect, photoelectric effect, electronics, coherer tube, antenna, phototube, iconoscope, kinescope, coaxial cable, tuning coil, vacuum tube.
2. What was Edison's contribution to the radio?
3. What was the main idea of Maxwell's theory?
4. What was the contribution of Hertz to the radio?
5. What is the difference between wireless telegraphy and the radio?
6. What was Marconi's contribution to the radio?
7. What is the principle of the coherer tube?
8. How did Hertz prove that electromagnetic waves would travel without wires?
9. Why was the coaxial cable developed?
10. Give a brief discussion of Marconi and his work.
11. Explain what is meant by tuning.
12. How are electromagnetic waves produced?
13. Who discovered the photoelectric effect?
14. What was Morse's chief contribution to the telegraph?

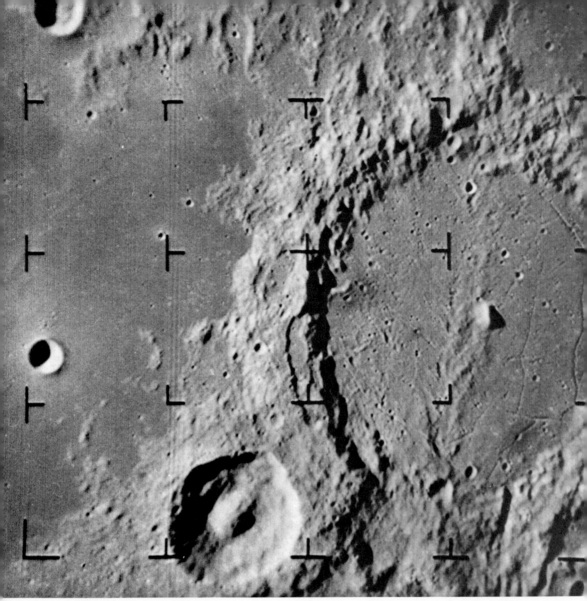

Television picture of the moon taken by Ranger IX prior to impact on March 24, 1965. The floor of the large crater, Alphonsus, shows an intricate pattern of ridges and rills. This view of the moon sent to the earth by television represented one of the major achievements of modern applied Science. (Courtesy, National Aeronautics and Space Administration)

Part **II**

Physical Science in the Modern World

THE SECOND HALF of this text, starting with Unit 7, is devoted to the study of the applications of physical science. The theories of physical science studied in Part I are subject to change, of course, but the changes are minor and infrequent. In contrast with the changes in the theories of physical science, the applications are changing rapidly, so fast, indeed, that a textbook cannot hope to keep up with the changes. New applications, now in developmental stages, will relegate many modern devices to the scrap heap. Part II presents the modern applications of physical science and indicates some of the future applications now in the laboratory stage.

It is difficult to label the present age. It has been called the age of electricity, the age of the automobiles and airplanes, the age of electronics and automation, the age of plastics, or the age of the "miracle" drugs. In summary, this second part of MAN'S PHYSICAL UNIVERSE will show that the present age is the age of physical science.

New York Airways Vertol tandem helicopter flying near the Statue of Liberty. New York City in the background. (Courtesy, The Boeing Company)

The Modern World
of Air-Conditioning,
the Automobile,
and the Airplane

God has placed no limit to the exercise of the intellect He has given us on this side of the grave.

FRANCIS BACON

*T*HIS UNIT starts with a study of the applications of physical changes in liquids and solids, among which heating systems, refrigeration, and air-conditioning are important. Such applications are not essential to life—many people in different parts of the world get along nicely without them—but for people living in our modern scientific society, these applications represent more comfortable living.

The latter part of this unit takes up the study of internal combustion engines, and their application to automobiles and airplanes which have revolutionized modern transportation. Typical of all applications of physical science, the automobile and airplane differ greatly from those of the previous generation, and they will be different in the next generation. These changes are based on a continuous program of research and development.

Liquids and Solids

There are two distinct classes of men: first, those who work at enlarging the boundaries of knowledge, and secondly, those who apply that knowledge to useful ends.

R. W. von Bunsen

INTRODUCTION

If the temperature could be raised sufficiently, all matter could be changed to the gaseous state. This is the actual condition of the matter in the sun. It is also generally recognized that nearly all solids may be changed to the liquid state by raising the temperature, provided that they do not decompose or sublime first. The great abundance of matter in a liquid state (such as water) and the fact that liquids are more tangible than gases caused some of their properties to be studied thousands of years ago, and several of the applications studied in this chapter have been known for a long time.

This chapter takes up some of the general and specific properties of liquids and solids, and their everyday applications.

The properties of liquids and solids were explained in terms of the kinetic-molecular theory in Chapter 6. This chapter should be reviewed at this time.

GENERAL PROPERTIES OF LIQUIDS

The general properties of liquids may be summarized as follows:

(1) Liquids are practically incompressible.

(2) Liquids retain their volume, regardless of the shape of the container.

(3) Liquids have no definite shape; they take the shape of a container and they go to the bottom of the container.

(4) Liquids diffuse slowly.

SPECIFIC PROPERTIES OF LIQUIDS

One specific characteristic of every pure liquid is that it has a definite boiling point. Another specific property is density. Such properties aid in the identification of liquids. Some other specific properties of liquids are viscosity and surface tension.

Viscosity

Liquids possess the property of **fluidity,** which *is a measure of the ease with which they flow.* **Viscosity** is a universal property of liquids. It *is the inverse of fluidity, for it is measured by the resistance to flow resulting from the internal friction of a liquid.* The viscosities of such liquids as molasses and tar are high at ordinary temperatures, while the viscosities of water and alcohol are much lower. It is a common observation that tar is heated in order to make it flow readily, and it is a general rule that viscosities of liquids decrease with increases in temperature.

Lubricating oil is purchased by the **S.A.E. number,** *which refers to the viscosity measured by standard methods prescribed by the Society of Automotive Engineers in America.*

The usual method of measuring viscosities is to determine the time required for a liquid to flow through a given tube or orifice at a standard temperature. A lubricating oil needs to have a sufficient viscosity to maintain a film of oil between the lubricated surfaces. Too low a viscosity results in inadequate lubrication, while too high a viscosity results in needless loss of power due to friction in the oil film itself. Oils used in cold weather should be of lower viscosity than those used in the summer because of the fact that the viscosity increases at lower temperatures, sometimes to the extent that cars cannot even be started.

Surface Tension

Liquids also exhibit a property called **surface tension.** This *is a force acting at the surface of a liquid which tends to cause the liquid to expose the least possible surface.* Water gathers into droplets on dirty or greasy surfaces because of surface tension. In the same way mercury forms drops when it is poured on a surface to which it will not adhere.

Surface tension causes liquids to spread out in thin films if they wet the surface.

When liquids are placed in capillary tubes, surface tension causes them to rise or sink in the tube above or below the level of the surrounding liquid, depending on whether they wet or do not wet the inner surface of the tube. Surface tension may, therefore, be measured by determining the rise (or fall) of liquids in capillaries. Slender capillaries account to a small extent for the rise of sap in plants, although evaporation at the leaf end of the capillary is quite important. The fibrous nature of blotting paper makes it absorbent, because the spaces between the fibers act as capillaries. Paper intended to be used with ink must be sized to prevent the spread of the ink due to this capillary action. Sponges and towels absorb water because of capillary action.

LIQUID PRESSURE

The pressure exerted by a liquid is equal to the sum of the external pressure on it and the pressure due to its own weight. **Pressure** is defined as the *force per unit area.* The meas-

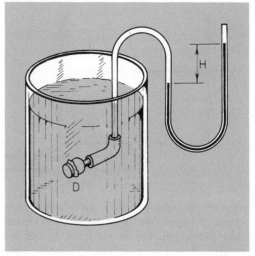

Figure 43–1. The difference in height *H* between the levels of the liquid in the U-tube shows the pressure of the liquid against the diaphragm *D.*

urement of the pressure at different places in a liquid would give results which may be summarized as follows:

(1) Pressure exists everywhere within a liquid.

(2) The pressure is the same at all points at the same level.

(3) The pressure increases with depth, and is directly proportional to the depth.

(4) The force against any small immersed object will be the same on all sides at a given depth.

The transmission of external pressure throughout a liquid was studied by the brilliant French experimentalist, Blaise Pascal (1623–1662). **Pascal's law** is stated as follows: *Whenever pressure is exerted at any part of a liquid, this pressure is transmitted to all parts of the liquid, and the transmitted pressure is the same at all points as the original pressure.*[1] Pascal also showed how this law could be applied to obtain large forces in the hydraulic press. In this press, there is a multiplication of the force in the ratio of the areas of two pistons. Thus a force of one pound on one piston would produce a force of six hundred pounds on a second piston having six hundred times the area of the first one. The hydraulic press is used for many

---

[1] This law also applies to gases.

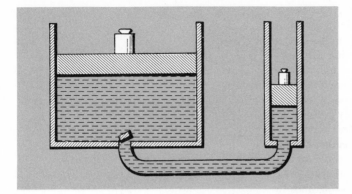

Figure 43–2. The principle of the hydraulic press.

purposes in industry; it is used to compress cotton or paper into bales, to extract the oil from cottonseed, and in machines to test the strength of various materials. Hydraulic automobile brakes and lifts are similar in principle to the hydraulic press.

ARCHIMEDES' PRINCIPLE OF FLOATING BODIES

Archimedes of Syracuse (287–212 B.C.) discovered the principle, known by his name, that *when a body is immersed in a liquid (or a gas) the loss in weight of the body will be equal to the weight of the liquid (or gas) displaced, and the body will be buoyed up by a force equal to the weight of the liquid (or gas) displaced by it.*

The story of this discovery is that Archimedes was given the problem of determining whether or not King Hiero's golden crown had been alloyed with silver. Archimedes was bathing one day, and noticed that he displaced water equal in volume to his own body. At once, he saw that the lighter alloy of gold and silver would displace more water than an equal weight of pure gold.

Why do bodies float when immersed in a liquid? What causes a diver to reach the surface of the water again? The pressure exerted by a liquid acts on all parts of the surface of a submerged body and always at right angles to it. Inasmuch as the pressure increases with depth, there is a greater pressure at the lower surface of the body than at the upper surface. The difference between these pressures causes the liquid to exert a buoyant force. The water in the Great Salt Lake has a greater buoyant effect than that of fresh water because its greater density produces a greater pressure at any given depth.

Archimedes' principle is applied in measuring the density of solids and liquids. One application of this principle is that of the hydrometer. **Hydrometers** *are floating vessels adjusted for certain ranges of density. They are buoyed up in proportion to the density of the liquid measured.* The percentage of alcohol in water can be determined, for example, by the hydrometer, because the density of mixtures of alcohol and water decreases with increasing concentrations of alcohol. Similarly, the density of sugar solutions is measured with a special type of hy-

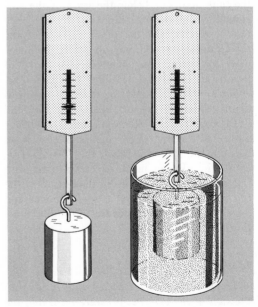

Figure 43–3. An illustration of Archimedes' principle. The "weight" displaces its own weight of water and it weighs less when immersed in water because of the buoyancy of water.

drometer. Among the many special uses for hydrometers, the battery tester is one that is very familiar to many people. It is based on the fact that the density of the sulfuric acid solution in a storage battery decreases as the battery is discharged. This decrease in the density of the sulfuric acid solution is caused by the removal of some of the sulfate ions as the battery is discharged.

Submarines are able to float or submerge by changing their weight. Water is allowed to enter a compartment in the submarine to add to the weight when it is desired to submerge it. When it is desired to bring the submarine to the surface again, it is raised by forcing the water out of the compartment with compressed air.

The density of a solid may be determined by weighing the solid in the air and then weighing it in water. The difference between the two weights represents the weight of water displaced by the body, that is, the weight of an equal volume of water. *The ratio of the weight of the body in air to the weight of an equal volume of water is the* **density** *of the body compared to water.* The weight of a boat could be obtained by measuring the amount of water displaced by it.

SOLIDS

Solids, like liquids, are practically incompressible. They maintain their volume and have definite shape. They diffuse very slowly.

Crystalline Solids

Many solids exist as crystals, which have a definite geometrical form characteristic of the substance in question. **Crystals** may be considered to be *huge molecules in which the atoms or molecules are arranged in orderly patterns, determined by the structures of the individual atoms or molecules.* The structure of crystals is obtained by passing a beam of X rays through them. Each atom deflects the X rays that fall on it and causes them to impinge on a photographic plate. A pattern of spots will be produced on the plate, representing the X rays that were deflected by the individual atoms. Such a pattern provides the necessary information to work out the structure of the crystal.

A **true solid,** like ice, is *crystalline in nature.* When heated to its melting point, its temperature remains constant until all of the solid is melted; a definite amount of heat is always used to melt a given weight of solid. This heat required to melt a solid is absorbed in breaking down the crystalline structure; at the melting point the whole structure collapses.

Noncrystalline Solids

In everyday usage, the term **solid** refers to *all types of materials that are sufficiently rigid to retain their shape in spite of gravity at ordinary temperatures;* this includes not only the crystalline solids but also *amorphous* (*Greek: formless*) **noncrystalline solids.** Such finely divided powders as flowers of sulfur or lampblack are often called amorphous solids, but they actually consist of very small crystals. Perhaps the closest approach to amorphous solids is the dark deposit found on the inside of incandescent light bulbs, bulbs of motion-picture projectors, and vacuum tubes. This metallic deposit is formed from the vapor of the metal that is formed when the filament is heated, in such a way that no regular crystalline structure is produced.

Plastics and glass are noncrystalline in nature and might, therefore, be called *amorphous solids.* Some people prefer to speak of these solids as **vitreous.** They *do not have a sharp melting point, but gradually soften as they are heated.* Sometimes, such solids as glass are said to be supercooled liquids. Many solids are *solidified solutions,* and are therefore called **solid solutions;** examples are some alloys and many rocks, such as lava or volcanic glass.

The majority of substances can be classified definitely as gases, liquids, or solids, but there are a few substances that show intermediate properties; thus vitreous liquids show by X-ray analysis that there are at least temporary crystalline structures present. Several hundred liquids that show crystalline properties are known.

SUBLIMATION OF SOLIDS

Some substances will pass from the solid state to the gaseous state without passing through the liquid state or vice versa. Thus camphor, naphthalene mothballs, or dichloro-benzene deodorant crystals, if left exposed to the air, will gradually sublime, i.e., change to a gaseous state. Iodine, which consists of black crystals, if heated will change to a beautiful purple gas, which will crystallize on a cold surface to form black platlets of iodine again, without first changing to a liquid. This process is also called **sublimation.** When sulfur is heated it will sublime and form finely divided "flowers of sulfur" on a cool surface. Ice and snow will likewise gradually disappear without melting. "Dry ice" is the common name for solid carbon dioxide. In recent years dry ice has replaced water ice for many purposes because it does not melt and produce a liquid as water ice does. In other words, dry ice sublimes.

SPECIFIC HEATS

The **specific heat** of a substance is *the ratio of the amount of heat required to raise the temperature of one gram of the substance one degree centigrade to the amount of heat required to cause the same temperature rise for the same weight of water.*

TABLE 43-1

SPECIFIC HEATS OF SOME COMMON SUBSTANCES

Water	1.00	Sand	0.19
Pine wood	0.65	Iron	0.113
Alcohol	0.60	Copper	0.094
Ice	0.50	Zinc	0.093
Aluminum	0.22	Mercury	0.033

The unusually high specific heat of water has a number of important applications. We have previously noted that the temperature of land areas near large bodies of water is kept equable by the breezes blowing from the water to the land areas. The temperature of large bodies of water changes very little during a hot day because of the high specific heat of water. On the other hand, large bodies of water do not cool very much at night for the same reason, Inasmuch as the specific heat of land areas is much less than that of water, they are more quickly heated and cooled than large bodies of water.

Hot-water heating systems are possible be-cause of the large amount of heat that is carried by the water and given off as the water slightly cools. The hot-water bottle is an application of the high specific heat of water. Iron would yield about one-tenth as much heat as water for an equivalent temperature drop.

THE HEAT OF FUSION OF ICE

When liquids solidify, heat is set free; and when solids melt, exactly equivalent amounts of heat are used up for equivalent amounts of the same substances. *The amount of heat in calories required to melt one gram of a true solid is* called *its* **heat of fusion.** The freezing of water liberates so much heat that winters are moderated and the advent of spring is delayed near large bodies of water, covered with ice, because of the heat absorbed by the ice as it melts.

The ice refrigerator illustrates an application of the high heat of fusion of ice. The heat in the refrigerator is removed by the melting of the ice.

TABLE 43-2

HEATS OF FUSION OF SOME COMMON SUBSTANCES

	Calories per Gram
Sodium chloride	124
Ice	79.8
Aluminum	76.8
Copper	43
Tin	14
Lead	5.4

EXPANSIBILITY OF SOLIDS

We have already seen that a change in volume is always brought about when a gas, liquid, or solid is heated. The majority of solids decrease in volume when cooled, but in a few cases, *the solid state occupies a greater volume than the liquid state of a substance;* this is one of the unusual properties of water. When water is cooled, it contracts until it reaches about 4° C. Below this temperature it expands upon cooling. The density of ice compared with water is 0.917. This means that ice is nearly one-tenth lighter than water; only about one-tenth of an iceberg floats above the surface of the water.

In some respects it is unfortunate that water expands upon freezing because it causes our water pipes and automobile radiators to burst in winter. The expansive force exerted by the freezing of water is so great that few containers are able to withstand it.

On the other hand, the principle of the expansion of water on freezing has many valuable applications in nature. It has already been pointed out that surface rocks are split apart as the moisture in them is frozen in the winter. If ice were more dense than water, it would sink in the ponds and rivers as fast as it was formed in the winter; such bodies of water would freeze solid and most of their animal life would be destroyed. The oceans, lakes, and rivers would all freeze from the bottom up, and summer melting would be confined to a little slush on top.

Figure 43–4. Expansion loops in pipelines in a chemical plant.

When water reaches the temperature of about 4° C, it begins to expand, and therefore remains at the surface of the body of water. The temperature of deep bodies of water does not change much, because both warm water and also water cooled below 4° C stays at the top.

Certain alloys of antimony, such as type metal (82 per cent lead, 15 per cent antimony, 3 per cent tin), are among the few substances that expand as they solidify. Coins made from copper, gold, silver, or nickel must be stamped on a metal disk with a heavy die rather than be cast because these metals contract as they solidify.

Allowances must be made for expansion and contraction in steam pipes and water pipes in buildings, in long pipelines, and in the construction of bridges, paving, and railroad tracks. Expansion in pipes is permitted by the use of tight sleeves, within which the pipes can work back and forth. Pipelines have large loops, whose change in curvature will take care of expansion and contraction.

Rivets in steel girders and sheets are put in place while hot, partly because they are softer and thus easier to work at high temperatures, but also because they contract on cooling to form very tight joints. Cracks are left between sections in concrete paving; these cracks are generally filled with tar. On a very hot day the tar may sometimes be seen to bulge up at the cracks due to the expansion of the concrete.

SUMMARY

Liquids

General Properties—Liquids are practically incompressible, they diffuse slowly, and they have a definite volume but no definite shape.

Specific Properties—Liquids have such specific properties as density, boiling point, viscosity, and surface tension.

The Laws—(1) *An increase in temperature decreases the viscosity and surface tension of liquids.* (2) **Pascal's Principle**—*Any pressure applied to any portion of a liquid will be transmitted undiminished to every portion of the liquid.* (3) **Archimedes' Principle**— *The upward force produced on a submerged or floating body is equal to the weight of the* *displaced liquid. (4) Liquids will rise or fall in capillaries, depending upon whether they wet the walls or not, in proportion to their surface tension.*

Solids

Classification—Solids may be classified as (1) true or crystalline solids which are characterized by definite melting points, specific heats, and heats of fusion, and (2) amorphous or noncrystalline solids, which include vitreous solids (supercooled liquids), and solid solutions.

General Properties—Solids have definite shapes, and volumes. They diffuse very slowly.

Specific Properties—The specific heats and heats of fusion of solids, as well as their expansibility, are specific properties of solids.

Sublimation—Some solids will sublime, i.e., change from the solid to the gaseous state or vice versa without passing through the liquid state.

Study Questions

1. DEFINE: hydrometer, density, viscosity, surface tension, liquid pressure, true solid, vitreous solid, solid solution, sublimation, solid, heat of fusion, specific heat, amorphous solid, fluidity, S.A.E. number, crystal, pressure.
2. State Archimedes' principle, and show how it is applied in the use of hydrometers.
3. What is surface tension? How may it be measured?
4. State Pascal's principle, and apply it to the action of the hydraulic press.
5. How is viscosity measured? Why are motorists advised to use oil of lower viscosity in cold weather?
6. What is the principle of the storage-battery hydrometer?
7. Why is ink paper sized?
8. Describe a convenient way to measure the density of liquids.
9. Name two devices that depend upon the transmission of pressure by fluids.
10. Why does a cork float on water?
11. Why is it easier to swim in salt water than in fresh water?
12. How could you determine the weight of a boat without weighing it?
13. How would the draft of a boat (depth to which the boat sinks in water) change on leaving a fresh-water harbor to go out to sea?
14. How does a true solid differ from a vitreous solid?
15. Give five examples of true solids and of vitreous solids.
16. Mention two respects in which water shows unusual properties.
17. Mention three advantages of dry ice as a refrigerant.
18. Mention some of the consequences of the fact that water has its maximum density at 4° C.
19. Explain how the formation of ice moderates winters.

Air-Conditioning, Refrigeration, and Heating Systems

Man is a minute mote in the vastness of nature. He has only just begun, through science, to see the world for what it is, and to find large-scale ways of controlling it in his long-term interests.

H. J. MULLER

INTRODUCTION

Many people do not understand the nature of air-conditioning, partly because they are not familiar with the basic physical principles upon which it is based. This section is a practical discussion of air-conditioning designed to help you with the problems of air-conditioning your own future home.

AIR-CONDITIONING

Air-conditioning is the modern way of creating a year-round climate, either for human comfort or to maintain constant conditions in laboratories and industries where it is important that *the temperature and relative humidity are kept relatively constant.* What constitutes a desirable climate? In general, the temperature should be between 68° and 78° F, depending upon the relative humidity and the presence of surfaces that radiate heat to or from the body. The relative humidity should be about 30 to 50 per cent. *The air should be free of objectionable gases, odors, smokes, dust, and pollens.* In this day, when tobacco smoking is so common, the problem of smog indoors is often worse than that outdoors. Therefore, *ventilation becomes important.* Outside air must be brought in, or the inside air must be circulated through purifying units. As a rule, outside air may contain dust, pollens, smoke, or smog which must be removed. Outside air may be too hot or too cold, so a provision must be made to cool it or heat it. It may be too dry or too humid, so the humidity must be controlled.

THE PURIFICATION OF AIR

One of the most difficult problems of air-conditioning is that of dust and dirt removal. Very small particles are difficult to remove, although human beings remove nearly 100 per cent of the dust from the air that they breathe. Unfortunately this dust often contains materials which are harmful to the lungs, where it accumulates.

As much as two quarts of dirt have been filtered from the air in an average home in one month. The removal of dirt from the air materially reduces the amount of housecleaning and dusting required. It has been calculated that up to 100 ounces of dust will filter into a 15,000-cubic-foot house in a year, under average conditions. In some air-conditioning systems air is filtered by passing it through specially treated steel wool or spun glass, but these filters are not very efficient compared to electrostatic filters. They seldom remove small pollen or smoke particles. Electrostatic devices depend upon the passage of air between plates on which a high voltage is maintained. The fine particles acquire an elec-

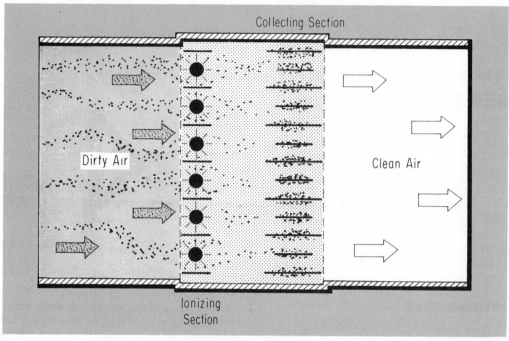

Figure 44–1. The principle of an electronic air cleaner. Particles of dirt are given a powerful electrical charge in the ionizing section, which are attracted to charged plates in the collecting section.

tric charge and are drawn to the plates of opposite charge, where they are precipitated.

AIR CIRCULATION

In homes lacking forced air circulation a person standing erect may be in a temperature of 70° F at the breathing line, his feet may be at a temperature of about 62° F, and the temperature at the ceiling may be nearly 80° F. This difference in temperature is reduced to only three or four degrees with a circulating system. Air circulation is also necessary in order to remove dust, smoke, grease droplets, odors, and excess humidity.

HEATING THE AIR

In many homes, the chief provision for controlling the indoor climate is that of heating. There have been many methods of heating, depending somewhat on the type of fuel available. There has been a gradual shift from the use of coal as a fuel to fuel oil and natural gas because of their convenience and economy. Now that natural gas has been made available

in most of the cities in the United States, its use has helped measurably in the elimination of the smoke nuisance, because natural gas is clean burning.

Warm air systems, using motor-driven fans to circulate the air, are popular—partly because modern automatic heaters take up little space—and are convenient and economical to use. When homes are properly insulated, they may be heated with electricity. If the cost of electric power is not too high it is often advantageous to use electric power for all purposes, thus taking advantage of the lower rates for larger amounts of power consumed. All-electric homes are desirable, because electricity contributes no smoke or fumes. One of the weaknesses of most gas or electric heating is that no provision is made for the control of humidity and the purification of the air.

Hot-water and steam radiators are sound in principle, in that they heat by radiation. Today, radiant heating is quite popular. It is based on the idea that people can be kept warm without heating the air to such high temperatures as is done by warm-air heating methods. The usual practice is to circulate hot water through copper tubing buried in a concrete floor. This requires that the floor be very well insulated. Covering the floor with thick carpets tends to decrease the amount of heat radiated, so it is better to heat panels in the walls and ceilings for radiant heating. Usually, such panels are heated by electricity, using resistance wires buried in plaster. This plan works for heating, but it does not provide for cooling. Why not run cold water through the copper tubing for cooling? The difficulty in this case would be that of providing a method of disposing of condensate. The weakness in most radiant heating systems is that no provision is made for circulating and purifying the air, and for maintaining the proper humidity.

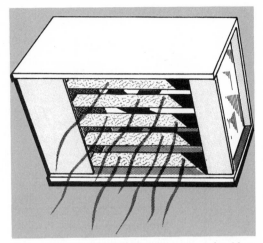

Figure 44–2. A very simple cooling unit. A fan blows air over long wet wicks.

COOLING THE AIR

Evaporative Air Coolers

When water evaporates, cooling results because heat is used up in changing water from the liquid to the gaseous state. Water has an unusually high heat of vaporization, and is therefore an excellent liquid to use for evaporative cooling. Nearly everyone has experienced the cooling of the body when wearing wet clothes, especially if the wind is blowing. Desert water bags keep the water cool by the evaporation of the moisture which seeps through the canvas. Figure 44-2 shows the principle of cooling by evaporation. An evaporative cooler consists of a porous material, which is kept wet, and a fan to move the air through the wet material. Evaporation is favored by low humidity and high temperatures, so evaporative coolers are most successful in desert regions, where the air is both hot and dry. Evaporative air coolers have the disadvantage that they add moisture to the air. The body cools itself by exaporation of perspiration. The higher the relative humidity the less the body is cooled in this way. It is common experience that hot dry air is much more comfortable than air of high relative humidity at a lower temperature. It would not do to recirculate the air in a house through an evaporative cooler because the air would soon become saturated with water vapor, the cooler would cease to function, and discomfort would

be the result. It is important that a relatively large amount of outside air be brought into a house in order to avoid building up too much humidity. The evaporative cooler washes and filters the air as it passes through wet, porous material, but the material must be replaced from time to time as dirt accumulates.

Cooling by Refrigeration

Cooling by refrigeration likewise depends upon the evaporation of a liquid to lower the temperature. There are two general methods of cooling air for home air-conditioning other than by evaporative coolers: (1) electrical, mechanical refrigeration, and (2) absorption.

1. Mechanical refrigeration—Figure 44-3 shows the principle of a mechanical refrigerator. A liquid, such as R-12 or R-22, which is readily vaporized, nontoxic and noncorrosive, evaporates in the cooling coil. The vapor is then carried to an electrically-operated compressor. It then goes to the condenser where it is cooled by air or water as it passes through a radiator. Here the vapor changes to a liquid, giving up heat in the process. The compressor thus serves to transfer heat from one place to another. In large refrigeration plants such as ice plants, the compressed gases are cooled by water, which is cooled, in turn, by vaporization in evaporation towers.

A mechanical refrigerating system, which is used for refrigeration, may be used to cool a house in the summer and heat it in the winter.

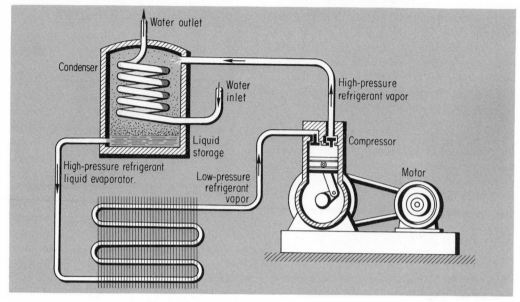

Figure 44–3. A vapor compression cooling system.

Thus, *by reversing the direction of heat transfer, the outdoor air may be used to heat the building in the winter.* This is the principle of the **heat pump,** which is becoming quite popular. It will be recalled that a mechanical refrigerating system has two coils: one cools the air, and the other is cooled by the air or condenser water or evaporative cooling (air and water). The system is merely a device to transfer heat from one place to another. When a compressor is used to cool a building, the heat is taken out of the building and absorbed by the outside air (or by water as mentioned above), which, though warm, is cooler than the compressed gas. In the winter, the heating coil is used to heat the inside air, while the heat is taken from the outside air, which is usually considerably warmer than the cooling coil.

The heat pump is most popular in temperate climates where the temperature does not get too low during the winter. In such climates, well water could serve as the source of heat, but adequate amounts of well water are not always easy to obtain. The colder the outside air is, the less efficient is the heat pump if the air is to be used to supply the heat. In some climates the humidity is high during the winter. In this case the heat pump is more expensive to operate because excessive amounts

of ice form on the cooling coils, and heat is required to remove this ice. Using outdoor air at 35° F, a compressor can raise its temperature to 70° F, expending only one-third as much electrical energy as would be required to heat the air by electrical-resistance heaters.

2. Cooling by Absorption—The gas-operated refrigerator originated as an invention of two Swedish students, Carl Munters and Baltzar van Platen, who made their brilliant discovery while still undergraduates at the Royal Institute of Technology at Stockholm. In general, it depends upon the driving off of ammonia from its water solution by heat, and then condensing the ammonia by cool water or by relatively cool air. The refrigeration coil is cooled by the expansion of the liquid ammonia, and the ammonia is reabsorbed by the water. The absorption of the ammonia in water corresponds to the compressor in the mechanical refrigeration unit.

In one type of air-conditioning equipment using the absorption principle, there are no moving parts except for the circulating fan. Cooling is accomplished by absorption of water vapor by a water solution of lithium bromide. The energy for the process is furnished by a gas burner which employs the principle of the gas refrigerator mentioned above.

THE CONTROL OF HUMIDITY

"Paul, a scientist of the Institute of Hygiene, Breslau, placed healthy persons in an airtight compartment of three cubic meters capacity and kept them there for varying periods up to four hours. First he kept the temperature and humidity low in this narrow space. The people in the experiment noticed no discomfort. Then the temperature was raised and the humidity was increased. Discomfort was apparent at once—depression, headache, dizziness, and even nausea. Paul admitted fresh air to the "victims" through a tube. This air was at the same temperature and relative humidity as the air in the cabinet. No relief was felt by the "victims."

They occupied a miniature "Blackhole of Calcutta," where, as history records, over 100 persons, imprisoned in a hot, humid space approximately 15 feet square, perished in a few hours from this same inability of the air to absorb body heat.

Paul then experimented with various methods for relieving the discomfort of those in the cabinet. First he dried the air, then he cooled it, and then he put it in motion with a fan. He made no chemical change in its content, however, but the sufferers were almost immediately relieved.

This revolutionary idea of ventilation proved that the discomfort felt by the persons in the cabinet was due not to breathing, but, primarily, to heat stagnation—inability of air which is too warm, too moist, or too quiet to carry away bodily heat—a vital contribution to the science of Air Conditioning.[1]

On a hot day with a temperature of 80° F and a relative humidity of 86 per cent, working capacity is reduced approximately 25 per cent, the appetite is reduced 13 per cent, and general discomfort ensues. Ideal conditions for most people are about 75° F with a relative humidity of about 50 per cent, although the ideal indoor temperature is controlled in part by the outdoor temperature. Some people consider 68° F to be an ideal temperature, but many people have found that they feel cold at considerably higher temperatures in the winter because of low relative humidity. Outdoor air in the winter contains little water because most of it is removed as the air is cooled to low temperatures. If this outdoor air is heated without adding moisture, it becomes relatively dry.

It is therefore desirable to add moisture to the indoor air in winter. The humidity of the air is usually controlled by passing it through a spray of water, thus adding water to dry air and removing excess water from moist air. Many people do not realize that the humidity of hot moist air can be decreased by passing it through a spray of cold water. Various devices for adding moisture in the winter have been used with rather indifferent effectiveness in the past. These devices include water pans in hot-air furnaces, troughs of water heated by radiators, and steam jets controlled by a humidistat. New humidifiers use atomizers.

One ingenious device for the control of humidity depends upon passing air through a spray of a solution of some salt, such as lithium chloride. The vapor pressure of this solution can be controlled by controlling the concentration of the salt in the solution, thus making it possible to obtain any desired humidity. Such a solution would take excess moisture from the air and would add the proper amount of moisture to air that is too dry.

A device that would control the relative humidity by passing the air through water or a water solution would have the advantage that it might purify the air at the same time.

In the refrigeration system of air cooling, moisture is condensed on the cooling surface. A considerable amount of the cost of air conditioning with a mechanical cooling system goes to the removal of moisture.

When mechanical refrigeration is used, the air in a house is recirculated as a rule. As much as 160 pounds of water may be removed daily in an average home. Clothes driers, dishwashers, bath showers, etc., contribute a great deal of moisture to the air. In an air-conditioned home, provision should be made to vent the moisture from clothes driers, showers, and other moisture sources.

Control of the humidity not only adds to the body comfort, but it also prevents the furniture and woodwork from drying out and cracking. Dry air robs the throat and nasal passages of moisture and renders them more susceptible to colds, pneumonia, and influenza.

---

[1] From "This Thing Called Air Conditioning," (Courtesy Honeywell Inc.).

The air in some homes in the winter is often drier than that in the Sahara Desert.

AIR-CONDITIONING HAS BEEN WIDELY ADOPTED FOR LARGE BUILDINGS

Motion-picture theaters were among the first types of large buildings to be air-conditioned. It is a distinct economy to remove the dirt from air in such buildings, thus reducing the cleaning expense and keeping the costly decorations clean much longer. The added feature of refrigeration soon pays for itself by increased patronage in the summer. Restaurants, beauty parlors, salesrooms, and retail establishments quickly adopted air-conditioning because of its sales appeal.

The Department of Interior Building at Washington, D.C., eight million cubic feet in size, was air-conditioned at a cost of about a million dollars. Most of the other United States Government buildings at Washington, including the White House, the Capitol, the Hall of the House of Representatives, and the Senate Chamber, have been air-conditioned.

The Ford Motor Company has completely air-conditioned its huge plant at River Rouge. It has been found that this results in better control of the accuracy of fine machining operations and provides protection from dust and dirt, as well as increased comfort and efficiency for the workmen.

Air-conditioning is now the rule in trains, buses, airplanes, and steamships, thus making travel much more enjoyable than it was in pre-air-conditioning days. Air-conditioned automobiles are almost a must for use in hot climates. Moisture condenses on their cooling coils thus washing the air and providing an added dividend.

THE IMPORTANCE OF INSULATION IN AIR-CONDITIONING

Air-conditioning is not practical unless a house is insulated. Insulation is of vital importance when electric heating or heat pumps are used, because excessive heat losses in the winter would otherwise make the cost of air-conditioning prohibitive. In the summer, in-sulation helps to keep the heat out, but without a provision for cooling the air during the summer, an insulated home has the disadvantage that it cools very slowly, once it becomes warm. As a result of insulating a home, the amount of money saved in heating the home in the winter must then be used to cool the home in the summer. The net result of year-round air-conditioning is increased body comfort, without a much greater cost except that of insulation and air-conditioning equipment.

All three methods of heat transfer, namely convection, radiation and conduction, must be considered in building a home.

If ceilings are insulated and the roof is not insulated, the space between the ceiling and roof may become very hot. For that reason provision should be made to provide outlets where the hot air may escape, and inlets where cool air may enter to take its place. Often, forced air ventilation by fans will more than pay for their cost.

Considerable heat may be transferred by radiation. Aluminum foil may be used under the siding and roofing to reflect heat. White paint or aluminum paint may be used on roofs to reflect radiant energy.

Most attention is generally given to the transfer of heat by conduction in insulating a house. A material having many dead-air spaces, such as mineral wool, glass wool, or asbestos fibers, is a poor conductor of heat. So a house is generally insulated by placing some such material in the walls and ceilings. In many cases it may even be desirable to insulate floors.

Double windows, with a dead air space between them, help to prevent heat transfer when there is considerable window area.

SUMMARY

Air-conditioning involves controlling the temperature and relative humidity, circulating the air, ventilation, and purification of the air.

Cooling may be accomplished by evaporative coolers, or by refrigeration, which may be done by electrical, mechanical compressors, or by an absorption type of refrigeration.

Heating may be done by radiant heating,

by the circulation of warm air by convection or fans, or by heat pumps.

Relative humidity is controlled by passing air through a spray of cold water.

Impurities may be removed from air, to a certain extent, by filtration, by electronic precipitation, and by washing with a spray of water.

Study Questions

1. DEFINE: air-conditioning, heat pump.
2. What does complete air-conditioning involve?
3. What is the most common cause of discomfort in crowded rooms?
4. In what respects would air-conditioning enter into the plans for a new home?
5. What is the best way to cool air?
6. What are the advantages of air-conditioning?
7. What is the principle of a heat pump?
8. Discuss the advantages of radiant heating and cooling.
9. How may humidity be controlled?
10. Why should provisions be made for ventilating the space under roofs?
11. How may heating by radiation be decreased?
12. What is the objection to an insulated house in the summer if no cooling device is used?
13. How are each of the three methods of heat transfer involved in preventing heat losses?
14. What is the principle of mechanical refrigerators?
15. What is the principle of the gas refrigerator?

Solutions—Colloids

With accurate experiment and observation to work upon, imagination becomes the architect of physical theory.

JOHN TYNDALL

INTRODUCTION

No matter what type of cell is examined under the microscope (a drop of blood the size of a pin's head contains millions of cells), it will always be found to contain a slimy, viscous, semifluid material called "protoplasm," which is the living material itself. This protoplasm and the cell walls in which it is retained are colloidal in nature. The materials in every cell reach it in the form of solutions. Colloids and solutions are the topic of this chapter. They represent two different kinds of mixtures.

All matter may be classified as (1) substances, or pure (homogeneous) materials, and (2) mixtures, or impure (heterogeneous) materials. Mixtures are of variable composition and consist of particles of more than one substance. *In any mixture, the substance present in largest amount is* called the **dispersion medium,** and *in it are* **dispersed** *the substances present in smaller amounts.*

CLASSIFICATION OF MIXTURES

Mixtures may be classified according to the size of the particles of one or both of these two phases in the mixture. A **phase** *is any portion of a mixture that is separated from any other portion by definite boundaries.* The following is an arbitrary classification of mixtures arranged in the order of decreasing size of particles.

Coarse Mixtures

Coarse mixtures *are mixtures in which the particles of one or more phases are of such size that they can be recognized easily by the naked eye.* The universe itself is a coarse mixture, whose particles range in size from visible dust particles to the largest stars. There is no upper limit for the size of particles of coarse mixtures, but the lower limit is set arbitrarily at 50,000 millimicrons[1] in diameter.

Fine Dispersions

In such mixtures the particles are of a size not easily recognized except with a microscope. They range in diameter from 100 to 50,000 millimicrons.

Colloidal Dispersions

Colloidal dispersions (**colloids,** or colloidal solutions) *are mixtures whose dispersed ingredients range in size from about 1 to 100 millimicrons in diameter.* The ingredients in a colloidal dispersion cannot be seen except with the aid of an ultramicroscope, and not always then.

Solutions

Solutions *are molecular dispersions; i.e., the particles of both phases are molecular in*

---

[1] A micron = 0.001 millimeter. A **millimicron** = 0.001 micron, or *one millionth of a millimeter.*

size. The diameters of such particles range from 0.2 to 1 millimicron.

COLLOIDS

Inasmuch as the dispersed and dispersion phases may exist in the solid, liquid, or gaseous states, eight types of colloidal dispersion would seem to be possible. These eight types are listed in Table 45-1, with examples illustrating the type in each case, although the dispersed phase in some of the mixtures listed is usually larger than colloidal in size.

A brief description of colloids was given in Chapter 5. It should be reviewed at this time.

Electric Charges on Colloidal Particles

Colloidal particles are usually electrically charged. Some colloids, such as ferric hydroxide suspensoid, are positively charged, while others, such as an arsenic sulfide suspensoid, or starch and oil emulsions, are negatively charged. This electrical charge on colloidal particles may readily be shown by **electrophoresis**—i.e., *the movement of the colloidal particles to an electrode of opposite charge.* Electrophoresis (sometimes called cataphoresis) has many useful applications; for example, the Cottrell smoke-precipitation process employs two highly charged plates that cause the colloidal smoke particles of opposite charge to precipitate out. The source of the charge on colloids is known to be due, in

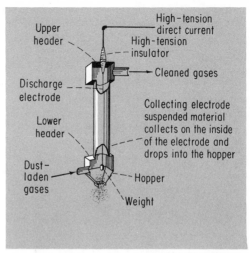

Figure 45–1. The principle of the Cottrell precipitator.

some cases at least, to the selective adsorption of ions; if only positively charged ions are adsorbed, the colloid will then be positively charged.

Adsorption by Colloids

The distinctive characteristic of colloids is their very small size. As particles are subdivided, the exposed surface is greatly increased. It has been calculated that a cubic centimeter of material, if ground into a powder of colloidal dimensions, would expose a surface of sixty square meters. Every solid or liquid surface exerts a pull upon molecules that come near it, and holds them as a per-

TABLE 45-1

TYPES OF COLLOIDS

State of Dispersion Medium	State of Dispersed Phase	Example
Solid	Solid	Chinaware or porcelain, gold in ruby glass
Solid	Liquid	Uncombined water in rocks
Solid	Gas	Biscuits, cake, or marshmallows (The dispersion medium in this case is a viscous solid.)
Liquid	Solid	Chocolate drink or muddy water
Liquid	Liquid	All such mixtures are called *emulsions* Examples: milk or mayonnaise
Liquid	Gas	Foam, whipped cream
Gas	Solid	Dust, smoke
Gas	Liquid	Fog, clouds
Gas	Gas	Impossible because all particles are molecular in size

Figure 45–2. Before and after photographs of a Cottrell Precipitator installation. (Courtesy, Western Precipitation Company)

manent film only a few (and perhaps just one) molecules deep. *This adhesion of one material to the surface of another* is called **adsorption.** (Note that absorption is not a surface phenomenon, but takes place within the liquid or solid, as the case may be.)

Activated charcoal adsorbs so much air that it fairly boils when it is heated, due to the evolution of adsorbed gases. Activated charcoal was used in gas masks during World War I to remove poison gases from the air before it reached the lungs. It is now used to remove objectionable odors and tastes from drinking water and to decolorize sugar solutions. Fuller's earth, a porous clay, is used to decolorize oils. Silica gel adsorbs gases, and is widely used in adsorbing gasoline from natural gas, and in household adsorbent-type refrigerators.

Stability of Colloids

Colloidal particles never settle out unless something is done to cause them to become larger in size. There are several reasons why colloids remain in suspension. In the first place, the Brownian movement tends to prevent the colloidal particles from settling out. Then again, the fact that every colloidal particle of a given colloid carries the same electrical charge causes the particles to be repelled as far apart as possible, according to the familiar law of repulsion of like electrical charges. Some colloids are also kept in suspension by protective films. Thus a kerosene and water colloid quickly separates into two layers unless it is emulsified with soap, which forms a protective film around each kerosene droplet, and thus prevents it from making contact with other kerosene droplets to form larger drops.

Two Kinds of Colloids

Many colloids are relatively unstable, and may be precipitated by slight traces of acids, bases, or salts (electrolytes), whose charged ions neutralize the charges on the colloidal particles. Such colloids are called **suspensoids,** or **sols.** The precipitation of suspensoids is well illustrated by the precipitation of suspended particles of mud by the ions of salt in sea water, when muddy river water mingles with sea water. Deltas are built by rivers where the mud is precipitated as the river water mixes with the sea water.

Many colloids, in contrast to the suspensoids, are not easily precipitated by electrolytes. Such colloids, called **emulsoids or gels,** *depend upon protective films rather than electrical charges for their stability.* Examples of such colloids are (1) milk, in which the butterfat is kept in suspension by a protective film of casein, (2) ice cream, in which gelatine has been added to prevent precipitation of milk sugar and the formation of ice crystals, and (3) mayonnaise dressing, in which egg proteins keep the oil from separating from the water.

Preparation of Colloids

Inasmuch as colloidal particles range in size from the smallest of about one hundred times the diameter of the hydrogen atom to particles visible under the microscope without the use of the Tyndall effect, it would appear that they could be prepared by combining many molecules or by breaking up larger particles.

When kerosene and a soap solution in water are violently shaken, the kerosene divides into colloidal-size particles. The whipping of cream, beating of egg whites, or mixing of mayonnaise is the same in principle. This

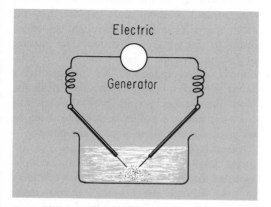

Electric

Generator

Figure 45–3. Bredig's electric arc method for the preparation of certain metallic colloids.

process of preparing emulsoids is called **emulsification.**

Suspensoids may be prepared from coarser particles by grinding them. Special grinding machines, called colloid mills, are available for this purpose. A cement mill is somewhat of a colloid mill; many of the cement particles are colloidal in size.

Metallic suspensoids are sometimes prepared by forming an electric arc between two electrodes of the metal in question. Small particles of the electrodes are violently disrupted and go into the water as colloidal particles. This is called **Bredig's electric-arc method.**

Colloidal particles may be prepared from smaller particles (i.e., the molecules in a solution) by chemical methods; for example, colloidal silver or gold may be prepared by mixing soluble silver or gold compounds with a reducing agent such as tannic acid.

SOLUTIONS

Solutions differ from coarse and fine dispersions, in that they *are homogeneous.* In this respect, they resemble substances; but *they must be regarded as mixtures,* nevertheless, *because their composition may be varied over rather wide limits without producing any abrupt change in their properties.*

The dispersed portion of a solution is called the **solute,** *while the dispersion medium is* called the **solvent.** The **solubility** *of a substance is the ratio of the quantity of solute to the quantity of solvent in a saturated solution.* A **saturated solution** is *a solution in which the dissolved solute is in equilibrium with the undissolved solute.* It represents a dynamic condition in which molecules of solute are dissolving just as rapidly as they are coming out of solution. A saturated solution of sugar in water can be prepared by stirring sugar in water until no more sugar dissolves. A quicker way to prepare it is to heat the water and stir in sugar hastily, making sure that there is an excess of undissolved sugar, and then cooling to the desired temperature.

Supersaturated Solutions

If a nearly saturated solution of sugar *is allowed to cool after removing the undissolved solute, the excess* sugar *might not* crystallize out, and the solution would be said to be **supersaturated.** If a crystal of undissolved solute is added to a supersaturated solution, the excess solute begins to crystallize at once. A supersaturated solution may be prepared for demonstration by melting crystalline "photographer's hypo" and allowing it to cool. The cold, supersaturated solution quickly crystallizes upon dropping in a small crystal of "hypo."

Supersaturated solutions are frequently met with in the home. Honey, for example, is a supersaturated solution. Sometimes crystals of sugar form in the honey. Addition of sugar would bring this about, but the usual cause of the formation of sugar crystals in honey is undue cooling. If a supersaturated solution is cooled sufficiently, the supersaturation becomes so great that crystals form even without seeding with sugar or some other small particles around which sugar might form. Honey is likely to "sugar" in the winter, and it is obvious that it should not be kept in a refrigerator. Jellies are supersaturated solutions, and sometimes the excess sugar crystallizes out in beautiful large cubes, called "rock candy."

In making some types of candy, it is desirable to obtain a supersaturated solution. Inasmuch as glucose crystallizes less readily than cane sugar, glucose is used in making such candies; they are stirred as little as possible. Taffy and butterscotch candy are typical supersaturated solutions. Fudge is crystalline, and it is stirred rapidly while cooling to insure the crystallization of extremely small crystals, which give a velvet texture to the fudge. Stirring is frequently all that is necessary to cause the excess solute in a supersaturated solution to crystallize.

Solutions of Gases in Liquids

Slightly soluble or fairly soluble gases follow the gas laws when they are dissolved in liquid solvents; it has been observed that *an increase in pressure will increase the weight of gas dissolved in a given volume of liquid.* This is a statement of **Henry's Law.**

The increased solubility of carbon dioxide in water with increased pressure is used in preparing carbonated drinks. When the cap of a soda-water bottle is removed, the liquid effervesces because the pressure has been released, thus allowing the extra gas to escape from solution. *The solubility of gases decreases as the temperature is raised, until, when the boiling point of the solvent is reached, most gases become completely insoluble.* All of the gases dissolved in water may be removed by boiling the water unless they form compounds with the water. It is the gases dissolved in ordinary water that give it the palatable properties to which we are accustomed. Freshly boiled water has an objectionable, flat taste which is removed by simply pouring it from one vessel to another through the air a few times, to dissolve some air.

When water is heated, bubbles of gas are observed to form on the side of the heating vessel, long before the boiling point is reached. These bubbles form, of course, because the solubility of the gas is reduced as the temperature is raised.

Although the solubility of oxygen in water is very small, it is very important. Most fish have gills with which to remove the dissolved oxygen from the water. The water of small aquariums should be changed or agitated regularly in order to dissolve more oxygen in the water to replace that taken out by the fish.

OSMOSIS AND DIALYSIS

If a membrane, such as parchment paper or an animal bladder, is placed between two solutions of different concentrations, it will be found that solvent particles will pass through the membrane, in the direction of the more concentrated solution, more rapidly than the solute particles will pass through the membrane in the opposite direction. *The passage of solvent through a membrane into a solution* is called **osmosis;** *the passage of a solute through a membrane* is called **dialysis.** Most membranes permit both dialysis and osmosis; but if a proper membrane could be secured, osmosis alone would take place.

Osmosis is explained in a number of different ways. The sieve theory, for example, assumes that the solute particles are too large to pass through the openings in the membrane, while the solvent molecules are sufficiently small to do so. There is considerable

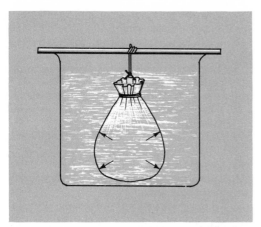

Figure 45–4. Dialysis. Crystalloids pass through a parchment bag suspended in water, but colloids do not. In this way crystalloids may be separated from colloids.

evidence that each solute particle is joined to one or more solvent particles in solution. This fits into the sieve theory nicely, and also explains why the gas laws do not apply to concentrated solutions. In such solutions, so much of the solvent would thus be joined to the solute particles that there would be a much smaller volume of free solvent than there is assumed to be in making calculations involving the volume.

Osmosis and dialysis have many important applications in living organisms, because every living cell is surrounded by a membrane through which it makes necessary interchanges with its environment.

If oysters are placed in distilled water, they swell because of osmosis, inasmuch as the solutions inside the oyster have a much higher concentration than distilled water (they have been in equilibrium with the sea water in which the oyster grew). Some unscrupulous market-men have taken advantage of this idea to increase the size and weight of their oysters before selling them.

If plant cells are placed in salt water, they wilt and lose their turgor. This is due to the fact that *water passes from the plant cells to the salt water*. Such a process is called **plasmolysis.**

One objection to the use of saline laxatives is that they not only remove water from the blood but that they also bring about a loss of valuable mineral substances by selective dialysis. One method of eliminating this objection is the practice that many people have of drinking a glass or two of lukewarm, **normal-saline solution** about a half-hour before breakfast. The term "normal" here refers to the fact that *the saline solution, which is about 0.9–1.0 per cent and contains two level teaspoons of common salt to a quart of water,* is **isotonic** with the blood. The body receives its food by dialysis through the membranes in the intestinal tract, so that both dialysis and osmosis take place at the same time. *A solution having the same osmotic pressure as the blood* would be called **isosmotic** with the blood, but such a solution might still change in concentration as the result of dialysis either from it to the blood or vice versa. *A solution that does not change either by osmosis or dialysis, when placed on the opposite side of the membrane to that of the blood,* is said to be **isotonic** with the blood.

The chemical garden is an excellent illustration of osmosis. It is prepared by dropping little crystals of very soluble colored salts such as ferric chloride, nickel chloride, cobalt nitrate, manganese nitrate, uranium nitrate, copper sulfate, etc., into a 10 per cent sodium silicate solution. These salts dissolve in the film of water surrounding the crystal, and the resulting solution reacts with the sodium silicate to form membranes. Water passes by osmosis into the crystal side of the membrane, and finally bursts the membrane. The solutions thus form new membranes, and the growth continues. Your instructor will undoubtedly demonstrate the chemical garden for you.

SUMMARY

Mixtures are classified as coarse, fine, colloidal, and molecular (solutions).

A solution is a molecular dispersion. It is homogeneous. A saturated solution is a solution in which the dissolved solute is in equilibrium with the undissolved solute. Supersaturated solutions are unstable, and can exist only in the absence of undissolved solute.

Henry's Law: An increase in pressure will increase the weight of gas dissolved in a given volume of a liquid.

Colloids are matter in a state of subdivision

in which the suspended particles are larger than molecules but too small to be seen with a microscope, except when a beam of light is employed to illuminate them.

Colloids remain in suspension as a result of the brownian movement, electrical charges, or protective films.

There are two kinds of colloids, the suspensoids and the emulsoids. Suspensoids may be precipitated by neutralizing their electric charges (the principle of the Cottrell precipitator). Emulsoids are coagulated by destroying their protective films.

Colloids are prepared by emulsification, grinding, Bredig's electric arc method, and by precipitation reactions.

Colloids expose a tremendous surface relative to their masses, and therefore have high adsorptive properties.

Study Questions

1. DEFINE: dialysis, osmosis, isotonic, isosmotic, normal-saline solution, colloid, saturated solution, supersaturated solution, phase, coarse mixture, fine dispersion, dispersion medium, millimicron, colloidal dispersion, electrophoresis, adsorption, suspensoid, emulsoid, solution, solute, solvent, solubility, plasmolysis, sol, gel.
2. Give an example of a supersaturated solution.
3. What is the basis for classification of mixtures?
4. Give examples of eight different kinds of colloidal dispersions.
5. What is the principle of the Cottrell precipitator?
6. Why are colloids such powerful adsorptive agents?
7. Give some of the uses of activated charcoal.
8. What causes colloids to remain in suspension?
9. Differentiate between suspensoids and emulsoids.
10. Give some examples of emulsoids.
11. Summarize the methods for the preparation of colloids.
12. What causes honey to form sugar crystals?
13. In what kinds of candy are crystals desirable?
14. What kinds of candy are supersaturated solutions?
15. What type of solid is taffy?
16. State Henry's Law.
17. Why does carbon dioxide escape when a soft drink bottle is opened?
18. What is the effect of temperature on the solubility of a gas in a liquid?
19. What is the effect of pressure on the solubility of a gas in a liquid?
20. What is osmosis? Describe an experiment illustrating osmosis.
21. How would you prepare a saturated solution?
22. How would you prepare a supersaturated solution?
23. Why do red blood cells burst when they are placed in distilled water?

CHAPTER 46

The Evolution of the Modern Automobile

A time to look back on the way we have come and forward to the summit whither our way lies.

J. H. BADLEY

INTRODUCTION

The development of the automobile typifies the technological progress, the social changes, and the social problems characteristic of the modern age of physical science. The automobile has made radical changes in the way people live. It has created millions of new jobs; today 11 million people depend upon business created by the automobile. Motels, trailer courts, service stations, restaurants, garages, vacation resorts, and sales are only a few of the non-manufacturing businesses created by the automobile.

The automobile has influenced the location and design of our homes, the schools we attend, the food that we eat, how we spend our leisure time, and even our courting habits. It has increased the tempo of life, made crime more difficult to control, and created many social problems.

The automobile driver is the fifth most important cause of death. In England 41,900 civilians were killed by German bombs during the eighteen-month period, January 1, 1940—July 1, 1941. England at war was a safer place than American highways.

Suburban living has become convenient and attractive, but it has created problems of transfer of business from cities to the suburbs, congested traffic, parking, and smog.

There are about 70 million automobiles in use today. For every mile of street or high-ways there are 20 motor vehicles. In the United States, there is about one mile of street or highway for every square mile of area.

NEW WAYS OF LIVING

The aluminum travel-trailer has revolutionized vacation travel, because it has made vacationists independent of motel and restaurant accommodations; it has become a home away from home.

There has been a tremendous growth of **mobile homes** *that are not intended for travel*, but which can be moved (in sections, in some cases) from factories to their destination, and also from place to place. A great many people (especially retired people) find that mobile homes meet their needs at a cost that they can afford.

Much of the increased leisure afforded by the machine age has been used in touring and holiday driving. Country people have visited the amusement places of the city, and city people have gone to the country for outings. Golf courses, bathing beaches, camping in the mountains, visits to national parks, and tours of the whole country have come within the reach of the masses. By making good used cars out of new cars, cars became available to almost everyone. The American people have been willing to sacrifice other things to ride like kings, and their vast petroleum resources

345

and high standards of living have made it possible.

NEW SPORTS AND HOBBIES

Automobile racing is a popular sport, and many men and boys build "hot rods" for a hobby. A **"hot rod"** *is an automobile that has been "souped up" or rebuilt to increase its speed.* "Drag" races have become popular among teen-agers. **"Drag races"** *consist of races against time, rather than against competing automobiles.*

Custom-built cars have furnished an interesting hobby for many people. Such cars involve the design of new body styles, and new approaches to old problems.

Collecting of old automobiles, and refinishing, refurbishing, and bringing them up to mechanical perfection is an interesting hobby.

THE EARLY HISTORY OF THE AUTOMOBILE

In 1885, Gottlieb Daimler patented a vertical high-speed gas engine, which was first used in 1885 to propel a motor bicycle and, in 1886, to propel a four-wheel vehicle. The gasoline, motor-driven carriage made its first appearance in the United States in 1893. In 1895, there were four automobiles manufactured in the United States. The first automobiles were crude contraptions with chain-driven rear axles and solid tires. Their engines had only one or two cylinders, and were very noisy.

Electric Cars

Electric cars were the most popular ones in 1900 because of their quiet operation and lack of fumes, but they possessed the disad-

Figure 46–1. Evolution of the automobile. (Courtesy, U.S. National Museum)

Figure 46–2. An early steam carriage. (Courtesy, U.S. National Museum)

vantage that they could not be driven more than 100 miles without recharging the batteries.

Steam Automobiles

In their day, steam automobiles were rivals of automobiles powered by internal combustion engines. They had a high torque[1] at low speeds. No transmission was required, and they accelerated rapidly. In 1906, a steam-powered automobile established a world's record speed of 127 miles per hour. However, there were handicaps. Open-flame burners and pilot lights were a hazard. Boilers corroded or burned out, and burners became clogged. Water tanks had to be replenished, and there was always the danger of a boiler explosion. And, of course, the car had to be drained and stored throughout the winter months, because the water would freeze in the boilers and reserve tanks.

MASS PRODUCTION

Precision manufacturing, interchangeable parts, and assembly line techniques speeded up the production of automobiles, and lowered their cost. Ransome E. Olds first used assembly line methods for the production of 2,500 Oldsmobiles in 1901.

Henry M. Leland (1843–1932), president of the Cadillac Automobile Company, pioneered in the use of interchangeable parts.

Henry Ford advanced mass production by using conveyor belts. In 1913, the Model T

---

[1] Torque is defined as a measure of twisting force.

Ford was assembled in 93 minutes, except for the body. These automobiles sold for as little as $400. By 1914, there were about a half million model T's in operation.

Increased production required the construction of marvelous new tools and machines, which made possible much better products at less cost. New alloys were used to permit higher-speed and lighter-weight engines and cars. Fuels and the efficiency of engines were improved, and more cylinders were added to provide smoother running and greater power.

EARLY IMPROVEMENTS

In 1895, the first pneumatic automobile tires were introduced. Improvements then piled up rapidly. Demountable rims were introduced; tires were improved; kerosene lights were replaced by carbide headlights, which were, in turn, replaced by electric lights run by a generator.

Charles F. Kettering (1876–1958) in 1911 perfected the electric self-starter, which appeared on the Cadillac in 1912. It eliminated the main obstacle for women, the old hand crank.

In 1920, the Essex car introduced a model with a closed body. By 1929, 90 per cent of the automobiles were closed models.

In 1922, Cadillac introduced thermostatic control of the air entering the carburetor, and in 1931, Oldsmobile introduced the automatic choke. In 1923, a counterbalanced crankshaft eliminated vibrations due to unbalanced forces. In the same year, four-wheel brakes were introduced.

In 1926, the first rubber engine mountings were used. In 1928, a mechanical fuel pump replaced the old pressure and vacuum tank systems. In 1931, the automatic spark control eliminated the old spark advance lever.

Between World War I and World War II, balloon tires, safety glass, lacquer finishes, sealed-beam headlights, no-draft ventilation, automatic transmissions, and independent wheel suspensions were added.

During World War II, the automobile manufacturers turned to making war goods. They produced 10 per cent of the airplanes, 47 per cent of the machine guns, 57 per cent of the tanks, and 87 per cent of the aircraft bombs.

POST-WAR AUTOMOBILES

After World War II, the trend was toward longer, lower, wider, and more powerful automobiles. Larger, heavier cars, required more powerful engines, better brakes, and power braking and steering. The engines supplied so much extra power that some of it was harnessed to power many electrical devices and air-conditioning.

HIGHWAY EXPANSION

In 1900, there were only 150 miles of dustless paved highways in the United States. When the weather was dry, dust rose in clouds from the horse-driven vehicles; and when it rained, the wheels sank hub-deep in mud.

The development of highway transportation is one of the most profound and far-reaching contributions to modern life. It has added immeasurably to the national wealth, and has added social and cultural enrichment to the lives of the people. Highways have made possible consolidations of schools and churches and quick movement of farm produce to city markets.

Improved highways have been recognized as an investment rather than an expense because they reduce the operating cost of automobiles by savings in gasoline, tires, depreciation, and repairs, and make possible quicker and usually year-round transportation. Improved highways also open up land and markets, and give isolated communities transportation.

In 1956, Congress passed the Federal-Aid Highway Act to provide 41,000 miles of new

Figure 46–3.   1850—Dark ages of the road. (Courtesy, Public Roads Administration)

Figure 46–4.   U.S. 1 between Richmond, Va., and Washington, D.C., in 1919. (Courtesy, Public Roads Administration)

interstate highways, and added a tax to existing state taxes that often increased the cost of gasoline by 10 cents or more per gallon.

AUTOMATIC TRANSMISSIONS

Today, automatic transmissions have replaced the clutch. There are two parts to an automatic transmission; (1) the **torque converter,** and (2) the **planetary gears.** The automatic transmission is first a fluid coupling that eliminates the need for a clutch. The fluid coupling consists essentially of two turbine wheels. One turbine is turned by the engine. The oil is driven by the first turbine against the blades of the second turbine. The driven turbine never turns as fast as the driving turbine, but at ordinary speeds the difference is negligible. However, at low speeds this difference is such that the driven turbine does not turn at all. For that reason the car can keep on running while waiting at a stop light.

At low speeds the engine does not deliver enough torque to turn the rear wheels. This problem was first solved by the clutch and gears, which made it possible to step up the torque at low speeds. So far, the fluid transmission simply acts as a fluid coupling. There has been no increase in torque. In the **torque converter,** *additional sets of blades are used, and a pump, which is driven by the engine, forces oil against the first set of blades.* By having the oil hit three rotors instead of one, the torque is increased sufficiently to meet the requirements for low speeds. For high speeds, however, there is more torque than is needed. The **planetary gears** *automatically connect the engine shaft directly to the propeller shaft for high speeds. The gears may also be used to obtain low gear ratios for climbing steep hills.*

THE CARBURETOR

The **carburetor** has two functions: (1) *to mix the air and fuel,* and (2) *to control the amount of the mixture taken into the cylinders.* The amount is controlled by the throttle valve, which is connected to the accelerator pedal. The throttle valve determines how much air and gasoline is pulled into the cylinders.

The second function of the carburetor is rather complicated, because different conditions require mixtures of air and fuel that vary in composition. The ideal mixture is about 15 pounds of air to one pound of fuel. However, gasoline will burn in mixtures having between 8 and 18 pounds of air per one pound of fuel. *A mixture of more than 15 to 1* is said to be **lean.** *If it is less than 15 to 1* it is called a **rich mixture.** Lean mixtures provide better gasoline mileage, while rich mixtures provide more power. The carburetor makes adjustments from lean to rich automatically, but for sudden acceleration or very high speeds, auxiliary devices are added. One of these is the automatic choke, which provides a richer mixture for starting in cold weather. In former days, the choke was controlled manually by adjusting the choke control on the dashboard.

Carburetors have been improved in many ways so as to meet the changing requirements at different speeds and different altitudes and temperatures. The better carburetors are so expensive that they are not used for regular automobile models. Expensive cars may have them, and racing car enthusiasts will put them on their cars. An expensive carburetor costs as much as a fuel injection system, and if there is a choice between a complicated carburetor or a fuel injection system, the latter would probably win out. Fuel injection would solve many problems. For example, it would make possible the lowering of the hood, which is a modern trend. This is not possible when a large, bulky carburetor must sit on top of the engine.

Fuel injection has been talked about for several years. Aside from its cost why has it not been adopted?

For a large automobile manufacturer, the tooling for an engine represents several hundred million dollars, which must be amortized over a period of years. The amortization period is usually about seven years, and the life of the tools is about ten years. Basic changes in engine design must wait for the next major program of retooling. In between such changes, most of the improvements must be in the nature of dual carburetors, dual tail-pipes, new power gadgets, new trim, and new paint colors.

TORQUE VERSUS HORSEPOWER

Horsepower ratings *represent the maximum horsepower developed at top speeds.* The higher the horsepower the higher the top speeds, but horsepower is only one of several factors which determine top speeds. In the average automobile, the addition of 25 horsepower will increase the maximum speed only about 4 to 5 miles per hour. Horsepower ratings tell little about engine performance, because maximum speeds are of little concern to anyone except racing drivers.

There is a difference between torque and horsepower. Horsepower is a consideration only at high speeds, but **torque** is what *determines the car performance at ordinary driving speeds.* Torque was previously defined as a measure of twisting force. The torque developed by the engine is more important to the average motorist than the peak horsepower. Torque is the force that does the work, while horsepower is a combination of torque and speed. Actually, the higher the horsepower the higher the torque for a given RPM (number of revolutions per minute), but by increasing the RPM, more torque is delivered at ordinary driving speeds. A high ratio of maximum horsepower to the weight of the car determines its speed, and is important in designing racing cars. On the other hand, a high torque-to-weight ratio supplies the **performance**, i.e., *fast starts and rapid acceleration.*

Today's high-speed (and often quite noisy) engines are designed to provide high performance at usual driving speeds. The modern high-speed engine has been the result of increasing the diameter of the cylinder and decreasing its length. This results in decreasing the length of the stroke and permits the piston to move up and down in the cylinder more rapidly. It also makes possible larger valves. Larger valves permit better breathing. Anything that the engine takes in it must get rid of. By exhaling more deeply there is a gain in efficiency and torque. Dual exhausts also aid in increasing the rate of getting rid of burned gases and decreasing back pressure. The change in the size of the cylinders mentioned above also decreases friction and wear.

INCREASING THE COMPRESSION RATIOS

The compression ratios of modern automobiles have been gradually increased, thus creating a demand for gasolines of higher octane ratings. When such fuels finally became available, the compression ratios were stepped up to about 10 to 1, which is regarded as about as high as it is economically sound to go.

New high-compression engines and other engineering advances, including the development of high-octane fuels, gave a 33 per cent saving in fuel, which amounted to a saving of 25 billion gallons of gasoline, or a saving of about $9 billion per year. This saving in fuel was calculated on the basis of equivalent horsepower. However, most of this potential saving was not realized, because of the development of automobiles of higher horsepower. Economy of operation has not improved very much. Any engineering advance that can increase the number of miles per gallon is important. An average increase of 1 mile per gallon would save 1.8 billion gallons of gasoline in a year.

THE HORSEPOWER RACE

In the late 1950's, there was a competition among the large automobile manufacturers to see which one could put out the largest automobiles, with the highest horsepower. Automobiles were pitted against each other in races, and the fastest cars were advertised as the best cars. Many of these monsters were too long for ordinary home garages, and they projected over the lines, both front and back in parking zones. They were much larger than they needed to be, and they had much more horsepower than common-sense driving could ever require. These automobiles did not represent increased miles per gallon of fuel. About this time, the new Federal Highway program got under way and the ever-increasing state and federal gasoline taxes furnished an incentive to buy the more economical, small foreign cars. Then, the automobile manufacturers began to turn out compact cars, and soon one-fourth of the cars sold were small cars.

Small cars have their advantages in city traffic, but for long trips, they are too small and subject to more serious accidents at the high speeds of superhighways. Will the next trend be toward a medium-size car that will give good mileage? Perhaps the time is now ripe for the turbine car discussed in the next chapter.

SUMMARY

The automobile and modern highways have revolutionized our ways of living, and have created many problems such as smog, crime, accidents and death, and traffic congestion in cities. Trailer living is a growing trend. New sports and hobbies have developed. In fact, the automobile is now considered to be one of the most important necessities of modern living.

Mass production, made possible by precision manufacturing, interchangeable parts, and assembly line techniques, resulted in economies that made possible better automobiles. New, annual models changed good new cars into good used cars, and thus made it possible for the masses to own automobiles.

Major improvements in the automobile were electric lights and batteries, self-starters, four-wheel brakes, better tires, automatic transmissions, knee-action suspensions, closed bodies, high-compression and high-torque engines, power steering, power brakes, and air-conditioners.

The trend in new cars has shifted from high horsepower to high torque. Compact cars have met the need for second and third family cars for economical city driving. Large, powerful cars meet the needs for long distance, high-speed traveling, and for pulling trailers.

Study Questions

1. DEFINE: torque, mobile home, horsepower rating, "hot-rod," "drag racing," torque converter, performance, lean mixture, rich mixture, planetary gear, carburetor.
2. List the various ways in which the automobile and modern highways have influenced our way of living.
3. List some of the social problems created by the automobile.
4. What are some of the things that have made it possible for the masses to own automobiles?
5. Compare large automobiles with small automobiles, for urban driving.
6. For what purposes are large, powerful automobiles superior to small automobiles?
7. What are the advantages of high-compression engines?
8. Compare high torque with high horsepower.
9. What changes in engine design have made high torque possible?
10. List the outstanding improvements in automobiles.
11. What developments made mass production possible?
12. What have been the trends in automobile manufacturing during the past twenty years?
13. What factors were responsible for the introduction of foreign cars and compact cars?
14. What is the principle of the torque converter?
15. Why have carburetors become so complex?
16. What would be the advantages of fuel injection?

Free-Piston and Turbine Internal-Combustion Engines

He who, by an exertion of mind or body, adds to the aggregate of enjoyable wealth, increases the sum of human knowledge, or gives to human life higher elevation or greater fullness—he is, in the larger meaning of the words, a "producer," a "working man," a "laborer," and is honestly earning honest wages.

HENRY GEORGE

INTRODUCTION

In Chapter 22, the advantages of rotary motion as compared with reciprocating motion were discussed. These advantages include greater efficiency, freedom from vibrations, much simpler lubrication, and fewer moving parts. In Chapter 26, the use of turbines in turbojet and turboprop airplanes was taken up. One would expect that automobiles of the future would be powered by turbine engines, because of their inherent advantages. The major automobile companies in the United States have been experimenting with turbine engines for some time. For example, the first Chrysler experimental turbine-powered automobile was unveiled in 1954. Ten years of research and development brought this automobile engine up to the limited-production model of 1964, discussed in this chapter.

In the previous chapter, the evolution of the modern reciprocating-engine powered automobile was outlined. Fifty years of continuous research went into these automobiles. They are good automobiles and the American people like them. It is to be expected that the automobile manufacturers will not change to turbine-powered automobiles quickly, but if the Chrysler limited-production car meets with approval it is likely that its production will be gradually increased. In the meantime, one can be sure that the other automobile manufacturers will not be caught napping.

Fortunately, the turbine-powered automobile can capitalize on the knowledge and manufacturing methods developed during the past fifty years with the piston automobile. Furthermore, modern metallurgy, called upon to meet the needs of 2,000-mile-per-hour airplanes, rockets, and jets, has developed the know-how to solve the special problems presented by the turbine engine.

THE SPECIAL PROBLEMS OF ADAPTING A TURBINE ENGINE TO POWER AN AUTOMOBILE

The requirements of an automobile turbine engine are considerably different from those of an aircraft turbine engine. It must operate at widely varying speeds, whereas the aircraft turbine operates at high speed most of the time. The automobile turbine engine must have quick response to varying power demands. The American public likes quick get away, get-up-and-go power: i.e., high performance. In addition, provision must be made for engine braking power.

Another major problem in the manufacture of turbine engines is to find materials for the turbines and combustion chambers which will stand up under the high temperatures. It is impractical to use metals such as are used in aircraft engines because they cost too much, and the world's supply of alloying metals would not support a possible wide adoption of turbine automobiles. A further requirement is that the engine must be quiet, and its manufacturing cost must be low.

SOLVING THE PROBLEMS OF TURBINE ENGINES

Chrysler metallurgists have developed new materials from plentiful and relatively inexpensive elements, which can be fabricated by conventional methods. These materials possess the necessary resistance to heat and oxidation. They are used to line the combustion chambers, and for casting the turbines in one piece, a process which is much less expensive than that used for the manufacture of aircraft turbines, as shown in Figure 47-2.

Engine braking power has been accomp-

lished by use of **variable nozzles,** *so that the direction of the airjets that impinge on the turbine can be reversed.* These variable nozzles also solve the problem of efficiency and flexibility. The latest experimental cars featured a major breakthrough—an acceleration time of one second from idle to maximum output.

An important engineering feature was the development of the two **regenerators,** i.e., *heat exchangers that extract heat from the exhaust gases to heat the incoming air.* These heat exchangers greatly improved the efficiency of the engine and provided lower exhaust temperatures. In fact, the gases issue from the exhaust at lower temperatures than is usually true of the piston automobile. The incoming air is compressed to one-fourth of its original volume, and in the process, the temperature is raised to 425° F. The regenerators heat this compressed air to about 1,000° F. In the burner chamber, it is heated

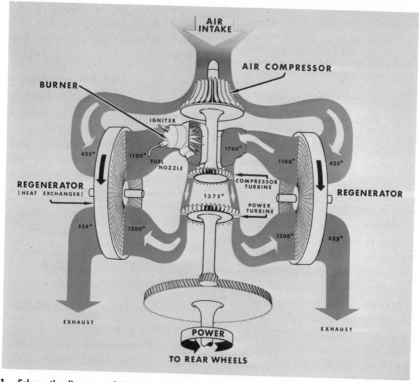

Figure 47–1. Schematic diagram of the Chrysler Corporation's twin-regenerator gas-turbine engine. The air is heated as it passes through the rotating heat exchangers. It is heated to 1700° F in the burner chamber, and then passes through the two turbines which are not connected to each other. One turbine operates the compressor and the other turbine furnishes the power to drive the car. (Courtesy, Chrysler Corporation)

Figure 47–2. Turbine wheel for Boeing T50 gas-turbine engine is shown here being assembled. Mechanically attached blades are held in place by metal keys. (Courtesy, The Boeing Company)

to 1,700° F by the combustion of the injected fuel. The hot gases expand through the turbine wheels and are exhausted through the heat exchangers. The hot gases are also used to heat the interior of the automobile, and thus make possible instant heating in the winter.

Undoubtedly, further research will lead to increased efficiency and improved performance, but the requirements of a successful turbine engine have already been met.

The new turbine engines are likely to lead to fresh approaches to old problems. For example, in the Chrysler turbine car, the starter also serves as a generator. It operates as a motor to rotate the gas generator to start the first stage turbine. When the gas generator reaches sustaining speed, the electric circuit is changed, so that the starter now becomes a generator. It will be recalled that a generator may become a motor by reversing the direction of the electric current.

Another fresh approach is that of combining the hydraulic and lubricating systems, so that one pump now replaces three pumps used in the modern piston cars.

THE ADVANTAGES OF THE TURBINE AUTOMOBILE ENGINE

Most of the advantages of the turbine engine may be summed up as greater economy of operation.

Maintenance

There are only about $\frac{1}{5}$ as many parts in a turbine engine as there are in a piston engine. There is no radiator, no fan or fanbelt, no water to freeze up in winter, no valves, no camshaft, crankshaft, distributor, water pump, carburetor, clutch, or voltage regulator. Only one igniter plug is used as compared to the six or eight spark plugs of the piston automobile engines. There are no mufflers to be replaced frequently. No tune-ups are required because (a) there is no series of timed events, and (b) a simple fuel control system replaces the complex carburetor and choke of the reciprocating engines.

Fuel Consumption

The turbine engine gives better fuel mileage than piston cars of equivalent horsepower. Expensive, high-test gasoline is not required. In fact, gasoline containing lead tetraethyl must not be used. The engine will use kerosene, diesel fuel, and low-test gasoline, and fuels may be changed or mixed without any adjustments being required.

Oil Consumption

The engine is almost friction free. The oil consumption is negligible because there are no cylinders or pistons to lubricate.

Lighter Automobiles

Turbine-powered automobiles are lighter than piston-powered automobiles. The heavy frames of the latter, which are required to resist twisting action, are not required. The turbine engine itself weighs about $\frac{1}{3}$ less than the reciprocating engine of equivalent horsepower.

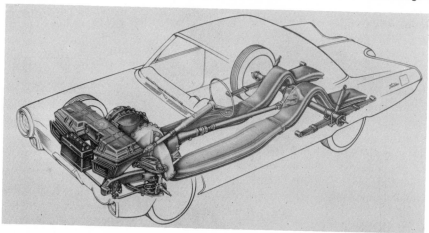

Figure 47–3. Turbine-car chassis components. Left portion of the phantom view of the Chrysler turbine car shows battery, air intake, engine and front suspension system. Front suspension, which is completely rubber isolated, has upper and lower control arms with ball joints, coil springs and sway bar. Shock absorbers are located within the coil springs. Center shows turbine-engine exhaust ducts. Rear suspension has two fore-and-aft leaf springs. (Courtesy, Chrysler Corporation)

Figure 47–4. The 1963 Chrysler Turbine Car. Fifty of these cars were manufactured in 1963 to determine the reaction of American drivers to this new car. (Courtesy, Chrysler Corporation)

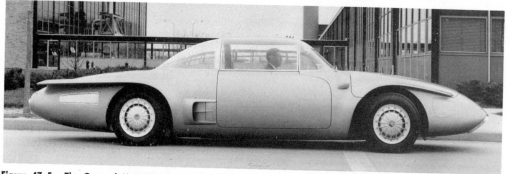

Figure 47–5. The General Motors' Firebird III. This turbine-powered experimental automobile incorporates many advanced ideas that may be found in automobiles of the future, which include a single control, and dual engines, one a turbine engine for propulsion, and a second accessory engine to furnish electricity for accessory units. (Courtesy, General Motors Corporation)

Additional Advantages of the Turbine Engine

Since the turbine engine operates with excess air, the fuel is completely burned, and practically no noxious gases, such as carbon monoxide, are formed. Furthermore, no smog-forming products resulting from the incomplete combustion of fuels are produced. The use of turbine engines in automobiles, trucks, and buses would help to alleviate the smog problem in cities and urban communities.

It is virtually impossible to stall the turbine engine, because increased power loads simply slow down the power turbine but have no effect on the gas generator.

Finally, the turbine engine is quiet and vibration-free, because it is a rotary engine rather than a reciprocating engine.

THE GENERAL MOTORS' FREE-PISTON ENGINE

Figure 47-6 shows the principle of the **free-piston engine.** *This engine has a horizontal cylinder containing two opposed pistons. The*

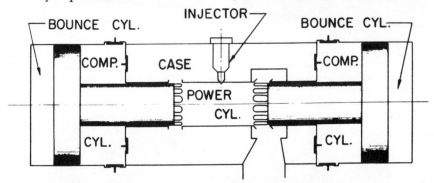

Position 1. Idealized section showing pistons in starting position. Intake and exhaust ports open. All valves closed.

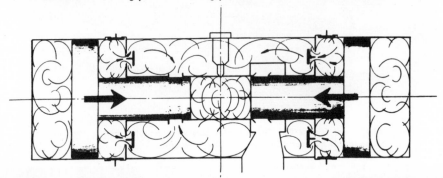

Position 2. Starting air pressure admitted to bounce cylinders. Pistons move inward, closing ports, compressing air in power cylinder, and forcing scavenging air from compressor cylinder into case.

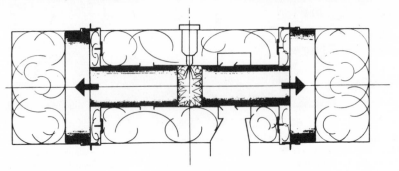

Position 3. Pistons complete inward travel. Fuel is injected into power cylinder. Combustion starts and power stroke begins.

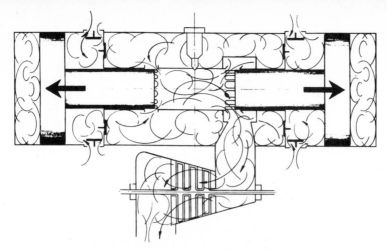

Position 4. Pistons continue outward travel. Air in bounce cylinders is compressed to store energy for return stroke. Compressor intake valves open. Exhaust ports open and gas is admitted to turbine.

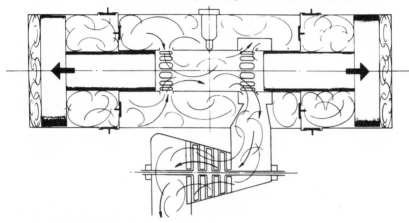

Position 5. Further outward movement of pistons opens intake ports, completing power stroke. Case air scavenges power cylinder and escapes to turbine.

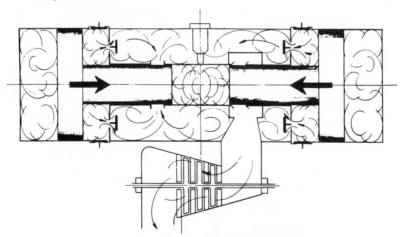

Position 6. Pressure in bounce cylinder moves pistons inward starting next cycle.

Figure 47–6. The principle of the free-piston engine. In position 1 the pistons are in the starting position and all valves are closed (position 2). Air pressure is admitted to the bounce cylinders which force the pistons toward the center of the cylinder thus compressing the air (position 3). Fuel is injected into the hot gases in the power cylinder, combustion starts and the power stroke begins (position 4). The hot gases may then be used to power a turbine. (Courtesy, General Motors Corporation)

inner ends of the pistons and the center part of the cylinder function as a very high compression, two-cycle Diesel engine. Figure 25-5 shows the principle of the two-stroke cycle Diesel engine.

The free-piston engine takes the place of the turbine used to compress the air, in the two-turbine automobile engine. The free-piston engine does not cause the vibrations and twisting action characteristic of the conventional piston engine. The pistons are cushioned by a layer of air, trapped in the rear of the cylinders, that bounces them back toward the combustion chamber. The sole purpose of the combustion chamber is to furnish hot, compressed gases to operate a turbine. Any number of free-piston engines could be used to increase the amount of gases delivered to a turbine.

This engine does not require warm-up time. All that is needed is a spark to start the fuel burning and the turbine turning. It runs more quietly than conventional piston engines, and emits no unburned fuel products through the exhaust, because excess air is used.

Experimental free-piston engines used in combination with gas-turbine engines have been developed by the Ford Motor Company to power farm tractors.

NEW APPROACHES TO THE IMPROVEMENT OF RECIPROCATING AUTOMOBILE ENGINES

The German automobile manufacturer, Daimler-Benz, has pioneered in the develop-

Figure 47–7. A free-piston experimental tractor power plant. (Courtesy, Ford Motor Company)

ment of several new piston-type automobiles. For example, the Mercedes-Benz automobile is available with a diesel engine that provides greater fuel economy. In London, there are more than 500 diesel taxicabs in operation, which just about cut in half their fuel costs, and go 150,000 to 200,000 miles before overhaul. The introduction of diesel engines would help to conserve fuels. The above company also produces the Das Kleine Wunder automobile, which is powered by a two-cycle engine, that uses an oil injection system and thus eliminates periodic oil changes and replacements of oil filters. The oil injection system supplies oil to the carburetor in exactly metered amounts depending upon the engine speed and load. This system is equivalent to one in which the oil is mixed with the fuel in the gasoline tank, but it eliminates the possibility of obtaining improper mixtures. This system of lubrication was made possible by (1) completely sealed, lifetime lubrication of crankshaft and main bearings, and (2) by the use of new alloys for the pistons, which reduce the need for lubrication.

SUMMARY

Adapting Turbine Power to Automobile Engines

Problem	Solution
1. Quick response to varying power demands.	Variable nozzle
2. Engine braking power	Variable nozzle
3. High temperatures	New alloy
4. Low cost	Cast turbines and inexpensive alloys, ⅕ as many parts
5. Quiet and vibration-free	Rotary versus reciprocating motion

Advantages of Turbine Power for Automobiles

1. Economy
   (a) Lower maintenance costs
   (b) Lower fuel and lubricating costs
   (c) Greater efficiency—higher miles per gallon
   (d) Lighter in weight

2. Other Advantages
   (a) Excess air for combustion means no incomplete combustion products to cause smog.
   (b) Will not stall.

The Free-Piston Engine

The free-piston engine is similar to a diesel engine except that the piston is not connected to other moving parts. The function of this engine is to produce hot gases under pressure to operate a turbine. It is used instead of the turbine compressor.

Study Questions

1. DEFINE: variable nozzles, regenerators, free-piston engine.
2. What are the special problems involved in adapting a turbine engine to power an automobile?
3. How does the Chrysler turbine engine provide for engine braking power?
4. Why is a turbine engine quieter and freer from vibrations than reciprocating engines?
5. Why is it more economical to operate a turbine automobile than a reciprocating-engine automobile of equivalent horsepower?
6. How did the Chrysler engineers manage to meet the "low cost" requirement?
7. What innovation in the lubricating system was introduced in the Chrysler turbine automobile?
8. Why is the cost of lubricating a turbine engine negligible?
9. How long does it take the Chrysler turbine engine to reach maximum speed from idle speed?
10. List the parts of a reciprocating-engine automobile that are not needed in a turbine-powered automobile.
11. What is the function of the heat exchangers in the Chrysler automobile turbine engine?
12. What is the principle of the free-piston engine? For what is it used?
13. What innovations have the Daimler-Benz Automobile Company introduced in piston-type automobiles?

The Airplane in the Jet Age

We are at the opening verse of the opening page of the chapter of endless possibilities.

RUDYARD KIPLING

INTRODUCTION

The airplane is a triumph of modern Science and technology. Its tremendous development in a very short period of time was made possible by the almost unlimited support of the United States government because of its importance to military defense and as a deterrent to enemy attack. The real significance of the development of the modern airplane is what can be accomplished by modern Science and technology when adequately supported.

The red-letter date of aviation was December 17, 1903, when the airplane designed by Orville Wright and Wilbur Wright was flown for a quarter of a minute with Orville Wright at the controls. From this time up to May 20–21, 1927, when Charles A. Lindbergh made the first nonstop solo flight from New York to Paris, airplanes were rapidly developed partly because World War I showed their importance. From this time down to the jet age, larger and larger airplanes were made possible by improved piston-type engines and by turboprop engines, in which four or more engines were used.

This chapter will emphasize the development of airplanes, starting with jet-propelled airplanes.

THE PRE-JET ERA IN AVIATION

1929—James Doolittle made the first demonstration "blind" landing at Mitchell Field, Long Island, New York. William Green developed the first automatic pilot.

1931—Igor Sikorsky built the first four-engine "clipper" flying boats.

1934—The American Airlines developed an automatic direction finder. The Electra Model 10 airplane advanced aviation with its all-metal construction.

1936—Lockheed Aircraft Corporation built the first pressurized cabin airplanes.

1938—Bell Telephone Laboratories developed the radio altimeter.

1939—Regular transatlantic airplane passenger service was begun by Pan American Airways.

1947—The U.S. Navy Constitution, four-engine airplane flew 180 passengers at 300 miles per hour, with a range of 6,000 miles.

1948—The B-36 giant six-engine bomber made a 6,000 mile nonstop flight.

1950—Turboprop transports flew at nearly 500 miles per hour.

1955—Airliners installed radar to detect storms.

1956—The C-130 Hercules propjet transport came into use for carrying troops and aerial refueling. Its cruising speed was 360 miles per hour. The Starliner Constellation's range was 6,300 miles.

1957—The C-133 Cargomaster transport could carry 26 tons a distance of 4,000 miles, at an average speed of 323 miles per hour.

THE AGE OF MILITARY JET-POWERED AIRPLANES

1941—Experimental jet-propelled aircraft were produced by Great Britain, Italy, and the

Figure 48–1. This 1912 hydroaeroplane carried three passengers at 60 miles per hour. We have come a long way in 50 years. (Courtesy, Lockheed Aircraft Company)

Figure 48–2. The Vega monoplane. Air pioneers set scores of records and wrote aviation history with this famous airplane. Top speed, 145 miles per hour. (Courtesy, Lockheed Aircraft Company)

Figure 48–3. The Electra (1934). (Courtesy, Lockheed Aircraft Company)

Figure 48–4. The C-130 Hercules (1956). (Courtesy, Lockheed Aircraft Company)

Figure 48–5. The Starliner (1956). (Courtesy, Lockheed Aircraft Company)

Figure 48–6. The C-133 Cargomaster (1959). (Courtesy, Douglas Aircraft Company)

Figure 48–7. F-104 Starfighter. (Courtesy, Lockheed Aircraft Company)

United States. During World War II, Great Britain was assigned the responsibility for the development of military jet airplanes.

1944—The Bell P-59A Aircomet was the first jet airplane to go into production in the United States.

1945—The Lockheed P-80 Shooting Star was hailed as the fastest fighter in the skies, with a speed of 550 miles per hour.

1946—The P-80 flew from Long Beach, California, to La Guardia Field, New York, in

4 hours and 13 minutes, averaging 584 miles per hour.

1948—The North American F-86 jet fighter set an official record of 671 miles per hour.

1953—The U.S. Navy Sea Dart was able to take off from and land on water.

1956—The U-2 high-altitude research airplane came into use for photoreconnaissance and weather observation at sustained altitudes unmatched by any other airplane.

1959—The Lockheed F-104 Starfighter set

Figure 48–8. The U-2 (top); the C-141 Starlifter (bottom). (Courtesy, Lockheed Aircraft Company)

a new altitude record of 103,395 feet for a jet airplane. It was in the Mach 2 class, flying more than 1,400 miles per hour.

1963—The C-141 Starlifter turbofan long-range transport came into service. It was hailed by President John F. Kennedy as the fastest cargo-carrying plane in the world. It can carry a payload of 90,000 pounds with a range of 3,675 miles.

TWO MAGNIFICENT JET AIRPLANES HEADED FOR THE SCRAPHEAP

The B-47 airplanes of 1947 were designed for long-range photoreconnaissance work, or to be used as bombers. In 1954, this airplane made a nonstop flight of 21,000 miles.

The B-58 Hustler is a supersonic bomber that flies at more than twice the speed of sound, 1,000 to 1,400 miles per hour, at an altitude of 60,000 feet. Two new "breakthroughs," (1) the area rule, or coke-bottle effect, and (2) gently curling the leading edge

downward, reduced the drag. It solved the heat problem with a honeycombed sandwich of metal and fiberglass, bonded with a very strong glue. Rivets and welds were eliminated, and a very smooth surface was thus made possible. A very powerful air-conditioning system cooled the inside of the airplane. This airplane was operated with a three-man crew and had a very sophisticated electronic system, including an automatic pilot. In 1957, it was the world's fastest bomber.

THE AGE OF CIVILIAN JET AIRLINERS

1952—England placed the first civilian jet airliner, the Comet I, into service.

1958—The first U.S. civilian jet airliners were placed in service. The Boeing 707 jet Stratoliner cruised at 591 miles per hour, at an altitude of 25,000 to 40,000 feet. In 1958, it crossed the Atlantic Ocean, a distance of 1,975 miles, in 3 hours and 47 minutes. The DC-8 jet transport cruised at 550–600 miles

Figure 48–9. The Boeing B-47 Stratojet, six-engine bomber. (Courtesy, The Boeing Company)

Figure 48–11. The Boeing 707 Stratoliner. (Courtesy, The Boeing Company)

Figure 48–10. The Convair B-58 Hustler. (Courtesy, General Dynamics)

Figure 48–12. The Douglas DC-8 transport. (Courtesy, Douglas Aircraft Company)

Figure 48–13. The Boeing 727. (Courtesy, The Boeing Company)

Figure 48–14. The Douglas DC-9. (Courtesy, Douglas Aircraft Company)

per hour, and had a range of about 6,000 miles.

WHISTLE-STOP JETS

More than half of the airline passengers travel less than 500 miles per trip. The short-haul airplanes have been mostly Electras (turboprops) and leftover, piston-engined airplanes, but the short-haul passengers also like the speed and comfort of jet-propelled airplanes. Figures 48-8 and 48-9 show two entries to the jet-hopping field. They use **turbofan engines.** *The fan bypasses cool air around the main part of the engine, and improves its efficiency.*

The DC-9 airplane uses two engines, while the 727 has three engines. In each case the engines are mounted in the rear. These airplanes will carry from 90 to 119 passengers at speeds of 600 miles per hour. They weigh less than half as much as the larger main-airliners, and can take off and land in shorter airfields. Thrust reversers are installed in the engines for use in landing.

TWO-THOUSAND-MILE-PER-HOUR AIRPLANES

The A-11 (Classified) airplane, in production in 1964, was flying regularly at speeds of about 2,000 miles per hour.

In 1964, the United States Government authorized the research and development of a 2,000-mile-per-hour supersonic airplane, scheduled for production by 1970. The information gained in the production and use of the A-11 would aid in the research and development of this new plane at an estimated cost of $1 billion.

Figure 48–15. The XB-70A Valkyrie bomber will fly at 2,000 miles per hour. (Courtesy, U.S. Air Force)

A 2,000-mile-per-hour airplane could fly from New York to Los Angeles in about 90 minutes. It could leave London at lunch time and arrive in New York in time for breakfast, because it would fly faster than the earth turns on its axis.

Such planes would undoubtedly use titanium and/or stainless steel, and they would be powered by new, more powerful jet engines. They would require air-conditioning equipment sufficient to cool a large theater. Such airplanes would not displace other airplanes because they would be good for long distances only. Furthermore, sonic booms might become a problem.

EXPERIMENTAL AIRPLANES

Many experimental airplanes have furnished the basic information required to develop later production models. The aerospace industry has accomplished one-third of all of the research and development in the United States during recent years.

The X-1 is a rocket-powered plane, which was the first airplane to be flown faster than the speed of sound. Note that the fuselage has the shape of a 0.50 caliber bullet. More recent experimental airplanes have shown that a bullet shape is not the ideal shape. This airplane was flown in 1947.

The X-2 has a skin of high-percentage nickel, stainless steel to resist the heat produced by friction at its top speed of 1,900 miles per hour, which is about Mach 3. The speed of sound at sea level is 763 miles per hour at 59° F, but at an altitude of 30,000 feet and temperature of −67° F, it is 660 miles per hour.

The X-3 Stiletto (1954) used straight wings instead of sweptback wings. The refrigeration of this airplane requires 2,600 horsepower.

Figure 48–16. The X-1. (Courtesy, Bell Aircraft Corporation)

Figure 48–17. The X-2. (Courtesy, Bell Aircraft Corporation)

Figure 48–18. The X-3. (Courtesy, Douglas Aircraft Company)

The high speeds developed by rocket planes produce so much heat by friction that refrigeration is a necessity.

The X-15 rocket-powered airplane in 1962 flew to an altitude of 314,750 feet at a speed of 4,151 miles per hour, more than 6 Mach. It was the first airplane designed to carry its pilot to the fringes of outer space.

Figure 48–19. The D 588-2 Skyrocket. (Courtesy, Douglas Aircraft Company)

The D-558-2 Skyrocket, a rocket-powered airplane, in 1953 flew at a speed of 1,327 miles per hour, more than Mach 2, and attained an altitude of 83,235 feet. Note the small, thin, sturdy, sweptback wings.

VTOL (VERTICAL TAKEOFF AND LANDING) AIRCRAFT

For many purposes, *vertical takeoff and landing*, and the ability to hover at low speeds are much more important than high-speed transportation. The helicopter was the first **VTOL** aircraft, being certificated in 1947. Since that time, helicopters have been used extensively in both military and civilian activities. Large tandem helicopters have been used for military transport and civilian airline passenger service. Larger, tandem helicopters, such as shown in Figure 48-15 have been made to carry heavy loads. In 1962, the Sikorsky S-64 Skycrane helicopter, using one main rotor with six blades, could transport loads up to 10 tons. It had a cruising speed of 110 miles per hour.

The Piasecki 16-H compound helicopter (1963) has short-span folding wings. The main rotor system is used for takeoff and landing. For conventional flight the propeller in the ring-tail takes over. It can fly at 170 miles per hour and carry 1,500 pounds a distance of 600 miles.

The Piasecki Airgeep, which does not depend upon the "ground effect" is a practical, wingless, VTOL aircraft. It houses all of the major components, the dual turbine engines, rotors, and controls in a low silhouette chassis. It can fly high or it can hug the ground. It can be wheeled (on its powered wheels) into a cargo-carrying airplane. Various other types of VTOL aircraft have been tried out.

Figure 48–20. The U.S. Airforce Piasechi Tandem Helicopter. (Courtesy, Piasechi Aircraft Corporation)

Figure 48–21. The Piasechi 16-H Compound Helicopter. (Courtesy, Piasechi Aircraft Corporation)

Figure 48–22. Sikorsky S-64 Skycrane. (Courtesy, Sikorsky Division, United Aircraft Corporation)

Figure 48–23. Piasechi Airgeep. (Courtesy, Piasechi Aircraft Corporation)

NEW ENGINES

Research is being devoted to the development of *ramjet engines,* which produce three to four times more thrust per pound of engine weight than the turbojet engine produces. One proposal to take advantage of the economy of ramjet engines is to equip a supersonic airplane with four turbojet engines for takeoff and landing, and four ramjet engines for supersonic flight. However, research is now being carried out to make one engine serve both purposes. Some kind of a device would be used to shut off the air inlet for the ramjet engine so that it could be used as a turbojet engine.

SUMMARY

Military Jet Airplanes

The development of jet-propelled airplanes in the United States started in 1944 with the Bell P-59A Aircomet. Most of the research and development of jet airplanes has been sponsored by the military services.

The military services have also sponsored a series of experimental rocket airplanes which have contributed to the knowledge required to develop the modern 2,000-mile-per-hour airplane.

Civilian Jet Airplanes

Civilian jet airplanes were first placed in service in 1958. They were large jet airliners designed for transcontinental and transocean flights, but recently short-haul jet airplanes have been developed.

VTOL Aircraft

The development of jet airplanes has emphasized the need for aircraft to move people to and from airports in less time. Helicopters, the original VTOL aircraft, are being used for this purpose, but a great deal of research has been devoted to the development of new types of VTOL aircraft.

Study Questions

1. DEFINE: VTOL aircraft, turbofan engine.
2. When did military jet airplanes first come into use in the United States?
3. From what year does the civilian, jet airplane age date?
4. List some of the problems which supersonic aircraft must overcome.
5. How do supersonic aircraft overcome the problem of heat?
6. Why is heat more of a problem for supersonic aircraft than for conventional jet airliners?
7. What are the advantages of jet aircraft transportation?
8. What have been the goals for the development of military aircraft?
9. Why are short-haul jet aircraft being produced?
10. Why is it suggested that the B-47's and B-58's are headed for the scrapheap?
11. What two aircraft design "break-throughs" helped to make the B-58 possible?
12. For what purposes are VTOL aircraft desirable?
13. What are the advantages and disadvantages of the helicopter?
14. What are the probable trends in the development of new airplane engines?

Aerial Navigation

> For I dipt into the future, far as human
> eye could see,
> Saw the Vision of the world, and all the
> wonders that would be;
> Saw the heavens fill with commerce,
> argosies of magic sails,
> Pilots of the purple twilight, dropping
> down with costly bales.
>
> From "Locksley Hall"
> ALFRED LORD TENNYSON

INTRODUCTION

The science of directing an aircraft from here to there is much different from that of traveling over well-marked highways by automobile. Familiar landmarks do not look the same from an airplane as they do from the ground. In bad weather and at night, even familiar landmarks are often lost to view. Once one has learned to fly, only half the battle has been won. The next problem is that of learning how to navigate an aircraft.

METHODS OF AERIAL NAVIGATION

There are four methods of navigating aircraft: (1) navigation by celestial observation, (2) navigation by terrestrial observation (pilotage), (3) navigation by dead reckoning, and (4) navigation by use of instruments.

Navigation by Celestial Observation

Navigation by celestial observation *can be used only when the sun or selected stars are visible and thus permit the determination of their angle of elevation, using the sextant.* The observations and computations require more

attention than a pilot can spare, so celestial navigation is only possible when a navigator can accompany the pilot.

Celestial navigation is practical, either day or night, provided one can fly above the clouds. It is especially valuable for flying across oceans, where there are no landmarks, and when flying in the substratosphere above an overcast, because radio signals are often affected unfavorably at these altitudes.

Celestial navigation is the same for both aerial and marine navigation, except that in aerial navigation the observations and computations are made less accurately, due to the unsteady and more rapid motion of the airplane.

Celestial navigation involves the following steps:

1. Determine the angle of elevation of the sun, or stars selected, with the sextant.

2. Note the exact time of the observation.

3. Compute the line of position from the sextant observation, and the time it was made.

4. Plot the line of position on a chart.

5. Determine a **fix** (i.e., *the position*) by plotting a line of position from a second star.

The **line of position** is *a short section of a circle, drawn with the radius, starting at a point directly under a given star at the time of observation, as obtained from an almanac, and extending a distance of 90°, minus the angle of elevation above the horizon, observed with the sextant.* This section of the circle is drawn for a short distance near the position where the airplane is thought to be. The intersection of this circle with the line of position obtained from another celestial object gives the position of the airplane.

Navigation by Terrestrial Observation (Pilotage)

Terrestrial observation is applicable only for short flights over familiar terrain or well-marked airways. It is not economical to follow highways or railroads because they seldom take the shortest path between two points. A pilot who is depending upon terrestrial observation would be lost if night overtook him or the visibility should become poor, due to a sudden change in weather.

Terrestrial navigation has been made easier by the erection of airway beacon lights, which may be recognized and followed by night with the use of charts (maps) of the civil airways. By day, these beacon stations may be recognized by the large numbers painted on the power sheds. Airport hangars generally have large identification marks or names on them.

Detailed aeronautical charts, revised every five years or less, show the important topographical information of a region, such as rivers and lakes; the cultural features, such as cities, highways, and railroads; the relief, i.e., the ridges, valleys, canyons, bluffs, and mountains with their altitudes; and such aeronautical data as airports, army fields, beacons, and radio stations.

Navigation by Dead Reckoning

Navigation by **dead reckoning** *depends upon the determination of positions by means of calculating their direction and distance from a known position from (1) the **true course, (TC)**, i.e., the line drawn from the point of departure to the destination, (2) the wind correction angle (WCA), which corrects for the effect of the speed and direction of the wind on the **heading**, i.e., the actual path of the airplane, and (3) the cruising air speed.* With the above information, the ground speed and the track are easily obtained by simple geometric plotting. The **track** is the **true heading,** i.e., *the true course (TC), minus the wind correction angle (WCA).* The **ground speed** *is the speed of the airplane relative to the ground.* The **air speed** is *the speed of the airplane relative to the air (wind),* and it may be more or less than the ground speed, depending upon whether the airplane has a tail wind or is heading into the wind.

Dead reckoning is used when other methods of navigation are not possible, and it is usually quite accurate.

Five fundamental instruments are essential for navigation by dead reckoning:

1. A clock or watch

2. An altimeter. An altimeter is an aneroid barometer that registers atmospheric pressure on a scale which is calibrated to read in feet above sea level. The altimeter has to be set just before leaving the ground in accordance with the atmospheric pressure at that time and the altitude of the airport. Inasmuch as an increase in temperature causes air to expand, the altimeter will give readings which are too low to the extent of about 2 per cent for each 10° F rise in temperature above standard air, 59° F. Sensitive altimeters are equipped with a setting device, which permits the pilot to correct the altimeter while in flight for any barometric pressure change that has occurred while he is in flight. A pilot may radio to the landing field and obtain the exact altimeter setting for that field. His instrument then will read the exact altitude of the field above sea level when landing.

3. The Magnetic Compass. The magnetic compass points in the direction of the earth's magnetic lines of force in any given location. The direction of the compass is caused to deviate by various magnetic attractions within the airplane. These deviations are reduced to a minimum by compensating magnets placed in the compass. The deviations of a compass vary according to the heading (the direction in which the airplane is pointed), so that a table of deviations at different headings must be prepared by actual observations.

Inasmuch as the earth's magnetic lines of force vary from a true north and south to a different extent at different locations, it is necessary to know the **magnetic variation,** i.e., *the angle between the true north and the magnetic north at any given location,* in order to be able to determine the **magnetic course (MC).**

The directional gyro (gyrocompass) contains a small gyroscope driven by suction from a venturi tube. The gyroscope compass will maintain for a short time a direction to which it is set, but due to precession, it changes direction at the rate of 3° every fifteen minutes, and therefore has to be reset frequently. The directional gyro may be used as a turn indicator. Another instrument using the gyroscope is the artificial horizon, or altitude indicator, which enables the pilot to tell whether he is climbing or descending, and the degree of bank.

4. The Air-Speed Indicator. The air-speed indicator is an instrument that measures the air-speed by measuring the pressure produced by the motion of the airplane relative to the air. The air-speed indicator is generally operated by a pitot tube, as described on page 209. The air-speed indicator reading decreases about 2 per cent for each 1,000 feet of altitude, and air-speed corrections must also be made for temperature changes.

5. The Drift Sight. Inasmuch as the velocity and direction of the wind change at different altitudes and at different times and places, wind direction and velocity must be observed while flying. The drift sight indicates the angular difference existing between the **heading** (*the direction in which the airplane is pointed*) and the track (the actual flight path of the airplane over the ground).

There are *two basic problems in* **dead reckoning:** (*1*) *determine from a chart the distance and compass heading to be followed between two points;* (*2*) *while in flight, determine and plot on the chart the track being made, on the basis of the observed compass heading, air speed, drift angle, and wind velocity.*

The **compass heading** is *the specific direction that the pilot will follow as read on his compass.* The direction that the compass must point in order to enable the airplane to follow the intended track must be determined by correcting the **true course** (i.e., *the course as indicated by the angle between the true north and the direction of motion on the chart*) *for magnetic variation, compass deviation, and effect of wind.*

While in flight, the track being made may be calculated by reference to the compass heading, the approximate ground speed, and the elapsed time. This process is essentially just the reverse of the first problem. The drift angle enables the pilot to make the correction for wind. When drift observations are impossible because of adverse weather, the wind correction is calculated on the basis of wind velocity and direction given in weather reports.

Navigation by dead reckoning not only enables the pilot to fly under adverse conditions, but it also enables him to come close enough to outstanding landmarks shown on charts to recognize them, and thus helps to keep the pilot from getting lost when flying by terrestrial navigation. Radio navigation is likewise supplemented by dead reckoning.

Slightly more complicated methods of plotting permit a pilot to know how far he can go in a given direction under given wind conditions and return to his base, or to an alternate base.

Instrument Navigation

Modern airliners and military airplanes employ many instruments, and even electronic computers, which make it possible for the airplane to fly to its destination by automatic pilots. The pilot monitors the instruments to be sure that they are functioning properly, but he does not actually control the flight of the airplane by manual control except in emergencies, and in takeoff and landing. Complex instruments are too expensive and too bulky for small airplanes. A small airplane can manage fairly well with a two-way radio, but most small airplanes will also use high-frequency (VOR) instruments.

All FAA (Federal Aviation Agency) airports require that all landing and departing airplanes be radio-equipped. Two-way radio communication adds greatly to the safety of flying. FAA stations provide weather information and other information for normal or emergency operation. Light "guns" on airport control towers provide information for takeoff and landing that can be used in case of radio failure.

When flying by Instrument Flight Rules (IFR), a special IFR license is required on controlled airways, and two-way radios are required. The airplanes must be flown at even thousands or odd thousands of feet altitude depending on the magnetic (compass) heading. On the other hand, pilots with only a VFR (Visual Flight Rules) license must fly even or odd thousands of feet, plus 500 feet, depending upon the compass heading.

Many small airplanes have Distance Measuring Equipment (DME), which beams radio signals to ground stations. The signals are returned from the ground station, and from the elapsed time between sending the signals and receiving the response, the distance from the station is obtained.

Another handy device for small airplanes is the Automatic Direction Finder (ADF), which uses a radio compass to indicate the direction of the station from which a signal is received. It can operate on signals from radio range stations, radio beacons, or commercial broadcast stations. It requires signals from two stations. It is susceptible to static interference, and does not compensate for wind drift as VOR does.

The radio altimeter now used by many airplanes, both small and large, can accurately measure an airplane's height above the terrain at low altitudes. It computes the altitude by beaming a radio signal straight down, and measuring the time required for the signal to be reflected back to the airplane.

VOR Navigation—Very High Frequency (VHF) radio signals are similar to television signals in that they provide "line of sight" transmission. Low Frequency (LF) signals have the advantage that they follow the curvature of the earth and, therefore, the stations may be farther apart. The LF signals are more accurate than VHF signals, but they are not weatherproof; they are subject to static disturbances, such as thunderstorms cause.

The Decca stations, widely employed in Europe, use LF signals.

The Omnirange system, in the United States, uses VHF signals, transmitted from stations not more than 90 miles apart. The omnirange (VOR) stations provide airway track guidance and enroute communications. Most VOR stations broadcast weather information at 15 and 45 minutes after each hour.

VOR (or VORTAC) omnirange stations project beams in all directions, like spokes in a wheel. Each beam is identified by its magnetic bearing. It is possible to fly to or from a VOR station by selecting the proper radial (beam). A position (fix) may be determined (fixed) by taking bearings from two VOR stations. The intersection of two radials shows the position. It is not necessary to know the wind correction when navigating by this system.

VOR receivers include four basic components: (1) a frequency selector, (2) an Omni-Bearing Selector (OBS), i.e., a course selector, (3) a To-From Indicator (TFI), which indicates whether the selected course is directed to or from the VOR station, and (4) a Course-Deviation Indicator, which indicates whether the airplane is on course or not.

The Instrument Landing System, (ILS)—The present ILS landing system consists of two signal devices on the runway. One signal, the localizer, tells the pilot where the center of the runway is. The other signal, called the glide-path, provides the pilot with a directional beam on which to descend. A barometric altimeter or a radio altimeter on the airplane tells the pilot his altitude above the ground. But neither the glide-path nor the altimeter is accurate enough to provide blind flying below a ceiling of 200 feet. The ceiling refers to distance above the ground below which the ground is visible. The gentlest glide path the ILS equipment can provide is too steep for actual landing. When the airplane reaches an altitude of 200 feet, the pilot must guide the plane visually on a gentler angle. Airplanes are not allowed to land if the ceiling is less than 200 feet. It is true that an operator on the ground, using ground-based radar, can "talk down" an airplane for a completely "blind" landing by giving verbal instructions to the pilot, but today's heavy traffic congestion makes this system impractical except for emergencies.

The government and the airlines are working toward a 100-foot ceiling limit, but it will take time and money to achieve this goal. For example, a $200,000 lighting system would be required for each runway.

The Flarescan Landing System—The Flarescan Landing System is scheduled to replace the ILS system when the supersonic era of the 1970's arrives. It embodies an oscillating transmitter on the ground to transmit beams that continuously report an airplane's altitude, rate of descent, and position relative to the airway. This information is fed into automatic pilots in the airplane, or it is used by pilots for manual control of the airplane. Instruments for the Flarescan system would cost about $8,000 to $10,000 per airplane, and the ground equipment would cost about $100,000 per runway. This is a simple system which begins to operate before the airplane reaches the bottom of its glide path.

The BLEU (Blind Landing Experimental Unit) Landing System—The British BLEU blind landing system uses a pair of cables stretching 5,000 feet beyond the runway and paralleling it. The cables operate magnetic instruments in the airplane. The British short-range jets, VC-10 and Trident, use *triple redundancy systems* in which three identical sets of instruments feed information to computers. These instruments measure altitude, air speed, distance from the runway, and other factors. As long as two instrument systems agree, the airplane is allowed to land. If three systems do not agree the airplane is not allowed to land. The BAC-111 short-range British transports, on order by airlines in the United States, will be equipped with these instruments, so the BLEU system (adequately tried out in London fogs) may be adopted in the United States.

The Hidan System of Navigation—The Hidan (High Density Air Navigation) system is entirely self-contained within an airplane. It can tell the pilot the exact location of his airplane, and can predict the time of his arrival at his destination. No costly ground navigation aids are required. It uses an airborne radar (Doppler) which sends beams downward, to the rear, ahead, and to either side. Electronic computers use the signals reflected back to the airplane to furnish the pilot with the information as to his location. The Doppler equipment has been installed on some transatlantic jet airliners. It enables the pilot to verify his course, surface speed, and exact remaining distance to be flown.

AIRWAY TRAFFIC CONTROL

Airway traffic control is built around radar, radar beacons, automatic data links between stations, and computers. Automatic data links keep ground control stations informed about an airplane's position, speed, and altitude while in flight, and they feed traffic and weather information to the pilot. Both long-range and short-range radar are required.

The problem of airway traffic control is becoming more acute each year. The advent of jet airliners accentuated the problem, because they would use too much fuel if they were required to stack up at airports waiting for an opportunity to land. Supersonic airliners promise to make the problem worse.

CONELRAD RADIO SIGNALS

Enemy airplanes could use commercial radio and television broadcast signals to direct them to any given target. Conelrad is a system of scrambling radio waves that would prevent an enemy pilot from using them to guide an airplane. Upon the detection of enemy aircraft, frequency modulation and television stations would be ordered off of the air, and amplitude modulation radio stations would operate on only 640 and 1240 kilocycles. Different stations would be going on and off the air on a split-second, random pattern schedule, and individual stations would alternate in the use of the 640 and 1240 frequencies.

THE ATRAN GUIDANCE SYSTEM

This system makes it possible to guide an airplane or a missile completely independent of human control subsequent to launching. The programmed information required to direct the aircraft is stored on a film and fed into an electronic computer which guides the aircraft. The information is obtained from topographical maps, and the system could not operate if accurate topographical maps were not available.

The Air Force's T.M.-76A Mace missile, in tactical status in West Germany, employs the ATRAN guidance system. It can carry a nuclear warhead a distance of 650 nautical miles, and flies just below the speed of sound. A nautical mile is 6,076.1 feet as compared with 5,280 feet for the statute mile. This low-cost, highly efficient missile replaced the Matador.

In the ATRAN system, no signals are sent out, so missiles cannot be detected by radio devices. Radio signals could not interfere with its operation. The missile automatically varies its course so as to avoid mountains or heavily fortified areas. It can be fired from unprepared sites. The launcher is towed by a special truck which can travel over steep gullies, swamps, or mountain terrain.

Project MAST (Missile Automatic Supply Technique) uses an electronic computer, transceiver system in a global hookup to keep tab on the Mace missile. It computes inventories at all stations instantly, and issues orders for needed parts or components to be flown to the stations where they are required.

SUMMARY

Aerial Navigation

There are four types of aerial navigation: (1) celestial, (2) terrestrial, (3) dead reckoning, and (4) instrument.

1. Celestial Navigation—An accurate timepiece and a sextant are required.

2. Terrestrial Navigation—Well-marked airways and aeronautical charts are the chief aids.

3. Dead Reckoning—Navigation would be simple if it were not for the wind. Dead reckoning makes it possible to plot a course by use of (a) a timepiece, an altimeter, a compass, an air-speed indicator, and a drift sight.

4. Instrument Navigation—a. Small airplanes —The minimum instrument requirement is a two-way radio. Most small airplanes are also equipped with a VOR instrument. Supplementary instruments include (a) distance measuring equipment (b) an automatic direction finder, and (c) a radio altimeter.

b. Large airplanes—Large airplanes usually are equipped with automatic pilots and special equipment for landing under low ceilings (200 feet). (a) The ILS system uses localizer beams and glide path beams to direct the path of the airplane. (b) The Flarescan landing system will eventually replace the ILS system.

Study Questions

1. DEFINE: dead reckoning, pilotage, true course, compass heading, track, ground speed, air speed, celestial navigation, true heading, magnetic course, magnetic variation, fix, line of position, heading.
2. Outline the two main problems of dead reckoning.
3. What aids does the radio make available to a pilot?
4. What aids are available for terrestrial navigation?
5. When in flight, how would one check his ground speed over a given course?
6. How would one know whether or not the direction of the wind shifted while in flight?
7. Differentiate between ground speed and air speed.
8. Compare the relative usefulness of the four types of aerial navigation, indicating the conditions under which each one could be used to best advantage.
9. What aids does the radio make available for aerial navigation?
10. What data are necessary for celestial observation?
11. What information do aeronautical charts contain?
12. How are civil airways marked?
13. Does an air-speed indicator give a true reading at various altitudes?
14. To what does the term, radar, refer? Discuss the various applications of radar.
15. How can pilots determine their position without reference to celestial navigation or dead reckoning?
16. What do the following abbreviations stand for? (1) FAA, (2) VOR, (3) IFR, (4) VFR, (5) DME, (6) ADF, (7) VHF, (8) LF, (9) OBS, (10) TFI, (11) ILS.
17. How does the ILS landing system operate?
18. What landing system will replace the ILS system in the supersonic era?

Josuah trees in the Mojave Desert, California. Top photograph taken with ordinary film. Bottom photograph taken with infra red sensitive film. Note how it has cut through the haze. (Courtesy, Eastman Kodak Company)

Light and Sound in Modern Life

Beauty is truth, truth beauty; that is all
Ye know on earth, and all ye need to know.

KEATS

AN IMPORTANT aspect of modern life is the widespread interest and participation in the humanities, particularly art and music. As man acquires more
leisure time he often uses it for the enjoyment of music and art. Many of the
students in physical science courses throughout the country are majoring in music
or art. Many more will find music or art to be important hobbies as time will
permit. The study of the physical science side of art and music should be of
value in the understanding, appreciation, and enjoyment of these important
aspects of modern life.

This unit also introduces some practical applications of light to optics and
photography. Sound, likewise, is of practical concern in the realm of insulation,
sound deadening, and acoustics, in which the primary concern is the elimination
of sound where it is not wanted. We also touch on one of the frontiers of physical
science, supersonics and ultrasonics, which will undoubtedly find many applications in the near future.

C H A P T E R   5 0

Ultraviolet and Infrared Radiation and Luminescence

Here is unfolded to us a new and astonishing world—one which it is hard to conceive should contain no possibilities of transmitting and receiving intelligence. Rays of light will not pierce through a wall, nor, as we know only too well, through a London fog. But the electrical vibrations of a yard or more in wavelength will easily pierce such medium, which to them will be transparent. . . . Granted a few reasonable postulates, the whole thing comes well within the realms of possible fulfillment.

SIR WILLIAM CROOKES

INTRODUCTION

Many substances radiate light when heated to a high temperature; this process is called **incandescence.** It is not necessary, however, to heat objects in order to cause them to emit light. *Various types of energy are used to produce cold light,* the process being called **luminescence.** Several forms of luminescence are still laboratory curiosities; but other forms, such as electroluminescence, fluorescence, and phosphorescence, discussed in this chapter, have graduated from the laboratory during the past forty years, and are being employed in many useful applications, even to the extent of revolutionizing such industries as electrical advertising and Mazda-lamp manufacture.

This chapter deals with wavelengths of radiation on each side of the visible spectrum, the shorter ultraviolet and the longer infrared wavelengths.

ELECTROLUMINESCENCE

George D. Destriau discovered electroluminescence in 1936. *The emission of light from phosphor powders embedded in an insulator,* such as a glass panel, *when an alternating electric current runs through it,* is called **electroluminescence.** By using a mixture of phosphors that emit different colors when activated with different electrical frequencies, the colors in a room may be changed by merely changing the frequency of the alternating current. For general home lighting, luminescent panels will provide a glareless, uniformly diffused light, once they become available at costs that will compete with other sources of illumination. Figure 50-1 shows the first experimental room illuminated with electroluminescent panels.

BIOLUMINESCENCE

There are many examples of **bioluminescence,** i.e. *luminescence produced by living organisms,* such as fireflies, glowworms, fish, and even bacteria. A harmless type of bacteria sometimes produces a glow as it acts on spoiling fish or meat. Fungi produce a greenish yellow glow on rotting wood.

Male fireflies flash on their light at regular six-second intervals, while female fireflies light up every two seconds, perhaps attracting the males in this way. In Siam and other parts of

the world, large numbers of fireflies flash in unison.

The railroad worm of South America has eleven pairs of greenish lights along its sides which it turns on when disturbed. The cucujo beetle, sometimes called the "automobile bug," has two brilliant lights near the head, and a strong glow on the underside of its body.

The so-called "phosphorescence" of ocean water is due to microscopic organisms which turn on their light when they are disturbed. A deepsea squid is known to shoot out clouds of luminescent material.

INFRARED RADIATION

Infrared radiation *consists of wavelengths of radiant energy found in sunlight that are longer than those of light.* The heating of objects by sunlight resembles fluorescence in that radiation of long wavelengths is emitted by objects which have been irradiated with infrared radiation of shorter wavelengths.

Sources of Infrared Radiation

Any hot object radiates infrared radiation. An electric heater uses electricity to heat a resistance wire to redness. Since infrared radiation can be reflected and refracted, such heaters usually contain shiny surfaces to reflect, or concave reflectors to focus, the radia-tion. Radiant heating, now so widely used for home heating, depends upon infrared radiation produced by heating devices in the floors, walls or ceilings.

An ordinary electric light bulb emits infrared radiation, which usually represents wasted electricity. The infrared lamp, on the other hand, is deliberately designed to emit infrared radiation with the minimum of visible radiation. Infrared lamps, often called heat lamps, are a very convenient source of soothing heat treatments in the home. Sometimes they are used in bathrooms to furnish a quick, convenient source of heat. They might also be used to thaw frozen pipes or to defrost refrigerators. Infrared lamps are used to bake cookies in commercial bakeries. Poultry producers heat their brooders with infrared lamps. Such lamps are used in cooking, drying, and dehydrating foods. Infrared lamps are widely used in industry in baking finishes on automobiles and household appliances.

Detection of Infrared Radiation

Infrared radiation can be refracted and reflected in the same manner as visible radiation. Heat-sensitive and photoconductive materials may be used to receive infrared radiation and change it into electrical energy. This electrical energy may then be amplified by electronic methods. Warm objects may be easily distinguished in this way from their

Figure 50–2. The Sierra Nevada range in the vicinity of Yosemite, photographed from Mount Hamilton by infrared light; distance to Half Dome, 120 miles. (Courtesy, Lick Observatory)

Figure 50–3. The photograph obtained using an emulsion sensitized to infrared radiations. The irons were not hot enough to produce any visible light in the perfectly dark room. (Courtesy, Eastman Kodak Company)

cooler surroundings. Smokestacks or airplane exhausts may be detected by the effect of their infrared radiations on sensitive thermocouples six miles away, and icebergs may be located in the fog by their coldness. A "fog-eye" designed to see through fog consists of a reflector that gathers in infrared rays and focuses them on a thermocouple. The electricity, generated by the thermocouple, is amplified millions of times, and may be used to ring warning gongs when a ship is approaching an iceberg. The "fog-eye" can detect a difference of temperature of one fifty-thousandth of a degree, which means that it should respond to the heat of a candle eight miles away.

Infrared detection devices have become a billion-dollar-a-year business. Because infrared wavelengths are shorter than radar wavelengths, smaller, less expensive devices may be used for their detection. For example, the four-inch infrared "seeker" in the nose of a Sidewinder missile can detect a burning cigarette a hundred yards away. It can detect airplanes or missiles at a distance of seven miles.

Infrared Photography

Inasmuch as infrared rays penetrate the atmosphere better than the radiations of shorter wavelength, and inasmuch as they affect certain photographic emulsions, infrared radiation may be used in photography, in cases where the shorter waves are scattered by the atmosphere. Excellent photographs are often made of distant objects on hazy days by use of films especially sensitive to infrared rays, and employing an infrared filter that screens out all but the infrared rays.

The photographs on page 376 show pictures taken with infrared-sensitive film as compared with ordinary film. Green leaves appear to be white in such photographs, and can be readily distinguished from green paint. Note that the sky appears to be dark because of the infrared radiation in sunlight. Daytime infrared photographs are often used to simulate moonlight effects.

Figure 50-2 shows how infrared-sensitive films may be used to penetrate haze.

Pictures have been taken in a dark room using the invisible radiation from a hot electric iron as shown in Figure 50-3.

The Greenhouse Effect

A closed automobile warms up when placed in sunlight because of two properties of glass. In the first place, glass transmits short infrared waves such as come from the sun, but it does not transmit the longer infrared rays such as come from warm objects in the car. In the second place, glass is a poor conductor of heat. Thus the automobile or the greenhouse acts like a heat trap. The transmission of short infrared rays by glass is a very important factor to be considered in air-conditioning. The behavior of glass toward infrared rays is applied in greenhouses and hotbeds.

ULTRAVIOLET LUMINESCENCE

About 1900, Peter Cooper Hewitt developed the mercury vapor lamp, which is a rich source of ultraviolet radiation. The visible radiation from such lamps may be screened out by the use of special glass filters, opaque to light but not to ultraviolet radiation. Some of the wavelengths of ultraviolet radiation have an effect on the body similar to sunlight. So-called "sunlamps" should be used with caution, because the wavelengths emitted are harmful to the eyes. The radiation from oxy-acetylene electric welding, or arc-lights is very rich in ultraviolet wavelengths. This is the reason why welders use special filters to protect their eyes. In some ultraviolet, mercury vapor lamps the harmful, shorter, ultraviolet wavelengths are screened out with special filters, and are, therefore, more suitable for experiments with ultraviolet radiation.

Germicidal Lamps

Mercury vapor lamps are used as sunlamps and germicidal lamps. Ultraviolet radiation will destroy bacteria in liquids and on the surfaces of solids. Often, germicidal lamps are used in refrigerators and meat display cases. Germicidal lamps may also be used in restaurants to sanitize drinking glasses and other utensils. In general, ultraviolet light is one of the most important prophylactic germicidal agents now available.

Duke hospital in Durham, North Carolina, has made extensive use of ultraviolet radiation to kill the staphylococci that have been giving so much trouble in hospitals because of their resistance to antibiotics. Ultraviolet radiation can be used at the scene of the operation by taking precautions to protect the eyes. This hospital reports results that are "nothing short of miraculous."

Other hospitals use powerful sources of ultraviolet radiation in air-conditioning ducts to sterilize the air for general use and for incubators.

Mount Sinai hospital, of Baltimore, Maryland, after six months of use of ultraviolet sterilization, reported that out of 1,600 surgical operations there was not a single case of infection.

FLUORESCENCE AND PHOSPHORESCENCE

Fluorescence and **phosphorescence** are types of photoluminescence in which *light is produced in certain substances*, called **phosphors,** *when they are subjected to invisible radiation such as ultraviolet, X rays or gamma rays.* George Stokes (1819–1903) suggested the name, fluorescence, after the green mineral fluorite, the strong fluorescence of which he observed in 1852.

Fluorescent light, like other types of luminescence is cold light. Both organic and inorganic substances exhibit fluorescence. **Fluorescent** *substances give off light of a longer wavelength than that of the radiation received, immediately after exposure to the radiation. The emission of light stops when the activating source is removed.*

Phosphorescence *differs from fluorescence in that the emission of light continues for some time after the activating source has been removed.* Phosphorescence may be of very short duration, or it may last up to four years, depending upon the phosphor used.

The theory of fluorescence and phosphorescence is that the activating radiation causes electrons to move from stable orbits to orbits farther from the nucleus. The electrons are thus in an unstable state and return to their original orbits, emitting radiation characteristic of the substance; usually the radiation

has a wavelength longer than that which activated them.

APPLICATIONS OF ULTRAVIOLET FLUORESCENCE

Modern "black light" analysis depends upon the fluorescence or phosphorescence produced in many substances by filtered ultraviolet radiations. Certain minerals possess a characteristic fluorescence when exposed to ultraviolet radiation, which is useful as a means of identification. In forensic chemistry, ultraviolet radiation makes it possible to detect forgeries and alterations in documents. In art, the authenticity of paintings and sculptures may be tested because overpainting, patches, etc., show up at once when irradiated with ultraviolet radiation.

Adulteration of foods and textiles can be discovered by differences in fluorescence. Dead or artificial teeth do not fluoresce as do natural teeth. The fluorescence of eggs increases with age. Hair dyes and oils show up under the fluorescent light. Cigarette stamps, made from materials containing quinine, will glow with a blue color in ultraviolet radia-

Figure 50–4. "Glowing Carpets" might be the appropriate name to apply to the fluorescent carpet which shines in brilliant colors when irradiated with ultraviolet light. (Courtesy, American Cyanamide Chemical Company)

Figure 50–5. Ice-skaters in ordinary light. (Courtesy, Switzer Brothers)

Figure 50–6. Ice-skaters' fluorescent costumes glow in ultraviolet light. (Courtesy, Switzer Brothers)

tion, thus differentiating them from counterfeit stamps that are not fluorescent.

Many inexpensive dyes are fluorescent, and thus make possible the manufacture of dyed carpets and dresses, etc., which will fluoresce brilliantly in ultraviolet rays. A number of theaters have their aisles covered with rugs dyed with fluorescent dyes. Figures 50-4, 50-5, and 50-6 show applications of fluorescent dyes.

By placing a fluorescent dye, such as fluorescein, in water, leaks in plumbing may be traced. A fluorescent dye thrown into sea water will attract the attention of airplane pilots searching for survivors who would be difficult to spot otherwise.

FLUORESCENT LAMPS

The fluorescent lamp is a long tube coated inside with a fluorescent material. The tube contains a small amount of mercury, which sets up a mercury arc when electricity is passed through the tube. This mercury arc produces ultraviolet radiations, which energize the fluorescent materials, causing them to give off visible light.

In addition to the trace of mercury, there is a small amount of argon gas at low pressure. The argon serves as a starter to conduct the current until the tube gets warm enough for the mercury vapor to do so. In general, fluorescent lamps are from 200 to 300 per cent more efficient in light output, color for color, than comparable incandescent sources. Incandescent lights waste, in the form of heat, much of the electrical energy used. The large light-producing area of fluorescent lamps, the high diffusion of the light from these lamps, their high efficiency, and low radiant heat make them very desirable for general illumination; and they have many excellent supplementary lighting applications.

NEON-TYPE LAMPS

Neon lamps were invented by a Frenchman, Georges Claude, who also invented a process for liquefying air that made it possible to obtain neon and the other rare gases from the air.

Claude found that the rare gases would glow when placed in tubes under low pressures, at relatively low temperatures, when a high-voltage current was passed through them. Neon vapor gives a red light; mercury vapor, a blue light; and helium, a white light. Other colors are produced by the use of tinted glass.

High-voltage fluorescent tubing known commercially as "zeon" (the N of Neon becomes the Z of Zeon when tipped on its side) lamps are similar to neon lamps in that they use long tubes and high-voltage circuits, but they differ from them in that the tubes are coated inside with fluorescent materials. Both neon and zeon lamps generate ultraviolet radiations, but these radiations are absorbed by the glass in neon lamps without producing useful illumination, while the fluorescent powders in zeon lamps convert the ultraviolet radiations into visible light. Any desired hue can be obtained with zeon lamps, while the choice is scant with neon lamps.

SUMMARY

Luminescence is cold light. Types of luminescence discussed in this section are electroluminescence, bioluminescence, and photoluminescence, which includes fluorescence, and phosphorescence.

Almost any kind of energy may produce luminescence. The basic principle of fluorescence and phosphorescence is that short-wave radiation causes electrons to move farther from the nucleus. They then return to their normal positions and emit radiation in the form of longer wavelengths of the visible spectrum. Infrared radiation may likewise be absorbed at one wavelength and be given off at a longer (but not visible) wavelength, as illustrated by the "greenhouse effect."

Fluorescent lamps are more efficient than incandescent lamps, because less energy is wasted in the form of heat.

Study Questions

1. DEFINE: luminescence, fluorescence, phosphorescence, phosphor, electroluminescence, incandescence, bioluminescence, infrared radiation, photoluminescence.
2. What is the source of the light in non-filament lamps?
3. List the different types of luminescence, and give an example of each type.
4. Differentiate between phosphorescence and fluorescence.
5. What type of luminescence is illustrated by the firefly?
6. Give a possible explanation of luminescence.
7. Discuss the sources of ultraviolet radiations.
8. Why is it that some ultraviolet lamps are dangerous to use while others are not?
9. Why did the introduction of neon lights revolutionize electrical advertising?
10. In what respects are "zeon" lights an improvement over neon lights?

11. Why are "zeon" and neon lights not used for lighting private residences?

12. Explain the high efficiency of fluorescent lamps.

13. What types of materials are used to produce fluorescence in fluorescent lamps?

14. Why are fluorescent lamps relatively expensive to install?

15. What are the advantages and disadvantages of fluorescent lamps as compared with incandescent filament lamps?

Color

I do not know what I may appear to the world, but to myself I seem to have been only like a boy playing on the seashore, and diverting myself in now and then finding a smoother pebble or a prettier shell than ordinary, whilst the great ocean of Truth lay all undiscovered before me.

ISAAC NEWTON

INTRODUCTION

The portions of the electromagnetic spectrum that are on either side of the visible spectrum were discussed in the last chapter. In general, these three—the infrared, the visible, and the ultraviolet are the segments of the electromagnetic spectrum that beneficially affect living organisms. The infrared portion conveys the sensation of heat, the visible portion provides for vision, and the ultraviolet provides the energy for the production of essential chemicals such as vitamin D. Of course, the amount of radiation is also important—too little or too much affect the organism adversely. The remainder of the electromagnetic spectrum may affect the living organism, but the effects are generally detrimental rather than beneficial.

In this chapter, we will consider only the part of the spectrum that is visible. Charts of the electromagnetic spectrum (see pages 266 and 271) are usually not drawn to scale, but show a significant portion for the visible radiation as a matter of emphasis. However, we actually see an extremely small segment of the entire spectrum. If the visible portion of the electromagnetic spectrum is represented by a segment 18 inches long (this is the length on some charts), then the length of the entire spectrum is more than 100 miles.

THE NATURE OF COLOR

In this chapter, we study **color,** which may be defined as *a learned psychological response to certain wavelengths of light.* The color of any object depends upon the capacity of the object to modify the wavelengths of light which are transmitted or reflected. The color of an incandescent object represents the wavelengths radiated by the object. *In general,* **colors** *refer to the wavelengths of the visible spectrum that produce the sensation we call* **color.**

Color is strictly subjective. Color does not exist in an object. Color is only the response of the eye and brain to radiant energy of one or more of the wavelengths found in white light. Color is a learned response. We say that something is red because that is what we have been taught. A color-blind person may not be able to see red, but may see green instead. However he would call what he sees red, because that is what he has been taught. The unaided, but trained, eye can recognize about 230 different hues, or colors, but an instrument, called the spectrophotometer, is capable of distinguishing about 30,000 different wavelengths in the visible spectrum. As previously mentioned, white light is a mixture of all of the colors in the rainbow, but no one would suspect it because the eye cannot analyze light.

The study of color includes the methods for the production of color and the applications of color in nature, art, and illumination.

The ability to experience color sensations is one of man's great blessings, but unfortunately there are about eight million people in the United States who are not so blessed; they are color-blind, to a certain extent. As a rule they cannot completely distinguish between red and green, or violet or yellow and grey. Some people see only green and others see only red. Many people are unaware of their disability.

COLOR THEORIES

There are various theories to account for the perception of color. The Helmholtz theory, first proposed by Thomas Young in 1801, and later modified and developed by Ludwig von Helmholtz, has been generally accepted; but Edwin Land's experiment, described below, suggests the need for a modification of this theory.

According to the Helmholtz tricolor theory of color vision, there are *three basic color sensations,* called **primary colors:** *red, green, and violet, to which separate sets of cone cells within the retina of the eye are sensitive.* These cones are shown in Figure 51-1. By adding these color sensations in varied proportions, all of the colors in the spectrum, such as the rainbow, or the continuous spectrum obtained with a spectrometer or diffraction grating, may be produced. If all of the cones are excited equally we experi-

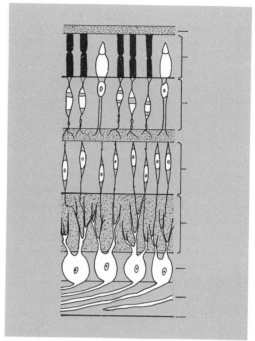

Figure 51–1. The structure of the retina. The cones, shown in white in the middle and upper layers, are thought to give rise to the sense of color. The rods, shown in black, are thought to be more sensitive to light but do not respond to color. The rods and cones terminate in the nerve cells which conduct light and color sensations to the optic nerve.

There are some 130,000,000 rods and some 7,000,000 cones in the retina of an eye.

ence the sensation of white. If none are excited the sensation is black. Figure 51-2 shows the range of the three types of color receptors according to the Helmholtz theory.

Edwin H. Land, in 1959, announced a

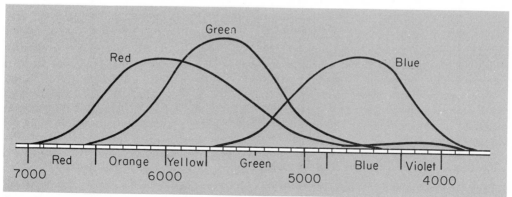

Figure 51–2.   The ranges of the three types of color receptors, according to the Young-Helmholtz theory (from Abney). The numbers represent wavelengths in millionths of millimeters (Angstrom units).

series of experiments dealing with new concepts of color sensation. One experiment utilized a pair of photographs taken from the same point on black-and-white panchromatic film, one through a filter passing the wavelengths of the visible spectrum, and one through a filter passing only the wavelengths in the middle of the visible spectrum.

When the photographs were projected and registered on a screen with a long-wavelength filter over the former, and a neutral filter over the latter, a variety of colors such as red, yellow, orange, green, blue, brown, and white were seen. Note that these colors were obtained from two black-and-white photographs. This shows that colors are not directly correlated with wavelength. The eye will see color in situations unpredictable on the basis of older hypotheses. Mr. Land concluded that the classical laws of color mixing conceal great basic laws of color vision.

THE PRODUCTION OF COLOR

Any method of separating the different wavelengths of white light should produce color. The wavelengths of white light may be separated by refraction, diffraction, interference, selective absorption or reflection, and scattering. The radiation of color may be produced by heat (incandescence) and by various forms of energy that result in cold light, which have been included under the general term of luminescence, as mentioned in the previous chapter.

Color Production by Refraction

Isaac Newton made the first important contribution to our knowledge of color. Chapter 37 presented Newton's experiments in which he produced all of the colors of the rainbow by the refraction of sunlight, using a glass prism. James Clerk Maxwell, using three projectors to project red, green, and blue light, combined the three light beams and obtained white light.

The Production of Color by Interference

Francesco Grimaldi (1618–1663) first showed that light could be **diffracted,** i.e.,

bent around corners, by passing it through very small openings. Later, his experiments were confirmed by Thomas Young, who explained diffraction in terms of interference around 1800. Young devised an ingenious plan whereby he obtained two sources of light in phase with each other by causing one source of light to shine through two closely spaced slits, thus producing a pattern of dark and light fringes, which he attributed to interference.

The rainbowlike colors of thin oil films on water and thin soap bubbles, are caused by interference. Films cause interference because the reflections from the two surfaces, if they are the proper distance apart, cancel each other. In other cases, only certain wavelengths of light will be canceled, thus leaving the noncanceled wavelengths as visible color.

If a wedge is made by placing two glass plates on top of each other and separating one end by a thin piece of Scotch tape, we will have a simple apparatus by which color is produced by interference. When light of a given color shines on the wedge, a series of light and dark bands of that color will be obtained. The distance between the bands will vary with the wavelength of the light and thus provides a method for its measurement. When white light shines on such a wedge, the characteristic rainbow spectrum is obtained, but the colors will be the reverse of those of a prism spectrum.

Iridescence, similar to colors of soap films or oil slicks, is often found in nature in butterfly wings or bird feathers, an outstanding example being the coloration of peacock feathers. Some insects, such as certain varieties of flies and beetles, show iridescence. The color in this case is the result of interference phenomena. The colors due to interference change with a change in the angle of incidence of light, or with a change in the thickness of a film. As one blows a soap bubble, the colors are observed to change as the bubble grows larger, and as the thickness of the film becomes correspondingly less.

The iridescence of a butterfly wing is due to layers of transparent scales. If a drop of ether is placed on the scales, the color will disappear because the airspaces between the scales are filled with the ether. When the ether evaporates the color returns.

The Production of Color by Selective Absorption

Colors may be formed by **pigments** (*colored opaque substances*) *that absorb certain wavelengths and reflect other wavelengths*. On the other hand, colors may be produced by absorption, as light is passed through transparent materials.

The Absorption of Color by Pigments—When white light shines on pigments, some wavelengths are absorbed and some are reflected; the color of the pigment is due to the wavelength of the reflected light. A mixture of pigments produces color by subtraction rather than by addition; for example, a mixture of red and yellow pigments produces an orange color, because the red pigment reflects only red wavelengths, while the yellow pigment reflects only yellow wavelengths.

The primary colors of the artist are reddish purple, yellow, and blue green, and are called **subtractive primary colors.** Figure 51-3 shows how the three primary pigments mix to form black. In case some white has been mixed in with the colored pigments, gray will be the result.

Color photographs and color printing depend upon the use of the three **additive primary colors**—*blue, red, and yellow.* A photographic color film consists of three dif-

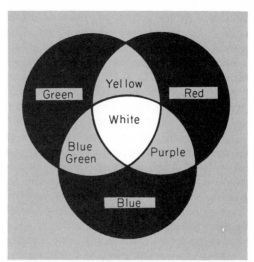

Figure 51-4.   Mixing additive colors of light.

ferent layers of emulsion, each of which is sensitive to one of the three primary colors. The development of such a film consists of the selective dying of each layer. A photograph may be made from a colored negative by making three different-colored prints in gelatin films and then superimposing them to produce the final color photograph. Similarly, three different engravings may be produced, each of which is printed with inks of the above three primary colors; the superimposed pictures in different colors produce the color printing with which we are familiar.

The Absorption of Color by Transparent Materials—When white light is passed through red glass, all of the wavelengths are absorbed except the red wavelengths, which are transmitted. This is an example of the general rule that transparent materials absorb all colors except the color of the absorbing material. Similarly, a green filter will screen out all of the wavelengths of white light except the green wavelengths. If the red light shines on a green paper the paper will appear to be black because the red wavelength is absorbed. Figure 51-4 shows that yellow may be obtained by mixing red and green light in the proper proportions. These three colors, blue, red, and yellow, are used for color television.

The Production of Gray Light by the Addition of Complementary Pigment Colors—**Comple-**

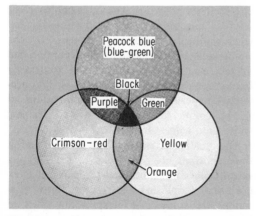

Figure 51-3.   The primary colors of pigments mix to form black.

mentary colors *consist of pairs of colors which, when mixed, will give gray light.* One method of determining complementary colors is based on the principle of retinal fatigue, mentioned above. If a circle of red paper, strongly illuminated by white light, is gazed at intently for about thirty seconds and is then replaced by a sheet of white paper, a bluish-green circle will appear to take the place of the red. The retina becomes fatigued by the red so that when acted on equally by all colors, it responds more strongly to the remaining colors in the spectrum. The red and bluish-green are complementary. Any one of the three primary pigment colors will produce its complementary color in the same manner. Complementary colors may also be determined by blending colors on a color wheel. Some other complementary color combinations are: orange and blue, yellow and blue-violet. In each of these cases the color is a primary color, and its complement is a result of a mixture of the other two primaries.

The Production of Color by Scattering

John Tyndall (1820–1893) demonstrated, about 100 years ago, that the color of the blue sky is caused by the scattering of sunlight by fine particles in the upper atmosphere.

The colors of the sky are due to the scattering of light by molecules of the air and particles of dust floating in the air, just as the waves of the sea are turned aside and scattered by rocks that rise above the surface. The short waves of light that compose the blue end of the spectrum are more easily turned aside than the longer red waves, just as ripples are turned aside by a rock over which the larger waves heave themselves and steadily advance. Thus a separation takes place and color is produced.

For example, the smoke rising from a chimney looks blue against a dark background, especially if the smoke particles are quite small. If, on the other hand, the smoke is viewed against a bright background of luminous cloud or even against the sun itself, the color that comes through is brown or red.

A red light carries better than a white light in a misty atmosphere because the water particles do not scatter the long, red rays as much as they scatter blue rays. Hence, infra-red photography is valuable in a hazy atmosphere.

COLOR IN NATURE

Green of chlorophyl is the primary color of the plant world, while the red of blood is the chief color of the animal world.

Many of the red and yellow colors of animals are the carotenoid pigments which they cannot produce, but which are obtained from plants that synthesize them. On the other hand, the red hemoglobin of the blood is a pigment synthesized by animals. The green color of a tomato worm or a green grasshopper is not due to chlorophyl, ingested or synthesized by such living organisms, but it is due to a mixture of yellow carotenoid pigments and blue bile salts produced by the organism.

COLOR IN ART

Color is used in the visual arts in various ways. The commercial artist utilizes color for advertising and the packaging of products. He selects attractive colors for packages to make them appeal to the customer. He uses the most vivid colors and the most brilliant hues in his advertising, in order to draw attention. The fashion artist uses color in designing fabrics and in the creation of clothing. For example, the blacks, charcoals, olives, and browns became so fashionable for men's clothing that it became difficult to find anything else in the mid-sixties. The interior decorator tries to harmonize colors of the interior finishes and in furnishing of homes. By the simple selection of colors, the decorator can make a room either exciting and restless or harmonious and tranquil, because the prolonged exposure to certain combinations of bright colors tends to excite and irritate, while pale colors are restful.

The creative artist considers color as one of the important considerations in making pictures. Colors are controlled to construct compositions (orphism), to reveal form (Cezanne), to study and interpret the effect of light on objects (impressionism), and to express emotions and ideas, gay or gloomy, light or profound (expressionism).

ATTRIBUTES (OR QUALITIES) OF COLOR

Hue

The spectral colors are **hues.** *Light of only one wavelength, called* **monochromatic light,** *is a hue.* The usual spectral color, such as yellow, represents a band of wavelengths (or frequencies) that conveys the sensation of one color to the eye. Typical hues are blue, red, yellow, and green.

A hue may be modified by adding other hues. Thus, a red may be made yellower or bluer, or a blue may be made redder or greener by adding other hues. By adding yellow to red another hue, orange, is obtained. The addition of blue to red converts it into violet.

Intensity

Intensity *refers to the brightness or dullness of a color.* A pure hue has high intensity, and a mixture of hues has a lower intensity. The intensity of a hue is decreased by adding its complementary color or by adding neutral gray.

Value

Value *refers to the dark or light quality of a color. White pigments may be added to a hue to make it lighter, thus producing what is known as a* **tint.** *The addition of black to a hue darkens it and thus produces a* **shade.**

Value is used in a different sense to compare the spectral colors. Thus, yellow is said to have a light value, while blue violet is said to have a dark value.

Hues are considered to convey emotional reactions. Thus, red is associated with rage, while blue is associated with sadness. Red, yellow, and orange are designated as warm colors (a desert in sunlight, for example), while blue and green are known as cool colors (night, sea water, ice, and snow, for example). Figure 51-5 shows the color wheel used by the commercial artist or the creative artist to select colors.

In the use of colors, the artist usually places warm colors near cool colors, and light against dark, in order to obtain pleasing contrasts. However, mixtures of hues are generally employed to make these contrasts more

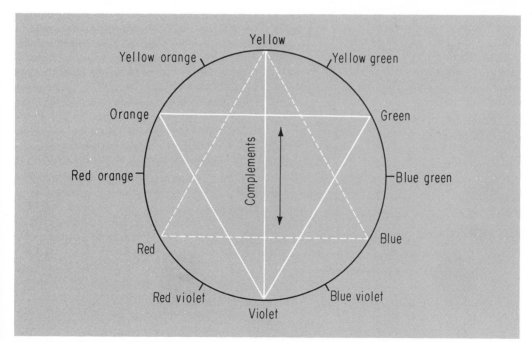

Figure 51–5. The color circle. Place an equilateral triangle anywhere on the circle to obtain colors which will harmonize with each other. When using pigments, the colors at opposite positions on the circle are complementary colors.

subtle. In nature, as well as in art, the general rule is that the brighter the color, the smaller the area.

SUMMARY

White light is a mixture of all of the colors in the visible spectrum.

Prisms and raindrops separate the colors in white light, because the short wavelengths are refracted more than the longer wavelengths as they pass from one medium to another.

The color of any object in white light is produced by the absorption of all frequencies but those which are transmitted or reflected.

Complementary colored lights are those which produce white light by addition. Primary additive colors may also produce white light by addition.

Complementary pigment colors produce gray by subtraction. Primary pigment colors produce black by subtraction.

The subtractive primary colors are reddish purple, yellow, and blue-green.

The additive primary colors are blue, red, and yellow.

A hue is a primary color, which, when mixed with white, produces a tint, and when mixed with black, produces a shade.

Color harmony is achieved by using color mixtures and by associating with any primary color the colors on either side of its opposite in the color circle.

Study Questions

1. DEFINE: color, complementary color, additive primary color, subtractive primary color, hue, tint, shade, value, diffraction, pigment, color intensity, color value, monochromatic light.
2. Differentiate between subtractive and additive primary colors.
3. In what ways does an artist use color as a means of expression?
4. What is the nature of the Helmholtz tricolor theory of color?
5. Describe the experiment conducted by Land, which suggests the need for a new theory of color.
6. List the different methods for the production of color.
7. Explain how a prism disperses white light.
8. Give some of the rules of the artist for the use of color.
9. Explain how the eye sees different colors.
10. What is meant by complementary colors?
11. What is the source of color in an object?
12. How do pigments destroy color?
13. How did Maxwell produce white light from three primary colors?
14. Give several examples of the production of color by selective absorption.
15. Describe a method for producing color by interference.
16. How are colors of soap bubbles produced?
17. Although kerosene is a colorless liquid, a trace of it on the surface of a pool of water will give a variety of colors. How are these colors produced?

Polarized Light and Illumination

Do not several sorts of rays make vibrations of several bignesses, which according to their bignesses excite sensations of several colours, much after the manner that the vibrations of the air, according to their several bignesses excite sensations of several sounds?

ISAAC NEWTON

INTRODUCTION

Illumination *deals with the problems of choosing suitable light sources to use for a given purpose, how much light is required, how the amount of light present can be measured, and where light sources should be placed.*

Tremendous strides have been made in the science of illumination, and yet few homes are properly illuminated. Proper illumination is desirable because it saves eyestrain. In this age, when the eyes are used so much in reading and close work, it is very important that everything possible be done to relieve the eyes from unnecessary strain.

One of the problems of illumination is the elimination of glare. **Glare** *is unwanted reflected light.* Reflected light is plane polarized to a considerable extent. The glare from store windows often makes it difficult to see what is behind them. The glare from a television screen may be a problem. The glare from automobile headlights makes night driving difficult. The glare from a coated paper may be a cause of eyestrain. The invention of polarizing screens seemed to offer a solution to glare because they could cancel out the plane polarized light in reflected light. Desk lamps, automobile visors, eyeglasses, and other applications of polarized light were widely marketed, but in most cases they possessed the disadvantage that the polarizing screen cut down the transmitted light too much to be satisfactory.

ILLUMINATING POWER

The value of any light source for illumination depends upon how much light it gives out. The unit of source intensity is called the **candle,** *which is equal to the intensity of a standard candle burning under specified conditions.* Obviously, the intensity of illumination by the light from a burning candle depends upon the distance one is from it, so that one must incorporate the idea of distance as well as that of source intensity into the measurement of illumination. See Figure 52-1. A **foot-candle** is the most convenient unit of intensity of illumination; it *represents the intensity of the light at a distance of one foot from a standard candle.*

The lumen is now replacing candle power in measuring illumination. The lumen is really a measure of the quantity of light, because it combines the idea of area with intensity. The **lumen** is *the amount of light falling upon a surface that has an area of one square foot, when every point of the area is one foot from a standard candle.* Light intensities are expressed in lumens per square meter, or in foot-candles; the foot-candle is one lumen per square foot.

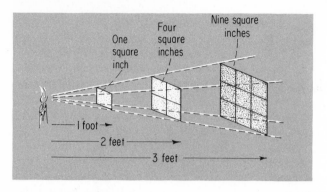

Figure 52–1. The quantity of light received per unit of surface is inversely proportional to the square of the distance from the light source.

THE MEASUREMENT OF ILLUMINATION

The strength of a light source is measured by use of a photometer, in which the distance of two light sources from a rod is varied until the shadows are of equal intensity. The relative strengths of the two light sources can then be computed on the basis of their relative distances from the rod.

The intensity of light is now measured for photographic purposes by means of light meters, which the photographer calls exposure meters. These are simply photoelectric cells in circuit with sensitive galvanometers, which measure the electric current from the photoelectric cell when light shines upon it.

THE AMOUNT OF ILLUMINATION REQUIRED FOR DIFFERENT PURPOSES

Different persons require different amounts of light, depending upon their sensitiveness to light. Certain conditions of eyestrain will cause such a sensitivity to light that people so afflicted can scarcely stay in the room that is adequately illuminated for other people. As a rule, old people require more light than young people.

The amount of light required for good illumination also depends upon the nature of what one is doing.

The following values represent good lighting practice:

3 foot-candles — stairways, passageways, etc.

3–10 foot-candles — power plants, elevators, etc.

5–10 foot-candles — general household work.

10–15 foot-candles — stores and general factory work.

10–20 foot-candles — offices and classrooms, general reading, writing, and sewing.

20–30 foot-candles — typing and average office work.

20–50 foot-candles — drafting and fine office work, prolonged reading, especially of fine print, fine needlework.

50–100 foot-candles — fine manufacture and inspection.

Your local power and light company will undoubtedly be glad to render you the service of measuring the intensity of illumination at various points in your home, office, or shop.

THE ELIMINATION OF GLARE AND SHADOWS IN ILLUMINATION

In designing a lighting system, whether for home, office, or factory, one should try to avoid glare and shadows that cause eyestrain. In general, one should keep in mind that it is not the light source that one wants to see, but rather the book, merchandise, or machine, as the case may be. Floor lamps and table lamps are good as decorations, but they are poor for general illumination, because they are in the direct line of vision. Flush-type ceiling lights, cove lighting, concealed floodlighting, and similar types of lighting represent good lighting practice, because light fixtures are kept out of sight, while the light is directed where it is needed.

Shadows, and all sharp contrasts in illumination, should be avoided because it takes some time for the eye to become adjusted to any given light intensity. A camera that has been adjusted to take a picture in the bright sunlight must have its diaphragm opened to allow more light to get in for exposure on a cloudy day. When one shifts his eye from a brightly illuminated book to an object in a poorly illuminated dark corner, it strains his eyes to see anything. Everyone knows that it takes time to adjust one's eyes to see outdoors at night when one steps out from a well-illuminated room, and everyone has experienced the almost blinding sensation of coming from a dark room into sunlight. Theater lights are turned on and off gradually in order to give the eye time to adjust to the change in illumination.

The reason eyestrain is caused by contrasts in illumination is that the iris of the eye, which corresponds to the diaphragm in a camera, opens or shuts with varying light intensities, and if the muscles that control the iris are kept constantly active, they become tired, and eye fatigue results.

In general illumination, it is obvious that contrasting regions of strong and faint illumination should be avoided. There should be some illumination in a room in which television is being watched, in order to avoid the contrast between the bright screen and the surrounding darkness. Equal, glareless illumination is accomplished by the proper spacing of light sources and by the proper diffusion of the light from these sources. When direct lighting is used, better illumination is obtained by the use of frosted-glass incandescent light bulbs than by clear-glass light bulbs. Opal glass is used in lamp globes and light fixtures to diffuse the light still more. Flush-type lights employ frosted glass; and when still better diffusion is desired, the frosted glass is replaced by "diffusex" or prism glass, the surface of which is molded into the form of small pyramids.

Light may also be diffused by reflection. Unpolished or rough surfaces reflect light in many different directions, and thus scatter or diffuse it. Indirect lighting depends upon the reflection of light from the ceiling and walls of rooms. The color of the finish on a ceiling

TABLE 52-1
LIGHT REFLECTION VALUES

Light—almost white	85 per cent
Cream	70–75 per cent
Yellow	55–65 per cent
Green	35–50 per cent
Blue	10–50 per cent

determines its reflecting power. Lighter shades reflect more than darker shades.

Indirect lighting is best for general illumination, and yet one does not want to illuminate every point in a large living room well enough to provide for reading fine print or doing fine needlework. Shaded reading lamps provide the localized light intensity required. The newer types of floor and table lamps combine direct and indirect lighting, but they still have the disadvantage that the light sources are in direct line of vision for general illumination, and that they seldom provide adequate general illumination. One method of providing the intensity of light required for special purposes is to place lights in the walls or ceiling behind small lenses which will focus the light where it is wanted.

THE EFFICIENCY OF INCANDESCENT LAMPS

An important fact that is unknown to many people is that more light is obtained from one 100-watt incandescent lamp than is obtained from two 50-watt incandescent lamps. For example, a 40-watt lamp will give about 25 candle power, whereas a 1000-watt lamp may give as much as 1500 candle power. Twenty-five 40-watt lamps would cost as much to operate as one 1000-watt lamp, but they would produce only 625 candle power.

It is important that lamps designed for a given voltage be used with that voltage. A 110-volt lamp used with a 130-volt circuit has a very short life, although greater illumination is obtained as long as it lasts because a higher temperature is attained. On the other hand, the same lamp used with a 100-volt circuit would last a long time, but it would give less illumination for a given expenditure of money. The maximum illumination per amount of money spent for both power and lamps is obtained when the lamps are properly matched with the voltage of the circuit. This is a problem worth investigating because the voltage in a circuit may not be what you think it is.

POLARIZED LIGHT

The first recorded discovery of polarized light was made by Bartholinus of Denmark, who in 1670 observed that an object viewed through Iceland spar appeared double. Bartholinus reasoned that the crystal separated the light into two beams. The later discovery of the physicist, Nicol, that Iceland spar crystals could be cut at certain angles and cemented together with Canada balsam to form prisms that would eliminate one of the above two beams of light, made possible the polarimeter and polarizing microscope, and thus harnessed polarized light for laboratory use.

THE INVENTION OF POLARIZING SCREENS

In 1852, W. D. Herapath discovered that quinine iodosulfate crystals would polarize a beam of light, but he did not succeed in mounting them in a satisfactory manner. It was the discovery of Edwin H. Land, announced in 1934, that these crystals could be suspended in a plastic cellulose acetate film and aligned by stretching the film, which

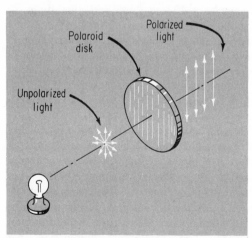

Figure 52–2. Polarization of light with a Polaroid polarizer.

made possible the polarization of light economically on a large scale. In 1941, Land produced a polarizing medium, which uses individual molecules rather than crystals to polarize light. These polarizing sheets are produced by stretching heated polyvinyl alcohol plastic, thus aligning the plastic molecules, and then allowing the plastic to imbibe an iodine solution. This new screen transmits one-third more light than the previous screen and polarizes 99.99 per cent of the light to which the eye is most sensitive. The principle of these screens, termed "Polaroid" by Land, is shown in Figure 52-2.

THE NATURE OF POLARIZED LIGHT

Light waves are transverse waves, that is, they vibrate at right angles to the direction that the light is traveling, just as waves set up in a pool of water by a stone thrown into it travel at right angles to the up-and-down direction in which the water surface moves. Ordinary light is a mixture of transverse vibrations in all possible directions. *When light is vibrating in one plane only, it is said to be* **plane polarized,** *or just* **polarized.** Figure 52-3 shows how crossed polarizing screens completely extinguish light.

POLARIZATION OF LIGHT BY REFLECTION

When light strikes a glass plate at an angle, about 5 per cent of the light is reflected, and a portion of this reflected light will be polarized. Figure 52-4 shows how light is polarized by reflection. A pile of glass plates not only produces polarized light by reflection but polarizes the transmitted light much as crystals do. The angle of a glass plate or mirror relative to the direction of the beam of light determines the relative amounts of ordinary reflected light and plane polarized light. The best angle, called the angle of polarization, is about 57 degrees, for ordinary glass.

Figure 52-5 shows how light is controlled in the windows of some railroad trains by the use of polarizing screens. Two polarizing discs are placed with their flat surfaces next to each other. They are mounted in such a

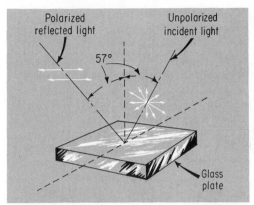

Figure 52–4. Polarization of light by reflection.

Figure 52–3. The rolled-up polarizing material at the left shows that one can see through several thicknesses if their "optical slots" are parallel. But when the "slots" are crossed, as they are in the fold at the right, no light passes. (Courtesy, Polaroid Corporation)

way that the outer disc is stationary to block all reflected light in the form of glare. The inner disc can be moved by turning a knob, whenever the passenger wants to reduce or increase the amount of light that enters the railroad car. When the polarizing discs are crossed no light can get through them.

COLOR PRODUCED BY DOUBLE REFRACTION

If a sheet of cellophane, mica, or cellulose tape is placed between two crossed polarizers so oriented that the light is eliminated, beautiful color effects will be produced.

When various crystals are placed between crossed polarizers they appear in beautiful colors. Polarizing microscopes are very useful for the examination of crystals. Roman Vishniac found that when polarized white light is used to examine microorganisms or human tissues by the use of a special optical

Figure 52–5. Control of light in a streamliner railroad car by means of Polaroid screens. (Courtesy, Polaroid Corporation)

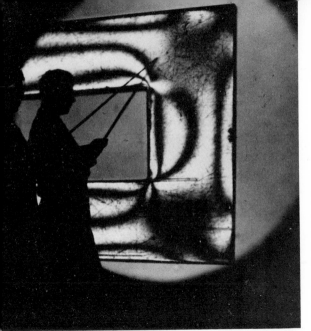

Figure 52–6. A "map" of the stress distribution appears in transparent plastic models under stress. (Courtesy, Polaroid Corporation)

DETECTION OF STRAINS IN TRANSPARENT MATERIAL WITH POLARIZED LIGHT

Strains in optical glass, radio tubes, mounted lenses, and glass apparatus may be detected by placing the object between two crossed polarizers. Such strains may result from poor annealing of glass. Glass which is poorly annealed is likely to crack when subjected to sudden temperature changes that would not crack glass free from strains. Gears, miniature bridge members, etc. may be made out of transparent plastic materials and then tested while placed in a beam of light between crossed polarizers. Such experiments enable engineers to determine the points of greatest strain under varying conditions.

SUMMARY

Illumination

Illumination is inversely proportional to the square of the distance from a light source.

Proper illumination involves the elimination

system, it is possible to repress one color and intensify another, thus making it possible to bring out details which cannot be seen with unpolarized white light.

Figure 52–7. Many crystals are revealed in much detail and beautiful colors when viewed by polarized light. (Courtesy, Polaroid Corporation)

of glare and contrasts. Light sources should be kept out of direct line of vision for general illumination.

Polarized Light

Polarized light is light that is vibrating in only one plane. Light may be polarized by double refraction in certain crystals. It may also be polarized by reflection. Glare consists of reflected light, much of which is polarized. The light from the blue sky, which is caused by scattering, is polarized to some extent. Polarized light is widely applied in the study of strains in transparent materials.

Study Questions

1. DEFINE: illumination, polarized light, glare, foot-candle, lumen, candle.
2. How is light intensity measured and expressed?
3. How does light intensity fall off with an increase in distance?
4. How is the candle power of a lamp measured?
5. What is the principle of the type of photographic exposure meter described in this chapter?
6. What intensity of light is considered desirable for studying?
7. What is the value of diffusing light for illumination?
8. How is light diffused for illumination?
9. Give a general rule concerning the position of light sources.
10. Why are table lamps and floor lamps used more widely than flush-type lights, cove lighting, and lens lighting?
11. Would you prefer to read out-of-doors in direct sunlight or diffused sunlight? Why?
12. In what three different ways may light be polarized?
13. What is the nature of a Polaroid screen?

CHAPTER 53

Optics

Knowledge comes by eyes always open and working hands; and there is no knowledge that is not power.

JEREMY TAYLOR

INTRODUCTION

The science of optics is concerned with light and vision. This chapter deals with optical devices and instruments, including the human eye and the camera, which resembles the eye in many respects. The defects of optical systems as well as a brief outline of the principles of photography is included. Photography is America's number one hobby, and rightly so, because it represents such an excellent blending of Art with Science. An estimated 52 million Americans own cameras and take more than 2 billion pictures per year.

LENSES

Figures 53-1 and 53-2 show how light is refracted by concave and convex lenses. *A convex lens brings light to a focus (converges it)* and is therefore said to be **convergent.** On the other hand, *a concave lens causes light to* **diverge.** The curvature of the lenses determines the extent to which they converge or diverge light.

ABERRATIONS IN LENSES

Spherical Aberration

The lack of sharpness of an image obtained with a spherical lens or mirror is called **spherical aberration.** Figure 53-3 shows this type of aberration.

The light rays passing through the outer edges of the lens converge at a point closer to the lens than do the light rays passing through the center of the lens. The smaller the field or the smaller the aperture, the sharper is the image. The wider the lens the more important spherical aberration becomes.

Chromatic Aberration

This type of aberration refers to *the decrease in the sharpness of the image, which is due to the fact that the light waves at the ultraviolet end of the visible spectrum are refracted more than the longer-wavelength rays at the infrared end of the visible spectrum.* Figure 53-4 illustrates this type of aberration.

Chromatic aberration can be eliminated by the use of monochromatic light, i.e., light of only one wavelength. A combination of lenses, each made of different types of glass having different refracting properties, will reduce this type of aberration. Figure 53-5 shows two such lenses, one made from crown (lime) glass and the other from flint (lead) glass. Such compound lenses are used to correct for chromatic aberrations in the lenses of telescopes, microscopes, and cameras.

MICROSCOPES

Modern light microscopes use a series of lenses to achieve a magnification of as much

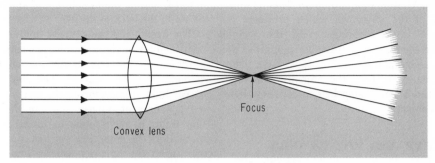

Figure 53–1. A convex lens converges parallel light rays.

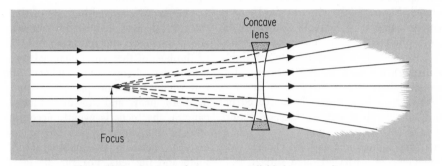

Figure 53–2. A concave lens causes parallel light rays to diverge.

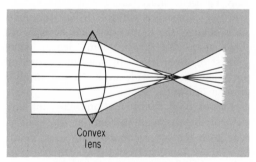

Figure 53–3. Spherical aberration.

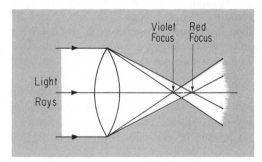

Figure 53–4. Chromatic aberration.

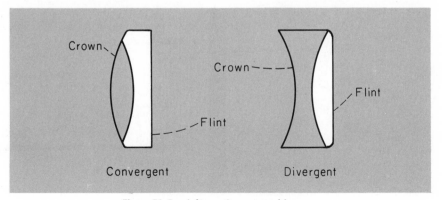

Figure 53–5. Achromatic compound lenses.

as 2,000 times. The two main lens systems consist of the objective, which produces an enlarged, inverted image; and the second lens, the eyepiece, which further magnifies the image. High-power microscopes have compound lenses in both the objective and eyepiece, and a condensing lens to converge light on the object.

THE EYE AND THE CAMERA

The human eye operates on much the same principle as the camera, but is more versatile and refined. Figure 53-6 compares the human eye with a camera. A pinhole camera will produce a photograph, but the exposure time is high because only a small amount of light passes through the pinhole. Furthermore, the image is not sharp unless the pinhole is very small. Now, if the hole is greatly increased in size and filled with a convex lens, a better picture is obtained in less time.

In both the human eye and the camera, an inverted image is projected on a screen, but in the case of the eye the retina replaces the photographic emulsion. The retina of the eye contains rod and cone cells which are the light receptors. The rod cells do not yield color sensations and are sensitive to dim light. The cone cells, on the other hand, are sensitive to bright light and colors.

The lens systems of both the eye and the camera cast the image of objects seen in an inverted position. This upside-down picture is registered on the film in the back of the camera, and in the eye, it is registered on the retina in the back of the eye.

The eyelid and the camera shutter serve to admit and stop light, while the camera diaphragm and the **iris** *of the eye control the amount of light received.* The iris prevents excess light from entering the eye when viewing a source of intense light. In the case of dim light, it opens wide in order to permit more light to enter the eye. In the camera, narrowing the opening usually improves the sharpness of the image, while enlarging the opening increases the speed of the exposure.

The flexible, crystalline lens of the eye, and the optical glass lens of the camera, focus a sharp image on the retina or film. The focus of the lens of the eye is changed by muscular action that changes the thickness and curvature of the lens, thus providing sharp images of both near and distant objects. In the camera, the focus is usually accomplished by devices that make it possible to change the distance between the photographic film or plate and the lens. For far distant and very close work, lenses of different focal lengths may be used. Many cameras now have "electric eye" exposure control, which automatically changes the shutter and time of exposure. They may also have "zoom" lenses which consist of three lenses in one, thus providing for telephoto and wide-angle "shots" in addition to ordinary "shots."

Figure 53-7 shows that muscles not only control the shape of the lens of the eye, but also turn the eye so that it can look in dif-

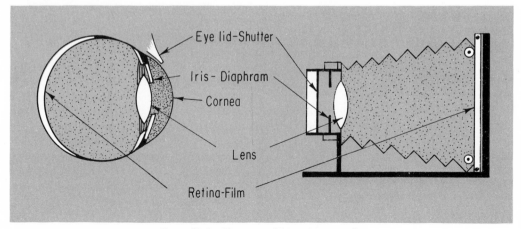

Figure 53-6. The eye and camera compared.

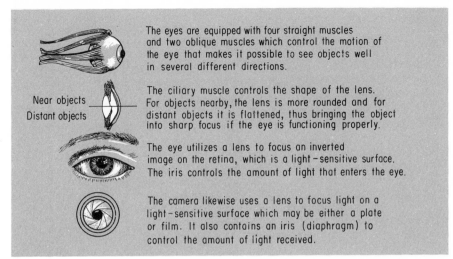

The eyes are equipped with four straight muscles and two oblique muscles which control the motion of the eye that makes it possible to see objects well in several different directions.

Near objects
Distant objects

The ciliary muscle controls the shape of the lens. For objects nearby, the lens is more rounded and for distant objects it is flattened, thus bringing the object into sharp focus if the eye is functioning properly.

The eye utilizes a lens to focus an inverted image on the retina, which is a light–sensitive surface. The iris controls the amount of light that enters the eye.

The camera likewise uses a lens to focus light on a light–sensitive surface which may be either a plate or film. It also contains an iris (diaphragm) to control the amount of light received.

Figure 53–7. The upper two figures show how the muscles of the eye control vision. The lower two figures compare the iris of the eye with the diaphragm of the camera.

ferent directions. The continued use of these muscles frequently results in fatigue and eyestrain.

THE F-VALUES OF APERTURE OPENINGS

The **f-value** is *the distance from the lens to the film divided by the diameter of the aperture. It is inversely proportional to the diameter of the aperture, since the distance is nearly constant.* The larger the *f*-value the smaller the opening, as is shown in Figure 53-8. The *f*-values shown in the scale have been calculated so that each smaller opening cuts down the light by one half.

EYE DEFECTS AND THEIR CORRECTION

Near-sightedness and **far-sightedness** *are the results of elongated and shortened eyeballs respectively.* People who have these defects either cannot bring near or distant objects into focus, or they subject their eyes to undue strain in so doing. Such defects are corrected by the use of concave or convex lenses, as shown in Figure 53-9.

Another common eye trouble is astigmatism. **Astigmatism** will cause more discomfort and eyestrain than any other type of eye defect. *The eyeballs in this case are slightly cylindrical in shape, so that two equally distant lines at right angles to each other will not be in focus at the same time.* Astigmatism is corrected by use of a cylindrical lens. Double vision or unequal focus, which at its worst is represented by crossed eyes, is due to muscle unbalance. Extreme cases may be overcome by delicate operations on the muscles, and less severe cases can be corrected by means of prismatic lenses.

Aniseikonia, Greek for *"unequal images,"* is *a condition in which the images received by the two eyes differ in size and shape.* People afflicted with this defect lack depth perception and distance sense and should not operate

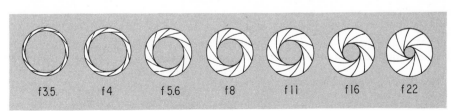

| f3.5 | f4 | f5.6 | f8 | f11 | f16 | f22 |

Figure 53–8. The camera lens opening. Note that the smaller the f-value is the larger is the opening.

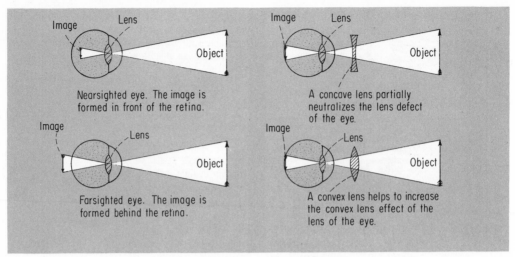

Nearsighted eye. The image is formed in front of the retina.

A concave lens partially neutralizes the lens defect of the eye.

Farsighted eye. The image is formed behind the retina.

A convex lens helps to increase the convex lens effect of the lens of the eye.

Figure 53–9. How near-sightedness and far-sightedness are corrected.

automobiles or airplanes. The eyestrain resulting from this disorder frequently causes headaches and stomach or nervous disorders. Aniseikonia can be corrected by special lenses.

THE PRINCIPLES OF PHOTOGRAPHY

It was known for a long time (J. H. Schulze, 1727) that light would blacken silver nitrate or silver chloride, but, for practical purposes, early photography had two great drawbacks: first, no means of fixing the images were known; second, the time required for the exposures was quite long. Louis Jacques Daguerre (1789–1851), in 1839, made public the details of his daguerreotype process of sensitizing a silver plate with iodine and developing it with mercury vapor. William Henry Fox-Talbot (1800–1877) found that if he treated paper with successive washings of a solution of common salt and a solution of silver nitrate, and exposed the wet paper to light, he could obtain a much more rapid blackening in light than he could obtain with silver nitrate alone. Unfortunately, a picture made with this paper would soon darken when exposed to light, because unreduced silver chloride had not been removed.

The Photographic Emulsion

Eventually, it was discovered that an emulsion of silver salts in gelatin could be coated on paper, glass, or plastic films. The silver-salt particles are colloidal in size, and therefore expose a relatively large light-sensitive surface. The size of the silver-salt particles can be controlled by controlling the conditions under which they are prepared.

It was found that larger crystalline particles were more readily activated than the smaller particles and that the sensitiveness to light could also be controlled by the use of the bromide and iodide of silver, as well as the chloride. Silver bromide is more sensitive to light than silver chloride. A mixture of the bromide and iodide (within certain limits) is more sensitive than either the pure bromide or iodide. Photographic films that are very sensitive to light are called fast films, because they can be used with a fast shutter speed (short exposure). A slow film, on the other hand, requires long exposures. Suspensions of these salts in specially prepared gelatin may be made extremely sensitive to infrared, ultraviolet, and other portions of the electromagnetic spectrum by the addition of special sensitizing agents and by heat treatment of the emulsion. One of the first observations that led to the modern sensitized films was based on the fact that photographic emulsions, which contained gelatin made from cows that had been eating plants containing mustard oil, were unusually sensitive. This observation led to the use of mustard oil to sensitize emulsions.

Developing

It was found that a silver-salt emulsion could be exposed to light without producing any visible change, but that *the portion of the salt* thus *activated,* even after a period of thirty or more years, *would be reduced by certain substances that develop this latent image,* and are therefore called **developers.** The portions of the emulsion not activated are not appreciably reduced during the short period of time required to reduce the activated portion, but continued exposure to the developer would eventually reduce nearly all of the silver salts in the emulsion. Fox-Talbot discovered the use of a developer (gallic acid), and reported it to the Royal Society in 1841.

After exposure to light, the film or plate is placed in the developing bath, which contains one or more of a number of substances to reduce the exposed areas, liberating free silver from its salts. The size of the silver particles and other factors determine the grain, which is important in enlarging. Developers which produce very small free silver particles are called fine-grain developers. The speed and contrast in developing are controlled by the use of substances such as sodium carbonate (the accelerator), to provide an alkaline solution, and potassium bromide (the restrainer), which helps to prevent reduction of the unactivated silver salts. Sodium sulfite (the preservative) is also added to the developing solution to prevent deterioration due to the action of the reducing agent with the oxygen of the air.

Fixing

The unexposed compounds remain unchanged after the reduction of the exposed portion. These unchanged compounds would also be reduced if left exposed to the light, *so they are treated with "hypo"* (*sodium thiosulfate*) *in the fixing bath, which dissolves these unreduced silver salts.* John Herschel (1792–1871) discovered the use of hypo as a fixing agent in 1819, and in 1839 he coined the word photography. An acid is generally added to the fixing bath to stop the action of the developer, because it neutralizes the alkali which is essential to the action of the developer. Potassium or chrome alum is added to harden the gelatin of the emulsion, which is softened and swollen by the sodium carbonate or other alkaline substance in the developing solution. Sodium sulfite is also added to oppose the decomposition of the "hypo."

Printing

Ordinary films and plates, when developed, are called **negatives.** A negative represents the reverse of *the light values of the original subject. By passing light through a negative, held in contact with a paper, film, or plate coated with photographic emulsion, the tone values are again reversed. This operation is* called **contact printing.** *By printing a negative,* a **positive** *print or film may be obtained. The light areas on the negative correspond to the dark areas on the positive.* If a lens is placed between the negative and the photographic printing paper, an enlarged or reduced image is obtained. *A device that makes it possible to vary the size of the image produced by changing the relative distance between the lens, the negative, and the unexposed emulsion surface is called an* **enlarger.**

Amateur motion-picture films do not need to be printed, because the original film is treated by a reversal process of developing, which produces a positive rather than a negative. In addition to processes of developing and fixing, there are the processes of **toning,** *in which the black silver is changed to a salt of another color,* and the processes of reduction and intensification, which are used to correct under- and over-exposed negatives.

PROJECTORS AND MOTION PICTURES

Projectors used for projecting slides or motion pictures *are similar in principle to photographic enlargers. Light is passed through the slide or motion picture film, and is then focused on a screen by means of a lens.* The lens inverts the image, so it is necessary to place the film or plate in the projector in an upside-down position.

The important characteristic of the eye that makes motion pictures possible is the fact that it retains a picture for about $\frac{1}{15}$ second and then erases it. If a series of images, changing at the rate of twenty or more per second is projected, the illusion of motion will result. In motion-picture projectors, the film is moved at a controlled rate by means of sprocket wheels and sprocket holes in the film. A shutter is closed between each picture (frame). It was the invention of the photographic film that enabled Thomas Edison to invent the motion-picture projector based on this principle. If films are run through a projector too slowly a flicker will result; if they are run through too fast the images will blur.

SUMMARY

Lenses

Convex lenses are convergent, and concave lenses are divergent. Lenses are subject to spherical and chromatic aberrations. Compound lenses may be used to eliminate chromatic aberrations.

Microscopes

Microscopes, like refracting telescopes, contain two lenses (or lens systems), (1) the objective which brings light to a focus, and (2) the eyepiece which magnifies the image.

Comparison of the Human Eye With a Camera

The Function	The Eye	The Camera
Control of the amount of light	iris	diaphragm
Length of exposure	eye lid	shutter
Focal length of lens	muscles	movable lens
Light-sensitive surface	retina	film or plate (emulsion)
Distant viewing	telescope or field glasses	telephoto lenses
Close viewing	microscope or magnifying glass	special lenses such as portrait lenses

Eye Defects

Near-sightedness—corrected by concave lens
Far-sightedness—corrected by convex lens
Astigmatism—corrected by cylindrical lens
Muscle unbalance—corrected by prismatic lens

Photography

Light activates photographic emulsions.
Developers reduce the activated portions of emulsions.
Fixers remove the unactivated portion of the emulsions.

Motion Pictures

Motion pictures depend on the fact that the eye retains an image for only about $\frac{1}{15}$ second. Motion picture projectors flash on a new image at the rate of about twenty per second, cutting off the light between each frame.

Study Questions

1. DEFINE: astigmatism, spherical aberration, chromatic aberration, developer, fixer, negative, positive, printing (photographic), convergent, diverge, iris, near-sightedness, far-sightedness, daguerreotype, projector, enlarger, f-value, toning, aniseikonia.
2. What are the shortcomings of a pinhole camera?
3. How do the objectives of microscopes differ from those of telescopes?
4. Why are compound lenses used in microscopes, telescopes, and cameras?
5. Show why a lens gives an inverted image.
6. How does a positive film differ from a negative film?
7. What discovery led to the invention of the motion-picture projector?
8. What characteristic of human eyes makes motion pictures possible?
9. What does a photographic developer do?
10. What are the functions of the different substances contained in a photographic developing solution?
11. What is the principle of the photographic enlarger?
12. How does a camera differ from a projector?
13. Compare a camera with the human eye.
14. List the common eye defects, and state how each one may be corrected.

Acoustics and Ultrasonics

Physicians have segregated the diseases of dirt. In a few more years we will find them classifying the diseases that come from noise.

RICHARDSON WRIGHT

INTRODUCTION

The brain classifies sound roughly as **noises,** *which are disagreeable or irritating,* and sounds that are received with pleasure or indifference. Sounds may be unpleasant because of excessive loudness or high pitch, or because they are of such complexity that they cannot be analyzed by the ear.

Excessive noise is not only unpleasant, but it may be harmful. It is a social problem characteristic of the machine age, in the same category with air and water pollution, and litter and trash along our highways.

Gradually, modern society is finding ways of eliminating noise. The science of acoustics has been developed to design and build auditoriums, business offices, and homes so as to eliminate or decrease objectionable noise.

NOISE

Noise is one of the chief drawbacks to the enjoyment of urban living. We are surrounded by the noises of trucks and jet airplanes, motorcycles, motorboats, power lawnmowers, sirens, barking dogs, sound trucks, automobile horns, and Diesel locomotives. Our homes are usually not designed to decrease noise, and many of our household appliances, such as vacuum cleaners, washing machines, or dishwashers contribute to the problem.

It is the opinion of students of the problem of noise that it impairs work efficiency, digestion, and peace of mind. It robs us of sleep and it may even cause deafness. Excessive noise causes nervous fatigue, which may be responsible for many accidents.

Investigations have shown that more energy is needed to work in noisy surroundings than in a quiet place. In one factory, putting new bearings in a ventilator fan to reduce the noise caused by excessive vibrations is reported to have increased output 9 per cent and reduced the typing errors by about one third.

RESONANCE

The intensity or loudness of a sounding body may be increased by use of a sounding board. This principle can be illustrated by striking a tuning fork and then holding it against a table top. The table top is caused to vibrate, and thus becomes a vibrating medium of greater intensity because it has a greater surface to agitate the air against it. Inasmuch as the energy of vibration is greater, it must last for a shorter time, the vibrations dying out much faster than when the tuning fork is held in the hand. *The original vibrating body* is called the **generator,** while *the sounding board is called the* **resonator.** Thus the strings in a piano make up the generator, while the sounding board is the resonator.

There are *two distinct kinds of resonators. One kind has no vibration frequency of its own and responds to all of the vibrations of the generator. Such vibrations are called* **forced vibrations.** *A second type of resona-*

407

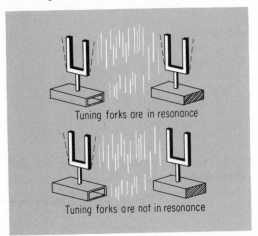

Tuning forks are in resonance

Tuning forks are not in resonance

Figure 54–1. When one tuning fork is set into vibration the other one will vibrate if it is in resonance with the first one.

tor possesses a natural frequency and strengthens sounds of its own pitch only. Such vibrations are called **sympathetic vibrations** or **resonance.** A tuning fork is usually mounted on a hollow box whose size is such that the air column will vibrate in resonance with the fork.

Just as a child in a swing can be made to swing farther by applying a gentle impulse at the proper time, so one tuning fork can be caused to vibrate by the vibrations of another fork in tune with it. See Figure 54-1. If the loud pedal of a piano is held down so that all of the strings are free to vibrate, that string will vibrate whose natural frequency corresponds to the frequency of a briefly sung note.

CANCELING SOUND WAVES BY INTERFERENCE

Mufflers used to absorb or minimize sound energy from internal-combustion engine exhausts, depend on the cancellation of sound waves by interference. Interference may be explained by referring to a boy in a swing. If a person gives the swing a push each time it reaches the end of a swing, the swing will swing farther and farther with each push; but if a person gives the swing a push when it is not at the end of the swing, the amplitude of the swing will be decreased. A push equal to the force of the swing, but in the opposite direction, when applied as the swing comes

to the position closest to the ground, will stop the motion entirely. *Sound waves are canceled in the same way by other sound waves which are out of phase with the incoming sound waves.* In one type of muffler, the length of the closed tube is one-fourth of the wavelength to be canceled. Waves entering the tube are reflected and returned to the main tube 90 degrees out of phase, thus canceling the incoming sound wave. In a second type of muffler, one path is longer than the other by one-half of the wavelength to be canceled, and the waves uniting at the outlet cancel each other. Such mufflers do not build up back pressures and should be of value in silencing airplane exhausts.

ACOUSTICS

Acoustics is *the science of sound and hearing, but, in common usage, it refers to the control of sound from the physical standpoint.* It is concerned chiefly with **reverberations,** i.e., *the reflection of sound waves.* However, sound deadening and sound absorption are important problems of acoustics.

Sounds are more intense in a room or hall, because they are reflected back by the walls. Sometimes, however, the sound has to travel so far that the reflected waves are not received at the same time that the original waves arrive. These echoes are one of the sources of poor acoustics in rooms. This difficulty can be remedied in part by hanging draperies against the walls or by lining the walls with materials that absorb rather than reflect sound. Clothing absorbs sound, and, as a result, the echoes characteristic of a large, empty hall are not so noticeable when it is filled with people.

In large auditoriums, sound waves are best reflected from large flat surfaces placed above, below, and behind both sides of the speaker. Curved surfaces are avoided because they concentrate the sound too much in certain spots. Ceiling domes, curved ceilings, and large reflective areas at the back of a room should be avoided.

A complete ceiling of acoustical material would be undesirable in a room where high-fidelity music reproduction is to be heard, because the sound would be lifeless. Some reverberations are desirable to give a lively quality to sound. Parallel wall surfaces of smooth, reflecting materials are the chief sources of poor hearing conditions in such rooms. Acoustical damping of sounds should be used on two walls that intersect rather than on opposite walls. Draperies often serve well for damping sounds for at least one of these walls.

A room which is quite satisfactory for speech might be too dead for music. Reverberations are needed for music to blend one tone with another. It would be desirable to have a sound-deadening curtain behind a speaker who is using a loud speaker, in order to prevent a feedback of reverberations into the microphone. Broadcasting studios are generally treated with sound-deadening materials to prevent reverberations. However, musicians prefer reflecting walls behind them in auditoriums in which a public address system is not used.

KITCHEN AND BATHROOM ACOUSTICS

Kitchens and bathrooms are generally noisy because they usually have smooth walls and floors which reflect sounds, and because they do not have such sound-deadening materials as rugs, draperies, and upholstered furniture. Furthermore, such rooms are the sources of many noises. The clatter of pots and pans, dishwashers, food disposal units, and noisy water pipes are common sound generators. Perhaps acoustical ceilings should be used in such rooms.

It is a well-known fact that people like to sing or whistle in a bathroom. Nearly everyone sounds like an artist (to himself) in a bathroom, because the reverberations in the bathroom enable the singer to hear his own voice as it is reflected back to him with little loss of energy.

The result of being unable to hear one's self sing results in tension and nervousness that decrease vocal efficiency. In the attempt to fill a hall with one's voice, one is apt to force it into too high a pitch. A modern device to aid an artist utilizes public-address units directed toward the artist so that he can hear himself sing.

SOUND ABSORPTION AND SOUND DEADENING

These two terms are often used interchangeably, but they are not synonymous. **Sound absorption** usually refers to *the elimination of reflections*, while **sound deadening** deals with *the prevention of the transmission of sound waves*. For example, an acoustically treated ceiling might be used in a restaurant or a bank to eliminate reverberations by sound absorption. But if there is a problem of sounds being transmitted through walls or floors, sound deadening is the solution.

Sound-absorbing materials are usually porous, or contain many small openings. Good heat insulating materials, such as rock wool, are also good sound absorbers, because of the dead-air spaces they contain. They absorb sound waves by converting them into heat. Sound absorption is best for high frequencies, which are the most objectionable ones anyway.

Sound deadening deals with such problems as keeping outdoor traffic noises out of buildings, or of preventing the transmission of sounds between units of multiple dwellings. Very dense materials, such as concrete, are excellent for deadening sounds. Dead-air spaces between partitions that are not joined in any way often are used to prevent the transmission of sounds.

Long hallways and hot-air ducts often transmit sounds by internal reflections. In such cases, the solution to the problem is to interpose some sound-absorbing materials somewhere along the duct or hallway.

Outside noises may be kept out by use of double doors such as one finds in motion-picture theaters, and by the elimination of doors and windows on the sides of buildings adjoining sources of objectionable noise. Weather stripping helps to keep out sounds. Heavy plate glass is much more rigid than ordinary window glass and should be used in windows which face noisy streets.

SHOCK WAVES

Shock waves *are very powerful waves in the atmosphere*, produced by violent explosions, or by jet airplanes as they crash through the sound barrier. In 1953, a Super Sabre jet airplane at a public air show near Palmdale, California, crashed through the sound barrier at a low altitude. Windows and doors of nearby buildings were smashed by the resulting shock waves. After this incident, regulations were set up to require that supersonic airplane flights not be allowed below an altitude of 10,000 feet, over inhabited areas or in the vicinity of commercial plants. However, it is difficult to police the atmosphere.

In Canada, an American F-104 Starfighter jet airplane, flying low over Ottawa's new Uplands Airport, accidentally slipped through the sound barrier and broke $100,000 worth of windows, in addition to doing other serious damage to the buildings.

SOUNDLESS VIBRATIONS IN MATTER

Infrasonic Waves

Waves of too low a frequency to be heard are called **infrasonic waves.** They may be received by microphones and converted into electrical impulses for detection and measurement. Earthquakes and severe tornadoes produce infrasonic waves.

The chemist's analytical balance, or the physicist's ballistic galvanometer, will not give accurate readings unless vibrations are eliminated. There are various methods of combatting vibrations by the use of sand, springs, and rubber mountings that may be used to decrease vibrations. Shock absorbers, and the liberal use of rubber, have been successful in reducing the vibrations in automobiles.

Bridges have been destroyed by the vibrations produced by strong winds. Serious accidents have been the result of vibrations set up in grandstands by a crowd of people pounding their feet in unison.

Ultrasonic Waves

Ultrasonic waves, sometimes called **supersonic waves,** are *vibrations having a frequency too high to be heard by the human ear.* They may be produced by transducers and magnetostrictors. A **transducer** *is a crystal that may be made to vibrate by the passage of an electric current of a frequency higher than 16,000 cycles per second.* The crystal

changes in shape with each alternation of the electric current. Ceramic slabs have also been used for transducers. The voltage from a vacuum-tube oscillator impresses alternating positive and negative charges on the top and bottom faces of the slab. When the charges are reversed, the slab becomes thinner. The slab thus sets up vibrations that are transmitted to a liquid, gas, or solid, as desired. Crystals may reverse the process, receiving waves and changing them into electrical impulses. Thus, transducers may serve as either sending or receiving devices. They are used in this way in radio microphones and phonograph pickups. For the production of higher-energy ultrasonic vibrations, the **magnetostrictor** is used. *It depends upon the property of certain metals, particularly nickel, to stretch and contract in a magnetic field.* An electric current of ultrasonic frequency, flowing through a coil surrounding a stack of nickel plates, will cause them to vibrate at the same frequency.

The production and uses of ultrasonic waves represents a scientific frontier in which only a relatively small amount of pioneering work has been done. Nevertheless, ultrasonics is already finding a place in almost every science and industry.

ULTRASONIC APPLICATIONS

Ultrasonics has a wide range of applications in such diverse fields as cleaning, the detection of flaws in metals, welding and soldering, physical therapy and medicine, impact grinding, and a guard system.

Cleaning

Ultrasonic waves at a frequency of about a million cycles per second, will shake off loose particles of dirt. Ultrasonic dishwashers and washing machines are being investigated. One may look forward to a time when pots and pans, even those with burned materials that are hard to scrub off, may be cleaned quickly in a special ultrasonic washer.

In industry, ultrasonic cleaning is used to clean metal surfaces for soldering, tinning, or galvanizing; to clean small parts such as electronic parts, watch parts, camera lenses, contact lenses, and even artificial dentures; to clean sewing machines; and to degrease jet engines.

In hospitals, ultrasonic cleaning is applied in the cleaning of surgical instruments.

The Detection of Flaws in Metals

Ultrasonic vibrations are used to detect flaws and bubbles in metals.

Welding and Soldering

Ultrasonic waves seem to break up the molecular structure of two surfaces and cause them to interlock. In this way, metals, which are difficult to weld by other processes, may be welded quickly without any melting or fusing.

Physical Therapy and Medicine

Ultrasonic diathermy treatments have been employed in the treatment of bursitis, lumbago, and arthritis. They can heal wounds, clear up infected sinuses, and relieve acute asthma. It is possible to create burns on the fingers by holding a glass rod which is dipped into ultrasonically vibrating oil, although the temperature of the oil is at ordinary room temperature. The glass conducts the sound to the fingers, because it is a better conductor than is the oil. The application of ultrasonic vibrations to an arm or leg will heat the marrow of the bone, although the bone remains at normal body temperature. Bone conducts vibrations, whereas flesh and marrow absorb them and, as a consequence, become heated. Much pioneering research must be done before ultrasonics finds widespread use in medicine.

Impact Grinding

By the use of a cutting tool of any intricate shape, vibrating into a slurry of abrasive material, patterns may be cut in glass, plastics, metals, and other materials, which would be very difficult to achieve by other methods.

Guard Systems

A guard system now in use, consists of an ultrasonic transmitter that transmits waves of 19,200 cycles per second, of a low enough frequency to be transmitted by air, but beyond the range of adult ears. If a person should enter a room so protected, the frequency of the waves would be disturbed, and an alarm would be sent to the control headquarters.

SONAR (SOUND, NAVIGATION, RANGING)

The Allies, during World War II, developed the use of ultrasonic waves to detect and locate enemy submarines. Transducers and magnetostrictors were used to set up "pings" that were reflected by the submarines. From the time required for a directed beam of waves to rebound and return, the position of the submarine could be determined.

Victory against the Nazi submarines was credited to sonar, but the United States alone lost 4,733 ships in the battle.

Several peacetime applications of the principle of sonar have been developed for navigation and fishing. By such devices, the depth of the ocean bottom may be determined continuously. Peaks in the rifts in the continental shelf, where fish like to feed, are located in this way. Such devices are also used by fishermen to locate schools of fish.

An interesting application of sonar for land use is to measure the depths of liquids in tanks.

Bats produce inaudible cries having a frequency of about 50,000 cycles per second, reflected by obstacles and received by their ears, which are sensitive to wave frequencies as high as 100,000 cycles per second. In this way, they can fly in the dark. The southern army moth is able to avoid bats at night because it, too, has ears sensitive to the frequencies broadcast by bats. Porpoises also use ultrasonic waves to avoid obstacles.

SOFAR (SOUND FIXING AND RANGING)

The velocity of sound waves increases with an increase in temperature or pressure. It has been found that at a depth of about 4,000 feet, sound waves will travel long distances in the oceans, because they are reflected downward by the warmer water at the surface levels and they are reflected upward by the increased pressure of the water at levels below 4,000 feet. Sound waves produced by small explosions at a depth of 4,000 feet have been received at a distance of about 3,000 miles, after traveling for about one hour. By the use of three receiving stations, the source of such an explosion can be located within one mile, just as the center of an earthquake disturbance can be located by the vibrations received at three stations.

SUMMARY

Acoustics deals with the elimination of noise. Noise is one of the problems of the machine age. It is a social problem, but its elimination is a problem of physical science.

Sound waves may be canceled by interference, for example, in mufflers.

The intensity of sound waves may be increased by resonance, using forced vibrations or sympathetic vibrations—applied in sounding boards in auditoriums.

Acoustics deals chiefly with the elimination or control of reverberations. Sound-absorbing materials are used to decrease reverberations. Sound deadening is used to decrease the transmission of sounds by structural members.

Infrasonic waves are those having a frequency too low to be detected by the human ear.

Ultrasonic waves or supersonic waves are waves of frequencies too high to be heard by the human ear. Ultrasonic waves have many possible applications. World War II applications included Sonar and Sofar.

Study Questions

1. DEFINE: acoustics, sound absorption, sound deadening, sofar, sonar, noise, reverberation, sound generator, resonance, forced vibration, sympathetic vibration, infrasonic, ultrasonic, transducer, magnetostrictor, resonator, shock wave, supersonic wave.

2. Discuss the factors that should be considered in providing proper acoustics for an auditorium.

3. Discuss the factors that should be taken into account in the design of a modern dwelling, and explain how each factor is controlled.

4. Would it be a good idea to put sound-absorbing material on the ceiling of a music studio?

5. What is the advantage of putting sound-absorbing materials on the ceilings and walls of offices, banks, and restaurants?

6. Why is the acoustics better in a crowded auditorium than in an empty auditorium?

7. Why do sounds travel better in an empty house than in a furnished house?

8. Why should we support antinoise campaigns?

9. How should a radio broadcasting room be constructed from the point of view of acoustics?

10. Why is the use of mufflers required by law?

11. Explain the method by which mufflers eliminate sound.

12. How does resonance increase the intensity of the sound waves produced by a generator?

13. Differentiate between the two kinds of resonators.

14. What are the causes of shock waves?

15. Why do some people like to sing in a bathroom?

16. Why should ducts and halls be acoustically treated?

17. What are the advantages of eliminating windows in buildings?

18. How are outside sounds kept out of motion-picture auditoriums?

19. Explain the difference in the acoustical problems of the treatment of an auditorium for speech and music concerts, with and without the use of public-address systems.

20. Discuss the causes of noise.

21. Why is noise a social problem?

22. Compare the acoustical treatment of a music studio and a broadcasting studio.

Musical Instruments

No man ever had genius who did not aim to execute more than he was able.

SIR HUMPHREY DAVY

INTRODUCTION

One of the fine things about modern education is the many opportunities that it provides for learning how to play musical instruments. And one of the fine things about modern young people is their participation in musical activities. Many of their parents have not had such opportunities, but they attend concerts and listen to musical programs broadcast by radio and television. Eventually, many young people and adults become dissatisfied with these sources of music and turn to the phonograph for their music. Young people and adults alike may appreciate music more if they understand the principles of musical instruments outlined in this chapter.

HOW MUSICAL INSTRUMENTS PRODUCE SOUNDS

All musical instruments consist of two parts, the generator and the amplifier. The **generator** *supplies the energy and fixes the frequency,* while the **amplifier** *enlarges the sound by forced vibration or resonance.* There are two main types of instruments, the stringed instruments and the wind instruments.

Stringed Instruments

The generator in stringed instruments consists of strings or wires which are bowed (as in the violin), plucked (as in the harp or violin), or struck with a hammer (as in the piano), in order to produce the vibrations.

The amplifier in such instruments may consist of a hollow wooden body (as in the violin) or a sounding board (as in the piano).

The different frequencies are produced in stringed instruments by the use of strings of different length, diameter, and tension. The heavier strings are wrapped with wire in order to provide inertia without impairing their flexibility. The piano and the harp contain many strings of fixed length, diameter, and tension, whereas other stringed instruments contain only a few strings whose effective length can be altered by pressing down on the strings at various positions, so as to cause the strings to vibrate in segments.

The strings of stringed instruments lose their tension by use and by changes in temperature and therefore must be "tuned" frequently.

The laws of vibrating strings may be summarized as follows: the *pitch is*

1. *inversely proportional to the length.*
2. *directly proportional to the square root of the tension.*
3. *inversely proportional to the square root of the linear density.*

Another way of expressing these laws is as follows:

Long, loose, large (thick and dense) strings produce low pitch. Short, stretched, small (thin and not dense) strings produce high pitch.

413

Wind Instruments

Wind instruments include the woodwinds: the clarinet, oboe, piccolo, flute, bassoon, English horn, and the saxophone; the brass instruments: the cornet, trombone, baritone, French horn, tuba, and trumpet; the human voice, the organ, and a variety of other instruments such as whistles.

There are two kinds of wind instruments: (1) those in which the generator consists of a mechanical vibrator, such as a reed or the player's lips, and (2) those in which the vibrations are caused by blowing across a column of air.

1. Mechanical Vibrators—The lips of the musician serve as the generator in the horn, the bugle, the trombone and similar instruments. Bugles produce differences in pitch with changes in the position of the lips, and with changes in the force of blowing, much as whistling with the lips is accomplished. In harmonicas and accordions wind produces their tones by causing vibrations of thin metal reeds. The clarinet generates sound by means of a single reed, which vibrates against the opening in the mouthpiece, while the oboe has a mouthpiece consisting of two reeds, which vibrate against each other.

2. Vibrations Caused by Blowing Across a Column of Air—In organ pipes and whistles, there are channels to guide the air up to and across the mouth of the pipe. All wind instruments contain air columns that amplify by means of resonance, which was discussed in the previous section. Such resonators can emit only their fundamentals, or one or more of their harmonic overtones. Differences in tones are produced in many wind instruments by changing the length of the resonator. This may be accomplished by opening side holes, as in the flute or clarinet, piccolo, oboe, English horn, saxophone, and bassoon. In other wind instruments the length of the resonator may be varied by use of valves which insert or cut out additional lengths of tubing, as in the case of the cornet. In the trombone, sliding tubes are used to change the length of the air columns.

Air columns are found to give the maximum sounds for vibrations of certain frequencies only. This is explained by the fact that sound waves reflected back in a tube may interfere with incoming waves, so that little or no sound is produced unless the incoming wave is of such a frequency that it is reinforced by the reflected wave; the column of air will be caused to vibrate with this frequency, producing an intense sound. There is a distinct relationship between the length of the tube and the frequency of the vibration. This accounts for the differences in the length of organ pipes. *The length of a sound wave is twice the length of an open tube and four times the length of a closed tube.* The shorter the air column, the higher is the pitch.

In most wind instruments, tones of higher pitch, the overtones, may be obtained by increasing the force of the wind; however, in organs, the wind is delivered at fairly constant pressure, so that the variations in pitch are taken care of by a multiplicity of pipes of different sizes. Some organs have as many as 30,000 pipes. The range for the organ is 16 to 4,138 complete vibrations per second. The organ pipe giving 16 complete vibrations per second is about 32 feet long. A few organs have pipes 64 feet long, which give only 8 complete vibrations per second. The organ pipe that has a frequency of 4,138 complete vibrations per second is only 1½ inches long.

Other Types of Musical Instruments

The chief type of musical instruments not included above is the percussion group—the drum, cymbal, bell, xylophone, marimba, triangle, and the tympani or kettle drums, in which vibrations in rods, membranes, or plates are caused by blows. The pitch is determined by the size of the vibrating object in some cases and, in the case of drums, by the size of the membranes and the tension on them.

THE HUMAN VOICE

The sounds of the human voice are produced by the vibrations of the vocal cords, which are housed in the larynx, much more prominent in men than in women, because the vocal cords of men are much larger than those of women. The vocal cords constitute a reed-like sound generator. The function of the air is to control the amplitude of the sound and to carry it out of the throat. The intensity of a sound is also controlled by changing the pitch, which is accomplished by changing the tension, the length, and the thickness of the vocal cords. The top range of vibrations for a bass voice would be about 256 per second, while that of a soprano would be over 768.

The air cavities of the head resonate when the vocal cords are vibrating. The shapes of these cavities thus control the quality of a person's voice. A cold in the head, adenoids, or enlarged tonsils influence the voice quality by changing the sizes and shapes of these cavities.

OVERTONES

A pure tone, produced by a simple vibration with no overtones, is unusual. Pure tones may be obtained with tuning forks, certain weak (stopped) organ pipes, or a flute or French horn softly blown. Most musical tones are rich in overtones. When the overtones predominate, the tone is likely to be strident or harsh. **Tones** are *sounds of such continuity and definiteness that their characteristics may be appreciated by the ear. If a string vibrates in only one loop,* as shown in Figure 55-1, *it produces its lowest tone,* which is called the **fundamental.** *If the string vibrates in two segments, a tone of higher pitch,* called the **overtone,** results. *If the overtone has a frequency which is an exact multiple*

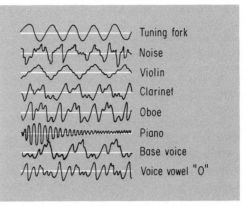

Figure 55–2. Typical wave patterns showing overtones.

of that of the fundamental, it is called **harmonic.** In this case, the *overtone is called the* **first harmonic.** *The string may be made to vibrate in more segments, thus producing additional overtones.* The violin and flute give notes with about six overtones, the oboe gives about a dozen, and the horn gives up to thirty.

When the set of vibrations has frequencies in the ratios of the natural numbers, 1 : 2; 3 : 4; etc., it is called a **harmonic series.** The overtones of many vibrating bodies are not harmonic. For example, the overtones in the xylophone are in the ratios 1 : 2.756 : 5.404, etc.

THE ANALYSIS OF MUSICAL TONES

For the analysis of sound waves, it is most convenient to use a device which will change the longitudinal sound waves into transverse waves.

The telephone diaphragm and the microphone generate oscillating currents from sound waves, which may be received by a cathode-ray type of oscillograph. The oscillograph will produce waves, such as are shown in Figure 55-2. This figure shows typical patterns of musical tones produced by various musical instruments. The top wave pattern shows the fundamental tone. Below that is the erratic pattern of noise. The other wave patterns show the overtones of several different musical instruments.

Pitch can be determined by means of tun-

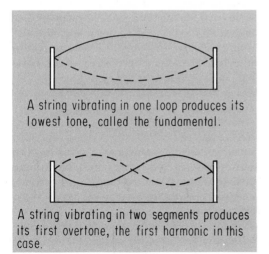

A string vibrating in one loop produces its lowest tone, called the fundamental.

A string vibrating in two segments produces its first overtone, the first harmonic in this case.

Figure 55–1. The fundamental and first harmonic shown by vibrating strings.

ing forks that vibrate with known frequencies. In comparing the pitch of a vibration, whose pitch is not known, with a known pitch of a tuning fork, *the difference in frequency between the tones is equal to the number of* **beats** *per second.* This is one method of tuning instruments.

QUALITY OF TONES PRODUCED BY MUSICAL INSTRUMENTS

Quality *depends upon the number and relative intensity of the overtones.* Overtones are determined in part by the nature of the material from which an instrument is made, but chiefly by the shape of the instrument. Cones in wind instruments help to provide the desired overtones. The slender conical tube of the horn may sometimes be more than eighteen feet long. Very long, straight horns are used by the Chinese, but the majority of horns are made spiral-shaped, in order to increase the ease of handling. The richness or the quality of a musical instrument, such as a piano or violin, depends upon the materials used, and the skill involved in creating resonating chambers or sounding boards of the proper size and shape.

ELECTRONIC MUSICAL INSTRUMENTS

Many new, experimental, electronic musical instruments have been invented. They give the musician more precise control of pitch, volume, and time, than classical musical instruments provide. Musicians have been limited in the past by their instruments, but the production of musical tones by electrical and electronic devices will permit musicians to express their feeling, intuitive understanding, and technical skill as never before. Some of the present electrical instruments are but primitive stages of what is to come.

For tuning the pitch of musical instruments, there is available an electronic device that provides a pure tone. Even expert piano tuners sometimes fail to tune pianos to the correct pitch.

Various types of electronic organs, pianos, and other devices are now available. In some organs, electronic tubes furnish the sound waves. In another type of organ, a perforated

disk, rotated in front of a light source, produces light waves that are received by two photoelectric cells. These cells change the light waves into electric impulses that actuate a loudspeaker. In still another electronic organ, synchronous motors are used to turn iron cogs near the coils of magnets, thus setting up electric waves that actuate a loudspeaker. An electronic piano employs reeds to set up the vibrations, which are amplified by electronic vacuum tubes, to actuate a loudspeaker.

Portable electronic pianos employ hammers to strike pieces of metal instead of strings, the sounds being electronically amplified.

SOUND RECORDING AND REPRODUCTION

The Phonograph

The phonograph was invented by Thomas A. Edison in 1877. His first phonograph made records on sheets of tin foil. Later, he introduced wax cylinders or disks. For making the sound tracks on the records, a stylus, which was controlled by a diaphragm sensitive to sound waves, was used. The sound was reproduced by moving a needle, which was attached to a similar diaphragm, over the sound track. The original phonographs used clockwork mechanisms, which were wound up by hand. There was no method of amplifying the sound beyond the use of a horn, similar to that of an ear-trumpet or a megaphone.

Modern phonograph machines employ electric motors to operate the turntables, and electronic pickups and amplification, similar in principle to those of the radio or television set. In fact, combination sets are available, which use the radio or television set for amplification.

Most sound motion pictures use a sound track produced on film by a device in which sound energy is transformed so as to vary the intensity of light falling on the film. Light passing through this sound track produces variations in the light received by a photoelectric cell, which changes the light into electrical impulses. These variations in electrical current are then amplified, as in the radio, by vacuum tubes, to a point where they can operate electromagnets powerful enough to cause rather large diaphragms to vibrate, and produce the usual sound of the loud-speaker.

Broadcasting stations frequently use video tape, on which both the picture and sound have been recorded. Magnetic tape recorders and wire recorders are available for home use. It is difficult to keep up with the technical advances in the field of sound recording and reproduction.

Phonograph records are first made in wax, dusted with graphite, and electroplated to make the master disks. These master disks are used to make faithful impressions on plastic materials of various compositions in the hydraulic press. The loudness of a sound produced by a record depends on the depth of the track, while the pitch depends upon the relative frequency of the elevations and depressions of the vertical-cut record. If the records are played too slowly the pitch is cut down. In the case of lateral-cut records, the loudness depends upon the swings of the track away from the center line.

High-Fidelity Sound Recording and Reproduction

Many console radio and television sets have a range of frequencies from 75 to 5,000. However, the human ear is sensitive to frequencies starting as low as 16 and going to as high as 16,000 to 20,000 or more. Many smaller radio sets are restricted to frequencies between 300 and 4,000 cycles per second. By omitting the higher frequencies, to which the human ear can respond, the higher overtones that give music its quality are eliminated. Furthermore, the lower base tones are not captured. The chief difference between high-fidelity music and ordinary reproduction is the quality of the equipment involved.

From the point of view of voice communication, ordinary radio or television reception is adequate, but more and more, radio and television sets are being depended upon as musical instruments. Since the music broadcast by most radio stations is of the latest "hit tune" variety there is little need for high-fidelity reproduction. **High-fidelity** *equipment reproduces all of the sound range with little distortion, thus giving a faithful reproduction of the original sound.* High-fidelity music is attained by the proper combination of recording and reproduction equipment, and proper acoustics of the rooms in which recordings are made and reproduced. Hence, once the novelty of the radio and television have worn off, and after listening to the too loud, too rapid, repetitious advertising of radio and television, many people turn to the phonograph as a source of music.

High-fidelity and stereophonic fans are often more concerned with the achievement of perfection in the realism of sound reproduction rather than music enjoyment. At first, they often turn up their sets too loud in order to obtain maximum enjoyment of such sound effects as a passing railroad train or fire engine, but eventually, they generally wind up as social-minded music lovers.

High-fidelity record players require special tuners, amplifiers, record-pickup devices, and loudspeakers. The pickup uses a stylus tipped with a sapphire or a diamond, and a crystal pickup to secure a wide range of frequency reproduction. Special noise suppressors may be used to decrease record scratch. Phonoequalizers may be added to the set to compensate for the sound exaggerations incorporated in records intended for ordinary phonographs. Speakers to handle both high and low frequencies require special designs. One solution to this problem is to use two speakers, *the one intended for high frequencies being called a* **"tweeter,"** and *the one intended for low frequencies* being called a **"woofer."** A high-fidelity speaker should occupy a cabinet with at least ten cubic feet of space. It should be sealed at the back and it should be lined with sound-absorbing material. Cabinets with open backs allow sounds to leak out. These sounds are then reflected and reach the ear out of phase with the original sound.

Special records are required to give the desired results with high-fidelity phonograph sets.

High-fidelity radio sets work best on frequency-modulation radio signals, because there is no static with frequency-modulation, radio reception.

An interesting method of amplification is the use of a polyethylene cylinder, about a foot in diameter, about eight feet long, and open at both ends. It is placed vertically in a room, and a good quality speaker is installed face down over the top opening. When the speaker is turned on, the whole column of air is caused to vibrate. It seems to bring the source of the music or other sounds on a record right into the room. Two such columns may be used for stereophonic reproduction.

Stereophonic Reproduction

The average radio or phonograph does not provide for stereophonic reception, i.e., sounds coming from different directions. The sounds obtained with a loudspeaker do not have the same quality as that of a concert hall because of the lack of reverberations.

Stereophonic reproduction *involves the use of two or more microphones to receive sound.* These sounds may be broadcast simultaneously on two different radio wavelengths, and then received by two different radio receivers to produce stereophonic reproduction. Radio stations are being equipped for stereophonic broadcasting, and radios designed to receive such broadcasts are on the market.

Stereophonic records are produced by the use of two vertical channels. For playing the records, special needles, tone arms, amplifiers, preamplifiers and stereophonic adapters are required.

THE DOPPLER EFFECT

One of the interesting sound effects on sound-effect records, for high fidelity fans, is the apparent change in pitch of a railroad-engine whistle as it approaches and passes by a given point. *This apparent change in frequency, produced by the relative motion of a sound source and that of the observer, is called the* **Doppler effect.** As the train approaches, the number of waves entering the ear in a given time is increased, and as it recedes, the number of waves is decreased. As a train passenger passes a ringing warning bell, the pitch of the bell appears to decrease, for the same reason.

SUMMARY

All musical instruments consist of a generator and an amplifier. The generator fixes the pitch and the amplifier enlarges the sound by resonance or forced vibrations.

Types of Musical Instruments

1. Stringed Instruments—The pitch is inversely proportional to the length, and to the square root of the linear density of the strings. It is directly proportional to the square root of the tension.

Long, loose, large (thick and dense) strings produce low pitch. Short, stretched, small (thin and not dense) strings produce high pitch.

2. Wind Instruments—These instruments produce sounds by mechanical vibrators, such as the lips or reeds, or by blowing across air columns. Tones are produced in air columns by resonance. The pitch of air columns is controlled by the length of the air column. The length of a sound wave is twice the length of an open tube, and four times the length of a closed tube.

3. Percussion Instruments—The sounds are generated by blows struck on rods, membranes, or plates, which serve as the amplifiers.

Quality of Musical Instruments

The quality of musical instruments is determined by the number and relative intensity of the overtones, which, in turn, depend upon the shape of the instrument and the nature of the material from which it is made.

Study Questions

1. DEFINE: amplifier, generator, overtone, high fidelity, stereophonic, Doppler effect, tweeter, woofer, tone, harmonic series, beats, fundamental, first harmonic, quality, harmonic.
2. Give the principle of the phonograph.
3. What is the frequency range to which the human ear is sensitive?
4. How does the human voice generate, amplify, and change the pitch of tones?
5. Why is it necessary to tune violin instruments frequently?
6. An organ pipe emits a certain tone when it is closed at the ends. What will happen to the pitch if the pipe is opened at one end?
7. How can musical tones be analyzed so as to show the overtones present?
8. What determines the quality of a musical tone?
9. How is the pitch determined in stringed instruments?
10. Give the general rules for the pitch of stringed instruments.
11. What are the methods of generating tones used in wind instruments?

The Physical Basis of Music

Scientific thought does not mean thought about scientific subjects with long names. There are no scientific subjects. The subject of science is the human universe; that is to say, everything that is, or has been, or may be related to man.

W. K. CLIFFORD

INTRODUCTION

Music undoubtedly gives greater pleasure to more people than any other art, and it can be even better appreciated or enjoyed if one knows something about its scientific basis. Just as the painter uses the knowledge of light and color to express his emotions, so the musician applies his knowledge of sound to express his feeling.

Music may be defined as *any succession of tones so modulated as to please the ear, or any combination of tones in harmony.* The pleasing arrangement of these tones, i.e., harmony, involves such relationships as rhythm, melody, and tone quality.

SOUNDS ARE CLASSIFIED AS NOISE AND TONES

The ear classifies sounds roughly into two classes: noises, which are disagreeable or irritating; and tones, which are received with pleasure or indifference, depending on the circumstances. *Tones, or any combination or succession of tones, received with pleasure are said to be* **musical.** There is no sharp borderline between a noise and a tone. Sounds classified as tones by some people are considered to be noise by other people. **Noise** *is generally a sound of too short a duration or of too great a complexity to be analyzed by the ear.*

TONES, NOTES, AND RESTS

A **musical tone** is *a sound of sustained pitch that can be recognized by the human ear.* A **note** is *a character designed to indicate the duration (time) of a tone, and by its position on a staff to indicate the pitch.* A **rest** is *a character designed to indicate the time interval between notes.* Table 56-1 shows the characters used to designate notes and rests.

TABLE 56-1

SYMBOLS FOR MUSICAL NOTES AND RESTS

Duration	Notes	Rests
Whole	o	▬
Half	♩	▬
Quarter	♩	⸱
Eighth	♪	𝄾
Sixteenth	♬	𝄿
Thirty second	♬	𝄿
Sixty fourth	♬	𝄿

PITCH

Pitch, which *represents the highness or lowness of a note,* is one of the most important characteristics of a musical note. *To the musician,* **pitch** *refers to the position of a note on a musical staff.* In scientific terms, **pitch** is *the number of complete vibrations per second, i.e., the frequency.* Figure 56-1

419

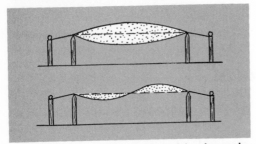

Figure 56–1. The pitch is determined by the number of vibrations per second.

shows how the pitch of a vibrating string is increased by increasing the number of vibrations per second.

Several terms are used in connection with pitch: (1) vibrato, (2) tremolo, (3) glide, (4) interval, and (5) octave.

Vibrato

Many singers are not able to maintain a constant pitch, but produce *a periodic and fairly even variation of tone due to variations in pitch,* and perhaps intensity or quality. In scientific terms, **vibrato** *represents variations in the predominating frequency, amplitude, or the number and intensity of the overtones.*

Tremolo

Tremolo is *a type of vibrato often deliberately produced in organ music. It refers to periodic variations in the amplitude of musical notes.*

Glide (Glissando)

The glide is a common fault of singers. *Instead of hitting the proper pitch they "glide" through a quick succession of adjacent changes in pitch, up or down.* In scientific terms, **glide** *refers to a gradual change in the frequency.*

Interval

A **musical interval** is *the difference between two pitches, i.e., the distance between two notes.* In scientific terms, a musical interval represents the ratio between the frequencies of two notes.

Octave

The **octave** is *a musical interval with a frequency ratio of nearly two to one.* A difference in pitch of two tones produces a number of beats, which depends upon the difference in pitch. Complex intervals produce tones that are unpleasant, because the number of beats is increased to such an extent that they cannot be differentiated by the hearing.

THE MOST COMMON MUSICAL INTERVALS

Unison 1:1	Minor third 6:5
Octave 2:1	Major sixth 5:3
Fifth 3:2	Minor sixth 8:5
Fourth 4:3	Major second 9:8
Major third 5:4	Major seventh 15:8
	Semitone 25:24

One who has no musical training or ability can make sounds with a musical instrument, but he cannot produce music, because he does not know what combinations of sounds will produce musical tones, and also because he has not developed skill in producing these sounds.

The Staff

The staff, shown in Figure 56-2 was invented by a Benedictine monk, Guido of Arezzo (995–1050), as a method of indicating the pitch of musical notes. *By placing the symbols for notes on the lines or spaces of the* **staff,** *the pitch of each note is indicated, because each line and space indicates a given pitch.*

If a greater range of pitch is to be shown, additional lines (ledger lines) may be placed above or below the staff, or they may be indicated as shown in Figure 56–2.

The Clef—The character placed at the beginning of the staff is the **clef.** It tells more about the pitch of a note. The character shown in the upper staff is the treble (or G) clef, which in this case, is played by the right hand on the piano. The lower staff designated by the character for the bass clef is played by the left hand. The character shown in the top staff indicates that the second line represents G above Middle C. The bass (or F) clef, shown on the lower staff, indicates that the fourth line represents F below Middle C. Thus, the clef adds to the range of the pitch which a staff can show.

*Sharps and Flats—*Sharps and flats represent a further refinement in designating pitch. The

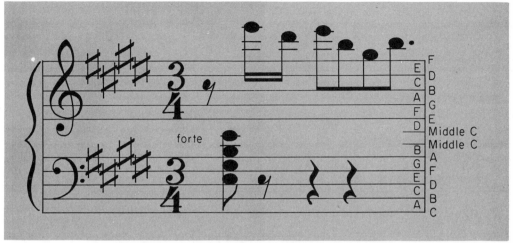

Figure 56–2. The first measure of a musical score for the piano.

key part of the signature indicates whether or not certain notes in the score are to be raised or lowered in pitch by half steps. In Figure 56-2, the sharps represent the key part of the signature. *Any note which occurs in the position in which a* **sharp** *occurs is not played as written, but is raised in pitch by one half-step. If* **flats** *had been shown in the signature, the corresponding notes would have been lowered by half steps.* Notes on the lines or spaces are played by the white keys on a piano, while the black keys are used to play sharps or flats, except in the case of Cb, B♯, Fb, and E♯.

Musical Scales

A **musical scale** is *a series of tones ascending or descending by regular intervals. The interval is the octave.* The **key** of any scale takes its name from the note on which it begins. Two tones that differ from each other in frequency by a factor of two are separated by an interval of one octave. An **octave** *consists of eight tones, and the frequency differences between each tone may be about the same as in the equal tempered scale, or they may vary as in the diatonic (see below) scales which are limited to one key.* Pope Gregory I, in the sixth century, set up the diatonic scale with eight notes, in which Middle C was given a frequency of 256, and the C above Middle C was given just twice this frequency, or 512. The chief disadvantage of this scale was that the frequency differ-

ences varied from note to note, and scales could not be started on any note except C.

About 250 years ago, Johann Sebastian Bach (1685–1750) suggested that the frequency of any note should be obtained from the one below it by multiplying it by the twelfth root of 2, or 1.05946. He developed his "well tempered clavichord," the forerunner of the modern piano, on the basis of the above suggestion. This plan makes *all of the intervals equal,* and hence the scale based on it is called the **equal-tempered scale.**

Bach's equal-tempered scale, like the modern equal-tempered scale, based on A above Middle C, with a frequency of 440, was devised to make it possible to begin a scale with any note. Anyone who knows Bach's music can appreciate the fact that he took ample advantage of his new-found freedom to compose scales in many keys.

All Scales Made Possible with Sharps and Flats

If a siren disk is made with four rows of holes, consisting of 24, 30, 36, and 48 holes to a row, respectively, and the disk is rotated uniformly, while a jet of air is blown through first one row of holes and then another, the familiar do-mi-sol-do scale will be produced. *Any series of four tones in the ratios of 24: 30: 36: 48 produces* **major chords.** Scales constructed on these ratios have the following frequency ratios:

C SCALE

Ratios	1	9/8	5/4	4/3	3/2	5/3	1 5/8	2
Keys	C	D	E	F	G	A	B	C
Frequencies	256	288	320	341.3	384	426.7	480	512

Now suppose that we construct another scale, called the D scale, as follows:

D SCALE

Ratios	1	9/8	5/4	4/3	3/2	5/3	1 5/8	2
Keys	D	E	F	G	A	B	C	D
Frequencies	288	324	360	384	432	480	540	576

COMPARISON OF FREQUENCIES IN THE C AND D SCALES

	C	D	E	F	G	A	B	C	D
C Scale	256	288	320	341.3	384	426.7	480	512	
D Scale		288	324	360	384	432	480	540	576

A comparison of the C and D major scales shows some discrepancies; for example, F is 341.3 cycles on the C scale but 360 cycles on the D scale. If one were playing the D scale on a piano, in which the keys were all tuned to the C scale, the F on the D scale would obviously lie about midway between F and G on the C scale. In order to make it possible to play all of the scales (C, D, E, F, etc.), the black keys were added to provide for frequencies lying between those on the C scale. These "in-between" frequencies are called sharps and flats.

Standard Pitch

The relative pitch of the notes on a score is shown by their position on the staff, by the clef, and by the key signature. However, there is a standard pitch that is represented by a certain frequency. In the United States, the manufacturers of musical instruments take A above middle C with a frequency of 440 vibrations per second as the standard pitch. This gives middle C a frequency of 264 on the consonant, diatonic scale, or 261.6 on the equal-tempered scale. The letters in Figure 56-2 would not be shown on a score, but they are included in this figure in order to show how lines and spaces are designated.

THE MUSICAL SCORE

A musical score may be very much more complicated than the sample shown in Figure 56-2. The musical score gives so much information concerning the pitch, duration, and intensity of tones that a great deal of study, training, and practice is required to read and interpret it. But beyond the ability to read a musical score there is required the skill in playing a musical instrument, which is acquired only at the expense of a great deal of practice. Music is challenging because it requires mental activity as well as muscular activity.

THE HUMAN VOICE

Perhaps the most difficult musical instrument to control is the human voice. To maintain the proper pitch without vibrato or glides, including the sharps and flats (the chromatics), and to maintain the proper rhythm, and at the same time vary the loudness and softness (the dynamics), is not easy. The quality of a human voice can be controlled to a limited extent by deliberate, intelligent effort, but to a large extent it depends upon the cavities in the head, which are not subject to much change, except for such things as removing tonsils or adenoids, or clearing up a cold.

TIME

The terms used to express time in music are (1) the meter (measure), (2) the metric signature, (3) the rhythm, (4) the rests, and (5) the tempo.

Meter

The **meter** is *the relative duration of a note or group of notes or rests expressed in time units. It is the time interval between accents, which is shown on a musical score as the distance between two bars on a staff.*

Metric Signature

The number of beats in a measure and the kind of note attached to each pulse is indicated by the **metric signature.** Basically, *it is the number of accented notes per unit of time.*

Rhythm

Musical rhythm *manifests itself in the association of pulsations, their multiples and fractions. It divides the time into regular and equal units, each one of which is called a* **beat.** The first note of each beat is generally accented unless otherwise directed. For example, **syncopation** *represents a shift of accent from the first notes in a beat or measure to other notes as desired, thus altering the rhythm.*

The numbers that represent the time part of the signature are placed on the staff after the key signature, to indicate the rhythm in which the music is to be played. The lower number indicates the value of each of the time units or beats, while the upper number shows the number of such beats per measure. In Figure 56-2, the time is called 3:4 time. It means that there are three beats per measure, each a quarter note in length. However, the quarter notes in this case are subdivided into eighth and sixteenth notes. *Each measure is separated by a* **bar** *on the staff.* The dot, shown in Table 56-1, always increases the duration of a note by one half.

Rests

In Figure 56-2, there is an eighth rest in each measure, and there are two quarter rests shown in the lower staff. Rests represent the silences in music, and are indicated by signs which correspond to each note. The duration of time indicated by rests is controlled by the duration of time indicated by the notes. The tempo controls both the notes and the rests.

Tempo

Tempo refers to *the speed.* The duration of a measure is determined by the musician, who may increase or decrease the tempo (*time interval between beats*). Often the musician will use a metronome or electronome to maintain a steady tempo at a predetermined rate. For an orchestra, the conductor indicates the tempo with the motion of his baton, hands or arms. The metronome, set at 60 ticks per minute, indicates that a quarter note is to be one second in length. A whole note in this case would consist of four beats. Some musical scores indicate the metronome setting, thus prescribing the time precisely, but, as a rule, such words as **adagio** (*slow*), **largo** (*faster*), **allegro** (*brisk*), and **presto** (*rapid*) are used to express the tempo. The tempo may vary from 42 to 152 ticks per minute, using the metronome. The tempo at which a score is played usually depends upon the judgment of the musician.

INTENSITY

Intensity refers to *the loudness or volume of a musical note.*

Loudness is *determined in part by the amplitude of a sound wave, and in part by its frequency.* Figure 56-3 shows how the amplitude of a string may be varied. For a given note, the loudness of a sound is determined by the amount of energy expended in producing the sound. A drum hit with great force will sound louder than when it is hit very lightly.

Common terms used in connection with intensity are **pianissimo** (*very soft*), and **forte** (*loud*). There is no scientific method of expressing intensity in music. Intensity is varied by the musician in order to express his feelings. A composer indicates relative intensities by the above terms, and the musician interprets them according to his own feelings.

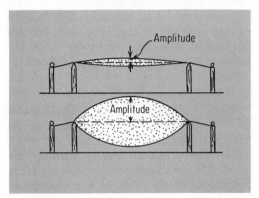

Figure 56–3. Intensity depends upon amplitude.

Three terms used in connection with intensity are (1) crescendo, (2) diminuendo, and (3) pulsation.

Crescendo

Crescendo refers to *the gradual increase in intensity, i.e., a gradual increase in amplitude.*

Diminuendo

Diminuendo refers to a *gradual decrease in intensity, i.e., a gradual decrease in amplitude.*

Pulsation

Pulsation refers to *the on and off fluctuation of a tone, or a variation in intensity.* In scientific terms, *it is the alternate canceling and reinforcing of sound waves resulting from interference.*

SUMMARY

Tones

Tones are pleasant sounds, the quality of which depends upon the number and relative intensity of the overtones. Tones refer to pitch.

Notes and Rests

Notes indicate the duration of a tone, and rests indicate the time interval between notes. The terms used to indicate time in music are the meter, the metric signature, the rhythm, the rests, and the tempo. The duration of a tone may be indicated by a metronome.

Pitch

Pitch refers to the number of vibrations per second. The musical staff serves to indicate pitch. Terms used in connection with pitch are vibrato, tremolo, glide, interval, and octave. An octave represents a musical interval having a frequency of nearly two to one. The clef on a staff provides information concerning the pitch that is not shown by the notes. The standard pitch in the United States is 440 vibrations per second for A above middle C.

Intensity

Intensity is determined largely by the amplitude of vibrations, but also somewhat by their frequency (pitch).

Study Questions

1. DEFINE: pitch, diminuendo, loudness, crescendo, vibrato, tremolo, glide, rhythm, scale, rest, octave, note, tone, interval, pulsation, beat, bar, metric signature, tempo, meter, clef, largo, allegro, presto, staff, key, syncopation, forte, music, musical tones, major chord, adagio, pianissimo, noise, equal-tempered scale, intensity, sharp, flat.
2. In what regards does a musician have latitude in interpreting a musical score?
3. In what regards must a musician follow a musical score exactly?
4. How is the time element expressed in music?
5. How is pitch expressed on the musical score?
6. What is the standard pitch in the United States?
7. What is the function of a metronome?
8. What determines the quality of a human voice?
9. Define pitch, quality, and intensity in physical terms.
10. What is rhythm, and how is it indicated on the staff?

11. What are the advantages of the equal-tempered scale?
12. What is music as differentiated from noise?
13. What does the elimination of overtones do to a tone?
14. What does the musician mean by the terms, harmony and discord?
15. Explain the necessity for the black keys on a piano.

Atomic cloud during Baker Bikini fission-fusion bomb explosion. A column of water a half-mile wide was sent thousands of feet up into the air. (Courtesy, U.S. Navy)

UNIT 9

The Frontiers of
Modern Physical Science

Still o'er the earth hastes opportunity
Seeking the hardy soul that seeks her.

J. R. LOWELL

THIS UNIT takes up the study of some of the important frontiers in the applications of physical science, such as fuel cells, electronics, and nuclear energy. Such developments, as in the case of electronics, are already ushering in a new revolution to modern living, in which man is building machines to aid his brain, in contrast to the industrial revolution in which machines were used to do physical work. These new machines can compute, sort, read, write, translate, and communicate. Their memories are extensive and their speed is amazing.

Nuclear energy is just beginning to be applied to modern life. It made a dramatic entrance when the atomic bomb was dropped on Hiroshima. Its development was stimulated by war, but it helped to bring about a rapid end to World War II. Perhaps its greatest contribution to the present and future will be its deterrent action in preventing future world wars.

The impact of nuclear energy on everyday living is small today, but it will surely be of importance in the future. The transformation of matter into energy is the most important accomplishment of physical science up to the present time. Perhaps the most ambitious goal of physical science today is that of harnessing fusion reactions which would liberate unlimited amounts of energy. Can we master this secret of the stars? Only time will tell.

The study of the electric current was reserved for this unit, because it is tied so closely to its various applications in vacuum tubes, semiconductors, photo-electric applications such as television, electronic computers, and the new laser technology studied in this unit.

Electrolysis and Fuel Cells

The life and soul of science is its practical application; and just as the great advances in mathematics have been made through the desire of discovering the solution of problems which were of a highly practical kind in mathematical science, so in physical science many of the greatest advances that have been made from the beginning of the world to the present time have been made in the earnest desire to turn the knowledge of the properties of matter to some purpose useful to mankind.

LORD KELVIN

INTRODUCTION

The basic principle of electrolysis was introduced in Chapter 32. In this chapter, applications of electrolysis in modern chemical industry will be presented. Such applications are the basis for some of the large chemical industries.

An interesting new development is the fuel cell, which is the reverse of electrolysis. A **fuel cell** *is an electrochemical cell or primary battery in which chemical energy is converted into electrical energy.* To this extent, this definition of a fuel cell does not differentiate it from any other electrochemical cell. *In the case of the* **fuel cell,** *however, the chemical energy supplied by the fuel and the oxidizer is supplied from an external source.* Fuel cells have been used to power electrical devices in satellites.

THE ELECTROLYSIS OF WATER

Electrolysis is a process by which a chemical reaction is caused at the electrodes in contact with an electrolyte when a direct electric current is passed between the electrodes.

A common laboratory experiment is the electrolysis of a water solution of sulfuric acid, using two platinum electrodes. In this experiment, hydrogen gas is evolved at the negative electrode (the cathode), and oxygen gas is evolved at the positive electrode (the anode). The basic chemical reaction is the production of hydrogen and oxygen from water. The process will continue as long as the supply of water holds out. The sulfuric acid supplies the ions to carry the electric current. Sulfuric acid ionizes in water to form two hydrogen ions and one sulfate ion per molecule. The hydrogen ions, being positively charged, migrate to the cathode, where they combine with electrons and become ordinary hydrogen gas. The sulfate ions, being negatively charged, migrate to the anode where they would give up their electrons if it were not for the fact that hydroxyl ions, which are also present, have a greater tendency to give up electrons. Water ionizes to form hydrogen (hydronium) ions and hydroxyl ions, and there is always an equilibrium between these ions. Even in an acid solution, there is a small concentration of hydroxyl ions. These hydroxyl ions go to the anode and give up their electrons. In the process, two hydroxyl ions are changed into one molecule of water and one atom of oxygen. The process continues, because additional hydroxyl ions are formed from the water as fast as they are used up, to maintain the equilibrium between water and its ions. The net result of the passage of the electric current through the solution is that two hydrogen atoms are liberated for each oxygen atom. This is verified by observing the volumes of the hydrogen and oxygen gases evolved at the two electrodes; the vol-

ume of the hydrogen gas is just twice that of the oxygen gas.

THE HYDROGEN-OXYGEN FUEL CELL

In the above laboratory experiment, the oxygen and hydrogen gases may be collected

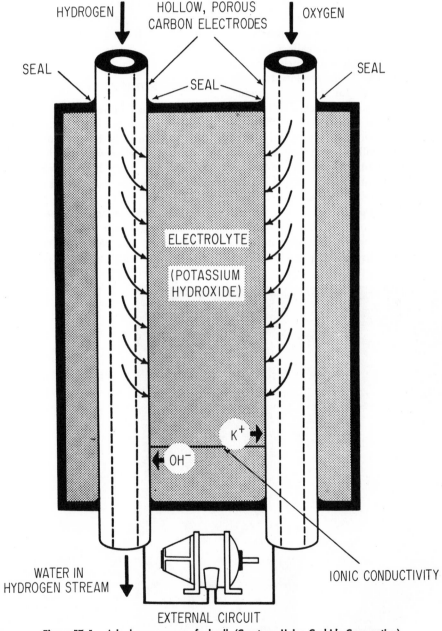

Figure 57–1.   A hydrogen-oxygen fuel cell. (Courtesy, Union Carbide Corporation)

in a rubber football bladder. The resulting gas mixture may then be used to blow soap bubbles, which explode with a loud, but harmless bang when they are ignited. This reaction is the reverse of the decomposition of water in electrolysis, since the hydrogen and oxygen have been combined to form water with the liberation of considerable energy. The hydrogen and oxygen gas explosion could be used to operate an internal-combustion engine, but this process is too inefficient, and hydrogen produced by electrolysis is too expensive to make such an engine economically sound.

A fuel cell, the principle of which is shown in Figure 57-1, has been developed to use hydrogen and oxygen for the direct production of an electric current. Such a cell ranges from 65 per cent to 80 per cent in efficiency as compared with an efficiency of only 25 to 30 per cent for gasoline internal engines, and 35 to 40 per cent for the best steam-turbine electrical power plants. Such cells will operate at room temperature. They are quiet because there are no moving parts.

The fuel cell shown in the above illustration consists of a jar in which hydrogen and oxygen gases are fed through chemically treated, hollow, porous carbon electrodes. The electrodes are immersed in a solution of potassium hydroxide. Such a cell does not require pure oxygen for its operation; air may be used as the source of oxygen.

Although the hydrogen fuel cell uses about one-half to two-thirds of the fuel consumption of the best Diesel-electric and steam-turbine electric generator systems, it is still not practical because hydrogen is too expensive. However, a relatively simple steam reforming unit can produce hydrogen from kerosene or natural gas.

OTHER FUEL CELLS

A great deal of research is being devoted to the development of fuel cells which will use less expensive fuels than hydrogen. Successful experimental cells have been developed to use alcohols and other liquid fuels, but natural gas fuel cells are receiving the most critical attention.

One might visualize electric automobiles for city driving, which would be powered by simple, quiet fuel cells. No fumes would be produced, and an important source of smog

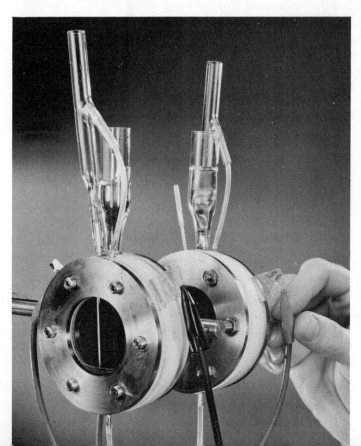

Figure 57–2. Two hydrocarbon fuel cells. These cells operate with such liquids as gasoline, diesel oil, or natural gas. Air is the source of oxygen. The fuel cells carry the reaction to completion, yielding carbon dioxide and water. (Courtesy, General Electric Company)

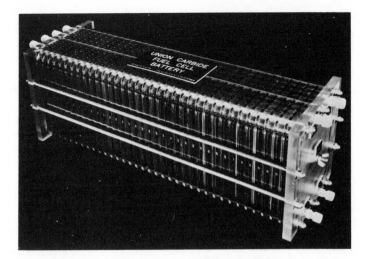

Figure 57–3. A hydrogen-oxygen fuel cell (1962), rated to produce 0.35 kilowatt at 28 volts, for continuous duty at room temperature. (Courtesy, Union Carbide Corporation)

would thus be removed. Their silent operation as compared with the noise of truck, bus, and automobile engines might prove to be a real blessing. One advantage of the fuel cell is that no fuel is used while it is not in operation.

The United States Army already has in operation portable fuel-cell-powered radar equipment.

An experimental fuel cell, weighing 30 pounds, will produce 200 watts at 24 volts. It will do the work of half a ton of freshly charged storage batteries. A metal hydride,

Figure 57–4. From basic research to space application. At left, the first hydrogen-air fuel cell of 1959. At the right, a fuel cell designed to furnish electricity to the astronauts in the two-man Gemini spacecraft. At the center, a portable fuel cell power supply for U.S. Marines and Army. Lower right, a small compact hydrogen-air fuel cell. This photograph made in 1963 shows the progress of fuel cell research during a four-year period. (Courtesy, General Electric Company)

such as lithium hydride, furnishes the hydrogen as it is needed. Such a fuel cell would be used only in situations in which the cost of operation is unimportant, because lithium hydride is quite expensive.

FUEL CELLS—A PRESENT SCIENTIFIC FRONTIER

The present experiments with fuel cells indicate that practical fuel cells may be expected in the future. Probably, many students now in college will make a living with fuel-cell applications in the future.

THE PREPARATION OF THE ACTIVE METALS BY ELECTROLYSIS

The active metals cannot be prepared economically by using cheap reducing agents, such as coke, to separate them from their compounds. More active metals, i.e., metals higher in the electromotive force series (see page 220), could be used to displace metals below them in the series, but these active metals would first have to be prepared for such a process. Electricity is used for the reduction of the compounds of the active metals. No active metal can be prepared by the electrolysis of a water solution of a salt of the metal, because hydrogen, rather than the metal, would be obtained in the process. However, molten salts are good conductors of an electric current, and, therefore, are used for the electrolytic production of such active metals as sodium, potassium, magnesium, and aluminum.

ELECTROLYSIS, A VERY IMPORTANT METALLURGICAL PROCESS

Electrolysis is used for reduction and refining of metals. **Electroreduction** *is employed to prepare metals from their compounds.* Water solutions are used if possible, but metals above hydrogen in the electromotive series must be deposited from molten salts as mentioned above. **Electrorefining** is *a method of purifying a metal.* The impure metal serves as an anode, from which it dissolves during electrolysis to form ions; the

ions of the electrolyte then deposit on the cathode. The impurities do not deposit on the cathode, but drop down to the bottom of the container as a sludge, or dissolve and remain in solution.

Zinc is produced by the electrolysis of zinc sulfate which is formed by the leaching of zinc ores with sulfuric acid. Copper may be produced by a similar process.

Lead, copper, nickel, cadmium, bismuth, cobalt, beryllium, tin, silver, and other metals are usually purified by electrorefining processes.

ELECTROPLATING

When metals are plated by electrolysis, the metal goes into solution at one electrode and plates out at the other; thus, in silver plating a brass spoon may be used as the cathode and a bar of silver as the anode, the electrolyte being a solution of some silver salt, usually the complex cyanide. Electrons are sent to the brass spoon and are taken up by the silver ions surrounding the brass spoon to form metallic silver, which is then deposited as a plate on the spoon. A corresponding amount of silver dissolves at the anode.

Silver plate and gold plate are common examples of metallic coatings that are applied by electrolysis. Nickel plate is used for many purposes, but for hardware and furniture, nickel plate is usually plated with chromium because of its greater resistance to tarnishing and its inherent beauty. Metallic articles may be coated with very thin or very thick layers of metal by electrolysis. A salt of the metal to be deposited is dissolved in water, and the metal object to be coated becomes the cathode. A direct electric current is passed through the solution, and the metal is deposited, the thickness of the coating depending upon the amount of electric current used. The type of solution and the method of plating are important considerations in obtaining a smooth, uniform plate. Thick plates are usually undesirable, because of unevenness and crystal growth.

ELECTROTYPING

Electrotyping is *a process whereby a complete object is built up by electrolysis.* Most books are printed by electrotype plates. A page of type set by machine or by hand is pressed into wax to make a clear impression. The impression is dusted with graphite powder to make it a conductor, and is then coated with copper by electrolysis. Molten lead is poured on to the back of the copper plate to give it strength. Electrotypes may be preserved for future use, whereas type would be too expensive to store away.

THE ELECTROLYSIS OF COMMON SALT

An important chemical industry is built around the electrolysis of common salt (sodium chloride). When a direct current of electricity is passed through a saturated water solution of sodium chloride in a chlorine cell, hydrogen gas is obtained at the cathode and chlorine gas collects at the anode. Sodium hydroxide, a strong base, and some sodium chloride are left in the solution. All that is needed to produce these three important products is common salt, water and electricity.

There is a large demand for chlorine in the elemental form for the chlorination of water supplies to kill any harmful bacteria that may be present, and for use as a bleaching agent.

Chlorine will react with sodium hydroxide (also obtained in the electrolysis of sodium chloride), or with sodium carbonate, to produce sodium hypochlorite, which sells as a 5 per cent solution in water under many names, such as "Clorox," and "Purex." This solution is one of the most powerful disinfectants and one of the least harmful to the delicate tissues. It is widely used under various fanciful names in disinfecting utensils in the dairy industry. Because of its bleaching action, it is also valuable in laundry work.

Sodium hydroxide, prepared by the electrolysis of common salt, is the cheapest strong base available, and hence has many applications where a base is needed. For example, an important use for sodium hydroxide is the manufacture of soap. Sodium hydroxide reacts with various animal and vegetable fats and oils to produce soaps. A by-product of this reaction is glycerin, a compound that has many uses. Potassium hydroxide may be prepared from the electrolysis of potassium chloride, and it may also be used to prepare soaps. Potassium hydroxide goes under the common name of caustic potash or lye. Sodium hydroxide is called caustic soda and sometimes it is also called lye. Sodium or potassium hydroxide may be used in the home to remove grease from drainpipes, in which the grease is converted into a soluble soap.

THE GROWTH OF AN ELECTROCHEMICAL PLANT

Just why a chemical plant is called a plant is uncertain. However, a chemical plant has one characteristic of living plants—it grows. To show how one product leads to another in chemical industries, let us consider a chemical company that was engaged in the production of chlorine by the electrolysis of a water solution of common salt. In this process, hydrogen gas and sodium hydroxide were obtained as by-products. This company had no use for the hydrogen at the outset. If the hydrogen-oxygen fuel cell had been available, it might have used the hydrogen for the direct production of electrical energy. This would have been a good idea, because electric power is the most expensive raw material in the electrolytic process. However, the company used the hydrogen for the preparation of ammonia by combining nitrogen with hydrogen in the presence of a catalyst. But this reaction required nitrogen, so some of the hydrogen was burned in air to remove the oxygen, thus leaving the nitrogen. This company soon found that it could not sell all of its chlorine for chlorinating water, bleaching, and other purposes. It then used part of its surplus hydrogen to combine it with chlorine to produce hydrogen chloride. There was a market for this chemical but the demand was not great, so some of the hydrogen chloride was combined with some of the ammonia to prepare ammonium chloride, which also had a limited sale. More uses for chlorine were needed, so the company then reacted chlorine with the hydrocarbons of natural gas to produce various chlorinated hydrocarbons. Eventually, this company became an **integrated chemical company,** *i.e., one that used its various products to prepare other products it could sell to advantage.* The above chemical company eventually merged with The Dow Chemical Company, which was also based on the electrolysis of sodium chloride and other salts.

THE DOW CHEMICAL COMPANY, A GOOD EXAMPLE OF AN ELECTROCHEMICAL INDUSTRY

In 1888, while a student at Case School of Applied Science, Herbert Dow invented a new and much less costly process for extracting bromine from brine. Two years later, he began the separation of bromine by electrolysis of the bromine-rich brines of Midland, Michigan, in a small flour-mill shed. By 1897, he was also producing chlorine by similar means, and subsequently developed a cell that produced both chlorine and sodium hydroxide by the electrolysis of a common salt solution. Seeking new outlets for chlorine, his young company then combined it with sulfur to form sulfur chloride, which was then treated with carbon disulfide, to produce carbon tetrachloride, an important solvent and fire extinguisher. Carbon tetrachloride was then treated with iron in the presence of water to produce chloroform, a widely used anesthetic, solvent, and organic intermediate.

The above reaction by which carbon tetrachloride was synthesized, was the first important synthetic organic reaction to be carried out on a commercial scale in the United States, and was but the forerunner of many synthetic organic chemicals to be manufactured by this company.

Dow was the first company to undertake commercial manufacture of synthetic phenol, an important basic chemical. Phenol is prepared from chlorobenzene, which is prepared by the reaction of chlorine with benzene. Chlorobenzene reacts with sodium hydroxide under pressure and relatively high temperature to produce phenol.

So broad are the chemical ramifications of chlorine that, while The Dow Chemical Company has for some years been by far its largest producer in the United States, the Company sells only a comparatively minute amount in elemental form. Almost all of the chlorine produced is used in processes such as already mentioned. Chlorine is also reacted

with iron to form iron chloride, with benzene to produce the insecticide, paradichlorobenzene, and with hydrocarbons to produce various chlorinated hydrocarbons.

From its Michigan brines, The Dow Chemical Company also separates magnesium chloride. This Company developed an electrolytic cell to produce magnesium metal and chlorine from magnesium chloride. It later built a plant at Freeport, Texas, to extract magnesium salts from sea water. Here, again, magnesium metal is produced by electrolysis.

One product led to another, until The Dow Chemical Company is now manufacturing more than 700 different industrial chemicals, agricultural chemicals, metals, plastics, and fibers.

SUMMARY

Fuel cells produce electricity directly by the oxidation of fuels. Fuel cells may become important future sources of power, because they possess the following advantages: (1) high efficiency; no mechanical cycle is required, (2) no moving parts, (3) no friction, and, hence, no need for lubricants, (4) silent operation.

A hydrogen-oxygen fuel cell has been developed, but its practical application requires an economical source of hydrogen.

Electrolysis is widely used in

1. electroplating
2. electrorefining of metals
3. electrotypes
4. electrolysis of such salts as sodium chloride and magnesium chloride to produce active metals and chlorine.

For the separation of the active metals the electrolysis of molten salts is used. Aluminum and magnesium are important metals produced by the above process.

Study Questions

1. DEFINE: integrated chemical company, fuel cell, electrotyping, electrorefining, electroreduction.
2. What are the advantages of fuel cells?
3. What is the chief obstacle to the use of the hydrogen-oxygen fuel cell?
4. Why may one speak of the hydrogen-oxygen fuel cell as the reverse of an electrolytic cell?

5. What are the three main products obtained in the electrolysis of sodium chloride?

6. Why must the electrolysis of molten salts be used for the preparation of the active metals?

7. What are some of the uses for sodium hydroxide?

8. What are the important uses of elemental chlorine?

9. How is electroplating accomplished?

10. What metals familiar to you are used for electroplating?

11. What metals are refined by electrorefining?

12. What are the products of the electrolysis of a sulfuric acid solution?

13. Electrolysis is the opposite of battery action. Can you think of an example in which electrolysis is used to charge a battery?

14. How may soap be considered to be a by-product of the electrolysis of common salt?

15. How is sodium hypochlorite prepared? Under what names may it be purchased?

16. How does a fuel cell differ from other electrochemical cells?

Current Electricity

Electricity, carrier of light and power, devourer of time and space, bearer of human speech over land and sea, greatest servant of mankind.

CHARLES ELIOT

INTRODUCTION

The high, steel towers of electric power lines are a frequent accompaniment of the modern landscape. Everyone knows that their purpose is to transmit electric power from generating plants to places, often at a considerable distance, where it is used. This chapter explains why such transmission towers are required. Again, the substations, with their steel framework, massive tanks containing transformers, and surrounded by steel fencing to keep people out, are a common sight near the outskirts of cities. This chapter also explains why they are necessary.

All of this expensive equipment designed to transmit electric power would be useless without the proper wiring system in homes. Unfortunately, many older homes and many tract-type new homes are not provided with electric circuits capable of handling the requirements of modern electric home appliances. The practical problems of home wiring are included in this chapter because such knowledge is a "must" in this age of electric servants.

GROUNDING

Grounding *refers to making an electrical connection with the ground or some object which has the capacity to receive electrons.* It should be kept in mind that an electric current cannot flow unless there is a complete circuit. The electric current will always take the most

direct path, and the object of a ground for electrical appliances is to provide a conductor through which an electric current will flow in preference to flowing through the human body. The human body itself may serve as a ground, i.e., it may acquire a charge even sufficient to cause the hair on the head to stand on end. This charge is not dangerous; it is the flow of a high-voltage electric current through the human body that is dangerous. Under ordinary conditions the body is insulated by rubber soles, leather, and clothing, but if it makes contact with water (which contains ions) a pathway is provided for an electric current to pass through the body. Again, a similar pathway may be made by touching a water pipe or an electrical conduit that makes an electrical contact with the ground.

It is considered to be good practice to ground all electric appliances. Of course, they are supposed to be wired in such a way that shocks will not be produced, but there may be short-circuits or other defects. Safety engineers recommend three-wire plugs and outlets for all home appliances, to reduce shock hazards. A three-wire plug can be recognized because it has three prongs. The third wire is not a part of the circuit but serves as a ground.

The use of three-wire plugs and outlets for electric appliances in the home is not very common. This means that one should avoid touching household appliances or even switches when taking a bath, because the water acts as a ground between the source of current and the ground. When using electric outdoor appliances, such as hedge trimmers, one should avoid making contact with moist soil. He should insulate himself with rubber soles, rubbers, or rubber gloves.

A familiar example of grounding is the electrical system of an automobile. The positive pole of the battery is connected directly to the automobile body, which thus serves as a ground. The "hot" wire leads from the negative pole of the battery to the load, such as a headlight or the starter. The load, in turn, is connected to the automobile frame, thus completing the circuit.

HIGH-VOLTAGE, DIRECT, ELECTRIC CURRENT

For some purposes a direct current is required. Batteries produce an electric current. In the automobile, a high-voltage electric current is necessary to produce the sparks in the ignition system. The voltage cannot be increased by the use of a transformer, which will operate only with an alternating current. To increase the voltage of a direct current an **induction coil** is used. *It applies the principle of direct and secondary windings found in alternating current transformers but it has in addition an interrupter, i.e., a vibrating device that will turn the electric current on and off.* Induction coils are capable of building up such high voltages that sparks may be made to jump several inches through the air. The distance a spark will jump through the air depends upon the dryness of the air, the difference in electrical potential, the shape of the conductors, and the form of the gap terminals. In ordinary air, an electromotive force of ten to thirty thousand volts is needed to make a spark jump across one centimeter. Induction coils are used where high voltage and low amperage are needed, as in furnishing a spark for igniting gases in internal-combustion engines, or in operating X-ray tubes.

THE DISTRIBUTION OF ELECTRIC POWER

The generation of electric power by turbines operated by water power would be relatively useless if the power could not be carried to distant cities where it is needed. Electric power plants usually have peak loads that could be aided by connecting power plants from different parts of the country in such a way that the surplus power from one plant could be delivered to another place where it is needed. Electricity cannot be carried very far by ordinary wires at ordinary voltages because of high losses due to their resistance. In order to transmit electric current over considerable distances, the voltage is stepped up and the amperage (flow of current) is decreased correspondingly. Line losses are chiefly due to resistance; the less the amount of current the less the resistance. Doubling the voltage doubles the power that can be transmitted over a single set of wires. The voltage of some transmission lines has been stepped up to as much as 500,000. The higher the voltage the less is the loss along the line.

Alternating current has been preferred for transmitting electric power because voltage can be readily stepped up or down by transformers with very little loss.

Super-voltage transmission lines require higher supporting towers and longer cross arms to provide greater spacing between the wires. Very large, and hence very heavy, cables are generally used for super-voltage transmission lines. Some modern cables are two inches in diameter. Aluminum cables are used in preference to copper cables, because aluminum is lighter and less expensive than copper. The cables are reinforced with a steel core surrounded with light-weight, insulating, filler material. New approaches to the problem of high-voltage transmission using direct current make it possible to transmit higher voltages over greater distances.

When power lines reach the edge of a town, they go to substations where huge transformers step down the voltage to about 20,000 volts, as shown in Figure 58-1. Other substations may step down the voltage to about 2,000 volts for various industrial uses. For home use, the voltage is further stepped down to about 110 volts by the familiar transformers, such as shown in Figure 58-2. Small transformers used for doorbells or toy railroads step down the voltage again to 6 or 8 volts.

Figure 58–1. Huge transformers installed at the Wilson Substation of the Great Western Power Company. (Courtesy, General Electric Company)

Figure 58–2. A pole-top mounted distribution transformer for residential districts. (Courtesy, Allis Chalmers Manufacturing Company)

CHANGING ALTERNATING CURRENT TO DIRECT CURRENT

The changing of an alternating current to a direct current is called rectification and the device used to do this is called a **rectifier.** A direct current may be generated by running a direct-current generator with an alternating-current motor. This is one of the best ways to produce a direct current when only alternating current is available.

Many types of one-way electron valves are used in rectifiers. Among these are some of the vacuum tubes and semiconductors described in the next chapter.

CIRCUIT BREAKERS AND FUSES

Excessive currents pass through wires when they are short-circuited, and many fires in automobiles and homes are caused in this way. A **short circuit** *is caused by connecting two wires through such a low resistance that the current flowing through the wire becomes very great, causing the wires themselves to become hot enough to start a fire or even melt*—all because of their own resistance.

In order to avoid such fires, fuses are introduced into the circuit. A **fuse** is *a wire or strip of some metal or alloy that has a low melting point and a comparatively high resistance, enclosed in a fireproof box.* As the current increases, the fuse is melted, and the circuit is broken before the copper wires get hot enough to cause any damage. Fuses are rated according to the current strength at which they will melt. Thus, a ten-ampere fuse will allow currents up to ten amperes to pass, but will melt when the current exceeds that strength. The practice of replacing a burned-out fuse with a penny or some other conductor that will not burn out is dangerous because, although it does permit current to flow once more, it offers no protection against and certainly no remedy for the situation that caused the fuse to blow out. An important safety precaution is never to replace a fuse with anything but a fuse, and never to replace a fuse with one of larger size.

Fuses break a circuit, but special devices called **circuit breakers** are often used instead of fuses. They have the advantage that they can be set again by a flip of a handle, whereas burned-out fuses must be replaced. The **circuit breaker** *may be an electromagnetic mechanism or it may be activated by a rise in temperature.*

HOME WIRING CIRCUITS

The main line from the power lines to the home comes to the main fuse box. From here, it divides into a number of branch circuits, which is determined by the number and kinds of loads to be serviced. There are four types of circuits often found in home wiring: (1) general purpose circuits for electric lights, which may use number 12 wire with 20-amp fuses, (2) small appliance circuits of the same capacity, such as one finds in wall outlets, (3) individual circuits for major appliances such as washing machines, ranges, dishwashers or circulating fan motors, and (4) 220-volt, three-wire circuits, for such appliances as ovens, ranges, clothes washers and driers, and air-conditioners. In the 220-volt, three-wire circuit, one wire serves as a ground. A circuit established between this ground wire and either one of the other two wires gives 110 volts, but a circuit between the other two wires give 220 volts.

In home wiring, the diameter of the wire is important. The size of the wire is indicated by numbers: the higher the number the smaller is the diameter of the wire. A number 14 wire uses a 15-ampere fuse (and no larger) and it can carry a load of only 1,750 watts, at 110 volts. An electric toaster may require up to 1,100 watts, and a coffee maker may also use up to 1,100 watts. Together, they are too much for a number 14 wire, but they would operate with a number 12 wire that uses a 20-ampere fuse and can carry a load of 2,400 watts.

The overloading of house wiring circuits is a frequent occurrence, often resulting in fires. Many older homes were not wired to accommodate the loads of modern home electric appliances. Because copper wires of small diameter cost a little less than wires of larger diameter, many tract-type homes have been wired with wires of too small a diameter for the loads they are likely to be called upon to handle. Such a small saving amounts to a considerable saving in a large tract. A further saving in construction costs is gained by providing relatively few electric circuits and outlets. New houses should always be wired with wire that is heavy enough and with a sufficient number of circuits to provide for the loads of electric devices likely to be used today, as well as those not yet invented.

THE KILOWATT-HOUR

Electric power is paid for in terms of watt-hours rather than volts or amperes. The watt is equal to the product of the voltage times the number of amperes.

The **kilowatt-hour,** the most common electric energy unit, is *the energy delivered in an hour at the constant rate of one kilowatt.*

ELECTRIC SERVANTS IN THE HOME

Everyone should be able to make the simple calculations that will make it possible to determine the loads on a given circuit, and the relative cost of operation of the various electrical appliances in the home. If the electric current costs 5¢ per kilowatt-hour, it will then cost 0.005¢ per watt-hour. The label on the appliance will generally list its wattage. The following table lists the wattage of typical appliances and their cost of operation for one hour at 5¢ per kilowatt-hour.

TABLE 58-1

Appliance	Wattage	Cost in Cents per Hour
Clock	2	0.01
Portable fan, radio, mixer, or 100-watt lamp	100	0.50
Vacuum cleaner	125	0.625
Refrigerator	150	0.75
Electric blanket	200	1.00
Television		
black and white	300	1.50
color	500	2.50
Freezer	350	1.75
Furnace fan	800	4.00
Portable heater or range—1 unit	1000	5.00
Toaster, Waffle iron, Coffee maker	1100	5.50
Clothes drier	4500	22.50

It will be noted that the most power is consumed by household appliances that transform electricity into heat.

ELECTRICAL MEASURING INSTRUMENTS

The **galvanometer** consists of *a coil of wire that is moved under the influence of the field of a permanent magnet, when the electric current passes through the coil.* The coil is attached to the pointer, which moves over the scale of the instrument. Of course, the coil could be fixed in position, and the permanent magnet moved, and some instruments are made that way. The relative motion of the coil and magnet may be thought of as the repulsion of like magnetic poles for each other. Galvanometers indicate a flow of current, but they may be so designed and connected in a circuit as *to measure* either *amperes* or *volts*, in which case they are called **ammeters** or **voltmeters**.

THE PRODUCTION OF HEAT BY AN ELECTRIC CURRENT

The production of heat by an electric current resembles the production of heat by friction; in fact, it is the resistance that the electrons encounter as they pass along a conductor that produces heat. If a conductor offered no resistance to the current, there would be no friction and no energy would be lost in the form of heat. The resistance of metals becomes greater as the temperature rises, because, according to one theory, it becomes increasingly difficult for the electrons to pass through the metal as the agitation of the molecules increases.

Certain metals and alloys, such as nichrome (nickel-chromium) wire, have a relatively high **specific resistance** (i.e., a high *resistance for a given length and cross section*), and are, therefore, used for electrical heating devices, such as toasters, irons, heaters, stoves, hot-water heaters, clothes driers, bottle warmers, blankets, and for wires in ceilings, walls, or floors of houses that are used for radiant heating. Most unprotected heating elements burn out eventually, i.e., the wires gradually become oxidized at high temperatures.

Electric welding is a process in which a large current is forced through two adjoining pieces of metal, whose resistance causes them to become so hot that they vaporize at the point of contact, thus making a high-temperature electric arc, hot enough to melt the surrounding metal. Electric furnaces are used to produce alloys such as stainless steel.

INCANDESCENT FILAMENT LAMPS

Thomas A. Edison (1847–1931) was the world's leading inventor. An inventor is not necessarily a scientist, for his researches are in the field of applications of known knowledge rather than in the realm of new contributions to knowledge. Both types of research are important, and it is a rare thing for a man to have ability to do both. Only a few men have this ability; two of them, Lord Kelvin and James Watt, have already been mentioned. Both the scientist and the inventor are benefactors of mankind. Thomas A. Edison was a great inventor because he had fertility of resource, quickness of perception, and, above all, unusual persistence. When Edison needed a material to use for the filament of the incandescent electric lamp, he searched far and wide for vegetable fibers that might carbonize properly, and finally used a strip of carbonized bamboo for the filament in his first lamp.

Among Edison's many important inventions were the phonograph, and the telephone and telegraph improvements already mentioned. In addition, he invented the mimeograph machine, the dictaphone, the motion-picture machine, and many other devices.

Edison's first lamp, made in 1879, contained a carbon filament in an evacuated bulb. If air had not been removed, the carbon would have been oxidized at once. Carbon-filament lamps were the only kind available for twenty-five years. In 1906, the carbon filament was replaced by the more economical tantalum, and tungsten filaments, which can be heated to higher temperatures, and yield a brighter light. The early, tungsten-filament lamps were not very successful, because the tungsten filament was so brittle and fragile that it broke easily, and because it vaporized so rapidly that the lamps had very short lives. W. D. Coolidge, of the Research Laboratory of the General Electric Company, worked for many years trying to accomplish the "impossible" feat of making tungsten ductile. At last his indomitable perseverance, backed by excellent facilities, brought the triumph that made the modern, inexpensive, economical, electric lamp possible. This invention did not solve all of the lamp manufacturer's problems. The bulbs began to blacken inside soon, and grew blacker with use. It was found that the blackening produced by the vaporization of the tungsten filament, and its subsequent deposition on the glass, could be greatly decreased by adding an inert gas like nitrogen or argon. This caused a decrease in the efficiency of the lamps, due to the heat transmitted by the gas, but this was more than overcome, in turn, by using concentrated filaments, or coils of filament. On the other hand, the presence of the inert gas made higher temperatures possible, and a brighter light was produced. The modern gas-filled, tungsten-filament lamp uses about one-fifth to one-sixth as much power as the carbon-filament lamps for the production of the same amount of light. Progress is still being made in the production of lamps with longer lives which produce more light at lower cost. For example, a simple change in the construction of 60-watt lamps, in the United States alone, gave users $12 million worth of additional light for their money in a single year.

SUMMARY

Power Transmission

Electric power is transmitted as high-voltage, low-amperage current to decrease losses due to resistance. Alternating current is used because it is readily transformed by transformers.

Grounding

Electric appliances should be grounded to prevent shocks. In making contacts with any

Figure 58–3. Edison's first successful lamp. (Courtesy, General Electric Company)

electric appliance, the human body should not be grounded. Three-wire outlets and plugs provide for proper grounding.

Induction Coils

Induction coils are used to provide high voltage from direct current.

Current Rectification—Alternating current is changed to direct current by rectifiers. Motor generators may also be used for this purpose.

Home Wiring

An adequate number of circuits and wire of proper size is important. Some appliances that use considerable power require 220-volt circuits, which consist of two 110-volt wires and a ground wire.

Circuit breakers and fuses are safety devices to prevent damage from short circuits or overloading of electric circuits.

Electric Power Units

The kilowatt-hour is the unit of electric power. Home appliances which convert electricity into heat consume the most power.

Incandescent Lamps

An important source of electric lighting is the incandescent lamp, in which a high-resistance wire filament, surrounded by an inert gas in a lamp, is heated to incandescence.

Study Questions

1. DEFINE: rectifier, induction coil, specific resistance, fuse, grounding, short circuit, kilowatt-hour, galvanometer, ammeter, voltmeter.
2. Why is electric power usually transmitted as alternating rather than direct current?
3. Why is electric power transmitted in the form of a high-voltage current?
4. How may alternating current be changed to a direct current?
5. How may the voltage of a direct current be stepped up?
6. How is the high-voltage, direct current, required for the ignition system of an automobile, obtained?
7. Why should electric household appliances be grounded?
8. How may electric household appliances be grounded?
9. Why should a person avoid being grounded when in contact with electric appliances of any kind?
10. Why is it particularly dangerous to touch an electric switch or appliance while taking a bath?
11. What are the relative advantages of fuses and circuit breakers?
12. Why is it that many homes are not wired to meet modern power loads?
13. How may one calculate the power load of the electric devices used on any given electric circuit?
14. What precautions should be observed in the wiring of a new home?
15. In what units is electric power sold? How may one calculate the relative cost of operation of the various electrical devices in the home?
16. If electricity costs 5¢ per kilowatt-hour how much would it cost to operate a 100-watt incandescent lamp for 10 hours?
17. Why should fuses never be replaced by anything but fuses?
18. Why is a circuit breaker safer than a fuse?

Vacuum Tubes and Semiconductors

A cold in the head causes less suffering than an idea.

JULES RENARD

One of the marvels of creation is the infinite capacity of the human brain to with-stand the introduction of knowledge.

THEODORE ROOSEVELT

INTRODUCTION

Electronics deals with the control of electrons. Broadly speaking, all equipment involving an electric current, would come under this heading. However, in practice, **electronics** has come to be the term used to describe *the control of electrons by vacuum tubes and, subsequently, by semiconductors, such as transistors.*

The production of transistors has become a tremendous industry. Transistors, which have replaced vacuum tubes for many purposes, are but the forerunners of many more devices based on the new study of the solid state of matter.

VACUUM TUBES

The crystal detectors, once used in radio receivers, were replaced by two-electrode vacuum tubes. Later, three-electrode vacuum tubes were introduced for receiving and, ultimately, for sending radio waves.

Thomas Edison made the first discovery that led to the modern vacuum tube. In connection with studies to determine the reason that black deposits formed in his incandescent lamps, he placed an insulated plate between the filament and the glass. When this plate was connected with the positive terminal of a battery through a projection fused through the glass, and the filament was connected with the negative pole of the battery, a current of electricity was found to flow through the wire. However, if the poles were reversed, no electric current was obtained. This effect, known as the **Edison effect,** remained unexplained for several years, although Edison rightly concluded that the current somehow leaped across the gap between the plate and the filament. Later experiments showed that this effect was due to *electrons emitted by hot metals.* See Figure 59-1.

Edison made a note of his discovery, but he did nothing about it. Thus, he missed inventing one of the most important devices ever made, i.e., the radio vacuum tube, which is as important as the incandescent filament lamp. Edison might well have concluded that he had discovered a one-way electron valve, but, at that time, there did not seem to be any practical application of the idea.

In an incandescent filament lamp, electrons are emitted by the heated filament. Since there is no place for the electrons to go, they accumulate in the form of a cloud that prevents more electrons from leaving the fila-

443

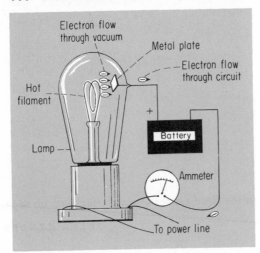

Figure 59–1. The Edison effect. Electrons flow from the filament to the plate when the plate is positively charged, but not when it is negatively charged.

ment. In Edison's tube, the positive plate, connected to the positive terminal of the battery, attracted the electrons. Thus, a path was provided for the electrons, and the circuit was completed. However, when the plate was connected to the negative pole of the battery, the negative charge on the plate repelled the flow of electrons from the heated filament.

It remained for others to apply the Edison effect, first, in the rectification of an alternating current, and second, in radio broadcasting and reception. The rectification of an alternating current, as mentioned in the previous section, can be accomplished in a variety of ways, but the use of a vacuum tube to do this provided a simple, compact device having many applications.

Sir John A. Fleming (1849–1945) improved this tube by making *the positive plate circular in shape, so that it surrounded the filament,* thus greatly increasing the efficiency of the tube as an electron valve. By this time the tube began to look much like a modern radio tube. In this form, it was called a **diode.** It has often been called a **Fleming valve.**

THE THREE-ELECTRODE VACUUM TUBE—THE TRIODE

Lee DeForest (1873–1961) invented the **triode,** in which *an electrified wire grid was*

placed between the heated filament and the plate. In other three-electrode vacuum tubes, the wire grid is replaced by a cylindrical perforated, metal plate. This grid controls the flow of electrons passing between the filament and the plate. If the grid is charged with electrons, it will repel the stream of electrons flowing from the filament to the plate. See Figure 59-2.

On the other hand, if the grid is positively charged relative to the cathode, it produces an opposite electrostatic field, which causes a heavier stream of electrons to flow from the hot filament than would otherwise leave it. Because the grid is much closer to the cathode, a given change in grid voltage has a much greater effect on the total emitted current, than an equal change of plate voltage. The operation of the tube depends upon grid voltage rather than current, thus making it possible to produce large changes in current in the plate circuit for very small input power to the grid. If the grid is furnished with a varying potential, corresponding variations in the flow of current through the tube will be produced. Since the variations in the current, flowing from the filament to the plate, may be much greater than the variations in the grid potential, it is possible to use the tube to detect and amplify variations of current, which could not otherwise be observed.

A single triode generally steps up voltage from five to twenty times. For use in radio circuits, the larger the number of triodes used, the greater the total amount of amplification. Only six tubes would amplify the voltage at least one million times. Thus, the triode tube could control a stream of electrons, interrupting it, reducing it, stopping it, or amplifying it. From this basic discovery came the tech-

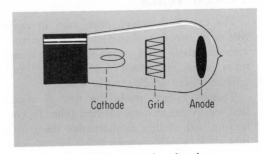

Cathode Grid Anode

Figure 59–2. A triode radio tube.

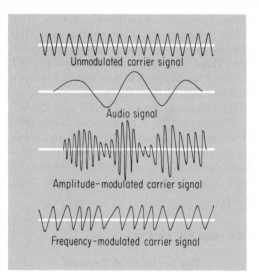

Figure 59–3. A comparison of amplitude and frequency modulation.

nology of radio, television, radar, electronic calculators, and many other devices.

Triodes made it possible for radio broadcasting stations to transmit variations on a carrier wave. By the use of induction coils and capacitors, high-frequency waves may be produced. They may then be amplified and carried to the antenna, which sends them out as carrier waves. These carrier waves may be varied (modulated) by feeding variations in an electric current produced by the sounds received by a microphone, into the carrier-wave circuit. These *variations in the electric current produce changes in the amplitude,* but not in the frequency of the carrier waves;

this change is called **amplitude modulation** (AM radio). *The frequency* of the carrier wave *may be modulated* instead of its amplitude; this change is called **frequency modulation** (FM radio). Frequency modulation has the advantage that electrical disturbances, such as lightning flashes, sparks from induction coils, and faulty automobile ignition systems will not produce static, which is so common in amplitude modulation. See Figure 59-3.

Edwin H. Armstrong (1890–1954) invented frequency modulation. Frequency modulation has the limitation that it employs ultrashort, radio waves, and, therefore, broadcasting beyond the horizon is not possible, because the ultrashort radio waves are not reflected back to the earth, as are the longer radio waves, by the ionized layer of gases known as the Heaviside layer, or ionosphere, in the upper atmosphere. This limitation of frequency-modulation broadcasting is really an advantage because there is no interference from distant stations. If two stations, using frequency modulation, were broadcasting on the same frequency, only the more powerful station would be heard. Frequency modulation makes possible many more broadcasting stations, and makes operation costs of a station much lower, because less power is required.

THE RADIO RECEIVER

The radio receiver reverses the process of the radio transmitter. First, the feeble current

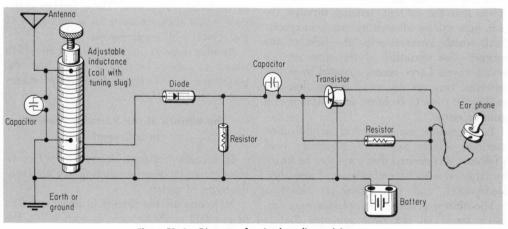

Figure 59–4. Diagram of a simple radio receiving set.

produced by the radio waves, as they move relative to the antenna, induces a current in the grid circuit. Keep in mind that an electric current is produced when electromagnetic lines of force move relative to a conductor, or vice versa. Then the radio receiver must be tuned to the frequency of the carrier wave sent out by the broadcasting station. Each broadcasting station will have its own particular frequency in a given section of the country, in order to avoid overlapping of programs. The receiver is tuned by turning a knob that turns a set of movable plates in the capacitor. The variations in the carrier wave produced by the sound waves are unscrambled by a triode to produce variations in an electric current. This current is then amplified by a string of triodes, and sent to the coil of a loud speaker, or a telephone receiver. Figure 59-4 shows the principle of a simple radio receiving set that employs a triode.

LOUDSPEAKERS AND MICROPHONES

Less distortion and greater volume of sound are obtained with the use of loudspeakers than with telephone receivers. In loudspeakers of the dynamic type, the current is sent through a coil of wire attached to a cone-shaped diaphragm. This coil surrounds a permanent magnet, or an electromagnet operated by a direct current. As the current in the coil varies, it causes the coil, with attached diaphragm, to vibrate back and forth. This can be easily understood when one considers that the current, passing through the coil, sets up an alternating, electromagnetic field, which interacts with the field of the magnet. The vibration of the cone sets up sound waves. Large cones, operated by strong currents, may set up sound waves that will enable the voice to be heard at a distance of a mile or more.

Loudspeakers and electrical amplification are now widely and very effectively used whenever it is desired that a speaker be heard by large crowds. A combination of amplifier, loudspeaker, and microphone is called a public-address system. Microphones were formerly based on the same principle that is employed in carbon-particle telephone transmitters, except that a double button, with carbon granules on each side of the diaphragm, permitted more faithful reproduction. These were too poor in response, and produced an undesirable hiss that led to their abandonment. Modern studio microphones are of the condenser type, in which one "plate" of a condenser is a light metal diaphragm, whose motion, caused by sound waves, alters the capacity of the condenser, and thus produces oscillations in the circuit. A number of other types of microphones are also used today.

THE SOLID STATE

The Surfaces of Crystals

One would expect the surface atoms of crystals to have special properties. Interior atoms in crystals bond in three dimensions, but this is not possible for surface atoms.

Finely divided charcoal or silica gel is used in gas masks to adsorb poisonous materials in the air. This process is selective and only polar molecules are adsorbed. Covalent molecules, like the nitrogen or oxygen molecules in the air, are not adsorbed. Poisonous substances are nearly always polar in nature, and are therefore adsorbed.

Defects in Crystals

Crystals are usually not pure. They *may grow around portions of gases or liquid solutions that have been adsorbed on their surfaces.* Such impurities are called **entrained,** or occluded, impurities. These foreign materials would show up upon the examination of the crystal with a microscope.

Another type of impurity is that in which traces of other substances enter into the empty spaces in a crystal. These empty spaces also represent defects.

The Nature of the Particles Present in a Crystal

In metallic crystals, electrons are free to wander about, thus accounting for the conductivity of metals.

Molecules are not present in ionic, metallic, or covalent solids because, in such solids, the ions or atoms form a giant particle similar to a molecule in structure. In a molecular solid, discrete molecules are joined to each other. Covalent molecules and ionic crystals are nonconductors of electricity. This fact indicates that the electrons in these crystals are not free to move about in the crystal.

Semiconductors

Some conductors conduct electricity to a limited extent, and they are therefore called **semiconductors.** Unlike metallic conductors, the electrical conductivity of semiconductors increases with an increase in temperature. In semiconductors, according to the electronic theory, there are holes or voids where electrons are needed to complete their stable arrangements. There are also free electrons present. An increase in temperature increases the number of free electrons.

Semiconductors are crystals, generally having a low conductivity, that are highly sensitive to light, radioactive irradiation, temperature, and impurities. The crystal detector, used in early radio receivers, is a semiconductor.

Thousands of different compounds may act as semiconductors, but their possible uses must await their preparation in the very high degree of purity required.

Transistors—Electronic vacuum tubes are now being replaced by transistors. In 1948, the transistor was invented by John Bardeen (1908–   ), W. H. Brattain (1902–   ), and William Shockley (1910–   ). The word **transistor** comes from its function, i.e., *it transfers an electric signal* across a resistor.

The early transistors consisted of silicon or germanium crystals having very small amounts of impurities. These crystals act like semiconductors in which the electrons bound up in the crystals are easily freed. Two of these types of transistors were called the point-contact type and the junction type. The point-contact type serves as an excellent high-speed switch for computers, and television and frequency-modulation radio receivers that operate at high frequencies. The junction-type transistor consists of layers of germanium or silicon of different types, the negative and positive types. Junction-type transistors have many applications. Depending upon the type of circuit used, they can amplify either voltage or current.

The Electron Theory of the Junction Transistor—Heat or light increases the conductivity of a semiconductor, such as germanium, because the crystal gives up electrons readily, and the motion of the free electrons constitutes an electric current. This *motion of free electrons* is called the **n-type (negative type) conductivity.** At the point where an electron is knocked out of the crystal, there is a broken bond or "hole" left by the electron. An electron from an adjacent bond may jump into the "hole" thus restoring the original bond, but leaving a new "hole." The *"hole" may thus travel in a direction opposite to that of the electrons, through the crystal, acting like a positive charge.* This type of conductivity is called **p-type (positive type).** Semiconductors may be made so as to be almost entirely one type or the other, by introducing minute amounts of impurities into

Figure 59–5. A tiny transistor used as an amplifier. (Courtesy, Bell Telephone Laboratories)

germanium or silicon before or during crystallization.

The boundaries between the two types are called *p-n* junctions, and serve as rectifiers. If direct current is applied to a crystal containing both types, so that the electrons and holes are both directed toward the junction, an electric current will flow; but, if the direction of the current is reversed, the electrons and holes will be pulled away from the junction and there will be no conduction. Multiple junctions such as *p-n-p*, or *n-p-n* make possible junction-type transistors, which may amplify either the voltage or the amperage.

Transistors, smaller than a grain of wheat, amplify current a hundred times or more, and are useful for high frequencies. Some transistors act like rectifiers to convert alternating current into direct current, and others reverse this process.

Advantages of Transistors—Vacuum tubes must be heated in order to drive electrons from the cathodes; the result is that they do not operate until they have been warmed up. In the transistor, however, the heat of the coldest day is sufficient to drive electrons from the impurities present; hence they do not require a warm-up period. They may be made very small, and thus make possible more compact electronic devices.

Applications of Transistors—Transistors may do anything that a vacuum tube can do, and they can usually do it better, quicker, and more economically. Transistors, together with printed circuits, tunnel diodes and other devices, discussed below, have made possible the miniaturization of many devices. Pocket radios are one application. Another is a midget broadcasting set, which can operate on the energy furnished by the sound waves of the human voice. Automobile radios, which use transistors, use about one-tenth as much power as radios using vacuum tubes. Therefore, they can operate for a much longer time without causing their batteries to run down.

Modern Semiconductor Developments

The *Tunnel Diode*—The **tunnel diode** *is about the size of a pinhead, about 1 per cent of the size of a transistor it replaces,* and uses about 1 per cent of the power required for the operation of a transistor. Also, it is about 100 times faster than a transistor. Like the transistor, it amplifies signals and controls electrical impulses. It contains a higher percentage of impurities than does a transistor. The impurities form a thin barrier in the crystal through which electrons tunnel. The use of tunnel diodes can make it possible to produce computing devices much smaller than present ones, which will operate at much greater speeds.

INTEGRATED CIRCUITS— MICROELECTRONICS

The integrated circuit is a part of the new technology called microelectronics or mole-

Figure 59–6. A Silicon power rectifier. This tiny semiconductor does the work of seven selenium-power rectifiers. (Courtesy, Bell Telephone Laboratories)

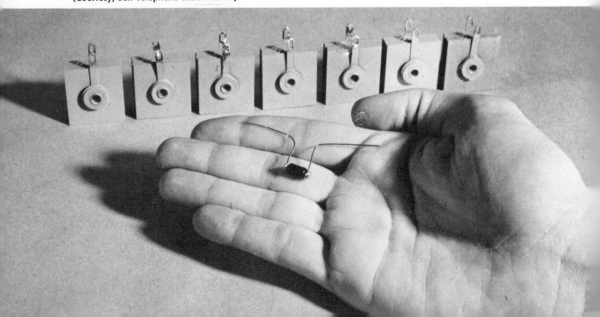

tronics (molecular electronics). It consists of a single chip of silicon, about 0.005 inch thick and $\frac{1}{16}$ inch long. By embedding microscopic particles of impurities in different parts of the chips, a number of units equivalent to transistors, diodes, etc. can be placed within the chip. These units are then connected by etching and other processes to form complete circuits, rather than a network of soldered components. The final product is encased in a container about the size of a button on a man's shirt. Inside the container, there may be the equivalent of ten or more different components, such as transistors, resistors, and rectifiers.

Integrated circuits make possible improved hearing aids and miniature electronic computers for rockets and satellites.

SUMMARY

Edison made the basic discovery that led to the development of vacuum tubes. The diode, based on his discovery, can serve as an electron valve. Triodes, the three-electrode vacuum tubes, can perform in any or all of the following ways:

1. convert radio-frequency electric currents into audio-frequency currents (detector tubes).

2. amplify electric currents (amplifier).

3. generate high-frequency radio carrier waves (oscillator).

4. rectify alternating current (rectifier).

Electromagnetic waves of very high frequency, such as are used for FM radio transmission, are not reflected by the Heaviside layer.

Either the frequency or the amplitude of carrier waves may be modulated.

The study of the solid state of matter is leading to many scientific advances, one of which is semiconductors. Transistors and other semiconductors will do everything that a vacuum tube will do. They do not require a warm-up time as do vacuum tubes. They require very little power. They are quite rugged, and may be very small, thus making possible the miniaturization of many types of electronic devices.

Study Questions

1. DEFINE: electronics, diode, triode, transistor, semiconductor, Edison effect, amplitude modulation, frequency modulation, Fleming valve, entrained impurity, n-type conductivity, p-type conductivity, tunnel diode.
2. What contribution did Edison make to the radio?
3. Explain what is meant by tuning.
4. Explain the action of the vacuum tube. For what purposes may vacuum tubes be used?
5. How are electromagnetic waves produced?
6. Describe the different types of vacuum tubes, and give the use of each.
7. What is the function of the ordinary radio receiving tube?
8. What is the principle of microphones?
9. What is the principle of the dynamic loudspeaker?
10. How does frequency modulation differ from ordinary radio broadcasting?
11. What are the advantages and disadvantages of frequency modulation?
12. Why is the range of FM broadcasting usually limited to the horizon?
13. Differentiate between frequency modulation and amplitude modulation.
14. Name two discoveries that made possible the miniaturization of electronic devices.
15. What is the nature of a semiconductor?
16. Explain how a triode acts as a rectifier.
17. How do transistors differ from tunnel diodes?

The Photoelectric Effect

We have a strong feeling that in a few years' time data communication will actually exceed, in sheer volume, communications of speech.

FREDERICK R. KAPPEL

INTRODUCTION

The simple discovery that *light would cause metals and other substances to emit electrons, to become better electrical conductors, or even to produce electric currents,* has had many important applications, suggesting the possibility of even more important things to come. This effect, called the **photoelectric effect,** is employed in photoelectric cells, the modern all-seeing "electric eyes."

PLANCK'S QUANTUM THEORY

Maxwell's electromagnetic theory of light explained many aspects of the nature of light, such as its method of transmission, its refraction by lenses, and its reflection, but it failed to explain some of the facts of radiation from a black body. Max Planck derived a theory that assumed that light was emitted in the form of discrete amounts of energy, which he called quanta, rather than continuously. His theory may be summarized as follows: *The electron can gain or lose energy only by making jumps from one discrete level to another. The energy emitted or absorbed by the electron during one of these jumps* is called a **quantum** (plural: **quanta**).

THE PHOTOELECTRIC EFFECT

H. R. Hertz had observed that a spark would jump more readily between the electrodes of his receiver of electromagnetic waves if they were irradiated with light. This was especially true of the radiation from the sparks of his transmitter, which was rich in ultraviolet wavelengths. Later, it was shown that the ultraviolet radiation caused electrons to be expelled from the receiver, which aided in the conduction of the electricity between the electrodes.

A simple device to demonstrate the production of electrons when radiant energy strikes a metallic surface is to connect a metallic plate to an uncharged electroscope. If an ultraviolet radiation source, such as a mercury vapor lamp, is used to irradiate the metallic plate the leaves of the electroscope will be observed to diverge. The leaves may be shown to have a positive charge, which means that negative charges (electrons) had been driven from the plate by the radiation. *This emission of electrons from metal surfaces when they are irradiated with electromagnetic radiation of certain wavelengths is* called the **photoelectric effect.**

The explanation of the photoelectric effect is based on the idea that the electrons in a metallic conductor are fairly free to move, but that the surface presents a barrier which they cannot surmount, unless they are given additional energy. The absorption of electromagnetic radiation by the electron furnishes this necessary energy.

Not all metals and not all wavelengths of radiant energy produce the photoelectric effect. For example, ultraviolet and shorter wavelengths will cause any metal to emit electrons, but visible light works only for the alkali metals, cesium, potassium and sodium, and the alkaline earth metals—calcium, strontium, and barium—which are high in the electronegativity series. (See page 259.) Blue wavelengths of light will eject electrons from sodium, but red wavelengths will not do so.

Experiments show that the number of electrons ejected depends upon the intensity of the radiation, but that their velocity is independent of the intensity of the radiation. However, the velocity of the ejected electrons does increase with an increase in the frequency of the radiation. As the frequency of the radiation is decreased, there will be a point where no electrons will be ejected. These ideas may be summarized in the following **laws of photoelectricity:**

1. *The number of electrons ejected is proportional to the intensity of the radiation striking the metal.*

2. *The maximum energy of the ejected electrons is independent of the intensity of the radiation.*

3. *For every metal there is a frequency below which electrons will not be ejected.*

4. *The maximum energy of the electrons depends on the frequency of the radiation.*

EINSTEIN'S PHOTON THEORY

The above laws could not be explained by Maxwell's theory. For example, his theory required that the intensity of radiation would determine both the number of electrons ejected and their velocities. The observation of the photoelectric effect of Hertz in 1890, and Planck's quantum theory, advanced in 1900, remained unexplained until 1905, when Albert Einstein proposed his photon theory of light.

Einstein's theory postulated that light is propagated through space in the form of individual *packets of energy* which he called **photons.** When a photon strikes a metal surface it gives up its entire energy to an electron and ceases to exist. If the photon has enough energy, the electron will be ejected from the metal. The amount of energy possessed by a photon was assumed to increase with the fre-

quency of the radiation. An increase in the intensity of radiation is the result of an increase in the number of photons rather than the energy of a photon. However, a photon, which represents radiation of greater frequency, will contain more energy than those of lesser frequency, and can thus accomplish more than many photons of lesser frequency.

According to the photon theory, the intensity of radiation depends on the closeness of the spacing of photons. As light spreads out from a given source, its intensity decreases because the photons become farther apart. When dealing with light in the usual experiments involving refraction, reflection, interference, diffraction, and polarization, we are working with enormous numbers of photons which travel in the form of waves, but when we are dealing with emission phenomena we are concerned with individual photons, and it is here that the particle-like nature of radiant energy becomes important.

THE COMPTON EFFECT

In 1923, A. H. Compton (1892–1962) observed that all substances will scatter X rays diffusely, i.e., in all directions. According to the classical electromagnetic theory, the scattered radiation should include the same wavelengths as the incident X rays. However, the scattered wavelengths included some wavelengths longer than those of the incident radiation. His explanation, which was strictly in accord with his experimental data, furnished additional evidence for the photon theory.

THE PHOTOTUBE

The photoelectric effect is very similar to the Edison effect. In the basic diode, electrons are emitted when certain metals are heated. These same metals will emit electrons when they are irradiated with certain wavelengths of radiant energy, depending upon the nature of the metal. The phototube, sometimes called a photoelectric cell, may be either gas-filled or of a high-vacuum type. It has no grid, but it does have two electrodes. Electrons are ejected from the cathode when it is irradiated. They are then attracted to the anode.

The small amount of electric current produced is then amplified by vacuum tube, or semiconductor amplifiers. A high-vacuum type of phototube is used in applications where great stability and instant response to light changes is necessary. The gas-filled tubes are used in applications requiring extreme sensitivity. They have a higher output than the vacuum-type tube. Phototubes can be designed to operate on either light, ultraviolet, or infrared radiation. The cathode is coated with a light-sensitive material, such as cesium.

PHOTOCONDUCTIVE DEVICES

There are other electronic devices that are sensitive to light. Thus, **photoconductive devices** *are based on the fact that certain substances, such as selenium, change in electrical resistance when exposed to light.* Selenium, for instance, greatly decreases in resistance when light shines on it. For some time selenium cells have been used to turn lights on at sunset and turn them off at sunrise. Selenium cells are unstable and relatively slow in responding to changes in light intensity.

Another kind of photoelectric cell is *the type that produces a current of electricity without the aid of an outside potential,* such as is needed for the types of cells mentioned above. These devices are called **photovoltaic** cells, and are very useful for measuring illumination, inasmuch as the current generated is sufficient to be registered by a microammeter, thus providing direct readings. These cells are widely used as "light meters" for photography and other purposes.

APPLICATIONS OF PHOTOELECTRIC TUBES

The kinds of jobs done by photoelectric tubes are generally familiar. Door openers depend upon the interruption of a light falling on a photoelectric cell. This results in a cutting off of the electric current that causes the door-opening mechanism to operate. This same idea can be applied in setting off burglar alarms, in which invisible wavelengths are used to activate the photoelectric tube. Hundreds, and perhaps thousands of different applications of photoelectric tubes depend upon the interruption of a beam of light. Automatic counting devices are typical of such applications. For example, in the Holland Vehicular Tunnel, photoelectric cells are used to count the vehicles, to turn on the fans when needed, and to warn toll takers to refuse admittance to trucks that are too high to clear the roof of the tunnel.

Photoelectric tubes may be made so as to be sensitive to different colors, and they may therefore be used in color matching. One application of color matching is the process control of coffee roasting, in which a light is directed upon the beans as they pass a window in the roaster. The quality of the light reflected from them depends upon how well done they are. When the beans are the right color, they are automatically ejected from the roaster. The spectrophotometer can detect two million different shades of color, and provide such specific information concerning any color, in terms of wavelengths, that it can be matched precisely on the basis of this information.

Many different kinds of sorting devices depend upon the use of photoelectric tubes. For example, in industry they are used to sort out cans that pass through a labeling machine without labels, or to sort out cigars.

Still other applications of photoelectric tubes depend upon their ability to distinguish between different light intensities. Thus, a photoelectric tube may be used to detect excessive belching of smoke from a chimney.

It is impossible to estimate how many workers have been displaced, or are at least not required, because of the ability of photoelectric tubes to perform such functions as counting, sorting, and grading. These functions can be carried out reliably and at low cost, thus cutting the costs of production, and freeing workers from such dull, routine tasks.

Photoelectric tubes are used to maintain precise register in color printing, and to detect minute holes in metallic sheets. However, all of the above applications are minor in importance to such applications as the sound-motion picture, television, the electron microscope, telephoto and facsimile transmission, and solar batteries mentioned below.

Figure 60–1. The Bell solar battery. This battery furnishes power directly to a telephone line. It will furnish power even in poor light. This typical application of the solar battery is one in which not much power is required. It requires very little attention and is recommended for remote places. (Courtesy, Bell Telephone Laboratories)

PHOTOTRANSISTORS AND THE SOLAR BATTERY

The **phototransistor** is similar to an electronic amplifying transistor except that *it is controlled by light rather than by an electric current*. It differs from a photoelectric tube in that it has no glass envelope, and it has no vacuum.

The Bell solar battery is an application of phototransistors. Such a battery is shown in Figure 60-1. The Bell experimental solar battery was first applied to furnish power for a telephone line, in 1955. It is not likely that the scientists who developed this battery could visualize its successful use in a "Telestar" communications satellite, by which television in color was transmitted from Europe to the United States, ten years later. Figure 60-2 shows this satellite under construction. The solar cell is made from a single, very pure, silicon crystal containing a trace of arsenic. A thin wafer is sawed off, and heated in a quartz tube with boron, which diffuses into the surface layer of the silicon. These wafers are then wired to other wafers to form the solar battery. This battery is capable of gen-

erating electric power from sunlight, at the rate of 90 watts per square yard of illuminated surface. Not all of the wavelengths of solar radiation may be changed into electricity, but about 45 per cent may be changed, which is enough to make the process practical.

In 1960, an experimental electric automobile was adapted to operate with 10,000 solar cells, mounted on a 26 square-foot panel on

Figure 60–2. An experimental "Telstar" communications satellite intended for use in overseas television transmission. Power to operate the satellite is furnished by batteries of solar cells which are covered with sapphires to protect the cells from space radiation. (Courtesy, Bell Telephone Laboratories)

the roof. Solar batteries served the Vanguard I solar-powered transmitters for almost three years.

Atomic batteries have been devised, on the principle of the solar battery, to change radiation from a radioactive isotope of strontium into electricity.

THE ELECTRON GUN AND THE OSCILLOSCOPE

The cathode-ray tube, used in the oscilloscope, is similar to the television receiving tube. The cathode-ray tube contains an electron gun, which emits a beam of electrons from a hot filament. Figure 60-3 shows the plan of the cathode-ray tube. The stream of electrons from the hot filament passes through a circular aperture in a negative electrode that controls the intensity of the beam. The electrons then pass through a circular aperture in a positive electrode that serves to attract and accelerate them. Next, the electrons pass through another aperture, which limits the size of the beam. Finally, the beam is focused by a magnetic, or electric field. If an electric or magnetic deflector is added, we have the basic principle of the cathode-ray tube, or the television tube. The purpose of the deflecting electrodes or coils is to cause the beam to move vertically or horizontally. When the beam strikes a fluorescent screen, it produces a luminous spot that moves with the beam.

The oscilloscope uses the cathode-ray tube to measure anything that can be expressed as variations in an electric current, such as pressure, temperature, and speed. The tube operates at the speed of light, but it has no memory and it makes no records. A special tube, the memotron, holds the tracings until they are erased. Another tube, the tonotron, will do the same thing.

The television receiver is a special type of cathode-ray tube, in which the cathode ray moves in perfect synchronization with the motion of the light in the camera tube. The television camera uses the principle of photoelectricity to change light into electric signals. The tube contains a nonconductive plate, covered with thousands of tiny silver globules, each one of which is coated with light-sensitive cesium. Each little globule serves as a photoelectric cell. A typical camera lens focuses the picture on the plate, and a beam of electrons sweeps across the plate in horizontal lines at the rate of 525 lines every $\frac{1}{30}$ second. Each globule gives off electrons when light falls on it according to the intensity of the light. The globule thus becomes positively charged. Then the lost electrons are restored by electrons streaming from the electron gun. Each time an electron is restored, an electric impulse is created in the metal backing sheet, and is sent over an attached wire, amplified, and broadcast.

THE ELECTRON MICROSCOPE

In 1926, H. Busch showed that symmetrical electric and magnetic fields act on streams of electrons much like lenses act on light rays, thus establishing the principle on which the cathode-ray tube operates. This same principle is applied in the electron microscope, in which electron beams take the place of light, and

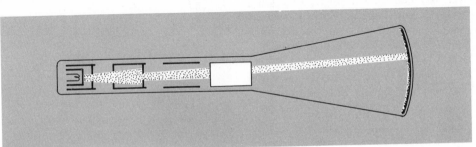

Figure 60–3. A cathode-ray tube. At the left end of the tube is an electron gun. To the right of it is one of a pair of deflection plates. Further along is another pair of plates at right angles to the first. By means of these four plates the beam can be made to paint an image on the fluorescent material which coats the end of the tube. (Courtesy, *Scientific American.*)

electric or magnetic fields take the place of the lenses. The electrons form images on a fluorescent screen or photographic film, and reveal far more detail than is possible with a light microscope. Magnification of about 100,000 times is possible with the electron microscope as compared to only about 2,000 times for a light microscope.

A light microscope is limited by the wavelengths of light and cannot resolve, or see, two points at a distance apart closer than the wavelength of the light used. The wavelength of an electron is much smaller and for that reason it has greater resolving power than light has. Up to this point, nothing has been said about the wave motion of electrons. In 1927, C. J. Davisson and L. H. Germer obtained photographs with moving electrons which showed diffraction patterns that could only be explained on the basis of waves. Now, an electron is considered to be a particle of matter, having a mass about $\frac{1}{1,845}$ the mass of a proton, and yet it behaves like radiant energy when it is in motion.

TELEPHOTO TRANSMISSION OF PHOTOGRAPHS

In 1947, the 1037-page book, *Gone With the Wind*, was transmitted in ninety seconds by Ultrafax, which combined high-speed photography and television. Ultrafax is the abbreviation of ultrafacsimile. **Facsimile transmission** is *an application of photoelectricity*. It is *based on the same principle as the television camera, in that a picture is illuminated a portion at a time*, and the light is then picked up with a phototube, and changed into a fluctuating electric current. The receiving set uses an electric light, which is sensitive to variations in the electric current, to produce an image on a photographic film.

SOUND, MOTION-PICTURE PROJECTORS

The sound, motion-picture projector has a phototube that converts the sound signals into electric signals. When the motion-picture film is made, variations in sound are changed into variations in an electric current controlling a beam of light that shines on the film, thus

producing the sound track. In the sound, motion-picture projector, a light beam passes through this sound track onto a phototube, which changes the variations in light to variations in an electric current. This electric current is then used to reproduce the original sound by use of a loudspeaker.

SUMMARY

Certain metals, notably the alkali metals, emit electrons when light shines on them. This is the photoelectric effect.

Certain substances, such as selenium, change in electric resistance when exposed to light, thus forming the basis for the photoconductive type of cell.

Certain combinations of substances will produce an electric current, without any outside source of electricity, thus forming the basis for photovoltaic cells.

Planck's Quantum Theory

A vibrating electron possesses energy in discrete packets called quanta, and it can gain or lose energy only in terms of multiples of these quanta.

Einstein's Photon Theory

Light is propagated through space in the form of individual packets of energy called photons. The amount of energy possessed by a photon increases with the frequency of the radiation. The intensity of radiation depends upon the number of photons.

Study Questions

1. DEFINE: photoelectric effect, quantum, photon, photoconductive cell, photovoltaic cell, phototransistor, facsimile transmission.
2. What is the function of the phototube in sound motion picture projectors?
3. What are some of the outstanding applications of the phototube?
4. Give the principle of the solar battery.
5. What are some of the applications of the solar battery?
6. List some of the things that phototubes will do to advantage in factories.
7. How may phototubes be used in burglar alarm systems?
8. What are the advantages of facsimile transmission?

9. For what is the oscilloscope used?
10. What is the basic principle of the television camera?
11. Why is it that an electron microscope has a higher magnification than the light microscope?
12. Explain the operation of automatic door openers that use photoelectric cells.
13. What determines the velocity of ejected electrons in the photoelectric effect?
14. How does the intensity of radiation affect the electrons ejected in the photoelectric effect?

CHAPTER 61

Electronics

Within a single generation, the science of electronics has contrived to revolutionize our way of life.

V. K. ZWORYKIN

I have no doubt that electronic computers are going to have a greater impact upon our society than atomic energy! In 15 to 20 years, perhaps less, the electronic-computer industry will be equal to the entire automotive industry.

JOHN W. CARR, III

INTRODUCTION

Electronics *deals with the flow of electrons through a vacuum or through gases, rather than through a wire.* It started with the vacuum tubes used in radio, as discussed in Chapter 59. Many types of vacuum tubes such as Phanotrons, Kenetrons, Pliotrons, Pentodes, and Thyratrons were soon developed for special purposes, and they were put to work in industry to measure and control industrial processes. They could measure and record temperature, light, time, voltage, power, weight, length, color, density, viscosity, turbidity, humidity, pressure, and electric conductivity. On the basis of such information, they could be used to control industrial processes. Prior to World War II, vacuum-tube electronics was spreading rapidly, but it was a mere drop in the bucket compared with what was to come.

During World War II, new types of tubes were invented, such as the cavity magnetron, and the klystron, which produced ultrashort (micro) radio waves of considerable power. These tubes were used to produce the microwaves used in radar to track airplanes and ships, to control gunfire and searchlights, and

for night fighter airplanes. The principle was that of transmitting microwaves, which were reflected back to the sender, in such a way as to indicate the distance and direction of the reflecting object. Radar came into use for blind landings for airplanes, and in the Loran system of navigation. The principle of radar was applied in the proximity fuse, which was used to explode shells as they neared their targets.

POST WAR ELECTRONIC DEVELOPMENTS

After World War II, microwaves came into use in microwave relay towers, which, supplemented by coaxial cables, made possible cross-country transmission of many simultaneous messages and television programs.

Vacuum tubes were then put to work in electronic calculators and data-processing machines. These complex devices were based on the simple idea that vaccum tubes can be made to switch a current off and on, billions of times per second. The possible applications of such machines in business and in government were tremendous. They could maintain inventory records, make out payrolls, and bill customers for insurance or electricity bills. In government, they could be used in maintaining social security records, handling census data, and eventually in processing mail. However, their first important applications were in the defense industry, as mentioned in Chapter 42.

These vacuum-tube electronic computers were limited somewhat because the tubes gave off too much heat, and required too much power. They were not reliable. For example, one of the early computers, the Eniac, had 18,000 vacuum tubes, any one of which was likely to burn out at any time. The equipment required considerable space, and required special provisions for cooling.

Vacuum tubes also had the disadvantage that they were poor detectors of very-short-wave signals. During World War II, scientists turned back to the idea of the original crystal detectors, and developed synthetic crystals. The study of such crystals led to the development of semiconductors, discussed in Chapter 59. Transistors played an important role in the new space age, in making possible miniature devices to operate satellites and relay information back to the earth. Within ten years of their invention, compact computers

were developed in which transistors replaced vacuum tubes, and the manufacture of electronic computers became a big business. Transistors and printed circuits soon made possible many different kinds of miniature electronic devices. Electronic research advanced rapidly. Microelectronic circuits were used in revolutionary, IBM System/360, data-processing machines announced by the International Business Machines Corporation in 1964. Transistors mounted in the circuits are only 0.028 inch square and are protected by glass films 60 millionths of an inch thick.

Not all of the recent electronic developments have centered on the use of semiconductors. New types of electron tubes have also been devised. For example, the nuvistor is a tiny electron tube that can be used in a scanning machine to read typed pages, and convert the characters into electrical signals at the rate of 200 per second. They can read numbers and punctuation marks, as well as letters, and store the information on punched paper tape, which may then be used to operate typewriters of a special kind. Other methods have also been invented to perform the function of character reading.

Compactons are tiny vacuum tubes that can do the work of five ordinary radio vacuum

Figure 61–1. An IBM 7080 Electronic Data Processing System used by the Pacific Gas and Electric Company for billing customers, accounting, payrolls, etc. (Courtesy, Pacific Gas and Electric Company)

Figure 61–2. An electrostatic printer tube. The tubes can print up to 20,000 characters per second. (Courtesy, Raytheon Company)

tubes or seven transistors. They may perform many functions, and they may be made even smaller than transistors.

The Raytheon printer-type tube deposits an electrostatic charge on a special paper which is developed in positively charged ink. The printing element is made of fine wires, imbedded in glass, that transmit electrons from the cathode ray tube to the outside surface. Such tubes are used in electronic machines, which can print 2 million labels in an 8-hour day.

THE LASER (Light Amplification by *Stimulated Emission of Radiation*)

The laser represents one of the most fascinating modern electronic developments because it opens up a wide range of new applications. The first successful laser was demonstrated in 1960. In this device, a flash tube was used to supply energy to electrons associated with chromium atoms in a ruby crystal. Electrons, thus "pumped" to an unnaturally high energy level by light from the flash tube, gave up their excess energy in the form of red light, when stimulated by light of the same wavelength. In a sort of chain reaction, all of the electrons gave off light of the same frequency, and the ruby emitted a brilliant flash of coherent light. Later experiments showed that laser action could be obtained by use of solids other than the ruby, and even by gases. However, all of these

Figure 61–3. An electrostatic printer tube printing labels for a magazine. (Courtesy, Raytheon Company)

devices used light-input sources, and the resulting light beam was very difficult to modulate.

The injection laser operates by supplying the energy input by passing an electric current through a semiconductor p-n junction, which results in the production of a continuous source of photons. It is a simple matter to modulate the semiconductor diode light output by simply modulating the incoming electric current.

One of the most useful features of the light emitted by lasers is that a very narrow beam is produced, spreading out very little as it travels through space. The great interest in lasers is largely the result of the fact that they produce nearly **coherent radiation** (i.e., *radiation of one wavelength only*), at much higher frequencies than radio wavelengths. Thus, they have the potential of providing communication channels with thousands of times the capacity of present overloaded radio channels.

THERMISTORS (THERMIONIC CONVERTERS)

Thomas John Seebeck, in 1821, discovered that *heating a circuit made up of two different metals produced an electric current.* This effect, called the **thermoelectric effect** is often called the **Seebeck effect** in recognition of his discovery although he did not realize its true significance. In 1834, Jean Charles Athanase Peltier discovered the reverse effect, namely that *the passage of an electric current through the junction of two different conductors would result in cooling or heating, depending upon the direction of current flow.* This effect is called the **Peltier effect.**

One of the important developments in electronics is in the field of thermoelectricity, in which miniature semiconductors, called thermistors and frigistors, are destined to play an important role. A **frigistor** consists of *a thermocouple or a semiconductor that cools when an electric current passes in one direction, and heats when the direction of the current is reversed.* Frigistors have already been applied in the manufacture of small, silent refrigerators with no moving parts. A possible application of thermistors would be wall panels that would heat or cool a room as desired.

Thermistors *can be used to generate either direct or alternating electricity directly from heat,* but their efficiency is low, only about 14 per cent. However, they offer possibilities in applications where the cost of equipment is of more concern than the cost of energy. For example, remote farms in Russia enjoy the advantages of electric lights and radio, thanks to the electric power obtained from a kerosene-heated thermoelectric generator.

Thermistors build up a resistance when the temperature increases, and this effect can be applied in temperature control systems. For example, they have been used to control the temperature of bottle warmers and hostess carts.

MAGNETOHYDRODYNAMIC GENERATORS

Hot ionized gases, when moved through a magnetic field, behave like the motion of an electric conductor in a magnetic field, which is the principle of the electric generator. **Magnetohydrodynamic** electric **generators** are made possible by super-conducting magnets. A great deal of research is being devoted to the investigation of this revolutionary method for the generation of electric power.

ELECTRONIC DATA-PROCESSING MACHINES

Computers, data-processing machines, and other machines use electronic devices to read, write, translate, memorize, and carry out complex mathematical calculations at lightning speeds. Some of these experimental machines can read printed material, understand some spoken words, monitor the operations in chemical plants, and operate controls to keep them running smoothly. They may operate metal working machines, and make engineering drawings or weather maps, using the data furnished them. These machines are not smart, but they are amazingly accurate and fast. They have to be told what to do, but instructions do not need to be repeated, and they are not forgotten. Modern electronic

Figure 61–4. This machine reads many styles of printing. It makes possible the processing of a wide range of printed material automatically without first converting it into machine language for data processing systems. (Courtesy, International Business Machines Corporation)

computers should be regarded as tools that extend man's abilities, particularly in the use of the brain.

Many large companies are using electronic machines to index and store printed information in their special fields, so that a quick search may be made on any topic. Electronic machines are used for general accounting, payroll calculations and payments, inventory control, preparation of sales records, financial statements, bills, dividend checks, social security records, and tax reports. A single machine, when furnished with instructions as to wage scales, overtime, deductions, etc., can type the payroll, calculate the tax deductions and union dues, write the checks, and charge them to the correct accounts for several thousand workers in less than four hours.

Information is fed into these machines by means of punched cards, punched tape, or magnetic tape. Here is where the real brain work is done, and it must be done by highly trained human beings, for whom there is an ever-increasing demand.

There are so many applications of electronic computers and data-processing machines in modern industry, that several large companies have invested huge sums of money in the development of new, different, and improved kinds of equipment. By 1961, more than 10,000 giant electronic computers were in operation. The cost of this equipment is decreasing, and more of it is being used. Special equipment, designed for small businesses, should result in more widespread adoptions. Many of the functions of stenographers, clerks, and bookkeepers will be taken over by machines, but, on the other hand, there will be a tremendous demand for workers trained to operate and service these machines.

Electronic machines now make it possible for stockbrokers' offices anywhere in the United States to obtain instant information concerning the price of any given stock at the last sale, the number of shares sold, the dividend percentage, etc., merely by punching three "call letters."

Figure 61–5. An electronic test-scoring machine, an important tool in modern education. (Courtesy, International Business Machines Corporation)

Some large banks employ electronic machines to help them decide which stocks or bonds to purchase.

The original selection of the seven astronauts, from among thousands of jet pilots, was done by an electronic computer. Space Technology Laboratories uses an IBM 7090 computer to match professional staff members to special problems.

Machines are now available that can select published information stored in their memory system, which deals with particular topics that are of concern to any given person. One could imagine a company that would store information concerning everything published, and provide a service to subscribers enabling them to keep up with the latest developments in their field, with the least amount of reading. For example, it is impossible for medical doctors to keep up with the growth of medical information. Such a service would be a must for practically every doctor. It could provide

general medical information, as well as information concerning the doctor's specialty. If all of the medical data concerning a patient could be placed on a special form, the data could be transmitted to a central office, which could then provide a possible diagnosis. Modern electronic communication machines, such as are described in Chapter 42, could make it possible to obtain special reports on any given topic. DIVOT is an experimental system, developed by the International Business Machines Corporation, which will receive a telephone request for information and return the reply in a matter of seconds.

The Rusdic is an electronic machine that can translate Russian words into English at the rate of 300,000 words per hour. Similar machines can be used to translate Chinese and other foreign languages.

Machines are being developed to aid almost every mental process. For example, electronic computers are being developed to automatically transcribe stenographic records. The next step would be to translate the spoken word directly into a typed or printed page, and work is being done to perfect machines to do this.

Machines are used by many banks to process checks, which have information printed on them with magnetic ink. The United States Post Office is experimenting with machines that will sort mail. A machine that could read some kinds of handwriting would exceed the capacity of the human brain. Perhaps a simpler approach would be the development of simple, low-cost machines to print special labels for addressing mail.

DATA, THE RAW MATERIAL OF SCIENTIFIC PROGRESS— INFORMATION RETRIEVAL

Scientists are unable to keep up with more than a fraction of the information becoming available in their special field. More than 55,000 journals and 60,000 books are published annually that contain scientific information of value. Much of the world's literature is printed in such languages as Russian or Japanese. Russian literature accounts for about 10 per cent of all scientific literature.

In the past, it has been axiomatic that any scientific investigation would begin with a search of the literature. **Complete retrieval of existing information** *requires the tapping of all pertinent sources of information.* The task of searching the literature is so monumental that one large corporation made the astounding statement,

If a research job costs less than $100,000 it is cheaper for us to do it than to find out if it has been done before and reported in the literature.

In Russia, the Institute of Scientific and Technical Information, processes 8,000 scientific journals from all parts of the world. It employs more than 2,000 people in its central office. In the United States, The National Science Foundation has been assigned the responsibility of providing a Science information service. Equipment to aid in this work includes reading, storing, searching, transmitting, and translating machines.

The Chemical Abstracts Service of the American Chemical Society, in Columbus, Ohio, uses an IBM 1401 computer to index chemical information and patents. Many of the large companies in the United States maintain their own computers to store scientific information and make searches of the literature. For example, The Lilly Research Laboratories have coded information on 800 antibiotics. Parke, Davis and Company has information concerning the biological activity of 40,000 compounds.

SUMMARY

Electronic tubes are gradually being replaced by semiconductors for electronic computers and data-processing machines, thus making it possible to reduce their size, cost, and maintenance, and to increase their reliability.

Electronic computers are tools that extend the capacities of human beings. They can

Figure 61–6. An electronic library—Document Storage and Retrieval System. This WALNUT system uses an image converter to reduce 35 mm microfilm images of documents to 1/1000 of their original size. Images can be retrieved in as little as five seconds and never leave their place in the file. (Courtesy, International Business Machines Corporation)

process any kinds of data obtained by automatic measuring and recording instruments, which may be used to operate machine tools, chemical plants, and many automatic labor-saving devices in business and industry.

Electronic devices extend the mental capacities of man, by electronic memories that can store tremendous amounts of information, which may be readily retrieved when it is needed. They perform all kinds of mathematical calculations. They are now being developed for reading printed or typewritten material, translating foreign languages, and transcribing spoken words into printed copy.

The laser can be used to amplify and modulate electromagnetic waves.

Thermistors and frigistors can use the electric current for either cooling or heating, thus performing the functions of the heat pump without involving such bulky equipment as electric motors and compressors.

Magnetohydrodynamic generators produce electric power by the motion of plasma (hot, ionized gases) through a magnetic field.

Study Questions

1. DEFINE: magnetohydrodynamic generator, laser, thermistor, frigistor, Peltier effect, Seebeck effect, information retrieval, coherent radiation, thermoelectric effect.
2. What scientific developments made electronics possible?
3. What are some of the mental functions that may be aided by the use of electronic computers and data-processing machines?
4. In what ways are electronic machines serving the business world?
5. How are electronic machines being used in schools?
6. Does your school use data-processing machines for registration procedures, attendance records, and maintaining academic records?
7. How are electronic machines used in manufacturing operations?
8. How may electronic machines cut down the time required for the search of scientific literature?
9. How could electronic machines serve the medical profession?
10. How could electronic machines be used to change library procedures?
11. What changes in job opportunities are being created by the use of electronic computers and data-processing machines?
12. How are electronic machines being used in many banks?
13. How are electronic machines being used by stockbrokers?

CHAPTER 62

Modern Alchemy

We find ourselves, in consequence of the progress of physical science, at the pinnacle of one ascent of civilization, taking the first step upward out on the lowest plane of the next. Above us rises indefinitely the ascent of physical power —far beyond the dream of mortals in any previous system of philosophy.

FREDERICK SODDY

INTRODUCTION

The experiments in which the three building stones of matter, the electrons, protons, and neutrons, were discovered had provided the basis for a nice, tidy theory of nuclear structure. This theory seemed to fit the facts; it accounted for atomic weights and atomic numbers. In 1919, Rutherford and his assistants, who had contributed so much to the knowledge of electrons and protons, carried out the first experiment of modern alchemy, in which one element was transmuted into another. Finally, transmutation, the goal of the alchemists, seemed to be in sight.

Not only did Rutherford's experiment usher in modern alchemy, but it also stimulated a new study of the atomic nucleus from which more than thirty fundamental particles have been produced. As a result, the neat theory of the structure of the atomic nucleus based on the three fundamental particles had to be broadened in some respects, as outlined in this chapter.

THE FIRST EXPERIMENT IN MODERN ALCHEMY

Rutherford and his assistants had been carrying out experiments in which alpha particles were fired at a screen coated with zinc sulfide. Each collision produced a tiny spark on the screen. They found that a metal disk would block the passage of alpha particles. Protons, produced by the bombardment of hydrogen with alpha particles, would pass through the disk and produce sparks that differed in appearance from the sparks produced by alpha particles. When nitrogen was substituted for hydrogen, the zinc sulfide screen still showed sparks identical in appearance to those obtained with hydrogen. Rutherford concluded that protons had been knocked out of the nitrogen nucleus. If his conclusion was correct, he had succeeded in carrying out the first atomic transmutation. Was his conclusion correct? If so, this experiment might prove to be tremendously significant. He now turned to the Wilson cloud chamber to test his hypothesis. In this cloud chamber, the usual alpha particle tracks showed up, but occasionally, an alpha particle track split into a forked track, when an alpha particle hit a nitrogen nucleus. One branch of this fork gave the characteristic track of a proton. The other branch was heavier in appearance, and was produced by what was left of the nitrogen nucleus. At the same time, the alpha particle vanished. Rutherford concluded that it had combined with the nitrogen nucleus when it hit the nucleus, displacing a proton in the process. Now the loss of a proton and the gain of an alpha particle by the nitrogen nucleus would produce a new element, an isotope of oxygen. This experiment, conducted in 1919 by Rutherford and his associates, was the pioneer experiment in modern alchemy.

It will be recalled that radioactive disintegration may result in the emission of alpha particles and the production of a lighter element. In the bombardment of nitrogen with alpha particles, a reverse reaction had taken place, in which the alpha particles had joined with the nitrogen nucleus to form a heavier element. Would it be possible to add alpha particles to the heaviest elements known and thus produce entirely new elements, having atomic numbers larger than those of any known element? This classical experiment of Rutherford suggested the possibility of other atomic transmutations and the race was on.

THE PRODUCTION OF NEUTRONS

In 1930, two German scientists had reported that a new radiation of great penetrating power had been obtained by the bombardment of beryllium atoms with alpha particles, but its significance was not understood.

In 1932, Frederick and Irene Joliot-Curie used this new radiation from beryllium to bombard paraffin, a compound of carbon and hydrogen. Protons were knocked out of the paraffin. In 1932, James Chadwick bombarded boron atoms with this radiation, and found that their mass was increased by a mass equal to that of the proton. Apparently, this new radiation was a stream of neutrons (neutral particles having the mass of the proton). Subsequent experiments resulted in a variety of methods for the production of neutrons. For example, when beryllium was bombarded with **deuterons,** *the nuclei of the hydrogen isotope with an atomic weight of 2,* a large number of neutrons were produced.

Later experiments showed that neutrons are quite unstable, the half-life of a free neutron being about 15 minutes. In a nucleus, where the neutron is not free, it is quite stable. It was found that the mass of a neutron is greater than the mass of a proton and an electron into which it disintegrated. The extra mass is changed into energy, the energy of the fast moving electron, which it ejects when

it undergoes radioactive decomposition. Neutrons were found to be excellent bullets for atomic bombardments, because they are neutral and are, therefore, not deflected by charged particles in the nucleus. Hence, they readily penetrate atomic nuclei.

ATOMIC BOMBARDMENT

All over the world, scientists began to bombard atoms, trying out different types of atomic particles as "bullets," and developing the *guns,* the **"atom smashers,"** to fire the "bullets." It also became necessary to develop methods of identifying the products of atomic bombardment.

Atomic "Bullets"

The use of alpha particles for bombardment experiments was soon replaced by the use of other positively charged particles, the protons, and the deuterons. However, as pointed out above, neutrons came into wide use because of their great penetrating ability, although they are more difficult to control, because of their lack of charge.

"Atom Smashers"—The Guns

"Atom smashers" must first produce the proper "bullets," and then accelerate them to provide sufficient speeds to give them the desired penetrating power.

In 1928, John D. Cockroft (1897–   ) and Ernest Walton (1903–   ) developed a device to impart an energy of 400,000 electron-volts to protons. The energy imparted to the "bullets" is generally expressed in terms of electron-volts, which is abbreviated to **ev.** *A million electron-volts,* is a **Mev,** and a *billion electron-volts* is a **Bev. An electron-volt** *represents the energy developed by an electron that has been accelerated by an electric field, having a potential of one volt.*

In 1931, the first *linear accelerator* was completed. It was based on the idea of adding energy to the bullets in a series of pushes as the bullet moved down a long sectional tube. However, attention was diverted from this to the *cyclotron,* invented by Ernest Orlando Lawrence (1901–1958), in 1939. In the cyclotron, the particles were bent into a circular path by powerful magnetic fields. They picked

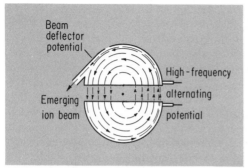

Figure 62–1. Principle of operation of the cyclotron.

up speed, and after circling in ever-widening paths, they were eventually shot out of the cyclotron with an energy of 20 Mev. Later variations of the cyclotron, called *synchro-cyclotrons*, yielded energies of 700 to 800 Mev. Figure 62-1 shows the principle of the cyclotron pictured in Figure 62-2.

In 1940, Donald Williams Kerst (1911–) designed a particle accelerator for electrons, which was called a *betatron*. It yielded electrons with an energy of 300 Mev. In 1954, there was developed a *bevatron*, at the University of California, which produced energies of 5 to 6 Bev. In 1957, the Soviet Union had a *phasotron* with a yield of 10 Bev. So the Mev-Bev race was on. In 1959, a new type of *synchrotron* was built in Geneva, Switzerland, by CERN, the European Committee for Nuclear Research, which had an energy of 28 Bev. This synchrotron is about three city blocks in diameter. In 1960, a 30-Bev, alternating gradient synchrotron was completed for the Brookhaven National Laboratory in New York.

Detection of the Products of Bombardment

The **Wilson cloud chamber** was the pioneer detecting device, and it made a great contribution to the advance of knowledge concerning the atomic nucleus. Eventually, the principle of the cloud chamber *in which vapor trails were formed in a gas,* was applied to **bubble chambers,** in which *a stream of bubbles is produced by nuclear particles.* Some of the latest bubble chambers use such rare liquids as liquid helium and liquid xenon. All detecting devices depend upon the fact that radiations, or particles, produce ions in the gases or liquids in which they travel. In bubble chambers, charged particles and even neutrons, speeding through the liquid in the chamber, produce tiny bubbles which may be photographed. The study of these photographs furnishes information concerning the velocities and the masses of the particles.

Figure 62–2. The Bevatron at the University of California. (Courtesy, University of California Radiation Laboratory)

Another detecting device, **the ionization chamber,** *contains two electrodes; one is charged and the other is grounded. The space between the electrodes is filled with an ionizable gas.* The introduction of radiation creates ions, giving rise to an ionization current, which may be detected by such electrical instruments as the electroscope or the electrometer.

Still another widely used, and well-known *detecting device* is the **Geiger-Müller counter,** which has been used extensively by prospectors in their search for uranium ores.

Scintillation *devices depend upon the use of a phosphor, such as zinc sulfide, that will give a momentary flash of light each time it is hit by* alpha or beta particles, or by photons of gamma rays.

Photographic methods depend upon the action of speeding particles on a thick photographic emulsion. The particles ionize the emulsion as they travel through it, and produce a latent image which shows up when the emulsion is developed.

NEW SUBATOMIC PARTICLES PRODUCED BY ATOMIC BOMBARDMENT

As a result of the bombardment experiments with very high-energy bullets, many new subatomic particles were discovered.

The Positron

Ever since the discovery of the mysterious cosmic rays, in 1911, by Victor Francis Hess (1883–   ) on a balloon flight into the upper atmosphere, many experiments to determine their nature have been undertaken. These cosmic rays were shown to have a very high energy content and tremendous penetrating power. It turned out that these **cosmic rays** were *naked atoms shorn of their electrons, consisting mostly of protons and, also, some nuclei of heavier elements.*

In 1932, Carl David Anderson (1905–   ) experimented with cosmic rays, using a Wilson cloud chamber containing a lead plate. A particle was knocked out of the lead, *which made a track like that of an electron, but had a positive charge.* This new particle was named the **positron.**

The positron existed for only a moment, and then joined with an electron to form gamma rays.

Since the positron and electron annihilated one another and disappeared in the process, the positron was called the "anti-particle" of the electron. Would it not be possible, likewise, to find another form of anti-particle that would obliterate the proton, and change it into energy? Interesting as this question was, there was a still more important significance to this experimental production of the positron. It was the production of energy from matter. This constituted another proof of Albert Einstein's suggestion that this should be possible.

The Anti-Proton and the Anti-Neutron

In 1955, Owen Chamberlain (1920–   ) and Emilio Gino Segre (1905–   ) bombarded copper with protons, having the energy of 6.2 Bev, and produced the anti-proton, the counterpart of the positron. When an anti-proton hits a proton, both particles may annihilate one another and emerge as a shower of gamma rays and mesons.

The Neutrino

When an electron is ejected from an atomic nucleus, it carries energy with it, which must have resulted from the conversion of some of the mass of the nucleus into energy. The actual decrease in mass was frequently found to be greater than that needed to provide the energy of the electron. This difference was accounted for by the hypothesis that there was also ejected, along with the electron, a neutral particle carrying the extra energy. In 1934, Enrico Fermi (1901–1955) named this hypothetical particle the neutrino.

It was predicted that the neutrino would be produced when a neutron disintegrates into a proton and an electron. So scientists began the very difficult search for the neutrino, a tiny particle with no mass and no charge. In 1956, this research first led to the discovery of the anti-neutrino, which was followed by the discovery of the neutrino itself.

Mesons and Hyperons

The researches carried out by scientists all over the world, using ever more powerful atom smashers, and more advanced detecting devices, soon turned up many more particles, called mesons. The **mesons** are *particles having atomic weights intermediate between the weights of the proton and the electron.* The first meson, having an atomic weight 200 times the weight of the electron, was called the mu meson, or the muon. Then came the pi meson or pion with an atomic weight 270 times that of the electron. The muons and the pions were found to exist in both positively and negatively charged forms, and there were found neutral forms of pions.

The discovery of the muons and pions was soon followed by the production of still heavier mesons, called K-mesons, which have a mass 966 times the mass of an electron. Next came the hyperons of several types, having still larger masses, existing in charged and neutral forms as well as in anti forms.

So in 1965, more than 30 different kinds of particles had been produced by the bombardment of atomic nuclei. Of course, new theories concerning the structure of the nucleus were required to explain these sub-atomic particles, and, as usual, a great deal of research will be necessary to confirm or refute these theories.

The fact that about thirty different particles are produced when atoms are bombarded, does not mean that all of these particles are contained in the nucleus, because they may result from the disintegration of the nuclei. It is considered that mesons represent the "glue" that holds a nucleus together. When one considers that like electric charges repel each other, it must take a powerful glue to hold the positively charged protons together in the nucleus.

CONVERSION OF ENERGY INTO MATTER

Having learned how to convert matter into energy, the question arises as to the possibility of the reverse process. What happens to the vast amounts of energy radiated by billions of stars, in such tremendous quantities, for billions of years? Is it possible that this energy is converted back into matter somewhere in space, to form new stars? Some astronomers think so, but can such a reaction be carried out experimentally? Yes, it

can, and it has been done. When gamma rays are passed through matter, positron-electron pairs are produced. It is interesting to note, however, that in all such creative events equal numbers of particles and anti-particles are produced. Therefore, astronomers have the problem of accounting for the whereabouts of the anti-particles.

ARTIFICIAL RADIOACTIVITY

In 1934, the Joliot-Curies bombarded aluminum with alpha particles and produced both protons and positrons. Strangely enough, when they stopped the bombardment, the aluminum kept on emitting positrons. They showed that a new radioactive isotope of phosphorus had been produced. Up to this time no one had been able to start, stop, or control the rate of natural radioactivity, but now, for the first time, artificial radioactivity had been produced. The Joliot-Curies analyzed the aluminum that had been bombarded, and they found a radioactive isotope of phosphorus having a half-life of about 2.5 minutes. This isotope decomposed to yield an isotope of silicon, and a positron. The positron had been formed by the conversion of a proton into a neutron and a positron. The Joliot-Curies and other scientists eventually found that all elements would become radioactive when bombarded with alpha particles. In this process, one or more radioactive isotopes not found in nature are produced. Most of these have short lives, sometimes as short as a fraction of a second.

NEW RADIOACTIVE ELEMENTS

Enrico Fermi found that the heaviest known element, uranium-239, when bombarded with neutrons, yielded three heavier radioactive elements, uranium-239, neptunium-239, and plutonium-239. Each of these new elements has the same atomic weight, but they differ in atomic numbers, and must, therefore, be different elements. In the above process, uranium-239 was the first of the radioactive decomposition series ending with uranium-235. Subsequently, the still heavier elements, americium and curium were obtained by bombardment of plutonium with alpha particles. Soon, the new elements, berkelium, californium, einsteinium, fermium, and mendelevium were prepared, and were found to fit into the periodic table in the blank spaces following uranium.

The gaps in the periodic table were filled by the synthesis of technetium, promethium, astatine, and francium, which had not been discovered previously because they are radioactive elements with short half-lives.

In 1961, a few atoms of element 103 were synthesized, thus completing the actinide series. It was produced by the bombardment of californium, element 98, with boron nuclei. Its suggested name was lawrencium, in honor of Ernest O. Lawrence, the founder of the laboratory in which it was prepared.

Why are the heavier radioactive elements not found in the earth's crust? It is quite possible that they were once present, but that their half-lives are so short that only a few of the original radioactive elements with long half-lives could have remained. It is quite reasonable to believe that the heavier elements, even elements still heavier than any of those synthesized so far, may exist in the centers of some stars.

RADIOACTIVE ISOTOPES

Since the first artificial radioactive isotope was produced, more than 1,300 radioactive isotopes have been obtained, many of them as by-products of atomic reactors, to be discussed in the next chapter. Many of these isotopes have such short lives that they are of little value. Others have been used in many ways in modern medicine, and in research.

One important use for radioactive isotopes has been that of indicators or tracers. Radioactive atoms or molecules may be traced in their paths through living organisms, because their radiation may be detected by a variety of methods.

SUMMARY

Modern Alchemy

Modern alchemy is the transmutation of elements by the bombardment of atomic nuclei with tiny, high-energy particles produced by "atom smashers."

The Guns—"Atom Smashers"—These huge machines are devices to impart tremendous energy to the "bullets" by accelerating them in magnetic or electric fields. The energy of a particle is expressed as electron-volts, Mev, and Bev.

The "Bullets"—The first "bullets" used were alpha particles. Later experiments employed deuterons, protons, and electrons, but the most useful bullets were neutrons.

The Products of the Bombardment of Atomic Nuclei—The bombardment of atomic nuclei produced more than 1,300 radioactive isotopes and more than 30 subatomic particles such as positrons, mesons, and neutrinos. For every particle there is believed to exist an anti-particle, or "anti-matter."

The Detection and Identification of the Products of Bombardment—This is accomplished by such devices as the Wilson cloud chamber, the bubble chamber, ionization chamber, Geiger-Müller counters, scintillation devices, and photographic methods.

Study Questions

1. DEFINE: deuteron, positron, "atom smasher," cloud chamber, bubble chamber, Geiger-Müller counter, cosmic ray, scintillation, Mev, Bev, electron-volt, ionization chamber, meson.
2. What are the most important "bullets" used in "atom smashers"?
3. What is the function of an "atom smasher"?
4. How was the first artificial radioactivity produced?
5. What kinds of anti-matter have been produced?
6. What was the first experiment in modern alchemy?
7. How are the products of atomic bombardment detected and analyzed?
8. Why are neutrons such good "bullets"?
9. How were americium and curium prepared?
10. How is the power of an "atom smasher" expressed?
11. What are some of the uses of radio isotopes?
12. What was the nature of the reaction in which matter was changed into energy, as described in this chapter?

CHAPTER 63

Nuclear Energy

The new discoveries made in physics in the last few years, and the ideas and potentialities suggested by them, have had an effect upon the workers in that subject akin to that produced in literature by the Renaissance.

Sir J. J. Thompson

INTRODUCTION

The atomic bomb dropped on Hiroshima on August 16, 1945, hastened the end of World War II, and vastly influenced the strategy of preparation for possible future wars. The results of a possible nuclear war are almost unthinkable. Many scientists have warned the world that it must choose between suicide or peace. If Science has made it necessary to outlaw wars as a method of "solving" international problems, it has rendered an outstanding contribution. In the meantime, our knowledge of nuclear energy has revolutionized scientific thinking in many fields.

This chapter tells the story of the development of nuclear energy in terms of the information released by the Atomic Energy Commission.

NUCLEAR FISSION—THE PIONEERING DISCOVERIES

In 1939, Irene Joliot-Curie and P. Savitch carried out an experiment in which they bombarded ordinary uranium with neutrons, and obtained an element that had the properties of a Lanthanum isotope, with an atomic

This chapter was based in part on the booklet, *Secret*, written by Wesley W. Stout, and published by the Chrysler Corporation in 1947. Permission for the use of this material was granted by the Chrysler Corporation.

number of 57. However, they did not believe that their results could be true, because they were not in accordance with theory current at that time. They thus missed the credit for one of the most important discoveries of the century, because, in this experiment, atomic fission had taken place.

In 1939, Otto Hahn (1879–   ) and Fritz Strassman repeated the experiment of Curie and Savitch, employing slowed-down neutrons to bombard uranium. They found barium to be present in the by-product of the reaction and radioactive radiation was produced. They attributed the barium to be due to an impurity, and they assumed that the radiation was caused by radium produced in the reaction, although they were not able to find any radium present. They had applied the discovery made by Enrico Fermi in Italy that neutrons must be slowed down in order to be effective in nuclear disintegration. He found that heavy water (deuterium oxide) would slow down neutrons satisfactorily.

This work had been begun by Lise Meitner (1878–   ), but having Jewish blood, she was forced to flee from Germany. Hahn and Strassman published a report of their experiment and, fortunately, they sent a copy of the report to Lise Meitner. Hahn and Strassman had not realized the significance of their experiment, but Lise Meitner surmised that the barium present had been produced by the splitting of the uranium atom. Her calculations

471

indicated that such a reaction should liberate an enormous amount of energy. See Figure 63-1. She wrote to Otto Robert Frisch (1904–   ), the son-in-law of Niels Bohr, who had fled from Denmark to Princeton University. Enrico Fermi was at Columbia University, having fled from Italy. Frisch believed that Meitner's conclusions were so important that he cabled to his father-in-law, Niels Bohr, in Sweden, on January 24, 1939. Bohr realized the tremendous significance of Lise Meitner's conclusions, and got in touch with George Pegram (1876–1958) and John Dunning (1907–   ) at Columbia University, who, a day later, carried out experiments that confirmed her conclusions. They communicated their findings to a meeting of physicists, and soon, similar confirming experiments had been carried out in a score of laboratories.

However, the experiments did not yield the amount of energy predicted. In 1935, Arthur Dempster (1886–   ) at the University of Chicago, had discovered that natural uranium consists of three kinds of isotopes, U-238, U-235, and U-234 (the numbers stand for the atomic weights). U-235 was present in the U-238 to the extent of less than 1 per cent, while U-234 was present in only minute amounts.

Niels Bohr, who had come to the United States, and J. A. Wheeler (1911–   )

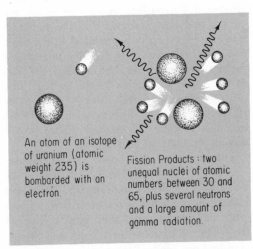

An atom of an isotope of uranium (atomic weight 235) is bombarded with an electron.

Fission Products : two unequal nuclei of atomic numbers between 30 and 65, plus several neutrons and a large amount of gamma radiation.

Figure 63–1. Nuclear fission, i.e., the splitting of large atoms into smaller ones, is one method of releasing nuclear energy. A portion of the original mass is changed into energy in the process.

reasoned that the amount of energy which would have resulted from a chain reaction was not produced because it was the U-235 isotope that had undergone fission, and the neutrons which should have produced the chain reaction must have been absorbed by the U-238 as fast as they were formed. To prove their theory, it was necessary to separate U-235 from natural uranium, a very difficult problem because both forms of uranium have identical chemical properties. However, a very small amount of U-235 was obtained and tested. Their theory was proven to be correct.

EARLY HISTORY OF THE NUCLEAR ENERGY PROGRAM IN THE UNITED STATES

Before World War II began, Fermi warned the United States Government concerning the military possibilities of atomic fission, but nothing resulted from this warning.

In August, 1939, gentle, peace-loving Albert Einstein, was prevailed upon by Leo Szilard (1898–   ) and others to write a letter to President Franklin D. Roosevelt. It was felt that Einstein would carry some weight because of his reputation as perhaps the greatest scientist of his generation. Albert Einstein had announced his conclusion that mass and energy were different forms of the same thing, back in 1905. However, few government officials knew anything about Einstein's theory or the first experimental fission discovery. Scientists knew that the scientists in Germany were working on the problem, and they felt that it was extremely urgent that the United States produce the atomic bomb before Hitler's Germany did so. How difficult it must have been for Einstein to write the following letter to President Roosevelt:

In the course of the past four months it has been made probable that a nuclear chain reaction can be set up in a large mass of uranium, by which vast amounts of power and large quantities of new radium-like elements would be generated. Now it appears almost certain that this could be achieved in the immediate future. This new phenomenon also would lead to the construction of bombs, and it is conceivable—though much less certain—that extremely powerful bombs of a new type, carried by boat or exploded in a port, might well destroy the whole port together with some of the surrounding territory. However such bombs might very well prove to be too heavy to transport by air.

The President appointed a committee, but nothing happened. In the meantime, in May, 1940, France had fallen to Germany. Einstein, dissatisfied with the inaction, wrote to President Roosevelt again. This time the President appointed Vannevar Bush (1890–   ) to head up a nuclear energy project.

The United States was not in the war yet, but even a year before Pearl Harbor, a voluntary censorship was imposed. There was a complete blackout in the newspapers and scientific magazines. Research continued, however, and by June, 1942, Vannevar Bush reported to President Roosevelt that an explosion equal to many thousand tons of TNT could be caused at any desired moment by the fission of U-235. He also reported that there were four different methods for obtaining U-235. (1) It could be done by converting uranium into a gas and separating the lighter isotope from the heavier isotope by diffusion. (2) It could be separated by the use of electromagnets, employing the principle of the mass spectrograph. (3) It could be separated by the use of centrifuges. (4) It could be separated by thermal diffusion.

Then, on December 6, 1942, nearly a year after Pearl Harbor, the first atomic reactor set up below the bleachers in Stagg Field at the University of Chicago, under the supervision of Enrico Fermi, produced plutonium from uranium by the process shown in Figure 63-2.

Plutonium was found to have properties similar to uranium-235, which made it suitable for fission reactions. So President Roosevelt secured the authorization for the expenditure of the huge sums of money that would be necessary for the production of the U-235 and plutonium, needed for fission reactions. These expenditures eventually amounted to more than one and a half billion dollars. It was quite an achievement to obtain an authorization for the expenditure of such a large amount of money from Congress without telling them what it was for.

The production of plutonium from uranium was centered at the huge plant in Hanford, Washington. Tons of uranium would be required and only a couple of ounces or so were available. A crash program to obtain uranium was undertaken. Uranium ore was first obtained from the Canadian wilds north of the Arctic Circle. Then a large stock of uranium ore, already mined, was found in Belgian Congo, and flown to the United States. Later, large amounts of uranium were obtained in the United States as the result of government subsidies.

In the United States, graphite was selected in preference to heavy water to produce slowed-down neutrons. The production of sufficient graphite of the desired purity was a big problem in itself, but it was solved.

The first few tons of metallic uranium were mixed with pure uranium oxide and a very little U-235 to start the chain reaction in the first **reactor,** sometimes called an **atomic pile,** at the University of Chicago. Bars of

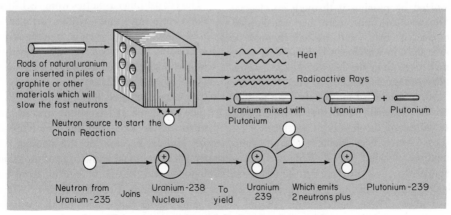

Figure 63–2. Production of plutonium from uranium.

neutron-resisting metals, such as cadmium, were used to moderate the rate of the reaction so as to prevent the chain reaction from reaching explosive violence.

Later, when pure graphite became available, a reactor using uranium rods and graphite rods was constructed at Oak Ridge, Tennessee. This reactor, operating continuously for a year, could not produce the required amount of U-235. So the huge Hanford plant was constructed, in 1943, in Eastern Washington, where the cooling water of the vast Columbia river was available. Here, plutonium was prepared from uranium, and then separated from it by chemical methods, remotely controlled and nearly automatic because of the radioactivity, which for one reactor is equal to a million pounds of radium.

The U-235 necessary to trigger the reaction in the Hanford reactors had been obtained by four different methods at Oak Ridge, Tennessee, where the power required in tremendous amounts was available.

The gas diffusion plant at Oak Ridge consisted of 63 buildings and cost more than half a billion dollars. Here, uranium was changed into the very corrosive gas, uranium hexafluoride, which was pumped through the nickel-plated diffusion barriers under a very high vacuum. The molecules of U-235 gas, being lighter, diffused faster than the heavier U-238 gas molecules. After thousands of cycles, a rich concentration of U-235 was obtained. To obtain the high vacuum, many pumps of new design were produced, after thousands of man-hours of research.

In the electromagnetic plant, a uranium gas was ionized by passing it through an electric arc. The resulting ions were then accelerated in an electric field, and passed through a magnetic field in which the U-235 atoms were deflected more than the heavier U-238 atoms. The electromagnets were 250 feet long and contained thousands of tons of steel. So powerful was the magnetic field, that it would pull iron tools out of the hands of workers.

At Los Alamos, New Mexico, a large group of scientists, headed by J. Robert Oppenheimer (1904–   ) worked out the technical details for manufacturing and exploding the fission bombs. These details still remain a secret in the United States, although other na-

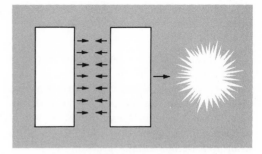

Figure 63-3. Why a fission bomb explodes.

tions have solved the problem for themselves.

Although the details are secret, the principle is known. For a given shape a critical mass is necessary. Below this mass an explosion will not take place. Above this critical mass, an explosion will take place, as shown in Figure 63-3. The solution of the problem is to divide the mass into two or more parts, and then bring them together at the instant that the explosion is desired. The two portions of the fissionable material were driven together by an ordinary explosive material. Perhaps, the fissionable material was imploded inward in a ball-like bomb.

FISSION BOMBS

For practical purposes, World War II ended when the first experimental atomic bomb was set off in the New Mexico desert on July 16, 1945. This experimental explosion was followed by the bombs dropped on Hiroshima on August 16, and on Nagasaki three days later. Five days later, Japan formally surrendered.

The Hiroshima casualties were 78,150 killed, 13,983 missing, and 37,425 injured. Two dozen men, without even a scratch, killed or wounded as many people as the United States had lost during the entire war. Of Hiroshima's 90,000 buildings, 62,000 were destroyed and 6,000 were damaged beyond repair.

The explosion at Hiroshima proved that the United States had won the "atomic" bomb race, largely because of the pooling of the very great technical knowledge of thousands of scientists, and the manufacturing know-how of many companies. President Harry S. Truman, in announcing the atomic bomb explosion at Hiroshima said: "What has been done is the greatest achievement of organized science in history."

THERMONUCLEAR ENERGY

Meanwhile, the fission bomb was dwarfed by the invention of the **fusion bomb.** In 1938, Hans Albrecht Bethe (1906–   ) had suggested several theoretical methods by which the energy of the stars could be produced by the *fusion of hydrogen atoms.* The secret of such a reaction is a very high temperature, such as exists in the centers of stars. For this reason, such reactions are called **thermonuclear reactions.** The high temperatures needed for a fusion reaction could be furnished by a fission reaction. Hydrogen, in the form of tritium, an isotope of hydrogen with an atomic weight of 3, was the fuel to be tried, because the theory indicated that it would react at a lower temperature than that required for ordinary hydrogen. This rare isotope of hydrogen had been prepared in reactors. The first fission-fusion bomb was exploded November 1, 1952.

THE FISSION-FUSION-FISSION (3F) BOMB

Another kind of fusion reaction may be carried out between lithium and deuterium. A solid compound of lithium hydride may serve as a compact fuel for a thermonuclear bomb.

Now, this reaction produces a large surplus of high-energy neutrons, so why not use these neutrons to cause the fission of ordinary uranium-238? So, to a lithium hydride fusion bomb, was added a shell of uranium-238. It was tried out at Bikini, in the Marshall Islands, on March 1, 1954. The figure shown on page 206 shows a photograph of the explosion of this bomb, while Figure 63-4 shows the possible nature of such a bomb. It proved to produce 150 times the energy of the Hiroshima bomb. On August 12, 1953, the Russians likewise set off a fission-fusion-fission bomb.

In addition to nuclear bombs, it is known that small-scale nuclear devices have been developed. The nuclear submarines of the United States are equipped with Polaris missiles having nuclear warheads. One of the smaller nuclear weapons is a nuclear device that may be shot from a bazooka by a single soldier. Nuclear shells, for use with artillery, are available. The assumption is that small nuclear devices would be used for "brushfire" wars, but such a war might soon get out of control.

The Soviet Union exploded her first fission bomb on September 22, 1949. On October 3, 1952, Great Britain exploded her first fission bomb, and on February 13, 1960, France

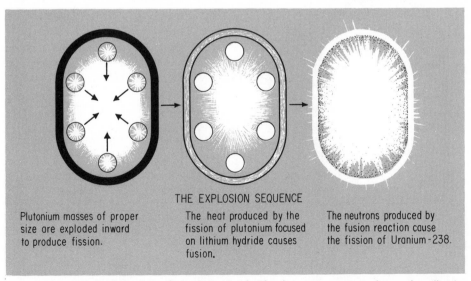

THE EXPLOSION SEQUENCE

Plutonium masses of proper size are exploded inward to produce fission.

The heat produced by the fission of plutonium focused on lithium hydride causes fusion.

The neutrons produced by the fusion reaction cause the fission of Uranium-238.

Figure 63–4. The principle of the fission-fusion-fission Bomb. The three-stage sequence lasts only millionths of a second.

joined the "club." In 1964, Communist China exploded a fission bomb.

RADIOACTIVE FALLOUT

When TNT is exploded, a sudden release of gases, with a temperature of about 5000° C, expands very rapidly and produces the pressure wave typical of an explosion.

In the case of a nuclear reaction, much more energy is released in a very short time, raising the temperature of the air to millions of degrees, and thereby forming a mass of hot, glowing gas in the atmosphere. This high temperature produces heat rays that burn everything in their path. Highly penetrating gamma rays are also produced, which may do severe damage to human bodies. Then, of course, there is the very powerful, and destructive explosion wave produced in the atmosphere, which virtually levels everything in wide areas.

However, if a person survives the first explosive blast, the heat rays, and the gamma radiation, he will still be exposed to the radiation from the radioactive disintegration products of the fission bomb. Most of these radioactive isotopes have quite short half-lives, so that, after about two weeks, most of these isotopes will have disintegrated into harmless substances.

One of the dangerous radioactive isotopes is strontium-90, which has a half-life of 28 years. It may fall on vegetable matter which may be eaten by animals. In human nutrition, the strontium-90 would become incorporated into the bones, where it would remain and continue to emit harmful radiation.

NUCLEAR REACTORS

A nuclear reactor (or pile) produces large amounts of heat, which may be used for the operation of electric power plants. It requires a nuclear fuel, either uranium-238 enriched with uranium-235, or some other fissionable material. Then a moderator, such as graphite or heavy water, is needed to slow down the neutrons. Control rods, usually made of cadmium or boron steel, are used to control the rate of neutron formation by moving the rods into or out of the reactor.

All reactors require heavy shielding of lead or other material to absorb the radioactive radiation. Nuclear reactors have proven to be practical for power plants in places where ordinary fuels cannot be obtained economically. As more knowledge is obtained concern-

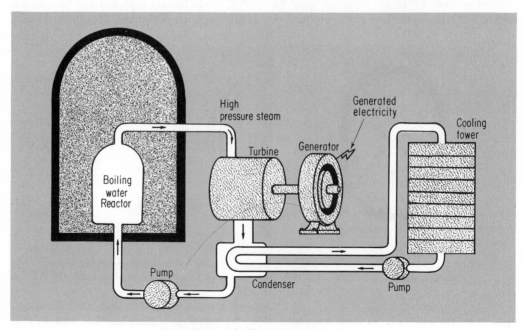

Figure 63–5. A boiling water atomic reactor.

ing their construction and operation, reactors may prove to be so economical to operate that private utility companies will build more nuclear power plants. The principle of one type of nuclear power reactor is shown in Figure 63-5. Already, nuclear power plants have been installed in many submarines.

Nuclear reactors not only produce radioactive by-products that are not wanted and constitute a problem for their disposal, but they may also produce desirable radioactive isotopes by introducing different elements into the reactor.

The first nuclear reactor built for the production of electric power for civilian use was started up in June, 1954, in the Soviet Union. In 1956, Great Britain placed its Calder Hall plant in operation, and on May 26, 1958, the United States started up its first civilian power reactor in Shippingport, Pennsylvania. All three nations have continued with the building of larger, and more efficient reactors.

BREEDER REACTORS

Uranium-235 is so scarce that the large-scale use of reactors as power plants would soon exhaust the supply. Now, it has been found that by omitting the moderator in a reactor, the fast-moving neutrons will convert uranium-238 into plutonium, so that the supply of plutonium will be produced faster than the uranium-235 is exhausted. Such a reactor, built in Arco, Idaho, in 1951, is called a breeder reactor. Thus all of the uranium-238 becomes a potential fuel in a breeder reactor.

THERMONUCLEAR (FUSION) REACTORS

A tremendous amount of research is being carried out to discover a method by which a thermonuclear reaction may be controlled. The main problem is to initiate the fusion of hydrogen or other light elements. The next problem is that of preventing the fusion reaction from becoming an explosion. A further problem is the problem of containing the nuclear fuel. No material could withstand the very high temperature required for the reaction.

SUMMARY

There are two types of nuclear reactions: fission and fusion.

Fission is produced by the bombardment of uranium with neutrons in which a chain reaction is set up. Neutrons may be obtained from U-235 or plutonium. Fission may be controlled by the use of materials which will absorb excess neutrons.

Fusion may be brought about between atoms of small atomic weight by means of high temperatures, which may be obtained with a fission reaction.

A **breeder reactor** *produces fissionable elements*.

Nuclear bombs do damage by (1) explosion waves, (2) high temperatures, (3) gamma rays, and (4) radioactive fallout.

Study Questions

1. DEFINE: atomic pile, breeder reactor.
2. What is the difference between nuclear fission and nuclear fusion?
3. What is a chain reaction? Give an example.
4. What is an atomic reactor, and for what is it used?
5. Describe the discovery of atomic fission.
6. What is the principle of the fission bomb?
7. What is the principle of the fusion bomb?
8. What is the principle of the 3F bomb?
9. Why is the thermonuclear reactor such a worthwhile goal?
10. What is a breeder reactor, and of what value is it?
11. Why is strontium-90 in radioactive fallout especially dangerous?
12. What are the various effects of a nuclear bomb, and what causes each result?

Hoover Dam. One of many dams constructed to conserve our most precious resource—water. (Courtesy, Allis-Chalmers Manufacturing Company)

10

Mastering the
Material World

I would . . . establish the conviction that Chemistry, as an independent science, offers one of the most powerful means towards the attainment of a higher mental cultivation; that the study of Chemistry is profitable, not only inasmuch as it promotes the material interests of mankind, but also because it furnishes us with insight into those wonders of creation which immediately surround us, and with which our existence, life and development, are most closely connected.

JUST VON LIEBIG

THE MAJOR raw materials of modern industry, with the exception of the carbon compounds, such as coal, petroleum, and natural gas (to be studied in the next unit), are air, water, a few nonmetals, such as the halogens, sulfur, and phosphorus; and a few metals, such as iron, aluminum, silicon, and titanium. This unit takes up the ways in which modern industry separates these materials and converts them into many important products that enter into modern living, such as glass, cement, metals, alloys, and even disinfectants and matches.

This unit also takes up the modern problems of water pollution, purification, and conservation. A similar problem, created by modern industry and automobiles as a by-product of the combustion of carbonaceous fuels to furnish power, is air pollution. These pressing problems must be solved if we want to continue to enjoy the "good life."

Fortunately, the solution to these problems is possible. The bacteria-resistant detergents which have been contaminating our water supplies may soon be replaced by detergents which can be broken down by bacteria. Atomic energy can be used to convert sea water into fresh water. Atomic energy can also be used to furnish much of the power required by industry. However, a pressing problem, not yet solved, is the contamination of the atmosphere with the fumes from internal combustion engines. Perhaps the solution to this problem is already in the laboratories, where new types of engines are being developed.

Sulfur and Phosphorus— Catalysis

The philosopher should be a man willing to listen to every suggestion, but determined to judge for himself. He should not be biased by appearance; have no favorite hypothesis; be of no school; and in doctrine have no master. He should not be a respecter of persons but of things. Truth should be his primary object. If to these qualities he add industry, he may indeed hope to walk within the veil of the temple of nature.

MICHAEL FARADAY

INTRODUCTION

Why have we introduced the subject of the rate of a chemical reaction, with emphasis on catalysis, in this chapter on sulfur and phosphorus? Perhaps there is no logical reason for doing so, but we offer as an excuse that sulfur and phosphorus are two active nonmetals that play an important role in all living matter, and that catalysis is the process by which living matter manages to carry out so many marvelous and complex chemical reactions.

Sulfur and phosphorus are important constituents of proteins, found in living protoplasm. For example, egg yolks and the seeds of plants are rich in both elements. Phosphorus is found in nerve tissue, and it has an important role in the release of energy in the muscles. It has been found that phosphorus compounds play an important part in photosynthesis. Phosphorus performs the most varied and basic functions in the chemical machinery of life. The bones and teeth of animals are composed largely of calcium phosphate. Soluble phosphates serve as buffer substances in the body fluids, to maintain the proper hydronium-ion concentration, i.e., the proper pH.

Both sulfur and phosphorus are quite active. One application of this activity is match manufacture.

PHOSPHORUS

The Occurrence of Phosphorus

Phosphorus is found in the form of calcium phosphate deposits, which were probably formed from the bones and teeth of animals. Extensive areas of phosphate rocks are found in Florida and several other southern states, as well as in the northern Rocky Mountains.

Elemental Phosphorus

Elemental phosphorus is prepared from phosphate rock by heating it with sand and coke in an electric furnace. There are two common varieties of phosphorus, white and red. White phosphorus is very active, and will ignite spontaneously at ordinary temperatures. White phosphorus glows in the dark as it reacts with the oxygen of the air. It is very poisonous, and has been used in rat poisons, but better and safer poisons are now available. Red phosphorus is not so active as white phosphorus, but it will burn in the air once it is ignited. It is not poisonous.

Uses of Phosphorus Compounds

The major uses of phosphorus and its compounds are in the match, fertilizer, and detergent industries. Phosphates are essential to plant life, and are usually deficient in the soil, so they are important ingredients in most fertilizers. Calcium phosphate is insoluble in water, and for that reason it would not be of value as a fertilizer. However, if phosphate rock is treated with sulfuric acid a soluble "super phosphate" is obtained.

Phosphorus forms many complex salts which are used in large quantities as water softeners, either alone, or as constituents of laundry soap powders and detergents. These compounds react with the ions that cause hardness in water to form complex ions that will not react with soaps.

MATCH MANUFACTURE

The two kinds of matches in common use are (1) the friction, or strike-anywhere match, and (2) the safety match.

The Friction Match

Friction matches are made of wood sticks, first dipped in an ammonium phosphate solution to prevent afterglow, and thus decrease the danger of fires being started by burning matches. The head of the match is then dipped into melted paraffin. Then a paste consisting of glue, sulfur or some other readily oxidizable matter; an oxidizing agent, such as potassium chlorate; and coloring matter is added. The tip of the match head consists of a sulfide of phosphorus, which may be ignited by friction. The ignition of the tip then causes the head to ignite, and this, in turn, ignites the paraffin and the match stick.

The Safety Match

The safety match is made from wood or light cardboard. The tip contains antimony trisulfide, glue, and an oxidizing agent. The match will not ignite unless it is struck on a surface of the match box or match folder, which is coated with a mixture of red phosphorus, glue, and powdered glass.

SULFUR

The Occurrence of Sulfur

Sulfur is widely distributed in nature in the form of sulfides of such metals as iron, silver, copper, lead, and nickel. Large deposits of gypsum (calcium sulfate) are used to make plaster of Paris and wallboard. Free sulfur has been found in large deposits in Texas and Louisiana, in the United States, and also in Mexico. Such deposits are frequently found in volcanic regions. Volcanic gases usually contain hydrogen sulfide and sulfur dioxide, which may interact to form free sulfur.

These underground deposits cannot be mined by ordinary shaft mining because of the presence of poisonous gases, such as hydrogen sulfide, the gas with the familiar rotten-egg odor. The deposits are found several hundred feet below the surface under layers of limestone and clay. In 1891, Herman Frasch (1851–1914) invented an ingenious process, illustrated by Figure 64-1. In the Frasch process, sulfur is melted in the ground by superheated water, and is then forced to the surface by compressed air.

Sulfur is recovered from natural gas and from various metallic sulfides. Iron pyrites, a sulfide of iron, is used in some parts of the world to produce sulfuric acid. In this case, the iron is a valuable by-product. In the case of sulfides of such metals as silver, copper, or lead, the metal is the main product, and the sulfur dioxide, which is recovered from roasting their ores, is the useful by-product.

Sulfur as a Raw Material

Sulfur is one of the cheapest raw materials, and one of the five most important ones used in the chemical industry. Besides serving as the starting point for the production of sulfuric acid, it is used in many other chemical reactions. Sulfur is used in the manufacture of gunpowder, fireworks, matches, rubber, plastics, and agricultural sprays.

Sulfur Dioxide and Sulfuric Acid

In the form of sulfur dioxide, sulfur is used in large quantities as an industrial bleaching agent, and in the production of wood pulp for

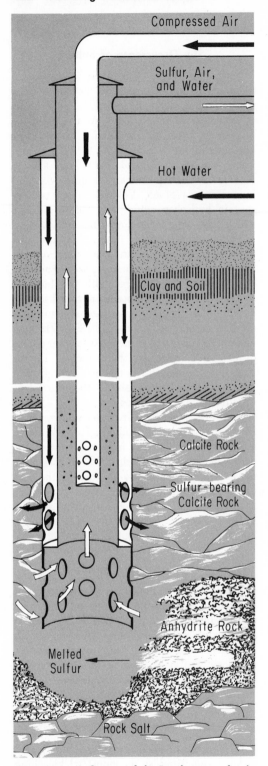

Compressed Air

Sulfur, Air, and Water

Hot Water

Clay and Soil

Calcite Rock

Sulfur-bearing Calcite Rock

Anhydrite Rock

Melted Sulfur

Rock Salt

Figure 64–1. A diagram of the Frasch process for the mining of sulfur.

the paper industry. It is also used to prevent various agricultural products, such as dried fruits, from spoiling.

Sulfuric acid is known as the workhorse of chemistry because it is used in such large quantities in a wide range of industries. Sulfuric acid is used in the refining of petroleum to remove objectionable unsaturated compounds. It is important in the production of several different fertilizer ingredients.

Perhaps the average person knows sulfuric acid best as the liquid contained in lead-acid storage batteries. He knows that this acid will corrode metals and eat holes in clothing.

HOW CHEMICAL REACTIONS ARE BROUGHT ABOUT

Activation

In many cases, substances will not react unless the reacting molecules have been given an extra amount of energy. This extra energy increases the motion of the molecules, and some electrons are energized to a higher state of activation. Some substances, such as phosphorus or sulfur, are quite active. This is another way of saying that not much energy is required to activate them. Other materials, such as ceramics or refractories, are not activated at temperatures as high as 1,000° F.

Chemical reactions between ions take place instantaneously because the ions are in an active (electrified) condition. Chemical reactions involving nonionic (covalent) compounds do not take place so readily. In many cases, the molecules must be activated with some form of energy, such as light, heat, or electricity. Once started, many of these reactions will continue because the reactions give off energy that serves to activate more molecules. The burning of wood is a typical example of this type of chemical reaction, which requires heat to get it started but gives off heat once it has begun. Such *a reaction, which evolves heat,* is called an **exothermic reaction.**

The reaction of the oxygen of the air with gasoline in the automobile engine evolves so much heat that a cooling system is necessary, even after the useful heat has been converted into mechanical energy. This is an example of an exothermic reaction which requires activation; it is the electric spark which activates the molecules. The source of the energy evolved is explained by the combining of high-energy-containing molecules, such as gasoline, with oxygen to form low-energy-containing molecules, such as carbon dioxide and water.

Many chemical reactions are **endothermic,** i.e., *the chemical reaction uses up heat.* Such reactions require the continuous application of heat in order to make them take place. The cooking of foods, and the heating of limestone to form lime, are examples of such reactions.

REACTION RATES

The rate, or speed, of a chemical reaction depends upon the following factors:

1. The nature of the reactants.
2. The concentration.
3. The state of subdivision.
4. The temperature.
5. Catalysis.

The Nature of the Reactants

One of the chief problems of the chemist is to find out how a desired reaction can be made to take place. This is no problem when we are dealing with solutions of electrolytes. All that is necessary is to mix the solutions; a reaction will take place if any combination of the ions present will react in some way so as to remove them from the solution. Such reactions take place instantaneously. For example, the neutralization of an acid by a base takes place instantaneously because the hydroxyl and hydronium ions combine to form water. Whenever precipitates or gases are formed, ions are removed from the solution.

Reactions between nonelectrolytes take place more slowly because two processes must often take place. First, the molecules must be broken down into smaller units; second, the molecules so formed must join with each other to form new compounds. Examples of such chemical reactions are the cooking of foods, the digestion of foods, or even the very slow processes involved in weathering.

The Concentration of the Reactants

Increasing the number of molecules of substances in solutions results in more frequent contacts between them, and the reactions are thus speeded up. For example, a very small amount of detergent, when added to a given volume of water, will not clean as fast as will a more concentrated solution. Reactions between gases are encouraged if the pressure is increased because the particles are brought close to each other.

The State of Subdivision

In many cases, chemical reactions will not take place unless the particles are quite small. Reactions between solids generally require that the solid particles be ground up into smaller ones, which expose a greater surface, because the reactions take place between the surface molecules. The setting of Portland cement is made possible because it has been ground up into a very fine powder.

The Temperature

An increase in temperature increases the rate of chemical reactions, because the molecules contain more kinetic energy, on the average, and, therefore, hit each other more often and with more force. The cooking of foods illustrates this principle. Pressure cookers cook foods more rapidly because the cooking temperatures are higher.

Catalysis

Many chemical changes take place in nature without high temperatures and pressures, and without activation. The secret of most of the chemical reactions in nature is catalysis. **Catalysis** is *a process in which a chemical reaction takes place in the presence of minute amounts of substances that remain unacted upon at the completion of the reaction.* In general, nearly every chemical reaction can be catalyzed. The problem is to find the proper catalyst.

Catalysis in More Detail—The German chemist, Johann Wolfgang Dobereiner, toward the end of the eighteenth century, found that platinum black would cause hydrogen to react with oxygen without burning. Other chemists observed similar chemical reactions, in which a very small amount of material caused chemical reactions to take place that would not take place in their absence, but which remained unchanged at the completion of the reaction. J. J. Berzelius called this phenomenon, catalysis, (from the Greek words, "to break down") because most of the catalytic processes with which he was familiar, such as the digestion of foods, or the fermentation of wines, involved decomposition of complex compounds into simpler ones.

A common classroom demonstration is the catalytic oxidation of acetone vapor by hot platinum black (finely divided platinum) deposited in asbestos. The acetone will react with the oxygen of the air, and keep the asbestos glowing until the acetone has been used up. Another interesting experiment is that of heating a copper penny in a flame, and then suspending it in a flask containing methyl alcohol vapor. The penny will glow in the dark until all of the alcohol vapor has reacted with the oxygen of the air.

A commercial catalyst called "oxycat" consists of a number of metal tubes coated with a catalyst. If these tubes are heated, a mixture of natural gas and air, when passed over the hot tubes, will react without producing a flame and yet produce the same products. The tubes will become red hot, due to the heat of the reactions, and will continue to glow as long as the air-gas mixture is passed over them. Similar catalysts are being tried out to oxidize the unburned gasoline in automobile, truck, and bus exhausts.

It has been found that some substances retard rather than speed up chemical reactions. These substances are called negative catalysts. Lead tetraethyl is a typical negative catalyst, used to retard the rate of the explosion of gasoline in the automobile engine. When an engine "knocks" it is because the reaction takes place too soon, and there is a resulting loss of power. Various **inhibitors,** such as substances put into lubricating oil to decrease the amount of corrosion in the engine, anti-rust compounds used in automobile radiators, and antioxidants added to rubber, *probably act as negative catalysts*, although their action is not well understood.

An important consideration in the use of catalysts is that certain substances, called **promoters,** *will increase their activity.* On the other hand, other substances, called **poisons,** *prevent the action of certain catalysts.* For example, mere traces of arsenic or phosphorus will poison the nickel catalyst used to cause hydrogen to join with unsaturated oils to form saturated fats, such as are found in shortenings and margarines.

Many important industrial processes depend upon the use of catalysts. The Haber process for the synthesis of ammonia from hydrogen and nitrogen by heating them under pressure in the presence of certain catalysts, is discussed in Chapter 65. Sulfuric acid is formed by the action of water with sulfur trioxide. Sulfur dioxide can be obtained by the direct union of sulfur and oxygen, but sulfur trioxide cannot be prepared in this way. A catalyst must be used to get sulfur dioxide to combine with oxygen to form sulfur trioxide. In one process, this is accomplished by use of an oxide of nitrogen that forms an intermediate compound with sulfur dioxide, which, in turn, reacts with oxygen to form sulfur trioxide, liberating the oxide of nitrogen. This formation of an intermediate compound is typical of many catalytic reactions.

Sulfur dioxide may also be combined with oxygen by bringing the mixture of the two gases in contact with certain catalysts. In this type of catalysis, called contact or surface catalysis, the theory is that the reactants are adsorbed on the surface of the catalyst, and thus are brought into close enough contact with each other to cause them to react.

It is typical of the processes of nature that practically all of them are catalyzed. Bacteria, for example, are called nature's chemists because they are responsible for so many chemical reactions. They accomplish their reactions by producing catalysts, which are known as enzymes. Enzymes and other catalysts, such as vitamins and hormones, by which living organisms bring about so many complex reactions, will be discussed in Chapter 81.

*Catalysis in World War II—*It will be recalled that Germany could not have carried on World War I without the Haber process for the fixation of nitrogen. In World War II, a similar situation existed, in which Germany could not have lasted as long as she did without a catalytic process for the preparation of hydrocarbons from coal. Large amounts of hydrocarbon fuels, such as gasoline, were required to propel her motorized army, but Germany did not possess oil wells. She was cut off from the Russian oil fields, and the Allies did their best to interfere with oil production in Rumania.

The German Bergius process for the direct hydrogenation of coal was perfected by Friedrich Bergius (1884–1949). It depended upon the use of catalysts. Later, the Fischer-Tropsch process for the catalytic hydrogenation of carbon monoxide was developed to provide liquid hydrocarbons. The carbon monoxide for this process was obtained by the action of steam on coal. Hydrogen was a by-product. Thus coal and steam furnished both of the reactants required for the production of hydrocarbons. Fortunately for Germany, plenty of coal was available.

SUMMARY

Sulfur and Phosphorus

These two active nonmetals are essential elements in living protoplasm.

Activation

Ionic reactions take place instantaneously because ions are activated. Many nonionic reactions require activation.

Exothermic and Endothermic Reactions

Exothermic reactions evolve heat, and once started, they continue with the evolution of more and more energy as more and more molecules become involved. Endothermic reactions will not take place unless energy is added.

Reaction Rates

Reaction rates depend on (1) the nature of the reactants, (2) the concentration, (3) the state of subdivision (in the case of solids), (4) the temperature, and (5) catalysis. The mechanism of catalysis is not well understood, but in some cases it seems to be the result of the formation of intermediate compounds, and, in other cases, it may be the result of contacts.

Some catalysts are influenced by promoters or poisons.

Extremely small amounts of catalysts may greatly increase the rate of chemical reactions.

Catalysts are specific. Probably all chemical reactions can be catalyzed if the proper catalysts can be found.

Study Questions

1. DEFINE: catalysis, promoter, poison, exothermic, endothermic, activation, inhibitor.
2. Give two theories of catalysis, and give an example of each type of catalysis.
3. Give an example of negative catalysis.
4. How do bacteria manage to bring about so many difficult chemical reactions?
5. Why does subdividing solid particles increase the rate of their reactions?
6. Explain how concentration, and temperature affect the rate of chemical reactions.
7. Give examples to show how the nature of the reactants is important in determining the rate of chemical reactions.
8. Why are sulfur and phosphorus considered to be important in living organisms?
9. Outline the preparation of matches.
10. How is phosphate rock rendered suitable as a fertilizer ingredient?
11. Explain the role of catalysis in the manufacture of sulfuric acid.
12. How is sulfur obtained from underground deposits?
13. From what processes is sulfur dioxide a by-product?
14. What are the important uses of sulfur and its compounds?
15. What are the important uses of phosphorus and its compounds?
16. How do white and red phosphorus differ from each other?
17. What are the functions of phosphorus in living organisms?
18. Discuss the occurrence of phosphorus.
19. Discuss the occurrence of sulfur.
20. Discuss the composition of strike-anywhere matches.
21. Discuss the manufacture of safety matches.
22. What is the function of phosphates used in laundry soaps and detergents?
23. Discuss the Haber process.

CHAPTER 6 5

Air and Air Pollution—Nitrogen, Oxygen, and the Rare Gases

Sit down before a fact as a little child, be prepared to give up every pre-conceived notion, follow humbly wherever and to whatever abysses nature leads, or you shall learn nothing.

THOMAS HUXLEY

INTRODUCTION

Water, air, coal, salt, sulfur, limestone, natural gas, and petroleum are the most important raw materials used in the chemical industry. In this chapter, air is considered as a raw material for nitrogen and oxygen.

Among all the elements, oxygen stands first in abundance. Not only is oxygen found in the atmosphere in the free state to the extent of about 21 per cent by weight, but it is also found in the combined state as water, sand, and in the majority of the materials which make up the earth's crust. Nearly two-thirds of the human body is oxygen. Oxygen constitutes about 50 per cent of all of the known material of the earth, including its atmosphere, hydrosphere, and lithosphere. Nitrogen exists in the atmosphere to the extent of about 80 per cent. The fact that it exists in the uncombined state indicates that this is the normal condition of nitrogen. It is difficult to get nitrogen to combine with other elements and, once combined, it may separate from its compounds with explosive violence, liberating the energy that was required to cause the nitrogen to combine in the first place. The nitrogen of the atmosphere is so inactive that few natural processes cause it to combine with other elements. Lightning flashes cause nitrogen and oxygen to combine to form oxides of nitrogen in relatively insignificant amounts.

Nitrogen fixation refers to *any process whereby the nitrogen of the atmosphere is caused to form compounds.*

AIR POLLUTION

Air pollution is one of the major threats to cities throughout the world. It is estimated that it costs city dwellers at least $50 a year per person in the form of doctors' bills, and damage to textiles, paint, and rubber.

Of course, air pollution is not entirely caused by the activities of man. Nature is a source of much air pollution. Plants add a million tons of pollens to the air in the United States each year. Volcanoes contribute dust, sometimes with a worldwide distribution. Winds blow dust clouds from desert regions. Sometimes man and nature work together. Man plows the fields and nature supplies the winds that result in dust storms. The summer heat haze observed over the valleys and plains, where there is considerable vegetation, is not due to forest fires, but rather to organic compounds, terpenes, and essential oils that emanate from plants and behave very much like petroleum products in the atmosphere. The haze over the Amazon is undoubtedly of plant origin.

Another way in which nature assists man in polluting the air is the temperature inver-

486

sion, so common in the Los Angeles basin, in which a warm air mass forms over a colder air mass at ground level and thus prevents vertical updrafts.

The black, soot-laden air of soft-coal-burning regions has been eliminated by the use of hard coal, fuel oil, and natural gas. But we still have the problems of refuse disposal on a home or community basis, oil refineries, power generation plants, steel plants, cement plants, smelters, lumber mills, and many other industrial plants that burn fuels and belch forth a large variety of chemicals into the atmosphere. Automobiles, trucks, and buses are an important source of air pollution in many cities. In the Los Angeles basin, about 2½ million such vehicles pour out 1,000 tons of contaminants daily.

Air pollution is harmful to plant growth. Often, air pollution results in smogs, which form when temperature inversions cause air pollutants to build up to a point where visibility is decreased, eyes become irritated, and nose, throat, and lung troubles appear. In extreme cases, smog has produced many deaths and a large number of illnesses.

Air pollution is one of the toughest problems that modern man has been called upon to solve. A great deal of research has been done on the problem of the exhaust fumes of automobiles, trucks and buses. In general, the chief smog producer in these exhaust fumes is the unburned hydrocarbons. Probably the best way to solve this problem would be a device to oxidize these hydrocarbons, perhaps with the aid of a catalyst.

THE RARE ELEMENTS OF THE ATMOSPHERE

The rare gases, helium, argon, neon, krypton, and xenon, are sometimes referred to as the old maids and bachelors of chemistry, because their chemical inactivity is their chief property. So inactive are these elements, that they do not combine to form diatomic molecules as most gases do; their molecules consist of one atom only.

Helium is next to the lightest gas known, having a lifting power 92 per cent of that of hydrogen, but, unlike hydrogen. it is not inflammable. The main sources of helium are the natural-gas wells of the central and western United States. It is used for airships and balloons, and for the prevention and treatment of "bends," the disease of deep-sea divers and high-altitude aviators.

Neon and argon are used in gas-filled glow lamps. Argon is also used in filling electric-light bulbs, thus reducing the tendency of the hot filaments to vaporize. Argon and neon are obtained, along with nitrogen and oxygen, in the fractional distillation of liquid air. Argon is present in air to the extent of 0.94 per cent by volume. One part in 65,000 parts of air is neon, while the other gases are present in such small proportions that they are too rare to have important uses.

LIQUID AIR—A SOURCE OF OXYGEN AND NITROGEN

In order to liquefy any gas or vapor, one need only cool it below the boiling point at standard pressure. Thus, steam may be liquefied at 100° C. Likewise, if one should cool air to a temperature of −190° C, it would liquefy. This is a very difficult process, however, and it has been found that air will liquefy at much higher temperatures by raising the boiling point, with a great increase in pressure. In order to liquefy air, therefore, it is only necessary to compress it, and allow a portion of it to expand. This expansion process cools the rest of the air, which has been compressed, and causes it to liquefy. If liquid air is allowed to boil, the nitrogen will boil off first, leaving liquid oxygen.

OXYGEN

For commercial purposes, air generally serves as a source of oxygen, inasmuch as the other gases in the atmosphere are inert. When relatively pure oxygen is needed, it may be prepared by the fractional distillation of liquid air, while still purer oxygen is obtained by the electrolysis of water.

The chief chemical characteristic of oxygen is its great readiness to combine with nearly all of the other elements, including both metals and nonmetals. The most important commercial use of oxygen is in the production of high temperatures by its reaction with hydrogen or acetylene for cutting, welding, and descaling of metals.

Pure oxygen is used for the treatment of such diseases as pneumonia in which the patient cannot inhale sufficient air to supply the oxygen requirements of the body. Cylinders of oxygen supply the oxygen needed by miners, when entering mines where the air is too poisonous to breathe, and by divers, aviators, and mountain climbers. Liquid oxygen is used in tremendous quantities in liquid-propelled rockets, as the oxidizing agent. Very large quantities are also now used in the steel industry to speed up the production of steel.

Oxygen may be converted into ozone by an electric discharge. Ozone is a form of oxygen that has three atoms per molecule, rather than two, as in ordinary oxygen. Ozone is used as a powerful bleaching agent, disinfectant, and deodorizer. Air and water may be purified by ozone, but ozone is poisonous, so it must not be used indiscriminately.

COMPOUNDS OF NITROGEN

Ammonia

Ammonia gas, a compound of nitrogen and hydrogen, reacts with water to form the weak base, ammonium hydroxide. Ordinary household ammonia is a 3 per cent solution of ammonium hydroxide. It is a valuable cleaning agent, especially for cleaning carpets and textiles, because it is too weak to damage the materials, and any excess evaporates, thus leaving no harmful residue.

Liquid ammonia is used as a refrigerant in large refrigerating plants. It is used as a fertilizer, either by direct injection into the ground, or in the form of nitrogen compounds.

It will react with oxygen in the presence of a catalyst to produce oxides of nitrogen, which will combine with water to form nitric acid. Nitric acid, in turn, is used for the preparation of explosives and fertilizers.

Gunpowder

Gunpowder was apparently first made by the Chinese about 1150 A.D., if not earlier, for the production of fireworks, not the least of which were firecrackers. The invention of gunpowder in the West is usually credited to

Roger Bacon, who, in about 1248, described the use of sulfur, charcoal, and saltpeter (potassium nitrate) to produce it. Gunpowder was first used by the English in the battle of Crecy in 1346.

Chile Saltpeter

Eventually, large deposits of the excreta of sea birds, called guano, were found in Chile. Guano is rich in phosphates and nitrates, and at one time most of the world depended upon these deposits as the chief sources of nitrates for gunpowder, high explosives, and fertilizers.

Nitric Acid, a Source of Explosives

Ammonia, prepared by the Haber process, may be oxidized by passing a mixture of ammonia and air through chambers containing such catalysts as iron oxide or platinum gauze to form nitrogen dioxide, which reacts with water to produce nitric acid. Nearly all of the commercial nitric acid used in the United States today is prepared by this method.

Nitric acid is one of the most important of the heavy chemicals. It reacts with many organic compounds: for example, with glycerol, it forms nitroglycerol, the principal active constituent of dynamite, which was discovered by Emanuel Nobel and his son Alfred when one of their cans of nitroglycerine leaked into the kieselguhr in which it was packed. This mixture was found to be more stable than nitroglycerine, and came to be known as dynamite. Nitric acid reacts with cellulose to form nitrocellulose, an ingredient of smokeless powder.

EXPLOSIVES

The black gunpowder of our forefathers was a mixture of charcoal, sulfur, and saltpeter. In 1865, the Prussian army used smokeless powder made from nitrocellulose and nitroglycerine. Picric acid, which is prepared by the action of phenol with nitric acid, came into use in the Boer and Russo-Japanese wars for high-explosive shells; and T.N.T. was used on a large scale in the high-explosive shells of the World War of 1914–1918. T.N.T. (trinitrotoluene) is prepared by the action of nitric acid on toluene.

Explosives have many peacetime applications in mining and construction operations that consume more than a million pounds a day.

THE NITROGEN PROBLEM IN WORLD WAR I

High explosives are made with nitric acid, and nitric acid is made from nitrates or ammonia. At the time of the first World War, Germany not only required additional nitrates for the production of foods, owing to the food blockade, but also for the production of explosives. The German High Command believed that this war would last only a few weeks and that her reserves, together with the ammonia, obtained from the destructive distillation of coal, would meet her needs. The German armies had the luck to capture several ships laden with Chile nitrate at Antwerp; otherwise their nitrate supply would have been exhausted long before the Haber process for the fixation of nitrogen was perfected. Four-fifths of the air is nitrogen, but nitrogen is so inert that, up to a few years before 1914, all efforts to combine it with other elements on a large scale had met with failure. Here was a job which required the aid of a catalyst.

Fritz Haber's nitrogen-fixation method, which *involved the heating of nitrogen and hydrogen under pressure in the presence of certain catalysts,* was rapidly developed on a large scale in Germany, when it became evident that the war was going to last longer than was expected. The hydrogen for this reaction was prepared from water by electrolysis, or by the action of steam on coke.

Kaiser Wilhelm believed that he could conquer the rest of the world because it did not have the Haber process, and did not have the raw materials or the scientific know-how or industry to produce gunpowder and other explosives. The Germans stationed a fleet off the coast of Chile to prevent the Allies from obtaining nitrates. Eventually this fleet was destroyed, but German submarines caused the Allies to pay a high price for their saltpeter.

In the meantime, the United States began a crash program to develop nitrogen fixation processes so that it would not be dependent upon Chile saltpeter. After the war broke out, it became difficult to obtain information concerning the new Haber process; so the United States, forced to provide a nitrogen supply that would not have to be transported by steamer from Chile, selected the **cyanamide process.** *This process consisted of the heating of calcium carbide to 1,000° C by an electric arc, and passing nitrogen over the carbide.* The resulting calcium cyanamide was then treated to obtain nitric acid for the production of explosives. During the war, Germany constructed several cyanamide plants, the one at Merseburg alone, having a production capacity corresponding to about two-thirds of the previous total annual shipments from Chile.

The first, commercially successful, nitrogen-fixation process was the electric-arc process, in which nitrogen and oxygen combine when passed through an electric arc. This process is too expensive, except where very cheap power is available, as in Norway. This fixation process has now been replaced by the Haber process. The Allies undertook the development of the Haber process to supplement the cyanamide process for the fixation of nitrogen, but it took a long time to learn how to make it work.

The first problem was to discover and produce satisfactory catalysts. The next problem was to obtain large amounts of pure nitrogen and hydrogen. Nitrogen was obtained by liquefying air, and separating the nitrogen by fractional distillation. Hydrogen was obtained by the electrolysis of water, by the cracking of natural gas, and by the action of steam on carbon. An important part of the cost of the Haber process is that of the purification of the gases. Impurities would poison the catalysts.

SOURCES OF NITROGEN FOR LIVING PLANTS

The maintenance of the nitrogen supply of the soil is probably the most difficult problem involved in keeping up the fertility of the soil, because nitrogen compounds are expensive, and easily lost from the soil. Why do plants require such relatively large amounts of nitrogen? The answer is that nitrogen compounds furnish the nitrogen for the proteins that plants manufacture. These proteins

Figure 65–1. A corn demonstration in Virginia. Rows to the right received nitrate; those to the left did not. (Courtesy, Chilean Nitrate Educational Bureau)

are the basic material from which the protoplasm of every living cell is made.

Nitrogen was formerly obtained from manures, and in some sections of the world, such as China, manures are still the chief source of nitrogen. Farms that raise crops to feed animals have returned to the soil a portion of the minerals, especially nitrogen, in the form of manures; but the modern tractor-operated farm, which raises no livestock, cannot return nitrogen to the soil through manures. The soil may be enriched by growing leguminous crops, in the roots of which there are small nodules that house nitrogen-fixing bacteria, but such crops take the soil out of production for other crops. Figure 65-1 shows the value of a nitrate fertilizer.

NITROGEN-CONTAINING
FERTILIZERS

Nature makes out reasonably well without the addition of nitrogen-containing fertilizers, when the vegetation is not removed. But when the vegetation is removed, as in harvesting crops, the raking of leaves, the catching of grass clippings, and the burning over of brush, the nitrogen balance is disturbed and nitrogen compounds must be returned to the soil in the form of fertilizers.

Fertilizers may contain nitrogen in the form of nitrates that are ready for use by plants. They may also consist of animal products, such as blood or fish meal, or manures, which the various types of bacteria will convert into nitrates. Today, nitrogen is often added to the soil by adding ammonia to irrigation wa-

ter. The nitrifying bacteria take over from there. Calcium cyanamide has the advantage of reacting slowly with water in the soil to form ammonia. Other sources of nitrogen in fertilizers are such ammonium salts as ammonium nitrate, ammonium phosphate, or ammonium sulfate. Such fertilizers thus use ammonia in combination with other desirable elements required by plants.

NITROGEN FIXATION BY
BACTERIA

Although higher plants and animals cannot make use of the nitrogen of the atmosphere, many bacteria can do so. The most important of the nitrogen-fixing bacteria are those that produce the nodules, or swellings, on the roots of certain leguminous plants such as cowpeas, clover, and alfalfa. These nodules, shown in

Figure 65–2. Soybean root showing nodules which harbor nitrogen-fixing bacteria. (Courtesy, U.S. Department of Agriculture)

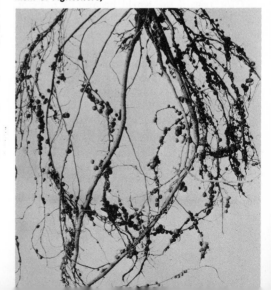

Figure 65-2, are modified rootlets swarming with bacteria. These bacteria furnish the nitrogen needed by the plant, and the plant host, in turn, furnishes the carbohydrates required by the bacteria—an example of many such cooperative relationships found in nature. These compounds, and those formed by the decomposition of dead plants and animals, are then transformed by various types of bacteria into a form in which they are utilized by plants to form more plant proteins. Thus, atoms of nitrogen are passed through plants and animals time after time. Without this cycle, life on earth would not have been possible.

THE NITROGEN CYCLE IN NATURE

Figure 65-3 shows a diagram of the nitrogen cycle in nature. Fortunately, natural processes provide a supply of nitrogen compounds for growing plants. Animals obtain their proteins from plants or animals. The proteins not retained are broken down by them into urea, and excreted as such. Certain types of bacteria act on urea in urine and other nitrogen compounds in manures to produce ammonia. Other bacterial specialists then convert ammonia into nitrites, and still other bacteria convert nitrites into nitrates.

SUMMARY

Separation of the Atmospheric Constituents

Nitrogen, oxygen, and the rare gases are obtained by the liquefaction of air, and its subsequent fractional distillation.

Nitrogen Fixation

Nitrogen may be fixed by (1) bacterial action, (2) electric discharges in air, (3) the catalytic combining of hydrogen and nitrogen (the Haber process), (4) the reaction of nitrogen with calcium carbide to form calcium cyanamide (the cyanamide process.)

Explosives

Most industrial and military explosives are nitrogen compounds.

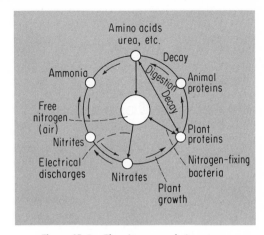

Figure 65–3.   The nitrogen cycle in nature.

Study Questions

1. DEFINE: nitrogen fixation, the cyanamide process.
2. List the most important raw materials used in chemical industry.
3. What important materials are made from atmospheric nitrogen?
4. Name the rare gases in the atmosphere, and give the uses of some of them.
5. What property of nitrogen causes it to exist in an uncombined condition in the atmosphere?
6. For what is liquid oxygen used?
7. How are oxygen and nitrogen obtained from the atmosphere?
8. Describe briefly the various processes for the fixation of nitrogen.
9. Why do soils need nitrogen-containing fertilizers?
10. Outline the nitrogen problem and how it was solved during World War I.
11. What is the chief method for the preparation of nitric acid?
12. What is the most important use of nitric acid?
13. What are the uses of ammonia?
14. How is ammonia usually prepared?
15. What are the major problems involved in the Haber process?
16. What are the main causes of air pollution?
17. What is the objection to air pollution?
18. What has been done about air pollution in some cities?
19. What is dynamite? How is it prepared? For what is it used?
20. What is the composition of smokeless powder?

CHAPTER 66

Water, Our Most Precious Resource

The scientist is a practical man and his are practical aims.

G. N. LEWIS

INTRODUCTION

Water is our most important and most abundant resource. It cannot be destroyed, and it is never used up. However, water resources are not equally distributed. There is plenty of water and sometimes too much in certain places, and not enough in other places.

By 1980, on the basis of an expected population of 270 million, it is estimated that the needs for water in the United States will exceed the water supplies available. Even today, as the result of the unequal distribution of water resources, many cities are finding that their needs are exceeding their resources.

The nation's water resources can be increased by conservation measures, and by the conversion of ocean water into fresh water. The first part of this chapter is devoted to conservation measures, which will be discussed under the following headings: (1) reduction of water runoff, (2) conservation of underground water, (3) reuse of industrial water, (4) reclamation of sewage water, (5) control of pollution, (6) control of loss by evaporation, and (7) elimination of unwanted water-consuming vegetation.

The processes of nature utilize the sun's energy to evaporate the water in the oceans, and to carry it to land areas, but it soon returns to the ocean if it is not used. The oceans thus constitute our huge natural reservoir of water. The Federal Office of Saline Water is sponsoring many research projects and demonstration projects using different methods for the conversion of seawater, to obtain information concerning the costs of different processes. Approximately 100 research centers and private firms have been spending about $50 million annually on research to convert saline water to fresh water. The target of this research is to find a method that will produce fresh water from seawater at a cost of not more than 35 cents per 1,000 gallons of water. Most cities in the United States now pay from 10 cents to 80 cents per 1,000 gallons of water.

Techniques are being perfected to obtain fresh water from seawater, and they cannot be perfected too soon. The various proposals for processes to convert seawater to fresh water are taken up at the close of this chapter.

THE PROBLEM—NOT ENOUGH FRESH WATER

The problem of water supply is a modern one. Today, with only 2.3 times the population of 1900, we use six or seven times as much water. The chief reason for the increased demands for water is the growth of irrigation and industry. People consume about 150 gallons per person daily, but this amounts to only about 8 per cent of the water consumption. Irrigation uses about 45 per cent, and industry uses another 45 per cent.

Four facets of the problem of inadequate water resources are (1) the unequal distri-

bution of water, (2) the increase of irrigation in water-short areas, (3) increasing
industrial water requirements, and (4) the
growth of industries in water-short communities.

The Unequal Distribution of Water

In the United States, the average rainfall
is about 30 inches per year, which amounts
to 10 million gallons per year for every
man, woman, and child. East of the 100th
meridian, which runs through the Dakotas,
Nebraska, Kansas, Oklahoma, and Texas,
there is usually sufficient water, and to the
west of it there is usually not enough water.
However, the thickly populated mid-Atlantic
states face increasing water shortages.

The Increase of Irrigation in Water-Short Areas

Irrigation is used chiefly in arid regions,
where there would not be sufficient water
otherwise to permit agricultural production.
The growth of irrigation has thus increased
the demand for water in regions that already
had a water shortage. For example, it was
the development of irrigation in Arizona that
resulted in the loss of water from the Colorado
River for southern California.

Increasing Industrial Water Requirements

Large industrial users of water are the steel
mills, textiles, petroleum products, rubber,
pulp, paper, meat packing, canning, preserving, freezing, brewing, dairy products, soap,
rayon, and tanning. It takes 110,000 gallons
of water to make a ton of rolled steel, and
90,000 gallons to make a ton of paperboard.
A ton of newsprint or rayon requires 240,000
gallons. More water is used for the manufacture of rayon and acetate fiber in the United
States than is used for all of the public water
supplies of the New England states.

Growth of Industries in Water-Short Communities

The arid southwestern states have serious
water shortages, but otherwise the climate is
so attractive that the population has been
growing rapidly, thus accentuating the problem.

THE WATER PROBLEM IN SOUTHERN CALIFORNIA

A notable example of the water problem
in the United States is that of southern California. Los Angeles has 4 per cent of the
nation's population in an area that receives
only 0.05 per cent of the nation's rainfall.
Northern California receives 98 per cent of
the state's water supply, but 77 per cent of
the water demand is in southern California.

The Colorado River water has been the
chief source of water for southern California,
but a decision of the United States Supreme
Court awarded a considerable amount of this
water to water-starved Arizona, so California
is now in the process of creating a new river
to carry water from northern California,
where excess water is available, to southern
California, where it is needed. This plan has
been called the "greatest mass movement of
water ever conceived or attempted by man."

Figure 66-1 shows a map of this project,
which will cost $1.75 billion dollars. It will
deliver water as far south as San Diego, a
distance of 750 miles, at a cost of about 15
to 20 cents per thousand gallons. The big
items are the Oroville Dam and reservoir,
which will dam up the waters of the Feather
River and prevent floods. This dam, costing
$458 million, will be the largest and most
expensive dam in the world. The Hoover Dam
that conserves the water of the Colorado cost
only $85 million. The completed water proj-
ect, scheduled for about 1980, will generate
2 billion killowatts of electricity, much of
which will be used to power huge pumps to
maintain the flow of water.

CONSERVATION OF THE NATION'S WATER RESOURCES

Reduction of Water Runoff

About 70 per cent of the water that falls
on the land area of the United States returns
to the atmosphere, as the result of transpira-
tion of vegetation and evaporation. The remaining 30 per cent flows down the rivers
into the oceans. This is all of the fresh water
that is available.

The seventeen western states already use

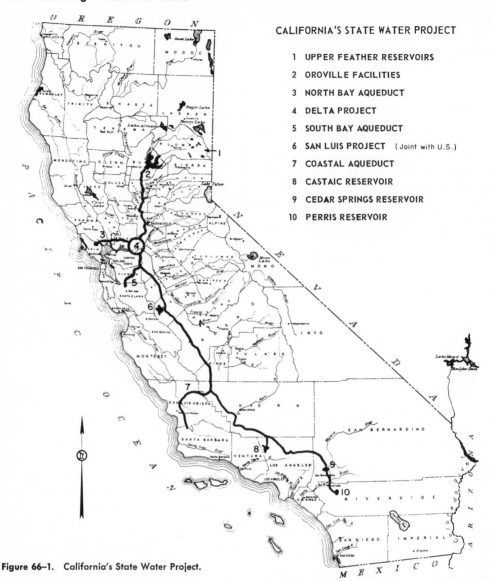

CALIFORNIA'S STATE WATER PROJECT

1   UPPER FEATHER RESERVOIRS

2   OROVILLE FACILITIES

3   NORTH BAY AQUEDUCT

4   DELTA PROJECT

5   SOUTH BAY AQUEDUCT

6   SAN LUIS PROJECT   (Joint with U.S.)

7   COASTAL AQUEDUCT

8   CASTAIC RESERVOIR

9   CEDAR SPRINGS RESERVOIR

10   PERRIS RESERVOIR

Figure 66-1. California's State Water Project.

about one-eighth of the available river water. More dams and reservoirs should be built, and more aqueducts should be provided to transport the water to places where it is needed.

Conservation of Underground Water

One community in southern California pumps the water reclaimed from sewage, into the ground, because the water table has been lowered by 110 feet as the result of excessive withdrawals. This community then obtains water from distant wells, although it could have used the purified sewage water directly, since it is chlorinated before being returned to the ground. In order to conserve our ground-water resources, excessive withdrawals and resulting lowering of water tables must be discontinued. Perhaps the above method would help to solve this problem.

Reuse of Industrial Water

Once the Federal and State Governments have required that industrial water be treated before returning it to the rivers, it may just as well be used over and over again. The cost of treating industrial waste water is usually no greater than 5 cents per 1,000 gallons.

The Kaiser Steel Company's Fontana, California, plant reuses its water and thus obtains a ton of steel with only 1,400 gallons of water, as compared with the 65,000 gallons that is used in the process.

Reclamation of Sewage

If industries can reuse their water, why should cities not reuse the water effluent from sewage disposal plants, which is purer than the raw water in the rivers, that is often the source of their water supplies? On the average, cities return about 90 per cent of their water to rivers in the form of effluent from sewage disposal plants, but there are notable exceptions. For example, the Bethlehem Steel company uses 50 million gallons of water per day, which has been reclaimed from the sewage of Baltimore, Maryland.

Los Angeles has embarked on a project to use water reclaimed from sewage to water its parks, and for industrial purposes. There is no reason why water reclaimed from sewage should not be used for irrigation.

Control of Pollution

Many communities have disposed of their sewage by discharging it into rivers or the oceans. However, Federal and State Health authorities have clamped down on pollution of our water resources by sewage, and most of our cities have instituted sewage treatment plants to purify the water before returning it to the rivers.

Many industries have wasted their water by returning it to the rivers in the form of waste that has created pollution problems. At one time, the Ohio River was literally a running sewer, created by the sewage from cities and industrial wastes, but through the cooperative efforts of five states bordering the Ohio River this pollution problem is being overcome.

Control of Loss by Evaporation

Evaporation losses from the lakes, reservoirs, and rivers in the United States exceeds the total amount of water used. The United States is entering a period of tremendous growth, in which the demand for good water

will be more than doubled. By 1980, water experts estimate that the reservoir capacity of the country must be increased from 275 million acre-feet to 600 million acre-feet.

The Australians pioneered in the use of cetyl alcohol, a pure, solid, long-chain alcohol, which will spread over water to form a layer one molecule deep. The molecules stand on end on the water surface, so closely packed that water molecules cannot pass between them. However, carbon dioxide and oxygen can pass through the films readily, so there is no danger of affecting the fish that depend upon dissolved oxygen. Such layers work nicely in calm weather, but high winds break up the films; the films reform when the winds die down. Certain types of bacteria feed on the films, so they must be renewed. These monomolecular films reduce water losses by evaporation by 30 to 50 per cent at a cost of 1.4 cents per 1,000 gallons of water.

The Elimination of Unwanted Water-Consuming Plants

In areas where the rainfall is adequate, water is conserved by vegetation, especially forests, but in areas where water is scarce, water is saved for crops by the elimination of weeds.

PROCESSES PROPOSED FOR THE CONVERSION OF SEAWATER INTO FRESH WATER

Oceans border twenty-three states, which have 65 per cent of the nation's industry, and 45 per cent of the population. Many cities located near the oceans may find it necessary to turn to them for their water supplies, regardless of cost.

The saltiness of saline waters varies from 0.7 per cent in the Baltic Sea to about 21 per cent in the Great Salt Lake. The average ocean salinity is about 3.5 per cent. The salt in seawater is mostly sodium chloride, but it includes up to 49 other elements. If a seawater conversion plant could be combined with a chemical plant to extract such elements as bromine, iodine, lithium, magnesium, and even gold, both processes might be economically sound.

The various methods of converting seawater into fresh water present a variety of applications of the basic laws dealing with the effects of temperature and pressure on physical changes, and the heat energy involved in these changes.

Among the hundreds of processes that have been proposed, the following are being investigated: (1) solar evaporation, (2) distillation, (3) freezing, (4) electrodialysis, (5) osmosis, and (6) formation of hydrates.

Solar Evaporation

For castaways, plastic films have been provided; they could be inflated and used to condense water evaporated by the sun's energy. This principle could be applied on a large scale. The advantage of such a process is that it uses solar energy, which costs nothing. The disadvantages are that the process is inefficient, takes up too much space, and requires too much maintenance.

Distillation

All navy ships and most passenger ships produce fresh water by distillation of seawater. Today, multistage evaporators are used in several commercial installations. The Pacific Gas and Electric Company has a huge electrical generating plant on Morro Bay,

California, where there is insufficient fresh water to meet the need for 144,000 gallons per day for its boilers. It produces fresh water from seawater by two triple-stage evaporators. *In the first stage of* **the multistage evaporator,** *water is evaporated to steam at atmospheric pressure or higher. The steam then passes through coils in a second evaporator, containing water at a lower pressure, which will, therefore, boil at a lower temperature. The steam from this stage may then pass to a third stage where water boils under a still lower pressure.* As the steam passes from one stage to another, it gradually gives up its heat and condenses, thus the original heat that was required to boil or evaporate the water in the first stage is conserved.

Figure 66-2 shows the first, large, experimental multistage flash plant in the United States, at San Diego, California. It was constructed to demonstrate the technical and economic feasibility of the multistage evaporation process. It began operating, March 10, 1962, and in less than twelve days it produced 515,950,000 gallons of fresh water from the Pacific Ocean. This plant was so successful that it was closed down on February 26, 1964, and dismantled for transportation to Guantanamo Naval Base, Cuba,

Figure 66–2. The San Diego multi-stage flash seawater conversion plant, which was transported to Guantanamo Naval Base. (Courtesy, Office of Saline Water, U.S. Department of Interior)

to make this base self-sufficient as far as fresh water is concerned. This action was undertaken as a result of Cuba's cutting off of the water supply for the base.

A large multistage distillation unit is used on the Caribbean Island of Aruba to supply its 55,000 inhabitants with 2.7 million gallons of fresh water daily, at a cost of $1.75 per 1,000 gallons. This plant burns heavy residual oil from a local oil refinery to supply the necessary heat. A similar process in Kuwait produces water at a cost of only 63 cents per 1,000 gallons of water for the entire population of 207,000 people, but, of course, this plant is located where there is an abundance of cheap fuel and labor.

It is likely that atomic-energy reactors will be used eventually to distill seawater, once their cost has been reduced so as to compete with other sources of energy. Such reactors would be ideal for communities where both fuel and water are scarce. Another suggestion is that waste radioactive isotopes be encased in metals and then used to operate distillation plants.

Freezing

Based on the amount of energy required, freezing processes could be the cheapest of all, provided that satisfactory methods of washing the ice crystals free from salt water can be perfected. Water taken from the ocean is already near its freezing point, and freezing requires much less energy than evaporation.

Freezing methods include: (1) partially freezing seawater by flash evaporation, and (2) evaporating a refrigerant in contact with precooled seawater.

Flash Evaporation—In Israel, there is a flash evaporation plant that is said to produce water at a cost as low as 40 cents per 1,000 gallons. In this process, salt water is sprayed into a vacuum tank where evaporation takes place rapidly enough to freeze the water. Ice crystals fall to the bottom, and are mechanically separated from the salt water. The vapor from one tank, which contains the heat liberated by the freezing process, is then used to melt the ice in a second tank.

Evaporating a Refrigerant in Contact with Precooled Seawater—In a typical process of this kind, a volatile liquid hydrocarbon, such as isobutane, is pumped into salt water, where it vaporizes and leaves behind an icy sludge.

Electrodialysis

Salt water is placed in a tank with a positive electrode at one end and a negative electrode at the other end. These electrodes attract the salt ions of opposite charge. If membranes are placed around the poles, the ions become trapped, and fresh water comes out in the middle.

One side of each compartment permits sodium ions to exit, but stops chloride ions from entering. The other side is a different plastic, which permits chloride ions to exit, but stops sodium ions from entering. The salt ions are removed from adjacent compartments.

This process uses considerable electricity and is too expensive for conversion of seawater to fresh water, but it is quite practical for the conversion of brackish water.

This process is used on the Bahrein Island, in the Persian Gulf, where it produces 90,000 gallons of fresh water daily.

A plant at Oxnard, California, produces water at 20 cents per 1,000 gallons, but it uses brackish water which is far less saline than seawater.

Osmosis

An osmotic process depends upon the use of a semipermeable membrane, impermeable to salt molecules, but permeable to water molecules. Ordinarily, water would pass from the dilute solution on one side of the membrane to the more concentrated solution on the other side of the membrane. However, the process can be reversed by applying a mechanical pressure on the salt water, thus forcing pure water through the membrane. One pass through the membrane removes about 90 to 95 per cent of the salt.

Formation of Hydrates

In this process, pumps and compressors force light hydrocarbons, such as propane, to the bottom of a pipe of fairly large diameter. The bottom end of the pipe is open and the upper end is closed. The hydrocarbon combines with water and carries it to the top of the pipe. The compressed gas condenses on the hydrate crystals as they rise to the top and thus furnishes the heat required to raise them to a temperature of 45° F at which they decompose, thus releasing fresh water. This process depends upon the fact that propane, for example, will combine with water in the ratio of one molecule of propane to seventeen molecules of water. There is a difference of about 10° F between the temperature at which the hydrate forms and the temperature at which it decomposes.

SUMMARY

The Water Problem—Not Enough Fresh Water

1. Unequal distribution of water.

2. Increase of irrigation in water-short areas.

3. Increase of industrial water requirements.

4. Growth of industries in water-short areas.

The Solution

1. Conservation Measures.
   a. Reduce water runoff by dams and aqueducts.
   b. Conserve underground water by returning water to the ground.
   c. Reuse industrial water.
   d. Reclaim sewage.
   e. Control pollution.
   f. Control loss by evaporation.
   g. Eliminate unwanted water-consuming plants.

2. Conversion of Salt to Fresh Water.
   a. Solar evaporation.
   b. Distillation.

   c. Freezing.
   d. Electrodialysis.
   e. Osmosis.
   f. Formation of hydrates.

Study Questions

1. DEFINE: electrodialysis, multistage evaporator.
2. What are the causes of the impending water problem in the United States?
3. What is the nature of the water problem?
4. What two general approaches will help to solve the problem of water shortage?
5. List the conservation measures which may be used to save fresh water.
6. Why would it be more economical for some cities to convert seawater to fresh water than to try to solve their problem by using fresh water supplies?
7. What are the causes of the water shortage in southern California?
8. How is the State of California planning to solve the water problem in southern California?
9. What are the possible uses for reclaimed sewage water other than for human consumption?
10. Is there any reason why water reclaimed from sewage should not be used for human consumption?
11. What were the causes of the pollution problem of the Ohio River?
12. What are the objections to water pollution?
13. List the various processes which have been suggested for the conversion of seawater into fresh water.
14. Give the principle of the hydrate process for the conversion of seawater.
15. Why is a freezing process for the conversion of seawater inherently economical?
16. Give the principle of multi-stage-evaporator distillation processes.

The Halogens—
Antiseptics and Disinfectants

Since the antiseptic treatment has been brought into full operation, and wounds and abscesses no longer poison the atmosphere with putrid exhalations, my wards, though in other respects under precisely the same circumstances as before, have completely changed their character; so that during the last nine months not a single instance of pyemia, hospital gangrene, or erysipelas has occurred in them.

As there appears to be no doubt regarding the cause of this change, the importance of the fact can hardly be exaggerated.

JOSEPH LISTER

INTRODUCTION

The **halogens,** so called because they are such *good salt formers* (from the Greek *halos*, meaning salt; and *genes*, meaning born), include fluorine, chlorine, bromine, iodine, and the very rare element, astatine. The halogens have been among the best sources of disinfectants, and for that reason, disinfectants are taken up in this chapter.

Chlorine, bromine, and iodine are found in the salts which are found in the ocean.

"The Romans found salt so necessary to the efficiency of their far flung armies that each soldier was provided with a special ration of it, or with the means of purchasing it. This stipend was called salarium argentum, and from it springs our English word salary. The expression "he is not worth his salt" also traces back to this source."[1]

From time immemorial, heavy taxes on salt, or government monopolies have been important sources of revenue. During the Middle

[1] Taken from *Salt—Its Romantic History, Its Refining and Its Many Uses,* an excellent reference for a more detailed study of salt, published by the Worcester Salt Company, New York City.

Ages in Europe, thousands of people every year were subjected to the lash or the rack or sent to the galleys for illegal preparation of salt. It was illegal for anyone to prepare salt from seawater for his own use, or even to save the water in which salt meat or fish had been cooked. The salt used in the leather industry was poisoned like our denatured alcohol is today, to prevent its internal use. Salt is one of our cheapest and most abundant necessities of life. Salt is obtained (1) by mining rock salt, and (2) by the evaporation of brine from the ocean or salt wells. Many large deposits of salt are widely distributed in the United States. For example, the Michigan salt beds, 32,000 square miles in area and from 1,000 to 5,000 feet thick, contain enough salt to supply the world for 1 million years.

THE HALOGENS

The halogens are a group of nonmetallic elements, very active, and similar to each other in chemical properties. They are highly electronegative, and form ionic salts. Fluorine is a pale yellow gas; chlorine is a yellowish green gas; bromine is a reddish brown liquid, and iodine is a black solid. Fluorine is the most active element known. The activity of the rest of the halogens decreases in the order in which they are listed above.

Nearly all of the salts of chlorine, bromine, and iodine are soluble, and for that reason they have been washed out of the soil and carried to the oceans. Sodium chloride, common salt, is the most abundant of the salts that impart the salty taste to seawater.

FLUORINE AND ITS COMPOUNDS

The calcium salts of fluorine, such as cryolite and fluorapatite, are insoluble in water, and deposits of these salts serve as the chief sources of fluorine. Fluorine is obtained by the electrolysis of its molten salts. Because of its high activity, fluorine is used as an oxidizing agent for some rockets. It forms very stable compounds, which accounts for its use in various synthetic plastics, fibers, rubbers, etc.

A relatively new family of organic chemicals, known as fluorocarbons, consists of compounds in which the hydrogen in hydrocarbons has been replaced with fluorine. It is a rule of chemistry that the most active elements form the most stable compounds. This rule is well illustrated in the case of fluorine, which is so active that it is only recently that ways have been devised to handle it. Fluorocarbons and their derivatives have great possibilities because of their unprecedented stability and noninflammability. Hydraulic fluids, lubricants, drugs, insecticides, dyes, plastics, coolants, and many other applications of fluorine are already in use. For example, uranium 235 was separated from uranium 239 by gaseous diffusion of uranium hexafluoride. Fluorine plastics are referred to on page 567. DFDT was used by Germany in World War II as an insecticide. It is similar to DDT except it is more effective for some insects.

The refrigeration coolant, Freon, is also used in aerosol bombs. Sodium fluoroacetate is one of the best rodenticides.

A few fluorine compounds hydrolyze, i.e., react with water, to produce hydrofluoric acid, which is destructive to animal life. Such compounds are therefore a frequent ingredient of insect and ant powders.

Hydrofluoric acid is used to etch glass, with which it reacts to form a soluble compound, silicon tetrafluoride.

A fluorine plastic, polytetrafluoroethylene, sold under the name of Teflon, has many desirable properties such as chemical inertness, resistance to corrosion and high temperature, and excellent electrical insulating ability.

There is considerable evidence that the addition of fluorides in a one-part-per-million proportion to drinking water reduces tooth decay, without harmful effects. More than one thousand cities have adopted fluoridation. The theory behind the use of fluorides is that they block the invasion routes by which bacteria enter the teeth. Fluorides may be applied directly by a dentist; the use of a dentrifice containing tin fluoride or other fluorides, may also produce the desired blocking.

The opposition to the addition of fluorides to the water supply in many communities is an indication of the fact that the scientific method does not yet influence the approach of many people to problems of everyday living.

CHLORINE

Chlorine is so abundant, so readily obtained by the electrolysis of common salt solutions, and so useful in preparing a very wide range of compounds, that we meet with it daily in the form of plastics, rubbers, fibers, and drugs. In the uncombined state, it is used chiefly to disinfect water, and as a bleaching agent.

BROMINE AND IODINE

Bromine is less than one hundredth as abundant as chlorine, and iodine is still less abundant. Bromides and iodides are widely used as silver salts to form photographic emulsions. Bromine is used to make dibromethane, to be added along with lead tetraethyl to prevent lead deposits from forming in the automobile engine.

THE DISCOVERY OF MICROORGANISMS

Anton Van Leeuwenhoek (1632–1723), a merchant in the city of Delft, became interested in the microscope as a hobby. Galileo had arranged the lenses of his telescope so that he could magnify close objects, and his idea was followed up by several people. But, Van Leeuwenhoek's great contribution was the carefully ground lens system with which he was able to obtain a magnification of as much as 200 times. He was the first man to observe yeast cells and small "animalcules" in stagnant water, and even **germs,** *which are now called* **bacteria.** Other workers improved microscopes to the extent that they were able to distinguish between **"bacilli"** (*little rods*) and **"spirilli"** (*spirals*). Soon, still smaller **"cocci"** (*berry-like*) microorganisms were seen. The German botanist, Ferdinand Julis Cohn (1828–1898) named these microorganisms bacteria. Pasteur introduced the term, **microbe** (*meaning small life*). Today, *any type of microscopic form of life, be it bacteria, yeasts, protozoa, etc.,* is called a **microorganism.**

PASTEUR'S ORIGIN OF THE GERM THEORY OF DISEASE

Louis Pasteur (1822–1895), a French chemist, found that a silkworm disease was caused by microorganisms, and he saved the silkworm industry by his plan of destroying all infected worms and leaves. On the basis of this idea, he originated the "germ" theory of disease, one of the most basic discoveries ever made in the field of medicine. Later, Pasteur laid the foundations for use of vaccines and antitoxins in the biological treatment of diseases caused by microorganisms. These new approaches, at first scorned by the leading doctors, finally saved the lives of millions of people who would otherwise have died from smallpox, cholera, typhoid fever, diphtheria, and other highly contagious diseases.

THE DEVELOPMENT OF ASEPTIC SURGERY

To Pasteur, and Joseph Lister (1827–1912), an English surgeon, we owe the introduction of **aseptic** *surgery,* i.e., *surgery under conditions which eliminate harmful bacteria.*

Prior to Pasteur's development of the germ theory, the Viennese physician, Ignas Semmelweiss, had observed that many women who had their babies in hospitals died of childbed fever (puerperal fever), while women who had their babies at home seldom contracted this disease. He reduced the death rate in maternity wards from 12 per cent to 1.5 per cent, by having the attending physicians wash their hands in a solution of chlorinated lime. Thus he introduced the use of a disinfectant even before Pasteur discovered that bacteria cause disease. His fellow physicians resisted these new "senseless" ideas, and drove him out of Vienna. Pasteur met with similar opposition to his new ideas by the leading physicians of his time, but this opposition simply drove him to experiments to prove the correctness of his theory. The physicians of Vienna went back to their former unsanitary practices, and Semmelweiss moved to Budapest where he introduced his ideas with success.

DISINFECTION BY HEAT— PASTEURIZATION

Pasteur had learned that bacteria could be killed by heat, and prevailed upon the physicians to boil their instruments and steam their bandages. He thus established the principle of **pasteurization,** *used to kill bacteria in milk and other materials.* A further application of the use of heat to destroy bacteria is illustrated by the tremendous canning industry of today. Autoclaves are now used to sterilize dressings, bandages, etc. used in surgery. Millions of lives have been saved by this one contribution of Pasteur.

DISINFECTION BY CHEMICALS

Lister introduced the idea of treating wounds with carbolic acid (phenol), and even sprayed his operating room with it. He met with opposition, but he won out, because Pasteur's germ theory had furnished a reasonable basis for what he was recommending. The use of carbolic acid tended to destroy tissues, and was hard on the people who had to breathe it. The result was that there began a never-ending search for new disinfectants that would not damage the tissues. The rest of this chapter outlines some of the results of this search.

ANTISEPTICS AND DISINFECTANTS

Microorganisms are able to survive in environments that prevent their growth, through the mechanism of changing into highly resistant spores. These spores may remain in the dormant state for long periods of time, even thousands of years, and recover their power to multiply, when conditions become favorable again. Substances that prevent the *growth (multiplication) of microorganisms but do not destroy them* are called **antiseptics,** while *substances that kill microorganisms outright* are called **disinfectants** or **germicides.** Some of the more common types of disinfectants are listed as follows:

Oxidizing Agents

The oxygen of the air, ozone, and hydrogen peroxide have been used for generations to kill bacteria. Oxygen is too weak; hydrogen peroxide has very limited applications; and ozone is highly irritant and toxic to the body. It is used to some extent to kill bacteria in water supplies. Thenardol, urea peroxide dissolved in glycerine, is a recent improvement on hydrogen peroxide for disinfecting wounds.

Halogens

The powerful disinfecting properties of the halogens—chlorine, bromine, iodine, and a number of their compounds have been applied ever since Semmelweiss' shrewd (or was it lucky?) use of chloride of lime.

It has already been pointed out that chlorine is obtained by the electrolysis of sodium chloride. Chlorine itself is a powerful disinfectant, and is used, as already mentioned, in the disinfection of water. It is also combined with lime to form bleaching powder, which may be used for the same purpose when chlorine is not available. A similar product is calcium hypochlorite, which is sold under various names, for the disinfection of home swimming pools.

Ordinary household bleach (a solution of sodium hypochlorite) is an excellent disin-fectant, but it is not recommended for application to the body. One interesting use of such household bleaches is their use in disinfecting water for drinking. Owners of travel trailers which have their own water tanks are generally advised to put a tablespoonful of household bleach in a twenty-gallon water tank when forced to use questionable water. Halazone tablets are specially designed to disinfect water. One or two tablets are placed in a pint of water, which is allowed to stand for a half hour before use. Hypochlorites are used under various fanciful names for disinfecting utensils in the dairy industry, and in disinfecting dishwashing solutions in restaurants. Dactin is an organic compound containing 66 per cent available chlorine, which is especially recommended for the above purposes.

The use of hypochlorites as disinfectants dates from World War I, when Dakin's solution, prepared by the action of chlorine on sodium carbonate, with the addition of a little boric acid, was the answer of Science to the call of military surgeons for a disinfectant to stop the tremendous loss of life due to infections. Chloramine T (also called Chlorazene) and Dichloramine T were later developed to replace the inorganic hypochlorites, because of their greater stability.

Iodine is still one of the best disinfectants, and the ordinary solution of iodine in alcohol, called tincture of iodine, is familiar to nearly everyone. Tincture of iodine contains 2 per cent of iodine dissolved in 50 per cent alcohol, which itself is a good disinfectant. If a bottle of tincture of iodine is not kept tightly closed, the alcohol will gradually evaporate and the concentration of iodine will increase to the point where its use will blister the skin. Tincture of iodine is poisonous if taken internally. It is still a widely used household disinfectant, but milder, equally effective disinfectants are now gradually replacing it.

Iodine has been used in the form of iodophors for sterilizing dishes in hospitals and restaurants. They consist of complex surfactant iodine mixtures.

Phenol and Related Compounds

Carbolic acid, the everyday name of phenol, is used as the standard for the comparison of the disinfecting properties of substances. The disinfecting power of a given substance is tested by determining the maximum dilution of the substance that will kill a given organism in a given length of time under specified conditions. Substances are usually compared with phenol as a standard, and their disinfecting power is expressed in phenol coefficients. The caustic action of phenol on the body tissues was a disadvantage, and the cresols, closely related to phenol, but less harmful to the tissues, soon replaced it for some uses. The cresols are used in the form of emulsions because of their limited solubility in water. Creosote, used to protect wood against termites or rot, and some household disinfectants containing a mixture of cresols, are being replaced gradually by more modern disinfectants. Pinosylvine, discovered in 1939, and found in the heartwood of pine trees, which it protects against decay, is reported to be from 7 to 30 times more powerful than phenol as a disinfectant. All of these substances are poisons, and should not be taken internally. They should be used with care when in contact with body tissues. A solution of fuchsin dye in carbolic acid is a powerful fungicide.

Compounds of Metals

Salts of nearly all of the metals, even common salt, have disinfectant or antiseptic properties, when used in sufficiently high concentrations. For example, a concentrated solution of common salt is often used as a mouth wash, and salt is widely used to preserve or pickle foods.

Compounds of antimony, arsenic, bismuth, mercury, and silver have been utilized in many applications as disinfectants. Mercuric chloride, corrosive sublimate, a deadly poison, has been used by physicians to wash their hands before an operation. Silver nitrate has been used to cauterize wounds, especially mad-dog bites. Water in swimming pools can be sterilized by the use of silver ions produced by electrolysis, in the ratio of one part of silver ion to 20,000,000 parts of water. Silver nitrate solution has been used to disinfect the eyes of newborn babies. Colloidal silver, Argyrol; colloidal silver bromide, Argental; and colloidal silver iodide, Neosilvol, are used to disinfect mucous membranes. Bismuth com-

pounds are often used for intestinal infections. Inorganic arsenic compounds are so poisonous to animals and plants that they are not suitable for use as disinfectants.

Alcohols

Ethyl alcohol is commonly used to disinfect thermometers and instruments, or to disinfect the skin before injecting a hypodermic needle. Propyl alcohol is often used instead of ethyl alcohol for the same purposes.

Triethylene glycol, an odorless liquid of high boiling point, when vaporized into the air will kill all of the microbes in the air. Propylene glycol acts the same as triethylene glycol. Phenoxetol, a relative of ethylene glycol, is an effective remedy for blue pus infections of wounds.

Certain Dyes

Malachite green was used in World War I as a skin disinfectant. Acriflavine, acriviolet, rivanol, brilliant green, and gentian violet are also used as disinfectants.

Picric acid, the high explosive, is a yellow dye that has been used for disinfecting surfaces of the body in preparation for an operation.

Mercurochrome, a dye containing mercury, has been widely used as a disinfectant, perhaps more so than its disinfecting properties warrant. Three other mercury compounds, Merthiolate, phenyl mercuric nitrate, and Metaphen have been found to be superior to Mercurochrome as disinfectants. A few years ago these compounds were replacing tincture of iodine as household disinfectants, but better disinfectants are now available.

Organic Acids and Esters

Benzoic and salicylic acids are weak disinfectants. Sodium benzoate is used as a food preservative. Undecyclenic acid and sodium proprionate are recently recommended remedies for athlete's foot and similar fungus diseases. Acetic acid, in the form of vinegar, is an everyday food preservative.

Miscellaneous Organic Compounds

Formaldehyde and its polymers were often used to fumigate buildings a few years ago.

Today, formaldehyde is chiefly used as a preservative of biological specimens.

Quarternary ammonium compounds, widely used detergents, are likewise excellent disinfectants. Their solutions are stable, nonvolatile, and are not destroyed by boiling. They are used to disinfect food utensils, dairy and hospital equipment, medical and dental instruments, and for the disinfection of wounds.

Hexetidine (sterisol) is a modern nontoxic oral antiseptic.

SUMMARY

The Halogens

The halogens, fluorine, chlorine, bromine, and iodine, are the most active nonmetallic elements. They are powerful oxidizing agents, and in the form of the free elements or various compounds, they serve as bleaching and disinfecting agents.

The salts of chlorine, bromine, and iodine, because of their solubility, are found in seawater and salt deposits formed from ancient seas.

The Germ Theory of Disease

Van Leeuwenhoek perfected the microscope, and thus was the first man to see microorganisms.

Louis Pasteur proved conclusively that many diseases are caused by bacteria, and he developed the use of vaccines and antitoxins to treat such diseases.

Pasteurization

Pasteur used heat to destroy microorganisms and established aseptic surgery. When heat is used to destroy bacteria in milk the process is called pasteurization, in honor of Pasteur. An important application of the use of heat to kill bacteria is the modern canning industry.

Antiseptics and Disinfectants

The first disinfectant was the chloride of lime recommended by Semmelweiss, for disinfecting the hands of physicians in maternity hospitals.

Lister introduced the use of carbolic acid to disinfect wounds, and by spraying, to disinfect the atmosphere.

The different kinds of modern disinfectants are classified as (1) oxidizing agents, such as hydrogen peroxide; (2) halogens, such as chlorine, hypochlorites, and tincture of iodine; (3) phenol; (4) compounds of metals, such as colloidal silver (Argyrol), and mercuric chloride; (5) alcohols, such as ethyl alcohol, propyl alcohol, and the glycols; (6) certain dyes, such as merthiolate, a mercury compond; (7) organic acids and esters, such as benzoic and acetic acids; and (8) miscellaneous organic compounds.

Study Questions

1. DEFINE: antiseptic, disinfectant, halogen, microbe, germ, bacteria, bacilli, spirilli, cocci, microorganism, aseptic, pasteurization, germicide.
2. What is "Chlorox"? For what is it used?
3. How could a solution of "Chlorox" be prepared?
4. Name the four most important members of the halogen family.
5. What is meant by the pasteurization of milk?
6. Name five different disinfectants that have been used as common household disinfectants.
7. Why are chlorides, bromides, and iodides, found in seawater?
8. Why are fluorides not found in seawater?
9. What is the outstanding property of fluorine?
10. How could impure drinking water be disinfected?
11. Name two uses of "Freon" that depend upon its stability and chemical inertness.
12. Who originated the germ theory?
13. Why is Louis Pasteur considered to be one of the greatest scientists that ever lived?
14. Name the first two disinfectants and the men who introduced them.
15. What was the value of the opposition to Pasteur's germ theory?
16. Suggest possible reasons for opposition to the germ theory and vaccination today.
17. Why do many people object to the addition of fluorides to drinking water, although they do not oppose the addition of chlorine?
18. Why is the addition of fluorides to drinking water recommended?
19. How could one take advantage of the protective action of fluorides on the teeth in

communities where fluorides are not added to drinking water?

20. How did Lister disinfect his operating room?

21. Give the origin of the word *salary*.

22. What is the composition of tincture of iodine?

23. What was Van Leeuwenhoek's contribution to the discovery of microorganisms?

Silicon, the Backbone of the Inorganic World

When you are studying any matter or considering any philosophy, ask yourself only what are the facts and . . . the truth that the facts bear out. Never let yourself be diverted either by what you would wish to believe or by what you think would have beneficent social effects if it were believed. But look only at . . . the facts.

BERTRAND RUSSELL

INTRODUCTION

Silicon and oxygen are the two most abundant elements in the earth's crust, including the atmosphere and the hydrosphere; 27.80 per cent silicon and 50.02 per cent oxygen by weight. Much of the silicon occurs in combination with oxygen in the form of sand or quartz. Silicon oxide is commonly called silica. The silicate minerals, which are compounds of silica with other metallic oxides, make up the backbone of the inorganic world, just as carbon compounds are the basic constituents of the organic, living world.

This chapter includes a study of such important silicon products as glass, ceramics, Portland cement, and silicones.

SILICON

Electronic Structure

Silicon is just below carbon in the fourth group of the periodic table. Like carbon, it has four electrons in its outside shell. In chemical reactions, it may either gain or lose four electrons, and it therefore exhibits both metallic and nonmetallic properties. However, since the outer shell of electrons is farther from the nucleus than in the case of carbon, electrons are more readily released and silicon is more metallic in nature than is carbon.

Carbon forms a tremendous number of compounds, partly because carbon atoms are able to join with other carbon atoms to form chains and rings. Unlike carbon, silicon atoms do not join with other silicon atoms, but are tied to each other with oxygen atoms. Since one, two, three, or four oxygen atoms can thus join a corresponding number of silicon atoms with a given silicon atom, many complex silicon-oxygen compounds, called silicates, are possible. Two oxygen atoms per silicon atom form chains. With three oxygen atoms per silicon atom, two-dimensional sheets are formed. Stacks of such sheets are found in mica and clay minerals. Such compounds become more complex when some silicon atoms are replaced with aluminum atoms. The resulting compounds are clays, such as kaolin. When each silicon atom is tied to four oxygen atoms, three-dimensional compounds are formed. Examples of such compounds are quartz, feldspars, and zeolites. Figure 68-1 shows a three-dimensional crystal of quartz, which is composed of many silicon dioxide molecules. Most sand particles consist of small quartz crystals. If the structure of silicon dioxide is orderly, a crystal, similar to that of quartz, is obtained. However, if silicon dioxide is melted, it can be blown into various forms for laboratory purposes. In this case, the silicon dioxide does not crystallize but remains in a vitreous condition, typical of glass. Silica glass transmits both visible and ultraviolet radiation and has a very low coefficient of expansion. It is inert to most chemicals.

Silicon dioxide (silica) occurs in such forms as quartz, sand, chalcedony, amethyst, onyx, jasper, opal, agate, and flint.

Figure 68-2 shows a picture of silicon carbide crystals, which are made by heating a mixture of coke, sand, sawdust, and salt in an electric furnace. Silicon carbide is known under the trade name of carborundum. Abrasive wheels are made by bonding the carborundum particles with various materials. Abrasive cloth and paper are made with carborundum crystals.

Silica Gels

Silica, combined with water in varying amounts, forms the various silicic acids. Many complex silicic acids may be formed from simple silicic acid by condensation, in which two or more molecules join with the loss of one or more molecules of water. The number of possible condensed acids that may be formed from simple silicic acid is large, and many of the salts of these complex acids exist in nature.

Waterglass is a water solution of a mixture of sodium salts of silicic acid. It is prepared by the reaction of silica with such compounds as sodium carbonate, sodium sulfate, or sodium hydroxide. Waterglass forms a thick, syrupy liquid that is widely used as an adhesive in joining sheets of paper to form paper boards, as a builder in soaps, in waterproofing plaster or cement, and in fireproofing wood and other inflammable materials.

When an inorganic acid reacts with sodium silicate (waterglass), a colloidal gel of hydrated silica is obtained. Water may be removed from silica gel to form dehydrated silica gel, a porous product which occupies a very large volume for its weight. Dehydrated silica gel has remarkable adsorbing powers. For example, it will adsorb water, and is therefore used as a drying agent. The swelling

Figure 68-1. A single quartz crystal grown by the Bell Telephone Laboratories in twenty days. Such synthetic, pure, quartz crystals are used to make solar cells and transistors. (Courtesy, Bell Telephone Laboratories)

of clays is due to the presence of gel-like materials which enable them to adsorb large amounts of water. Agates, flint, and onyx are solid dehydrated silica gels.

Silicon Minerals

In the form of complex silicates of aluminum, iron, magnesium, and other metals, silica accounts for most of the substances found in rocks, clays, and soils. The chief

Figure 68-2. A mass of silicon carbide crystals as it comes from the electric furnace. (Courtesy, The Carborundum Company)

types of silicate rocks are silicates formed from various proportions of silicon dioxide, magnesium oxide, calcium oxide, boron oxide, and an iron oxide. By melting together various combinations of these oxides, a great variety of complex silicates may be obtained. Indeed, this is the process by which glass, cements, and ceramics are made. Such products may be considered to be rocks made to order.

Certain minute aquatic organisms (diatoms, infusoria) and some varieties of sponges develop silicious skeletons. Deposits of such skeletons have been found in layers up to a thousand feet in depth in the United States. This material, called diatomaceous earth (kieselguhr), has been used as a constituent of scouring powders.

Asbestos is hydrated magnesium silicate, which owes its fibrous structure to the linking of silicate groups in continuous double chains. It occurs as both short and long fibers. Short-fiber varieties are used to pack steam pipes, while long-fiber varieties may be woven into fireproof fabrics. Closely related to asbestos is talc, a white mineral with a flaky texture. It is soft enough to be readily scratched with one's finger nail, and so smooth as to be almost greasy to the touch, which accounts for its use in talcum powder. Soapstone is a relative of talc. Mica is a hydrated potassium aluminum silicate, which may be split into transparent sheets as little as 1/2500 of an inch in thickness.

GLASS

Glass may be considered to be *a non-crystalline, supercooled solution of various inorganic compounds, usually metallic oxides, which have been melted together.* When cooled, the product is a glass that breaks with a characteristic fracture, and possesses a luster and some degree of transparency.

The earth's crust contains an abundance of glass-making materials. In fact, if the entire crust were to be melted, the product would be glass. The first known glass was natural glass produced by volcanic activity. This glass, known as obsidian, was used by the American Indians to make arrowheads, spearheads, and tools.

Glass has many valuable properties, among which may be listed its resistance to scratching, chemical attack, and heat. With the exception of the precious metals such as gold or platinum it is one of the most chemically resistant materials. Glass also has a high electrical resistance, mechanical strength, the ability to be molded, drawn, or blown into many forms, and desirable optical properties.

Many different kinds of glass have come out of the research laboratories, and more are on the way. Already, very strong glass materials are used in building construction, because of their beauty and low maintenance cost.

Common window glass consists of compounds of silicon dioxide, calcium oxide, and sodium oxide. It is prepared by melting calcium carbonate (limestone), sodium carbonate, and quartz sand in a furnace. A variety of other oxides may replace those in common window glass, usually referred to as lime-soda glass, or as soft glass, because it has a relatively low melting point. Increased resistance to mechanical and thermal shocks is obtained by substituting boron oxide for part of the silica in glass. Such a glass is referred to as hard glass, because of its relatively high melting point. Pyrex glassware is such a glass. It was developed in the United States to manufacture laboratory glassware. Pyrex is a trade name and similar glassware is manufactured under other trade names. Similar types of glassware have found their way into the home for use in ovenware and glass cooking utensils.

Glass making is an ancient art, although the earliest glasses were of very inferior quality and contained many impurities. By way of contrast, let us consider modern optical glass, which must be uniform in composition, free from impurities and defects due to air bubbles. Such glass is used to make lenses for eyeglasses or lenses for microscopes and telescopes, cameras, and scientific instruments.

Flint glass, otherwise known as lead glass because it contains lead oxide, has a high density and a high index of refraction. It is soft and brilliant, and is therefore used to make ornamental cut glassware.

Colored glass is obtained by adding small traces of the oxides of heavy metals; thus, cobalt oxide imparts a blue color; selenium oxide, a ruby red; chromium trioxide, a green; manganese dioxide, a violet; and iron oxide, an amber color.

Glass Wool and Fibers

An inexpensive glass wool may be made from a waste product, such as slag, by blowing a stream of air or steam into the molten material as it runs out of a furnace. Such a product is known as mineral wool. It is used for insulation. Glass wool is a similar, but improved product made from pure glass.

Glass fibers are made by drawing out pure molten glass into fibers less than one-tenth the diameter of a human hair, so small, indeed, that a pound of glass would contain enough fibers to wind around the earth at its equator fifteen times. Glass fibers are widely used for insulation, and to make textiles that are not affected by moisture, vermin, mildew, sunlight, or oxidation. They are fireproof. Because of their electrical insulating properties, glass fabrics are used in the electrical industry for such applications as battery-plate separators. Because of their strength, glass fibers are used to reinforce plastics in such articles as fishing rods, boats, skis, and furniture. Glass cloth may be dyed or printed with deep brilliant colors by first treating them with a silicone, discussed later in this chapter.

Glass is gradually being replaced by synthetic plastics for many purposes, such as unbreakable bottles and laboratory ware. However, glass and plastics often team up to take advantage of the good properties of each member of the team. For example, safety glass is made by joining two sheets of glass with a plastic sheet to make a transparent sandwich that resists splintering on impact.

Glass Fiber Optics

It has been found that bundles of glass fibers will transmit light by total internal reflection. They are used to make optical devices to examine the inside of the stomach and similar hard-to-see places.

Some New Types of Glasses

Heat-Absorbing Glass—A transparent, heat-absorbing glass, with a pale bluish tint for glare reduction, is now being used for automobiles.

Photosensitive Glass—A number of years ago, the Corning Glass Company scientists came up with a photosensitive glass that made it possible to produce photographs in the glass. There has not been much demand for such a product, but research on this glass showed that the photosensitized part of the glass was fifteen times more soluble in hydrofluoric acid than the rest of the glass was. This discovery led to a process for the manufacture of color television tubes. A 21-inch color television tube must have 400,000 tiny, tapered holes, accurately spaced. Furthermore, because the surface of the tube is curved, each hole must be properly focused. Such a manufacturing task seemed to be almost impossible, but the use of hydrofluoric acid on photosensitive glass solved the problem.

Pyroceram—Pyroceram is not just one material, but it is a new class of materials that can be mass-produced to replace almost any object that can be made from glass. At least 5,000 different kinds of pyrocerams, with widely varying properties, have been produced in the laboratory. Pyroceram is twenty-seven times more resistant to sandblasting than glass. It is harder than hardened steel, and will scratch steel or brass. It is very resistant to heat; it is still rigid at 2,200° F. Some pyrocerams are stronger than cast iron or brass. Pyrocerams are as light in weight as aluminum. They are smooth as glass, and are easy to keep clean. They may be made white and in color, and some varieties are even transparent. Pyroceram cooking utensils have already found their way into many homes.

Pyrocerams start out as glass, but they are not glass after they have been given a special heat treatment. Glass is noncrystalline in nature. However, pyrocerams are made from glass by adding nucleating agents, such as titanium oxide, to cause it to crystallize upon careful heat treatment. By controlling the heat treatment, the size of the crystals may be controlled. The result is that pyrocerams, like steel, may be adapted to a wide variety of applications.

CERAMICS

True **ceramic** *products such as pottery, earthenware, and porcelain have a composi-*

tion intermediate between glass and cement. Ceramic products are classified into three groups: (1) unglazed, porous materials such as bricks, pottery, and terra cotta, (2) glazed, porous materials such as earthenware, and (3) nonporous materials such as stoneware, chinaware, and porcelain. *Such* **ceramic** *products are made from clay.* A pure form of clay is kaolin, a hydrated aluminum silicate. Other ingredients commonly found in clay are oxides of iron and carbonates of calcium and magnesium. Kaolin will absorb large amounts of water to form a plastic mass that can be readily molded. When heated, this moist clay loses its water and a hard, rock-like product is obtained. The nature of the product depends upon the kind of clay used, the temperature used for firing, and the types of glazes used. Ordinary bricks contain considerable iron oxide and sand; the oxide is responsible for their color. Purer clays are used for pottery. Porcelain is made from pure kaolin, powdered silica, and feldspar. Glazes are produced by applying oxide pastes, which will fuse into the surface to form a glass.

REFRACTORIES

Modern technology requires better and better refractories. A **refractory** is *a substance of an extremely infusible nature.* Firebricks, made from a special type of clay, called fireclay, have been used for many years to line furnaces and fireplaces. However, modern technology has required improved refractories that will withstand the very high temperatures of jet engines and rockets. Pyroceram is one solution to the problem. Cermets furnish another solution. A **cermet** is *a mixture of metal and ceramic grains fused together.* Metal-bonded titanium carbide, for example, displays adequate strength at temperatures as high as 1,800° F.

PORTLAND CEMENT

Ordinary **mortar,** such as is used between bricks, *consists of a mixture of slaked lime, sand, and water.* The mortar sets by combining with carbon dioxide obtained from the air, thus forming what amounts to synthetic limestone, reinforced with sand. *Hydraulic mortar differs from ordinary mortar in its capacity to set under water, and in the absence of carbon dioxide.* **Portland cement,** so called because of its resemblance in color to the celebrated building stone quarried near Portland, England, *is a hydraulic mortar.*

Modern Portland cement is produced by treating a raw material rich in lime, such as limestone, with other materials rich in alumina and silica. Alumina and silica are furnished by clay, shale, slate, and even by blast-furnace slag.

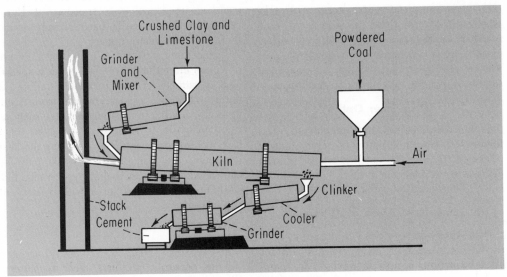

Figure 68–3. The process of making Portland cement.

The manufacture of cement takes place in four steps: (1) the mixture of raw materials is finely ground with water to form a slurry; (2) the slurry is heated in rotary kilns, and is partially fused to form a clinker; (3) the clinker is then cooled and mixed with 2 to 3 per cent of gypsum, which lengthens the time required for the cement to set; (4) the mixture is then ground so fine that it can pass through silk cloth. If quick setting cements are desired, the alumina content is increased and the lime content is decreased.

Portland cement differs from glass in that it has a much higher lime content.

CONCRETE

When Portland cement is mixed with water or with a mixture of water, sand, and gravel to form **concrete,** it takes an initial set within a few hours, and continues to harden slowly for months or years. This hardening process consists, in part at least, in the **hydration,** i.e., *chemical combination with water,* of the anhydrous compounds produced during the burning of the cement, to produce synthetic silicate rocks. These synthetic rocks may be made stronger than natural rocks by the use of reinforcing steel. Concrete should be kept wet when setting in order to provide plenty of water for the hydrating process.

SILICONES

Silicones are *organic carbon compounds in which silicon dioxide replaces some of the carbon groups.* Their unique properties are due to the unusually stable silicon-oxygen bond. Thousands of silicones have been made, and a tremendous amount of research is devoted to the production of new silicones, and to many new applications.

Silicone liquids are used as lubricants, because they remain fluid at quite low temperatures, and because they resist decomposition at higher temperatures. Their constancy of viscosity makes it possible to operate engines in the polar regions, and at the low temperatures of high altitudes.

Silicone rubber is valuable because it retains its elasticity even at low temperatures, and because it resists oxidation and elevated temperatures. An interesting laboratory curiosity is bouncing putty, which is soft and pliable like clay, and yet bounces like rubber. It has been used in the center of golf balls.

A silicone aluminum paint will withstand temperatures up to 1,200° F, and is therefore useful for painting smokestacks. A silicone glaze for baker's pans eliminates the necessity of greasing them, prevents sticking, and eliminates subsequent cleaning. A similar treatment given to skillets or pancake griddles prevents sticking without the use of grease. Shoes, clothing, or masonry may be treated with a silicone liquid to prevent them from being wet with water. Eyeglasses may be kept from fogging. Silicone coatings may be used to protect metals against corrosion.

The above applications are but a few of the examples in which silicones are playing a part in contributing to the comforts of everyday living, all because of the happy marriage of carbon and silicon chemistry.

SUMMARY

Compounds of Silicon

The wide variety of silicon compounds is largely due to the fact that silicon atoms may be joined by oxygen atoms to form complex combinations.

Waterglass—is a sodium silicate used as an adhesive.

Silica gel—is a dehydrated silicic acid used as an adsorbing agent for water.

Silicon Carbide—is a very hard material used as an abrasive.

Glass—Glass is a supercooled melted mixture of various metallic oxides.

Pyroceram—is a glass in which crystals have been formed by adding nucleating agents and by heat treatment.

Ceramics—ceramics are products made from clay.

Portland Cement—consists of a mixture of oxides of calcium, aluminum, and silicon.

Concrete—consists of a mixture of Portland cement, water, sand, and gravel.

Mortar—consists of a mixture of slaked lime, water, and sand.

Silicones—are organic compounds containing silicon.

Study Questions

1. DEFINE: glass, ceramic, cermet, silicone, pyroceram, Portland cement, mortar, concrete, refractory, hydraulic mortar, hydration.
2. Why is silicon said to be the backbone of the inorganic world?
3. Name several silicon minerals.
4. What types of rocks are silicious in nature?
5. What types of rocks are not silicious in nature?
6. To what are the advantageous properties of silicones attributed?
7. List some of the improvements in the properties of rubber and lubricants made possible with silicones.
8. In what regard are silicon and carbon similar?
9. How may one account for the vast number of silicon compounds found in nature?
10. How is waterglass made, and for what is it used?
11. What is pyroceram? How is it made? What are its superior properties?
12. What is the composition of Portland cement? How does it differ from mortar? How is it prepared?
13. What is concrete? How does it differ from mortar?
14. How does Pyrex glass differ from ordinary window glass?
15. Outline the types of ceramics. From what are they made?

CHAPTER 69

Metals and Metallurgy

Science is the great instrument of social change, all the greater because its object is not change but knowledge; and its silent appropriation of this dominant function, amid the din of political and religious strife, is the most vital of all the revolutions which have marked the development of modern civilization.

A. J. BALFOUR

INTRODUCTION

The use of coal to replace charcoal in the smelting of iron, and the invention of the steam engine, inaugurated the industrial revolution. Our modern industrial civilization is still based on iron, and every year has witnessed new methods of producing harder, tougher, and stronger iron alloys (steels).

Every year sees fresh progress in the field of metallurgy, and there is hardly any branch of the history of civilization more fascinating than that which traces the development of man from the Stone Age through the Bronze Age, the Iron Age, and the modern age of new metals, such as aluminum, and magnesium. It is interesting to note that some of our most outstanding scientific achievements, such as atomic energy and artificial satellites, were made possible by the use of new "wonder" metals.

METALLURGY THROUGH THE AGES

The separation of metals from their ores was an art practiced long before it became a science. For example, the making of brass articles in China was an art passed down from one generation to another for thousands of years. Each city became famous for the characteristic kind of brass which it made.

The particular kind of brass was probably determined by the nature of the ores used. The ancient Egyptians and Babylonians, and primitive people throughout the world, separated copper, iron, and a few other metals, from their ores, by processes that were the same in principle as those used today.

The history of metallurgy reveals the relative difficulty of separating metals from their ores. Gold has been known for a long time because it occurs **free**, i.e., *in an uncombined state*, in nature. Gold was well known by ancient peoples. Probably its chief early uses were in the fabrication of ornaments. It could be beaten into sheets and pulled into wires. It had a pleasing appearance, and it did not corrode. Copper, which has been found in limited quantities in the free state, was probably the first metal to be separated from its compounds, usually oxides or sulfides, by reduction with charcoal. Tin was similarly obtained. Perhaps the first **bronzes** (*alloys of copper and tin*) were obtained by reduction of naturally occurring mixtures of oxides or sulfides of copper and tin. The Bronze Age replaced the Stone Age in Europe and western Asia about 3500 B.C., and in southeastern Europe about 2000 B.C.

Throughout the ages, the production of metals has been stimulated by their contributions to warfare. Early uses were for swords, spearheads, and daggers. Then the use of armor was developed as a counter measure. Mercury and lead were known by the ancient Egyptians and Babylonians. The alchemists added bismuth, zinc, and arsenic to the list of known metals. Gold, silver, copper, tin, iron, and lead were known by the ancient Egyptians, and are mentioned in the Old Testament. Mercury was referred to by Aristotle about 350 B.C., and in A.D. 10, Strabo referred to zinc. Iron was known as early as bronze, but it is probable that the only sources of iron for a long time were meteorites. Iron smelting began somewhere in Asia Minor about 1400 B.C. An iron-equipped army could route a bronze-equipped army, because iron was harder, and could cut through bronze shields. The use of iron weapons by the Hittites in Asia Minor probably accounted for their rise to power. Later, the Assyrians had all-iron weapons which, about 800 B.C., enabled them to dominate Egypt and western Asia for about 250 years. The Achaeans of Greece were defeated by the iron-equipped Dorians because they clung to bronze weapons.

THE NATURE OF METALS

The Chemical Nature of Metals

The metallic elements give up electrons, and thus form positive ions in solution. **Metals** are *base forming, i.e., their oxides will react with water to form bases.*

An outstanding characteristic of metals is the difference in their chemical activities. Some metals, like the alkali and alkaline-earth metals, are so active that they react with oxygen and water vapor in the atmosphere at ordinary temperatures. Other metals, the so-called noble metals such as gold, platinum, and iridium, are so inactive that they are not acted upon appreciably when exposed to the air, even after several thousand years. We have already learned that these differences among the metals are the result of their varying attraction for electrons. It will be recalled that this difference in the attraction for electrons is shown by the table of electronegativities on page 259. The electromotive series, page 220, also lists the elements in the order of their attraction for electrons.

The Physical Properties of Metals

One of the properties that distinguishes metals from nonmetals is their **luster**, i.e., *their ability to reflect light.* Another characteristic of some metals is that they are good conductors of heat and electricity. Most of the metals have too few electrons in their outside shells or orbits to form covalent bonds such as those formed by carbon or silicon, but act like a mass of positive ions in a cloud of electrons. Both the positive ions and the electrons are free to move. Heat, or electrical conductivity, is considered to be the result of the motion of electrons, while the diffusion of one metal into another is thought to be due to the diffusion of positive ions.

Some metals are relatively soft and **malleable**, which means that *they can be drawn out and extended by beating.* For example, gold may be formed into "gold leaf," an exceedingly thin sheet of gold. Many metals are **ductile**, i.e., *they may be drawn out into wires.* Other physical properties characteristic of metals are their relatively high density, and hardness.

METALLURGY

Metallurgy is *the science and art of preparing metals from their ores.* The metallurgical processes depend upon the nature of the ore and the metal to be separated. The metallurgy of the heavy metals differs in general from that of lighter ones.

The metallurgical operations (often called smelting) of the heavy metals fall into four groups:

Concentration

The ore is separated from *useless foreign material* (the **gangue**) by various **concentration** methods. This is done by hand selection, sifting, washing with a stream of water, and froth flotation. In many cases the ore must be crushed before separation by gravity processes, which may be done with or without the use of water. When the mineral and the gangue are of about the same density, gravity processes will not work. In this case, froth flotation often brings about a separation, be-

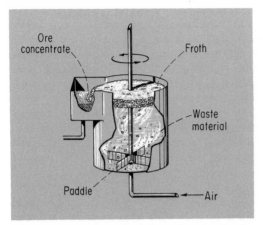

Ore concentrate

Froth

Waste material

Paddle

Air

Figure 69–1. Concentration of ore by the flotation process.

cause one of the two materials present will stick to the oily surface of a bubble and be carried to the surface with the bubble, leaving the nonwetted material behind. See Figure 69-1.

Sometimes chemical separation is possible when a chemical can be found that will dissolve the mineral and not dissolve the gangue. An example of this process is the separation of gold from a finely powdered ore by dissolving the gold in a cyanide solution. Many improved types of concentrating machinery have made it possible to reopen abandoned mines, and to run them at a profit.

Roasting

After concentration, many ores need to be **roasted,** i.e., *heated in an excess of air to convert compounds of sulfur and arsenic into oxides.*

Reduction

The metallic oxides, formed by roasting, must be **reduced,** i.e., *the oxygen must be removed.* Reduction may be accomplished by the use of:

Carbon—Carbon was used in earlier days, in the form of wood charcoal, but today, coke is used instead. Coke is obtained by heating bituminous coal in the absence of air. When coke is used, a **flux** is added *to combine with the gangue in the ore and in the coke to form a crude form of glass* (the **slag**), which floats to the top of the molten metal, and, inciden-

tally, protects it against oxidation. Lime and silica are the principal components of ordinary glass. If the gangue is high in silica, limestone is added as a flux, and if the gangue is high in lime, sand is added as the flux.

Hydrogen—Hydrogen is used in the reduction of tungsten oxide, and it has even been used in making some kinds of steel.

Active metals—Such active metals as sodium or aluminum may be used as reducing agents.

Electricity—Very active metals, such as sodium, potassium, magnesium, and aluminum, are prepared by the reduction of their compounds by the electrolysis of their molten salts.

Refining

After reduction, the crude metal must usually be *freed from impurities* by **refining** processes which may involve resmelting, distillation, or electrolysis.

THE METALLURGY OF IRON

Iron was obtained in ancient times by heating iron ore, usually ferric oxide, with charcoal. The temperatures used were not high enough to melt the iron produced, so it was *wrought into shape by hammering.* The product was **wrought iron.** In the middle ages, about A.D. 1600, improved furnaces made it possible to *melt the iron so that it could be poured into molds.* This "cast-iron" was more brittle than wrought iron, because it *contained several per cent of carbon and silicon.*

ALUMINUM

Aluminum is the third most abundant element in the earth's crust. Deposits of aluminum oxide (bauxite) are fairly abundant, but the most common compound of aluminum is clay.

In 1884, Frank M. Jewett of Oberlin College, standing before his class, predicted:

The man who makes aluminum available for commercial use will be a benefactor to the world. He will also be able to lay up for himself a great fortune.

Charles Martin Hall, one of the members of the class, took up the challenge. Less than a year after his graduation, he invented a method of preparing aluminum by the electrolysis of aluminum oxide which was dissolved in molten cryolite.

On February 23, 1886, he rushed from his father's woodshed laboratory to show his sisters the first buttons of aluminum he had made, and then with boyish enthusiasm he hurried to the college and shouted, "Professor, I've got it!"

Charles Martin Hall left a great fortune to his alma mater when he died, and his process, which is still used today, has been of great benefit to the world. By it, aluminum is now produced from bauxite (aluminum oxide) ore and sold at about 25 cents a pound, whereas it cost eight dollars a pound when Hall began his experiments.

Aluminum has two great advantages over steel: (1) it is only about one-third the density of steel, and (2) it corrodes only slightly, forming a thin coating of aluminum oxide that prevents further corrosion. The modern process of anodizing aluminum by electrolysis gives it a bright finish that is even more resistant. Pure aluminum is rather soft, but alloying takes care of that. Some aluminum alloys are even stronger than steel.

Aluminum is finding extensive applications in transportation on land, air, and water; as a material for electric conductors, cooking utensils, machinery, and electrical appliances; in the metallurgy of iron and steel; in building construction; and as a material for containers and other equipment in the chemical, food, and beverage industries. Not only is pure aluminum used for some of these applications, but aluminum is given strength and other desirable properties by alloying it with magnesium, silicon, copper, and other metals. Some desirable properties, such as increased strength, may be produced in the case of certain alloys by heat treatment. As an example of the numerous applications of aluminum, there may be cited the more than half a million miles of aluminum, steel-reinforced, high-tension, electrical transmission cable installed in the United States alone. Aluminum and its alloys make possible modern transportation by the all-metal airplane, the streamlined train, and trucks, where dead weight must be eliminated. It is even finding application in the construction of bridges, booms, and other structures where lightness is at a premium.

Aluminum is being used more and more in building construction for doors, window frames, siding, and roofing, because of its resistance to corrosion. Modern travel trailers and mobile homes likewise use aluminum because of its resistance to corrosion, and also because of its relatively low density.

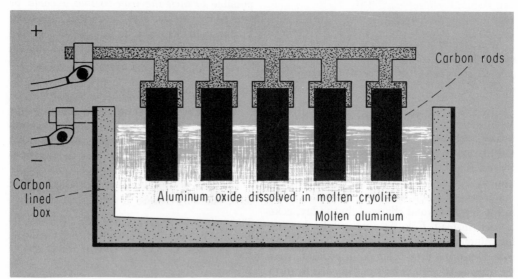

Figure 69–2. Aluminum is produced by the electrolysis of aluminum oxide which has been dissolved in molten cryolite.

MAGNESIUM

Aluminum is now meeting with some competition from magnesium.

Magnesium is quite an active metal. It is above hydrogen in the electromotive series, and, for that reason, it cannot be obtained by the electrolysis of a water solution of one of its salts. It was produced during World War II by reduction of magnesium oxide with carbon, but this process is more expensive than the modern process of electrolysis of molten magnesium chloride. Magnesium, like calcium, sodium, potassium, and lithium, as a result of natural chemical processes forms soluble salts, which are carried to the oceans. During the earth's history, the evaporation of inland seas left huge deposits of these salts. Formerly, magnesium chloride was obtained from the brine of salt wells, but today, seawater is its principal source. To the ocean water lime is added to precipitate magnesium hydroxide, well known in many households in the form of milk of magnesia. Lime could be obtained by heating limestone, but oyster shells have served as the chief source of lime for this process. The precipitate of magnesium hydroxide is treated with hydrochloric acid to produce magnesium chloride. The magnesium chloride solution must then be evaporated to obtain the dry salt for electrolysis. Chlorine is a by-product of the electrolysis process. It can be used to prepare the hydrochloric acid required earlier in the process. A cubic mile of seawater is estimated to contain 23 million tons of magnesium, so there is an inexhaustible supply.

Magnesium is even lighter than aluminum, and only one-fourth as abundant. It is acted upon by moist air to form a protective coating that does not scale off as iron rust does. When heated, magnesium burns with an intensely hot flame and gives off a dazzling light. It has been used for flashlight powders, flares and fireworks. During World War II, tremendous quantities were used in incendiary bombs. The chief uses of magnesium will be in the form of alloys that take advantage of its low density. Such alloys of magnesium as Dowmetal (90 per cent magnesium and 10 per cent aluminum) and magnalium (30 per cent magnesium and 70 per cent aluminum)

have been widely used in airplane construction. The extraction of magnesium from seawater is a rather expensive process, and it is the relatively high price of magnesium that is holding back its more widespread use.

TITANIUM

About 80 per cent of the elements are metals, and, of these metals, there are only seven really common ones: iron, aluminum, magnesium, sodium, potassium, calcium, and titanium. Sodium, potassium, and calcium are far too active to be used as construction materials. Titanium will undoubtedly become the "wonder metal" of the future because of its extraordinary combination of good qualities. Its density is about half as much as that of steel, and it is stronger than steel or aluminum, weight for weight. It can withstand high temperatures, and it is resistant to corrosion. Titanium oxide is highly valued as a white pigment for paints. Titanium is the tenth most abundant element. Metallic titanium has been used to prepare alloys that will withstand the high temperatures of jet engines and turbines.

SOME COMMON, BUT LESS ABUNDANT METALS

Nickel, copper, lead and zinc, which are so common in everyday life, are relatively inexpensive because they have been segregated by natural processes into rich deposits of ore, from which they can be extracted at relatively low cost by roasting and smelting.

Nickel (the United States nickel coin is 75 per cent copper and 25 per cent nickel) is especially valuable in the preparation of alloys. Nickel imparts toughness, heat resistance, and noncorrosive qualities to other metals. Stainless steels have a high nickel content, while monel metal is an alloy of nickel and copper. German silver is an alloy of nickel, copper, and zinc.

Copper also plays a versatile role in alloys, but its most important applications are in the electrical industry, because it is the most economical electrical conductor.

Silver is a common metal, valued because of its use in preparing photographic emulsions, coins, tableware, jewelry, and mirrors. There is such a demand for silver that it exceeds the supply. It is the best conductor of heat and electricity known, and would find extensive applications in the electrical industry if sufficient quantities were available. Silver does not tarnish except in the presence of sulfur or some of its compounds, which form a black coating. This tarnish is readily removed by placing the silver in an aluminum pan, or in contact with a piece of magnesium, and adding some warm water containing baking soda, as the electrolyte. Since aluminum or magnesium are above silver in the electromotive series, they displace the silver from the silver sulfide.

Tungsten is a metal with many valuable properties. It is very hard, insoluble in acids, and has a very high melting point. Because of its high melting point and low electrical resistance, it is used as an electric-light filament.

Platinum is a very useful metal, but its very high cost restricts its use to jewelry and a few special applications. Many substitutes for platinum are available. The other members of the platinum family, palladium, rhodium, osmium, and iridium, are now used for many purposes where a metal that will resist corrosion is needed.

NEW RARE METALS

Among the rarer metals, zirconium is valuable because of its resistance to acids. It does not absorb neutrons, and it is, therefore, used in building atomic reactors. Rhenium, a metal more costly than gold, has some important applications, because of its very high melting point and superior electrical properties. Niobium is another metal of superior heat and corrosion resistance. Such rarer metals help to make rockets and artificial satellites possible. Hafnium is used for control rods in nuclear reactors.

Indium has been used to prepare several alloys that meet specific needs, such as bearing metal. The addition of 1 per cent of indium nearly doubles the tensile strength of lead. It makes desirable alloys with gold, silver, and copper.

Beryllium is another contender among the light metals. It is a very light metal; but, un-

fortunately, large deposits are not available, and it is expensive to extract from its ores. However, it is a valuable alloying element in small amounts in other metals; a good example is beryllium bronze. Unfortunately, beryllium and its compounds are very poisonous and must be used with care.

SUMMARY

Metallurgy is the process of obtaining metals from their ores. It may involve one or more of the following processes: (1) concentration, (2) roasting, (3) reduction by carbon, hydrogen, active metals or electricity, and (4) refining.

Aluminum and other active metals are obtained by the electrolysis of their fused salts.

Magnesium and titanium are the coming metals, but some of the rarer metals are now produced for atomic reactors, artificial satellites and other modern applications that depend upon their high melting points and other desirable properties.

Study Questions

1. DEFINE: metallurgy, slag, bronze, luster, flux, malleable, ductile, roasting, reduction, refining, concentration, cast iron, wrought iron, free state, gangue, metal.
2. Which of the metals were known in ancient times? Why were these metals, rather than others, known then?
3. Outline the operations of metallurgy.
4. List ten metals, and mention at least one important use of each.
5. What are the reducing agents most commonly used in metallurgical operations?
6. Aluminum is a more abundant element than iron. How, then, do you account for the fact that aluminum is so much more costly than iron?
7. Why does aluminum not corrode readily?
8. Give a few examples to show how warfare has stimulated the production of new metals.
9. Give some of the important physical properties of metals.
10. What properties of aluminum account for its many uses?
11. List some of the most important chemical properties of metals.
12. How may the chemical properties of metals be accounted for?

13. What is the process known as froth flotation?
14. What is the principle of cleaning silver articles by placing them in a baking soda solution in an aluminum pan?
15. Why is titanium one of the coming metals?
16. Outline the process for the extraction of magnesium from seawater.
17. What factors determine which reducing process will be used in metallurgy?
18. What is the purpose of roasting an ore?
19. What metals are obtained by roasting and smelting?
20. List some of the properties of silver that account for its uses.

CHAPTER 70

Alloys and Corrosion

Discoveries are not terminals—they are fresh starting points from which we climb to new knowledge.

W. R. WHITNEY

INTRODUCTION

There is a constant battle to liberate metals from their compounds faster than corrosion reverses the process. It has been estimated that corrosion costs more than 5 billion dollars per year in the United States. Large amounts of money are spent in the effort to protect metals against corrosion.

Natural gas and water pipes corrode, and must be replaced, but there is usually considerable loss of natural gas or water before the damage is discovered. Automobile radiators, tailpipes and mufflers corrode so frequently that their replacement represents a considerable cost of automobile ownership. One of the chief causes of automobile engine wear is corrosion. Corrosion is a constant problem on ships and bridges, especially those exposed to salt spray. Farm equipment, industrial equipment, railroad tracks and rolling stock, oil-field pipes and pumps, power-plant boilers, and home hot-water tanks are some of the important fields in which corrosion seems to be winning the battle. This chapter surveys the methods of combatting corrosion, including the preparation of alloys which resist corrosion.

THE CAUSES OF CORROSION

The chief cause of **corrosion** *is the chemical action of metals with constituents of the air, water, and various chemicals such as acids.* Corrosion is speeded up at elevated temperatures, because the speed of these chemical reactions is increased.

An important cause of corrosion is cell action. Any two metals in contact with an electrolyte constitute a cell. If the metals are connected by a wire, or if they are in contact with each other, cell action will take place, with the result that one of the metals will be acted upon, i.e., corroded.

CATHODIC PROTECTION

It has been found that *cell action can be used to protect a given metal against corrosion by placing it in contact with more active metals which serve as anodes.* For example, blocks of magnesium have been welded to the hulls of steel ships to prevent corrosion. The magnesium will be acted upon in preference to the steel. It is a common practice to melt ice and snow with salt in many cities during the winter. The salt water causes metal automobile bodies to corrode very rapidly. Perhaps it would be a good idea to try the use of magnesium anodes on them. These active metal anodes are spoken of as sacrificial, galvanic anodes. The "galvanic" part of this term is based on the fact that the two metals, in contact, constitute a galvanic electric cell. The sacrificial metal should always be a metal higher in the electrochemical series than the metal being protected. Like magnesium, anodes of zinc have been used to protect boat hulls and pipelines. Galvanized iron is an application of cathodic protection. The metal to be protected, usually iron, is either dipped into molten zinc or zinc is deposited on it by electrolysis. The metal so protected will not corrode as long as any zinc remains in contact with it. The modern method of coating steel with aluminum for use in automobile mufflers and tailpipes is another example of cathodic protection.

ELECTROLYTIC, ANODIC PROTECTION

In contrast with galvanic cathodic protection, which depends upon simple cell action, *electrolytic* **anodic protection** *employs an external source of direct current to maintain the proper potential difference between the metal being protected, which serves as the anode, and the cathode.* The cathode may be of an expendable type or a nonexpendable type. Expendable metals, such as iron, steel, or aluminum are gradually expended by electrolytic action when they serve as cathodes. Nonexpendable cathodes include carbon, graphite, and platinum.

OTHER METHODS OF COMBATTING CORROSION

It has been found that much of the damage to automobile engines is due to corrosion rather than wear. Acids formed in the crankcase together with relatively high temperatures, have been an important cause of corrosion. Keep in mind that the speed of a chemical reaction is roughly doubled for every 10° C rise in temperature. Inhibitors, i.e., negative catalysts, are now being added to some lubricating oils to decrease engine corrosion. Another frequent problem with automobiles is the corrosion of radiators. The automobile cooling system presents an ideal arrangement for corrosion, i.e., two or more different metals in contact with an electrolyte. Chemical inhibitors are now available to add to radiator water to decrease corrosion.

Although corrosion is a very complex problem, great progress is being made in methods of combatting it. For some purposes, corrosion is prevented by covering the metal with a surface film that will prevent contact with oxygen or water. Iron, properly cleaned and

dried, may be painted; as long as the paint film is maintained intact and impervious to moisture, no corrosion will take place. The first coat of paint usually contains red lead as the pigment, although zinc chromate is replacing it, particularly for underwater work. Exposure to sunlight, water, and air quickly oxidizes the paint vehicle and therefore allows the pigment to dust off. Iron may also be protected for some uses by giving it an initial protective coating of iron oxide. This is done in a number of different ways. Black iron oxide is produced by dipping the articles in melted potassium nitrate. This produces the familiar blue coat on such articles as rifles. A film of oil or grease prevents rust. Likewise, the porcelain-like enamel of stoves and kitchenware prevents rust as long as no portions are cracked or chipped off. Once broken, however, the rust spreads under the enamel, and it begins to scale off. In many cases, rusting is prevented by coating the iron with a metal that is not so easily corroded. Nickel was once used widely for this purpose, but it is now supplanted by chromium, which is even less corrodible and more beautiful. Copper is sometimes used to coat iron, but copper is so readily tarnished itself that it is not always a desirable coating for iron, although it will prevent rust as long as it covers the whole surface.

Metallic coats may be applied by electrolysis; by electrochemical displacement, as in the case of copper, zinc, tin, nickel, chromium, and cadmium; by dipping the iron into the molten metal, as in the case of zinc, tin, and aluminum; by spraying with the recently invented metallic spray guns, which melt the metal and spray it on a surface in one operation; by **cladding,** i.e., *heating thin sheets of such metals as copper, nickel, or aluminum into the surface;* by using the finely divided metal as a paint pigment; and by various other methods. As mentioned above, tin and zinc may be applied to iron by dipping it into the molten metal. Tin has been the usual coating material for cans. It affords excellent protection as long as the surface is unbroken, because it reacts with the oxygen of the air to form on its surface a thin film of tin oxide, which resists further action. Tin is below iron in the electrochemical series, and therefore accepts electrons from the iron once the surface is scratched, so that the iron then rusts even more rapidly than it would in the absence of the tin. Zinc, on the other hand, is above iron in the electrochemical series, and all of the zinc will go into solution before the iron is attacked. Galvanized iron is therefore preferred to tin for many purposes, but it cannot be used in contact with foods because it may dissolve to produce toxic zinc compounds.

Cadmium, a metal similar to zinc, is now being used as a metallic coating, especially for hardware articles.

Zinc may be applied to iron by the sherardizing process, in which the articles are heated with zinc dust in a tight drum to 800° F, thus forming alloys at the surface.

Aluminum powder, in fine flakelike form, is now widely used as a pigment in paints for the protection of bridges, oil tanks, and many other metal structures. Aluminum, like tin, does not easily corrode, because it forms a protecting layer of aluminum oxide on its surface; if it were not for this fact, aluminum would corrode more readily than iron, because it is above iron in the electrochemical series and therefore has a greater tendency to give up electrons.

In 1907, Thomas Coslett, an English chemist, invented the process now known as the parkerizing process. It consists of producing a coating of basic iron phosphate by dipping the iron into a hot, dilute solution of iron phosphate. This process gives a pleasing dull black finish that serves as an excellent base for paint or enamel.

ALLOYS

The Nature of Alloys

Alloys are produced by melting two or more metals together and then allowing the molten mixture to cool. An **alloy** is *a mixture of metals, either homogeneous or heterogeneous, that has metallic properties.* Sterling silver, for example, is an alloy consisting of a solid solution of copper in silver. Alloys are classified in terms of what happens when a molten mixture cools, as follows: (1) *a mixture of crystals* may be obtained. An example is

solder, an alloy of tin and lead. Such an alloy is heterogeneous, and would show crystals of one metal imbedded in the other metal if examined with a microscope. (2) *A solid solution* of the metals in each other is obtained. Like all other solutions, this type of alloy would appear to be homogeneous when examined with a microscope. A silver coin, which is an alloy of silver and copper, is an example of this type of alloy. (3) *A metallic compound* is formed. Bronze is an example of a metallic compound.

Steel, an Important Alloy

The History of Steel Making—In the previous chapter, the production of cast iron, wrought iron, and malleable iron was briefly mentioned. During the middle ages, the art of steel making developed. Steel differs from cast iron in that it contains less carbon, only about 0.2 to 1.5 per cent. It is tougher, harder, and stronger than cast iron or wrought iron. Cast iron, wrought iron, and malleable iron, unlike steel, cannot be annealed, hardened, or tempered. In early days, steel making was more of an art than a science. It was made in small amounts by carefully adding carbon to wrought iron, which itself was difficult to make, so steel swords were highly prized. The age of steel began in the mid-nineteenth century, when Henry Bessemer, a British engineer, became interested in the production of cannon. Cast iron was too brittle for this purpose. Bessemer invented the process of removing excess carbon from cast iron by blowing air through the molten iron. His blast furnace was announced in 1856. At first, the steel produced by this process was not satisfactory, because of its phosphorus content, but this problem was whipped by lining the furnaces with limestone and magnesia.

In 1882, Robert Hatfield found that, by adding 13 per cent of manganese to steel, a much harder product was obtained. In 1900, it was found that the addition of tungsten and chromium further improved steel. In 1913, the British metallurgist, Harry Brearly, accidentally discovered that the addition of nickel and chromium to steel produced stainless steel, which was the first steel which would not rust or corrode.

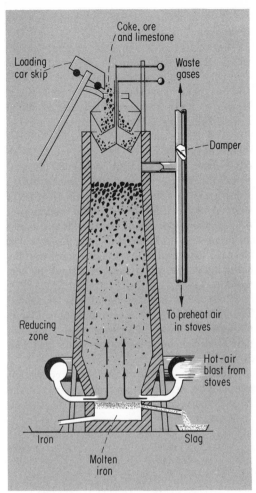

Coke, ore
and limestone

Loading
car skip

Waste
gases

Damper

Reducing
zone

To preheat air
in stoves

Hot-air
blast from
stoves

Iron

Slag

Molten
iron

Figure 70–1. A Diagram of a Blast Furnace.

Steel Manufacture—Steel is made by the following processes:

1. *Crucible steel* is made by melting wrought iron with charcoal in a graphite or fireclay crucible. Carbon is thus added to the iron to produce a uniform, hard, brittle product especially adapted for use in such articles as watch springs, razor and knife blades, and other tools in which the selling price per pound of steel is high.

2. *Bessemer steel* is obtained from molten pig iron by oxidizing the impurities with a blast of air, and then adding the desired amount of carbon and manganese. It may be produced very cheaply. The invention of the Bessemer process was perfected just before

the American Civil War, and has been largely responsible for the tremendous expansion of railroads since that time.

3. *Open-hearth steel* is superior to Bessemer steel in that impurities are more completely removed by oxidation in a large open hearth, heated with producer gas or natural gas. It yields a more uniform product than does the Bessemer process, and today about 80 per cent of the steel is produced by the open-hearth process. It is used for rails, bridge girders, armor plate, and other products requiring a strong but cheap material in large quantity. A new steel-making process is the use of oxygen to replace the open-hearth furnace. This device, called the *converter*, has the advantages of lower initial capital costs, substantial savings in production costs, and much faster production per batch of metal. The oxygen serves to burn off impurities in the iron.

4. Electric steel is obtained by use of the electric furnace, which permits the iron to be kept in a fluid condition in a controlled atmosphere, while other substances are added as desired. The best alloy steels are made in this way. Such steels are used when a very tough, dependable product is needed, regardless of cost, as in the manufacture of certain parts of modern automobiles and machinery.

Heat Treatment of Steel—The properties of steels depend quite as much on heat treatment as on chemical composition. *When red-hot steel is slowly cooled, it is said to be* **annealed.** *If it is cooled very suddenly, as by quenching in water or oil*, it is **hardened.**

The Value of Alloys

Alloys of the precious metals, such as gold or platinum, are often used instead of the pure metals, because of the improved physical properties of the alloy. For example, platinum usually contains about 10 per cent iridium, which hardens the otherwise rather soft platinum.

Alloy steels possess many superior properties; chromium imparts hardness, toughness, and strength; nickel also imparts strength. Both metals are used to manufacture stainless steel, one of modern Science's chief contributions to the elimination of corrosion. One of the rarer elements, niobium, has been found to produce superior stainless steel.

Literally thousands of different mixtures of metals (i.e., alloys) have been investigated. Corrosion-resistant steels are now produced by adding silicon to produce such products as "duriron." Tungsten, titanium, nickel, vanadium, cobalt, and molybdenum are added to produce other valuable properties, and a variation of 0.1 per cent in some of these metals will produce a marked change in properties. A steel containing 11 to 14 per cent manganese is too hard to be machined, and is therefore used in constructing burglarproof safes and armor plate. The addition of a little zirconium (0.3 per cent) to nickel steel makes it very resistant to perforation by bullets. The addition of tungsten and other elements produces high-speed cutting steels that do not lose their cutting power even at white heat. These new cutting steels revolutionized shop practice by enabling cutting tools to plow through steel ten times as fast as formerly. "Invar" is a nickel steel that contracts or expands very little with changes of temperature, and is

therefore used in watches and measuring instruments.

There are many alloys of copper, two of which, brass and bronze, are well known. Ordinary brass is an alloy of copper and zinc (67 per cent copper and 33 per cent zinc). However, there are many different kinds of brass, containing different percentages of copper and zinc, and to which various other metals have been added. For example, German silver contains 55 per cent copper, 26 per cent zinc, and 20 per cent nickel. Bronze differs from brass in that it contains tin instead of zinc. A typical bronze formula consists of 67 per cent copper and 33 per cent tin. Many different types of bronzes have been made. Bronzes are usually preferred to brasses because they are much more resistant to corrosion.

There are many different kinds of solder. The formula for ordinary plumbers' solder is 67 per cent lead and 33 per cent tin. Half-and-half solder consists of 50 per cent lead and 50 per cent tin.

Most of the coins of the world consist of alloys. For example the nickel coins of the

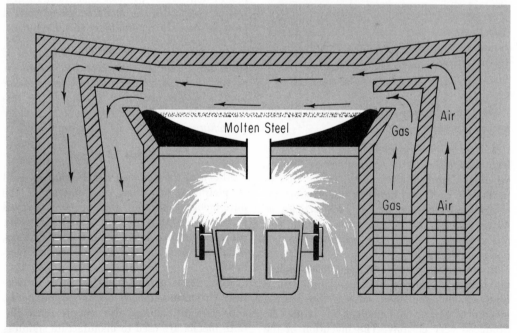

Figure 70–2. A Diagram of an open-hearth furnace. The open-hearth furnace consists of a shallow, saucer-like hearth in which molten iron is heated by flames from the hot, combustible gases that are passed over it. Separate streams of air and combustible gases burn to produce a temperature of about 1600° C.

United States of America consist of 75 per cent copper and 25 per cent nickel. However, many countries use pure nickel for coins. Silver coins of the United States of America consisted of 90 per cent silver and 10 per cent copper, up to 1965.

Silver used for jewelry usually consists of 80 per cent silver and 20 per cent copper. Gold jewelry usually contains 76 per cent gold and 24 per cent copper. The percentage of gold present is called **fineness** and is expressed in carats. If the gold alloy is divided into 24 equal parts, the *number of* **carats** *represents the number of 24ths that are pure gold*. Thus 24-carat gold would be pure gold.

Amalgams

Alloys of mercury are solid solutions of mercury in other metals. They are called **amalgams.** The term, amalgam, may have been derived from the Arabic, *al magma*, or Greek, *migma*, which refer to a mixture. Some amalgams crystallize and break up into powder soon after they are formed. This action explains the disintegration of brass or lead plumbing fixtures, such as pipes and traps, not long after mercury dissolves in them. This same action is the basis for warning people to keep mercury away from jewelry. A mercury amalgam with silver, soft at first, soon hardens, and is therefore frequently used as a tooth filling.

SUMMARY

Corrosion

Corrosion is caused by chemical reactions of metals with other substances. It is accelerated by cell action, according to present theory.

Corrosion may be combatted by cathodic protection in which a cell is set up; the metal to be protected is the cathode, and another more active metal, such as aluminum, magnesium, or zinc, serves as the sacrificial anode.

Corrosion may also be combatted by electrolysis, which is the reverse of cell action.

One of the outstanding methods of combatting corrosion is the use of alloys that resist corrosion.

Alloys

An alloy is a mixture of metals obtained by melting them together, and allowing the melt to cool. It may consist of a mixture of crystals, a solid solution, or a metallic compound.

Steel

Steel is obtained from pig iron by removing the impurities and adding carbon, manganese, or other elements in the proper proportions. There are four processes for making steel: (1) crucible steel, (2) Bessemer steel, (3) open-hearth or converter, and (4) electric steel.

Study Questions

1. DEFINE: alloy, corrosion, cathodic protection, anodic protection, amalgam, annealing, hardening, fineness, cladding, carat.
2. List the three types of alloys, and give an example of each type.
3. Steel is an example of which of the three types of alloys?
4. List the different types of steel.
5. Which type of steel is used most widely?
6. What are the advantages of the use of oxygen to replace air in the open-hearth process?
7. What does heat treatment do to steel?
8. Why does cell action increase corrosion?
9. Why is the rate of corrosion increased with an increase in temperature?
10. Give examples of the use of inhibitors to decrease corrosion.
11. Explain how cathodic protection works.
12. What is the principle of anodic protection against corrosion?

A typical petrochemical plant. The propylene oxide plant of Wyandotte Chemicals Corporation, Wyandotte, Michigan. (Courtesy, Wyandotte Chemicals Corporation)

11

Creative Chemistry

Nature is so varied in her manifestations and phenomena, and the difficulty of elucidating their causes is so great, that many must unite their knowledge and efforts in order to comprehend her and force her to reveal her laws.

LaPlace

*C*HEMISTRY plays a vital part in man's mastery of his material world, because, as we have learned in a previous unit, chemistry is the science which deals with the transformations of matter. It is the purpose of this unit not only to provide an appreciation of the accomplishments of chemistry in producing better things for better living, but also to show how essential chemical research is to the success of industry in this modern world.

The picture to be presented is very incomplete because, in every field of Science, the story of accomplishment is always accompanied by the story of new problems to be solved. There is always room for improvement. The ideal synthetic fiber has yet to be made, and contrary to some overenthusiastic advertising, the automobile tire that will last as long as the automobile has not yet been made.

Chemistry is bringing profound changes to our way of living as it provides better products to take care of old necessities, and creates new necessities.

During the 1850's the per capita consumption of petroleum was less than one teaspoonful per year. Its major use was medicinal, and after a taste of the putrid stuff, it is easy to see why its consumption was so low. Today, oil is taken from the ground by a very complex industry at the rate of 1.4 billion gallons per day. It is refined by highly automated refineries. The relative cheapness of petroleum fuels and other products is a tribute to the efficiency of the entire industry.

Petroleum and natural gas, with which it is closely associated, have gradually replaced the use of coal as a fuel. Another important use of coal was that of coal tar, a by-product of the coke (and steel) industry that served as the starting point for the first contributions of creative chemistry in the form of new, synthetic dyes, drugs, perfumes, flavors, and high explosives. The present generation has witnessed the development of a tremendous new industry, the petrochemical industry, in which petroleum and natural gas are replacing coal as a raw material for the chemical industry. This unit tells the story of the development of the petrochemical industry and the new products it has created.

What are the raw materials used to produce the better things for better living?

527

Are these raw materials inexhaustible? If not, what conservation measures should be undertaken? To what extent is the United States endowed with these essential raw materials? Such are some of the vital topics considered in this unit.

CHAPTER 71

Carbon, the Energy Carrier

There's hardly a thing that a man can name
Of use or beauty in life's small game
But you can extract in alembic or jar
From the "physical basis" of black coal tar—
Oil and ointment, and wax and wine,
And the lovely colors called aniline;
You can make anything from salve to a star,
If you only know how, from black coal tar.

Punch, LONDON

INTRODUCTION

With the exception of atomic energy, the energy that we use comes from the sun. The power of winds, tides, and water are types of energy which have been obtained from the energy of the sun. However, most of the energy that we use today represents energy of the sun, which was stored in the form of the chemical energy in coal, petroleum, and natural gas. These sources of energy were produced by photosynthesis thousands and millions of years ago. Photosynthesis converts the sun's energy into chemical energy today in the form of foods, fibers, wood, and many other things produced by growing plants.

The carbon dioxide cycle in nature, in which the carbon dioxide is used by plants to produce fuels, and in which fuels, in turn, are burned to return carbon dioxide to the atmosphere, is one of the wonderful natural processes that make life possible.

In this chapter, coal will be considered as a fuel, and also as a raw material for the chemical industry.

THE CARBONACEOUS FUELS

The United States, with about 7 per cent of the world's population, accounts for about one-half of the world's fuel consumption. The shift from coal to fuel oil and natural gas has been very rapid. Less than half a century ago, coal furnished about 45 per cent of the fuel, petroleum about 33 per cent, natural gas about 13 per cent, and water power, foods, and wood, the remaining 9 per cent. However, the use of coal has not increased, and, in fact, it has decreased somewhat. On the other hand, fuel oils displaced coal to a large extent, and recently, natural gas has been displacing both coal and fuel oils.

Wood

In the early pioneer days in the United States wood was the chief fuel. Magnificent hardwood forests in the eastern and central states were cut down, and the land was cleared for farming. Some of the wood was used as a fuel or for the construction of buildings, but the rest was burned to get rid of it. Today, wood is so important as a building material, and as the raw material from which paper is made, that its use as a fuel amounts to less than 1 per cent of the total amount of fuel consumed in the United States.

Coal

Coal soon replaced wood as the chief source of energy for power-driven machines. Coal had the advantage that it was a much more concentrated source of energy, as shown in Table 71-1. Two forms of coal came into use, **anthracite** (*hard*) coal and **bituminous** (*soft*) coal. **Anthracite** *coal is nearly pure amorphous carbon.* It has been used as the chief fuel in regions where its transportation would not be too expensive. It burns with a clean, nearly smokeless flame, and leaves little ash.

Bituminous coal burns with the production of so much soot and smoke that it is gradually being replaced by petroleum and natural gas, because the smoke nuisance has been greatly accentuated with the growth of industry and the shift of the population to the cities. For about one hundred years, bituminous coal was used as a source of coke, for the production of steel.

Anthracite Coal

Coal is produced by changes in plant matter, and anthracite coal is the product in which these changes have gone the farthest. The various stages in the decomposition of plant materials (chiefly cellulose) are represented by peat, lignite, bituminous coal (soft coal), and anthracite coal (hard coal).

Anthracite is a very desirable fuel because it burns with the production of the maximum amount of heat and the minimum amount of smoke and sulfurous fumes. Only about 0.65 per cent of the coal resources of the United States are of the anthracite variety. At the present rate of consumption, our anthracite coal resources will be exhausted in about one hundred years.

Coke

When bituminous coal is heated in the absence of air, fuel gases (artificial gas), ammonia, and coal tar are important materials that are driven off from the coal, leaving the mineral matter and carbon in a porous form, called "coke." This process is called **destructive distillation.**

THE ALLOTROPIC FORMS OF CARBON

Carbon occurs in nature in the two crystalline allotropic forms, graphite and diamond,

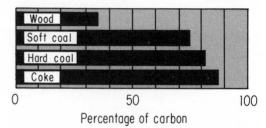

TABLE 71–1
The percentage of carbon in equal weights of different fuels.

Wood
Soft coal
Hard coal
Coke

0   50   100
Percentage of carbon

and as amorphous carbon. *Such forms of substances, identical in chemical composition, but differing in energy content, are called* **allotropic forms.**

Graphite

Graphite is widely used as the "leads" in pencils, as a lubricant, and as a paint pigment, because of its soft, greasy, chemically inert properties. It is an electrical conductor, and is used to make electrodes for dry cells and electric furnaces, commutator brushes for generators, and in making electrotypes for printing. Because of its inertness and resistance to high temperatures, it is used to make refractory bricks and crucibles. Graphite may be prepared by heating anthracite coal in an electric furnace. Prepared in this way, graphite is generally superior to naturally occurring graphite.

The Diamond

The crystalline, colorless, transparent properties of pure diamonds cause them to be highly prized as gems, but it is the great hardness of diamonds that makes them of importance in industry, in providing a cutting edge for core drills, and for grinding or cutting wheels. Diamonds that contain colored impurities are used for industrial purposes. Artificial diamonds of small size have been made by crystalizing carbon in cast iron under very high pressure, but no synthetic diamonds have been produced large enough for use as gems.

Amorphous Forms of Carbon

Carbon Black and Lampblack—When a natural gas flame is directed against a cold metal surface, a black, fluffy, finely divided powder, called "carbon black," is produced. Lampblack is a similar material produced by burning fuel gases in a supply of air insufficient to completely oxidize them. Lampblack will deposit on cooking utensils when they are placed over a yellow gas flame, which is the result of an improper mixture of air with the natural gas in the burner.

Carbon black and lampblack are used to add strength and resiliency to rubber tires, and in the preparation of inks, paints, shoe polish, phonograph records, and black concrete.

Charcoal—In *heating wood in the absence of air,* many valuable by-products, such as acetic acid, acetone, and wood alcohol, are obtained from the gases that are driven off from the wood, leaving the minerals and carbon in the form of charcoal. This process is another example of **destructive distillation.**

Charcoal is used where relatively pure forms of carbon are needed in the reduction of metals, as in the production of crucible steel.

Animal charcoal (bone black) is obtained by the destructive distillation of bones.

CARBON MONOXIDE

Carbon monoxide is produced when carbon and other fuels are burned in a limited supply of air. Inasmuch as it represents only a partial oxidation of carbon, it is readily oxidized to carbon dioxide, and thus serves as a fuel gas.

Carbon monoxide is not suitable for use in homes because it is poisonous. However, it is an important industrial fuel. Hot carbon will react with steam to yield water gas, which is a mixture of carbon monoxide and hydrogen. Producer gas is a similar fuel, containing nitrogen in addition to hydrogen and carbon monoxide, because it is prepared by heating bituminous coal with a mixture of air and steam. Carbon will react with carbon dioxide to yield carbon monoxide.

Carbon monoxide combines with the red blood corpuscles more easily than oxygen does, thus making the blood incapable of serving as an oxygen carrier. Continued breathing of air containing 0.15 per cent of carbon monoxide may be fatal.

Carbon monoxide is odorless, and thus fails to warn of its presence. It is likely to be produced in any stove, furnace, or combustion engine. A small automobile may produce enough carbon monoxide in a closed garage to kill a man within three minutes. Sometimes, carbon monoxide leaks from defective exhausts into closed cars, and is thus responsible for an unknown number of accidents. Protection against carbon monoxide poisoning requires that all exhaust gases be carried away through adequate flues, chimneys, and exhausts. Flues and chimneys should be checked occasionally to make sure that they are not stopped up with soot.

CALCIUM CARBIDE

Limestone may be decomposed by heat to form lime (calcium oxide) and carbon dioxide. Lime may then be heated in an electric furnace with carbon, in the form of coke, to form calcium carbide. Calcium carbide is extremely important, because it will react with water to furnish acetylene, which is used not only in oxyacetylene welding, but also as a starting point in the synthesis of many organic compounds. This is another source of hydrocarbon fuels to replace petroleum and natural gas. Already, acetylene is often preferred to petroleum and natural gas as a raw material because of its great chemical activity. For example, two molecules of acetylene may be combined (polymerized) to form monovinyl acetylene. This compound may then be treated with hydrochloric acid to produce chloroprene.

Several molecules of chloroprene may now be polymerized to form large molecules, to produce a plastic material similar to natural rubber in many respects, and superior to it in other respects. This product is the synthetic rubber, neoprene.

Acetylene is also the starting point for the synthesis of ethylene, acetic acid, acetone, ethyl alcohol, and many other important compounds.

Calcium carbide offers still other interesting possibilities. For example, it will combine with nitrogen to form calcium cyanamide, which may be used directly as a fertilizer, or treated with steam to produce ammonia. The ammonia may then be used to produce ammonium salts for fertilizers. Calcium cyanamide may also be readily converted into urea, which is used in synthetic plastic manufacture, and as a stabilizer for explosives. Calcium cyanamide may also be converted into sodium cyanide, which is used for the extraction of gold by the cyanide process.

THE DEVELOPMENT OF THE COAL TAR INDUSTRY

When soft (bituminous) coal is heated in the absence of air to produce coke, tar is one of the by-products. Previous to the World War of 1914–1918, much of this tar produced in the United States was thrown away. Germany, to be sure, had learned how to use coal tar, but it required the World War to teach the rest of the world that coal tar is one of its most useful raw materials.

In 1919, the United States Senate Finance Committee held hearings on the serious question: Should the United States Government "promote the establishment of the manufacture of coal tar products in the United States?"

Marston Taylor Bogert, Professor of Chemistry at Columbia University, testified before the committee that "a well-developed synthetic dye-stuffs industry is absolutely necessary for the security of our country." Twenty years later, as the result of an intensive program of chemical research, the United States had become one of the leaders in the production of new synthetic dyes, pharmaceuticals, flavors, perfumes, and other products. In 1914, we made only 10 per cent of our dyes, while in 1940, we produced about 95 per cent of our dyes and exported more than 25 million pounds.

Tremendous developments have taken place since 1940. Petroleum and natural gas proved to be better raw materials than coal for the chemical industry, and a huge petrochemical industry is now turning out billions of pounds each year of plastics, fibers, detergents, and synthetic rubber, based on petroleum and natural gas as raw materials. For that reason, the use of coal as a raw material for the chemical industry has been tied in closely with the steel industry, because the steel industry needs coke, and coke is obtained from coal, coal tar being a by-product of the production of coke. The new oxygen process for the production of steel requires less coke than was formerly used in the open-hearth process for the manufacture of steel, so the coal tar industry may lapse for a while. Eventually, however, when the supplies of natural gas and petroleum run out, the huge reserves of coal will then become the chief raw material of the organic chemical industry. Several processes for the production of chemicals from coal have been developed on a relatively small scale, so future use of coal as a raw material in the organic chemical industry will not depend upon coal tar. Two of these processes are the Bergius process for the direct hydrogenation of coal and the Fischer-Tropsch process for the synthesis of carbon compounds, using coal as a raw material. Both of these processes were developed in Germany. These processes depended on the use of catalysts, and were discussed in Chapter 65.

COAL TAR COMPOUNDS

One of the important compounds obtained from coal tar is benzene, a ring hydrocarbon composed of six carbon atoms and six hydrogen atoms. To show how it serves as the starting point for many other compounds, we will trace some of the organic reactions using benzene as the starting point, without attempting to indicate the mechanism of the reactions.

For example, if a hydroxyl group consisting of one hydrogen and one oxygen atom is substituted for one hydrogen atom in benzene, phenol (carbolic acid) is obtained. Carbolic acid is well known as a powerful disinfectant. By adding another group of atoms, the carboxyl group, composed of one carbon, one hydrogen, and two oxygen atoms, salicylic acid is obtained. Salicylic acid may be readily changed to methyl salicylate, commonly known as oil of wintergreen. Salicylic acid may also be used to prepare acetyl salicylic acid, commonly known as aspirin. Phenol may be treated with nitric acid to form picric acid, a yellow dye and high explosive. Again, phenol may be combined with formaldehyde to produce the plastic, Bakelite.

Starting with benzene again, a methyl group, composed of one carbon and three hydrogen atoms, may be substituted for one hydrogen atom, to produce the hydrocarbon, toluene. Toluene may be treated with nitric acid to give the high explosive, T.N.T., tri-nitrotoluene. Toluene also serves as the starting point for benzaldehyde, which is synthetic almond flavor. Saccharin, a sweetening agent, may also be made from toluene.

Starting with benzene again, a couple of simple steps lead to aniline, the starting point for indigo and many other "aniline" dyes.

Coal tar also contains the double-ring and triple-ring compounds, naphthalene and anthracene. Napthalene comes in the form of white crystals, commonly known as "moth balls" when compressed into the shape of balls. From naphthalene and anthracene, many dyes and other useful products are obtained.

Many of our most valuable drugs, perfumes, and flavors are derived from the raw materials in coal tar. In fact, benzene and toluene have been in such demand that the coal tar industry could no longer produce adequate amounts. Methods have been developed for the preparation of these ring hydrocarbons from the chain hydrocarbons found in petroleum.

SYNTHETIC PERFUMES AND FLAVORS

Centuries ago, adventurous merchants braved unknown deserts and uncharted seas to search the world for rare perfumes, spices, and drugs, because of the high prices they would bring.

Coal tar is the chief source of raw materials for the production of perfumes. It is possible to duplicate any natural perfume, once its composition is known, but inasmuch as thirty or forty ingredients must often be skillfully blended to produce a given perfume, one can understand why cheap perfumes, which contain only a few ingredients, do not have the quality of perfumes of a more complex nature.

Such essential oils as jasmine, orange blossom, musk, heliotrope, tuberose, and ylang-ylang can now be synthesized from coal tar compounds. Coumarin, which is used in perfumes having the "new-mown hay" odor, and as a substitute for vanilla in cheap extracts,

can now be synthesized. Vanillin, the chief flavoring ingredient of vanilla beans, is synthesized today on a large scale.

Perfumes are being used in increasing amounts, as they have become available at reasonable cost. They have been used for a long time in soaps and cosmetics, but now they are used in detergents and scouring powders. Merchandisers are using perfumes in many ways to influence people through their olfactory sense.

DYES

The development of synthetic dyestuffs had its origin in the accidental discovery of mauve in 1856 by William Henry Perkin (1838–1907), during his research on quinine. Today, the chemist synthesizes from coal tar products dyes that are very much cheaper than the inferior natural colors they replace. The famous Tyrian purple obtained from shellfish was so expensive that only kings could afford it, and purple came to be considered the badge of royalty. This dye was obtained from tiny sacs behind the heads of a kind of shellfish of the eastern coast of the Mediterranean Sea. In 1909, Friedlander analyzed this dye and found that it had already been synthesized and discarded because of its inferiority to other dyes never found in nature. Any dye found in nature can be duplicated and prepared in a purer condition in the laboratory, once its composition has been determined. The knowledge of its composition is like an architect's blueprint, for anyone who understands the methods of building molecules can follow the plan once it becomes available. The analysis of dyes is not a simple process. Thus, the Badische Anilin und Soda-Fabrik spent $5 million and seventeen years in chemical research learning to make indigo. Then they reduced the price from $4 a pound to 15 cents a pound, and received over $12 million a year from their sale of this one dye. Not only is synthetic indigo cheaper, but it is purer and more uniform than vegetable indigo. Previous to the synthesis of indigo, it had been obtained from India, where nearly a million acres produced an annual crop valued at about $20 million. Within less than twenty years this profitable industry was wiped out.

Though it was a loss to India, it was a gain to the world.

Today, thanks to a well-developed coal tar chemical dye industry in the United States, there is available a wide range of synthetic dyes far superior to, and surpassing in beauty, brilliance, fastness, and variety of hue, those found in nature. Some dyes, called direct dyes, are especially adapted to combine with such fibers as silk or wool; others, called mordant dyes, require a third substance (mordant) to bind the dye to the textile material.

SUMMARY

Carbon and its compounds, found in coal, natural gas, and petroleum are the chief energy sources of the present age, and they are also the chief raw materials for the organic chemical industry, which makes so many "better things for better living." Coal tar, obtained by the destructive distillation of coal, is the chief source of the ring hydrocarbons. The two important forms of coal are anthracite, high in carbon content and relatively scarce, and bituminous, from which coke and coal tar are obtained by destructive distillation.

Carbon exists in such allotropic forms as the diamond, graphite, lampblack, wood charcoal, and coke.

Study Questions

1. DEFINE: destructive distillation, bituminous coal, anthracite coal, allotropic forms, coke.
2. What is meant by a synthetic product?
3. Discuss synthetic dyes as to (a) raw materials, (b) comparison with natural dyes.
4. What types of products are obtained from coal tar?
5. How is acetylene obtained from coal?
6. List some of the important substances that can be prepared from acetylene.
7. What important products are obtained in the hydrogenation of coal?
8. Describe the carbon dioxide cycle in nature.
9. What is the source of the carbonaceous fuels?
10. Why is it a good thing that natural gas and petroleum products have largely replaced bituminous coal as domestic fuels?
11. List some of the products made from coke.
12. List some of the uses of graphite and indicate what properties of graphite make these uses possible.
13. What is the source of activated charcoal and for what is it used?
14. Why is it that so many people die from carbon monoxide poisoning?
15. How is carbon monoxide prepared and for what is it used?
16. Why has there been so much unemployment in the bituminous coal industry in recent years?
17. How could coal be used as a raw material for the organic chemical industry without being subjected to destructive distillation?

C H A P T E R   7 2

Cellulose and Lignin

For countless jobs, in home, in industry, and in commerce . . . wood—rather than the new synthetics—is the true miracle product of our times.

THOMAS J. MCHUGH

INTRODUCTION

Wood has been used as a structural material because of its low cost, natural beauty, and ease of fabrication. But it has its weaknesses as a building material. It dries, shrinks, warps, rots and burns. Ways have been found to treat wood so as to remove these defects, but they also increase its cost. As wood becomes scarcer and the demand increases, its price increases. So today, concrete, steel, and aluminum are replacing wood as a structural building material. Wood still has many uses because of its natural beauty, which is preserved in the widely used plywood or laminated boards.

Wood owes its desirable qualities, as well as its weaknesses, to the presence of two groups of complex substances that make up its structure—namely, cellulose and lignin. **Cellulose** *refers to a group of carbohydrates of high molecular weight built up from the simple sugar, glucose, by oxygen linkages.* The fibrous part of wood consists of relatively pure celluloses. There are also present non-fiber celluloses, called hemicelluloses. Together, these cellulose compounds make up about two-thirds of wood. Nearly all of the remaining third of wood is lignin, which serves as a natural plastic to bind the cellulose fibers into a strong material.

LIGNIN

Lignin is *a very complex compound or mixture of compounds, so complex that its* structure has only been partially determined. However, it is known that the chief building blocks of lignin are ring compounds. It is thought that lignin is the chief parent of coal, and that the aromatic compounds found in coal tar were originally produced by plants in the form of lignin. Lignins have been found to vary slightly in their composition in different kinds of wood, and are probably the chief compounds that give different kinds of wood their distinctive properties.

It has been found that if sawdust is mixed with bacteria of certain kinds and left to stand for some time, the bacteria change the sawdust into a product resembling humus, a valuable agricultural material. Naturally-occurring peat moss, so popular among home gardeners, may possibly be replaced by sawdust "humus" in the future. At present, however, it is cheaper to harvest peat moss.

Plastics can be made from lignin, and one might visualize a huge industry in which lignin plastics are used to bind sawdust and woodchips to form hardboards which could replace wood for many building purposes. At present, other sources of adhesives and plastics are now used to produce such products, because they can be made more readily and at less cost from natural gas and petroleum than from lignin. The chief difficulty in the use of lignin is that it is such a complex material that expensive chemical treatments would probably be necessary to separate it from cellulose in a usable form. Methods of doing this have not yet been developed. In the meantime, we are rapidly using up our precious

535

natural gas and petroleum resources that cannot be renewed; whereas wood, a renewable resource, is being wasted. It is all a matter of economics. For the present, it is more economical to exploit our natural gas and petroleum resources, and leave wood to fall back on when these resources are depleted. That is all the more reason why our wood resources should be conserved, so that wood will be available when it is needed.

Lignin is a major industrial waste. If economical uses for lignin can be developed, it may well become more important than coal, petroleum, or natural gas as a raw material. Enough is now known about lignin to suggest that it may prove to be a raw material for the aromatic products now made from coal. However, if the use of lignin must wait until the world's lignite and coal resources are exhausted, it will be a matter of several thousand years. **Lignite** is *brown coal, a sort of half-way product between wood and coal*. Peat probably represents a still earlier step in the natural processes which produce coal.

The pulpwood industry alone, in the United States, produces about twenty million tons of lignin each year. This lignin is a nuisance. It is either burned, or sluiced into streams in order to get rid of it. When sluiced into streams, it kills the fish and creates more of a nuisance. The pulpwood industry must dispose of twelve million gallons of lignin solution each day. Millions of tons of lignin are available in such agricultural wastes as corncobs, grain hulls, bagasse, and waste straw. Such an enormous supply of lignin not only taxes our ingenuity in disposing of it, but also challenges us to do the necessary research to discover its true chemical nature, and utilize it as a raw material in the manufacture of still more "better things for better living." Lignin not only binds the cellulose fibers together but also enables them to resist chemical attack. There is no known solvent that can act on the cellulose until the lignin has been removed. It requires powerful treatments to destroy the lignin molecules, and the lignin fragments differ according to the method of attack. During the latter part of the 19th century, the sulfite process was introduced to obtain cellulose from wood. Wood chips are boiled with sulfites in this process to produce water-soluble lignin compounds. Attempts have been made to utilize these waste lignin products, but so far the chief product has been synthetic vanillin, used in vanilla extract, for which there is not a large tonnage demand.

CELLULOSE AS A FOOD

Man can digest starches and gums, but he is not able to digest cellulose. Cellulose, in the form of sawdust, may be hydrolyzed with an acid to produce sugars, but this process has not been used extensively because there are cheaper sources of sugars. Certain animals, the ruminants, have special stomachs in which bacteria produce enzymes that break down cellulose. Termites are experts at digesting cellulose, but again it is done with the help of bacteria.

PROGRESS IN THE UTILIZATION OF WOOD PRODUCTS

Particle Board

Wood chips and shavings, once wasted, are now being bonded together to form what is known as particle board. Particle board is used as an inexpensive base upon which thin films of more expensive wood are fixed. Such boards have made possible the production of furniture that would otherwise be available only at prohibitive prices, if it were to be made from solid hardwoods. Particle board is not used as much as it might be because it costs about as much as raw lumber.

Hardboard

Hardboard was discovered accidentally, in the early 1920's, by William H. Mason, who developed "Masonite." Masonite points the way for future utilization of waste wood products. To produce masonite, sawdust or chips are subjected to high pressures, which are suddenly released, with a resulting tearing apart of the fibers and activation of the lignin. The mass is washed, screened, rolled, dried, and pressed into sheets under high temperature and pressure.

Plywood

Plywood is made by gluing together thin layers of wood in a crisscross manner. It is used as a construction material because of the advantages of sheets over boards, because of their strength, and because selected woods of great beauty may be used to produce the outside layer.

PAPER

Paper is made by two general processes, the mechanical and chemical processes. Newsprint is a cheap paper made by grinding logs in such a way that the fibers are torn from the coarse materials. About one part of chemically-treated wood pulp is added to three parts of the pulp obtained by the mechanical process. The resulting mixture is then spread out as thin sheets, drained, compressed, and dried in huge paper-making machines.

The chemical process is the sulfite process already described, which produces quite pure cellulose pulp that is used for finer grades of paper. Many different kinds of paper are obtained by adding to the cellulose pulp various substances such as clay, rosin, glue, starch, size, and dyes.

Paper may be made from almost any kind of fibers. Wood pulp is the chief source, but for some purposes, paper made from rags is preferred. Rice, wheat straw, cornstalks, and other cellulose products can be used. Even synthetic fibers have been used for some special types of paper.

About 400 pounds of paper products per capita are used in the United States each year.

THE MAIN TYPES OF CELLULOSE DERIVATIVES

The industries using cellulose are divided into three main groups on the basis of the extent to which the cellulose molecules are transformed in the manufacturing processes involved.

Cellulose in Slightly Altered Form

The use of cellulose in the form of lumber, textiles, and paper involves little more than certain physical processes, such as carving, spinning, and weaving. As lumber becomes scarce, however, it is to be expected that many lumber substitutes will be devised which will use less wood and utilize waste products. Such developments as plywood come under this class. Sawdust, cork, sugar cane refuse, etc. are now used to prepare various types of composition boards.

Mercerized cotton is an example of a slightly altered form of cellulose. In 1844, John Mercer discovered that cotton fibers can be shortened and strengthened by passing them through a cold solution of lye. Later it was found that these fibers would change into smooth, silklike tubes by stretching them during the drying process; thus mercerized cotton came into use.

Parchment paper resembles mercerized cotton in that the surface is partially dissolved by sulfuric acid and is then allowed to dry. In parchment paper, the fibers are bound together to the extent that the paper can be used as a dishrag without disintegration. Foods may be tied up in parchment paper and cooked, thus preventing loss of flavors, natural juices, and water-soluble substances, such as minerals, sugars, and vitamins.

Vulcanized fiber partially resembles parchment paper. It is produced by running paper through a solution of zinc chloride, which produces a gelatinous hydrated cellulose on the surface. The paper is then washed to remove zinc salts, wound in rolls, and pressed to produce a material harder than wood, but just as easily worked, nearly oilproof, and having good electrical insulating properties.

Lumber may now be treated with the appropriate chemicals to prevent dry rot, infestation by termites, or shrinking and swelling in dry and damp weather.

Wood can be made plastic by soaking it in a concentrated solution of urea, drying, and then heating it to the boiling point of water, at which temperature it can be readily shaped. When cooled, the wood retains its shape and resists further action of moisture. Sawdust and chips can be treated in this way and then pressed in molds when hot, forming products practically as strong as wood.

Cellulose Dissolved and Reprecipitated

Cellulose may be dissolved and reprecipitated to form the several different types of rayon, which will be discussed in Chapter 75.

Esters

Christian Friedrich Schönbein (1799–1868), in 1846, accidentally discovered that if cellulose was treated with a mixture of nitric and sulfuric acids, an explosive compound was obtained that was more powerful than any known up to that time. He had spilled the acid mixture on the floor of his home and had wiped it up with his wife's cotton apron. He hung it up to dry in front of a fire, and as soon as it was dry it burned up with a sudden puff. The above material came to be known as nitrocellulose or guncotton. Nitrocellulose was tried out as a military explosive because it would explode without producing smoke, but its use was given up because it was so explosive that it usually exploded at the wrong time.

Later experiments produced a safer product. The impurities were removed, and it was mixed with nitroglycerine and vaseline to make the useful, smokeless powder known as cordite.

In the same year that Schönbein discovered nitrocellulose, Ascanio Sobrero also discovered by accident that a high explosive was obtained when glycerine was treated with a mixture of nitric and sulfuric acids. He nearly lost his life in the explosion that resulted, and it is not surprising that he left this process alone after that experience.

Alfred Nobel found that a mixture of nitroglycerine and kieselguhr, an absorbent diatomaceous earth, was safe to handle, but that it could be exploded with a percussion cap. This product came to be known as dynamite. When Nobel died in 1896, he left his fortune, made from the manufacture of dynamite and other explosives, to a fund for the granting of the annual Nobel Prizes in chemistry, physics, medicine, physiology, literature, and peace.

It was found that *cellulose* could be *partially nitrated with nitric acid*, and that the product would not explode, although it would burn rapidly. It was given the name **pyroxylin** (from the Greek words for fire-wood). *Pyroxylin would dissolve in a mixture of alcohol and ether. By evaporating the solution, a tough, transparent film, the first synthetic plastic film, was produced.* It was given the name **collodion.** An early application of this solution was its use as "liquid court plaster." It was sold under the name "new skin." This was back in the days when "court plaster" was widely used to cover cuts so as to keep dirt out of them.

In 1865, Alexander Parkes discovered that *by adding camphor to a solution of collodion, a transparent plastic was obtained,* which could be heated to form a soft, malleable material that could be molded into almost any shape. Camphor thus became the first plasticizer. Today many different substances are used as plasticizers.

In 1869, John Wesley Hyatt won a prize of $10,000 by developing a process to manufacture billiard balls from this plastic. Prior to that time billiard balls were made from ivory and both the ivory and the process of fashioning it into billiard balls were quite expensive. He called this new plastic material **celluloid.** Celluloid came to be used to make many different products, just as polyethlyene is used today. For example, celluloid collars were popular, because they did not require laundering. Soon celluloid was used to make flexible, thin films which formed the base for the first photographic films. Unfortunately, celluloid was quite inflammable, and articles such as motion picture films were dangerous to use because they would burn with extreme rapidity. Eventually, it was found that acetate groups (found in acetic acid, for example) could be substituted for the nitrate groups in nitrocellulose to form cellulose acetate, which burned much less readily. After World War I, cellulose acetate came into wide use as the base for photographic films, and it has been only recently that some of the new synthetic films have begun to compete with it.

One type of rayon, viscose, is made from a carbon disulfide solution of cellulose. If this solution is extruded through a slit, it forms a thin, transparent film, which came to be known as cellophane. Cellophane was the forerunner of many new, transparent films, which, like new fibers, had their origin in petroleum, natural gas, and coal.

A generation ago, lacquers were the latest finishes for automobiles and many other objects. Lacquers were solutions of pyroxylin, to which dyes or pigments could be added if desired. They revolutionized automobile finishes because they dried in so much less time than the old varnishes and enamels which they replaced. Today, however, lacquers have been largely replaced by new superior synthetic enamels, based on coal, petroleum, and natural gas as raw materials.

A generation ago, cellulose nitrate and cellulose acetate were widely used to produce the new "wonder" plastics, such as "Xylonite" and "Pyralin." They were obtainable in practically any shade or hue in beautiful transparent, translucent, mottled, opaque, and pearl effects, and were used to manufacture fountain pens, toiletware, radio dials, optical frames, buttons, and many other articles. These early plastic articles did not stand up very well, but they served as the opening wedge in this modern age of plastics.

Pyroxylin solutions came into use for the coating of canvas and other fabrics for the production of durable materials, which were used in bookbinding, automobile seatcovers, etc. They were known as artificial leather. Today new types of very much improved artificial leather are produced from new materials based on coal, petroleum, and natural gas.

FOREST CONSERVATION

In Asia, most of the land has been stripped of its trees and much valuable soil has been lost by erosion. Disastrous floods have been a yearly experience because of the lack of forested areas to retain water. In the United States we have followed in the footsteps of the Chinese, except that we have employed power-driven saws to cut down trees, and powerful trucks to haul them to the mills, thus speeding up the process. About 90 per cent of the original forests in North America have disappeared. America is extremely wasteful in its utilization of its remaining wood. The waste begins in the forests, where about half of the tree remains on the ground as a fire hazard unless it is burned. Of the wood that is removed from the forest, from 40 to 70 per cent is wasted in the sawmills, especially the smaller ones, which cannot maintain integrated operations to save the waste products.

There are two approaches to the conservation of this valuable resource. In the first place, methods must be found to utilize the waste products, and in the second place, sound management of our remaining forest lands must be instituted so that the amount of wood cut down each year will be balanced by an equivalent growth of new wood. This kind of management is very difficult in a democracy where 345 million acres of the 461 million acres of commercial forest lands are privately owned. The Federal Government owns 89 million acres, and smaller governmental units own 27 million acres. About 3,600 individuals have holdings of 5,000 acres or more, while more than 4 million individuals own smaller acreages. About 75 per cent of the privately held commercial forest lands are in these smaller holdings, the average number of acres per owner being about 62 acres. A completely socialistic government might solve the problem quickly by nationalizing all forest lands. In a democracy, a way must be found to conserve our wood resources in such a way as to safeguard individual enterprise. Many of the large lumber, paper, and pulp companies are instituting wise forest management policies, and about 3,500 tree farms have been established, but they represent only about 7 per cent of the commercial forest lands.

The conservation of our forests is desirable for many reasons other than that of assuring an adequate wood supply. Forests play an important part in conserving water supplies and preventing floods. They also serve as the home of our wild animals, and as recreational areas.

THE GOAT—DESPOILER OF THE EARTH

Goats have been one of the chief despoilers of forests throughout the world. The whole Mediterranean basin has been stripped of trees by herds of goats. Goats are not satisfied with grazing on grass. They tear up roots and eat seedlings and shrubs, destroying every trace of vegetation. Much of Spain has been stripped by flocks of sheep and goats. The Berber country in North Africa, Morocco, and the western Sahara was made barren by goats. The limestone mountains of Syria, Lebanon, and Israel were likewise laid bare by goats. The once prosperous area of the Tacaqua river bed in Venezuela was ruined by goats.

Most of the regions that once supported man's most advanced cultures became sterile and unproductive because the forests were cut down and goats were introduced. As a result, such regions today are populated by backward people.

Perhaps we owe more than we realize to the development of synthetic fibers which make us no longer dependent on goats for textile fibers.

SUMMARY

Wood is composed of cellulose and lignin. Lignin is a potential raw material of great promise, but its use awaits the discovery of methods of separating it from wood without destroying it, and the discovery of its structure.

Cellulose may be obtained from wood by mechanical and chemical methods to obtain wood pulp for making paper. The chemical method employs sulfites to break down and dissolve the lignin. The wood pulp may then be bleached and mixed with other materials to produce a wide variety of papers.

Cellulose has been used as a raw material to produce nitrocellulose, for the manufacture of guncotton, and smokeless powder. Pyroxylin was made by the partial nitration of cellulose, and from it celluloid, photographic film base, lacquers, and artificial leather were made. Cellulose acetate replaced cellulose nitrate as a film base, and came into wide use in the manufacture of rayon and plastics.

The use of cellulose as a raw material for the manufacture of many products has gradually been replaced by coal, petroleum, and natural gas.

Wood is an important natural resource that has been dwindling rapidly. It should be conserved.

Study Questions

1. DEFINE: cellulose, lignin, pyroxylin, collodion, lignite, celluloid.
2. What is cellulose?
3. What products are obtained from cellulose by simple physical changes?
4. Is the preparation of rayon a physical or a chemical change?
5. Give the basic principles involved in the preparation of "cellophane."
6. List the products obtained from cellulose by dissolving and reprecipitating it.
7. What is lignin, and why does it constitute a problem for research today?
8. What are the disadvantages of lumber that the chemist might try to eliminate either by treating the lumber, or by producing new materials to replace it?
9. Why is it important that our forests should be conserved?
10. How is wood pulp manufactured?
11. What happens to lignin in the making of wood pulp from wood?
12. For what may wood pulp be used?
13. What is smokeless powder? What are its advantages as compared with the old black gunpowder?
14. Why was cellulose acetate used in preference to cellulose nitrate for photographic films?
15. For what was celluloid used? How was it made?
16. Why have coal, petroleum, and natural gas replaced cellulose as a raw material in recent years?
17. Why is wood gradually being replaced by other building materials?
18. Why is the conservation of our forests a very difficult problem?
19. As wood products become scarce it is likely that their price will rise. What would be the normal economic results of higher wood prices on the depletion of our wood resources?
20. What were the results of the cutting down of the forests in China?

Petroleum

We are so breathless with the progress already made that few of us are able to see where this road along which we have moved so rapidly over the last few years will lead us. Apparently it is leading us in the direction of converting the natural hydrocarbons of petroleum into simpler compounds of less molecular weight, and then recombining these simpler compounds in new ways to obtain an entirely new molecule having the characteristic that we want, and which we cannot obtain in the natural molecule.

F. A. HOWARD

INTRODUCTION

The growth of the petroleum industry has been one of the most dramatic chapters in the history of America. Fifty years ago it was an infant, supplying us with a small number of products. Now it is a giant. It has been called upon to supply gasoline to power our automobiles and airplanes, diesel oil to power our trains, trucks, and buses, fuel oil to heat our buildings, and lubricants to keep our machines running. In addition it has become the source of many of the raw materials for the huge petrochemical industry. It is estimated that the hydrocarbons in petroleum and natural gas could be used to produce about a million different compounds. Today, many products based on petroleum and natural gas, such as plastics, synthetic rubber, fibers, fertilizers, and detergents, are made in billions of pounds per year. In fact, more than 60 billion pounds of petrochemicals are produced each year. Since many of the gaseous by-products of petroleum refining are similar to the gaseous compounds found in natural gas, both of these sources furnish the raw materials for the petrochemical industry. The petrochemical industry will be taken up in the next chapter in connection with the study of natural gas.

HISTORY OF PETROLEUM

From the earliest times, petroleum, found seeping from the ground, has been used for many purposes. The Bible mentions pitch in several places. The Babylonian King, Nebuchadnezzar, used asphalt to pave roads and to make mortar for his palace. Reeds dipped in oil were burned as a light source. About 450 B.C., Herodotus described a Persian oil well, and in the first century A.D., Pliny, the historian, described many uses of oil from Sicilian springs. During the crusades, petroleum flame throwers were used in storming the walls of Constantinople. Marco Polo, in the 13th century, described a fountain of oil in Baku.

In 1859, Edwin L. Drake obtained about thirty barrels of oil per day from the first oil well drilled in the United States. Soon, other oil wells were drilled, as petroleum came into use as a source of kerosene for lamps. Oil seeps in different parts of the world were recognized as signs of oil deposits and soon became the scenes of oil well drilling.

In 1901, a "gusher" near Beaumont, Texas produced 100 thousand barrels per day. In a few months other "gushers" were obtained in this same area, known as the Spindletop oil field. In 1910, "gushers" opened several

541

new oil fields in Mexico, thereby increasing its production fourfold in one year. By 1929, the United States was producing two-thirds of the world's oil. After World War II, new oil fields were discovered in the Middle East, where about two-thirds of the world's proved crude oil reserves are found, almost 200 billion barrels, as compared with roughly 13 per cent of the world's oil reserves on North America. Today, the United States produces somewhat less than a third of the world's oil, and imports oil from various parts of the world. Vigorous exploration in the United States has added to the known reserves. New oil fields in Canada have made that country an important oil-producing nation.

THE ORIGIN OF PETROLEUM

The origin of petroleum is uncertain, but the preponderance of opinion is that it was not formed from such sources as cellulose and lignin, from which coal deposits were formed. Petroleum deposits are found in the beds of ancient seas, many of which are now covered by dry land. It is generally believed that petroleum (and natural gas) were formed from the bodies of small marine animals, from marine plants, and, perhaps, from organic matter carried to the oceans by rivers. It appears that these organic sediments were compacted into hard deposits of clay, sandstone, dolomite, and limestone, layer upon layer. As these layers were buried deeper and deeper, tremendous pressures, heat, and perhaps radioactivity and bacterial action,

changed the organic matter into hydrocarbons. These hydrocarbons were squeezed out and perhaps emulsified in the form of small droplets, which were absorbed into the more porous sandstone or loose sand deposits, or in porous limestone or dolomite. The original horizontal ocean floors were folded and faulted by movements of the earth's crust. Oil and natural gas collected in domes and pockets produced by these crustal movements. These oil traps are found in anticlines (upraised arches), faults, and stratigraphic traps. Faults may result in cutting off of porous layers by nonporous layers. Stratigraphic traps result from the pressure of adjoining nonporous layers on porous layers, which squeezes the oil into pockets.

Natural gas collects at the top of a dome (anticline). *If the top of the dome is penetrated first by an oil well, a "**gasser**" will result.* Below the petroleum there is likely to be salt water, which corroborates the theory that petroleum and natural gas had a marine origin.

PETROLEUM PROSPECTING

The geologist begins the search for oil by surveying the surface formations and the data obtained from wells or small bore holes which may have been drilled in the area. He will be looking for layers of limestone, dolomite, and sandstone, where oil and natural gas are most likely to be found.

If the preliminary surveys show possible favorable indications, the geophysicist enters the picture. His chief tools are the gravimeter, the seismograph, and the magnetometer. The gravimeter is used to measure the force of gravity at the surface. Large masses of dense rock will show a larger gravitational force than less dense formations. The seismograph is used to measure the intensity and speed of shock waves produced by explosions of dynamite charges, and reflected from the surfaces of subsurface formations. The magnetometer indicates variations in the magnetic fields of

Figure 73–1. Cores from an oil well in Kettleman Hills. These cores, obtained as the well is drilled, are tested for the presence of oil. A geologist can identify the stratum being drilled by observing the types of fossils in the cores. (Courtesy, Union Oil Company of California)

subsurface formations. Airborne magnetometers are often used to survey large areas.

Small bore holes may be drilled, and the drill cores may then be examined by a paleontologist (a fossile expert), who can identify a rock layer by noting the kinds of fossils, if any, which are contained in it.

GEOCHEMICAL METHODS OF CHECKING THE PROGRESS OF OIL-WELL DRILLING

On the basis of scientific oil exploration, the possibility of finding oil may result in the decision to drill an oil well. However, the petroleum expert will do better than the national average if he hits more than one producing oil or gas well in nine tries. Once oil drilling is started, geochemical methods may be used to check the progress of the drilling.

The mass-spectrograph is the modern device used to analyze samples of drillings. Analyses may be made on samples of gases smaller in volume than the head of a pin, and the results may be obtained within ten minutes.

Another modern device is an electric eye which is very sensitive to gamma rays. It is lowered into a well, where it responds to varying emissions of gamma rays from different strata, thus helping to identify them.

DRILLING OIL WELLS

Petroleum geologists and geophysicists determine whether or not oil is likely to be found in a given place, but only the oil-well drilling crew can determine whether or not it is there. Sometimes **"wildcatting,"** i.e., *the drilling of a well where neither oil nor gas have yet been found,* opens up new oil fields. Once a producer has been discovered, other oil wells are drilled to develop the field.

The drilling of oil wells is a highly technical problem. The deepest well drilled to date reached 25,340 feet. It was a "dry hole," producing neither oil nor gas. But sedimentary rock formations which might contain petroleum are as much as fifty thousand feet thick, so deeper wells may be drilled. As wells become deeper the problems increase. Tem-

peratures as high as 400° F might be encountered at fifty thousand feet below the surface.

Various methods of drilling have been used throughout the world. Early oil wells were drilled by a percussion method in which heavy drills were lifted and then allowed to drop. This is known as cable-tool drilling. In this method, it is difficult to control the direction that the drill will take. Today, the majority of wells drilled in the United States use rotary drills, mounted on the ends of long steel pipes. Sections of pipe are added as the drill progresses downward. Drilling bits have to be replaced frequently, and it is quite a chore to pull up a mile or so of steel pipe and to separate the sections. Other techniques have been used, in which electric motors or mud-driven turbines have been used at the bottom of the hole to furnish the power for drilling, rather than at the top as in conventional methods. One of the newer methods of drilling uses the percussion principle, in which sonic generators, using magnetostrictors, cause the bit to hammer at high rates of speed, while the drill is slowly rotated to make a symmetrical hole.

PETROLEUM RESOURCES

Tremendous deposits of shale, containing petroleum have been discovered. The oil shale beds of Colorado, Wyoming, and Utah, up to 2,000 feet in depth, constitute a fabulous petroleum reserve. It is estimated that this one formation, 16,500 square miles in area, has trapped within it 1,473 billion barrels of oil, three times the total world's proved crude oil reserves today.

An oil-shale industry has been in operation in Scotland for more than a hundred years. Sweden also produces oil from shale, and has been testing one method of drilling into the deposit and heating the shale by electricity. Such a process requires a low-cost source of power, such as the water power in Sweden provides. Oil-shale deposits have been worked in France and Estonia. Pilot plant experiments in the United States show that its oil-shale deposits can one day serve as economical sources of oil.

The tremendous Athabasca tar-sands of

northern Alberta, in Canada, are estimated to contain 300 to 600 billion barrels of petroleum. Sulfur is also locked into these tar-sands.

Proved reserves of crude oil in the United States now approximate 31 billion barrels, and with continued exploration, new reserves are found each year. At the same time, however, the United States now produces 2.8 billion barrels of crude oil annually. In order to conserve our petroleum reserves, various conservation methods have been adopted, including the prorating of production to market demand, well spacing, and secondary recovery methods.

Oil should not be withdrawn from wells too rapidly, because the underground pressure equilibrium between oil, gas, and water would be destroyed and all of the oil contained in the reservoir could not be recovered. Several states have adopted conservation laws to prorate production of oil among fields or wells to prevent waste, and to regulate the spacing, drilling, casing, completion, and operation of oil and gas wells. The Interstate Oil Compact Commission also has been an effective instrument in conserving the petroleum resources of the United States, as an advisory group of thirty-three member states that is continually studying oil conservation practices.

The Middle East oil fields harbor the richest concentrations of petroleum on earth, the average output per well being about 4,000 barrels per day as compared with 12.6 barrels per day in the United States.

The world's truly giant oil fields, which the scientists say are those with reserves of more than 10 billion barrels each, are confined to the Middle East, with the exception of one in western Venezuela. Middle East oil reserves are more than 50 times greater than those of North America, and nearly 100 times greater than those in South America. Most of the Middle East fields have a total of 1 billion or more barrels of oil each, while few of North American oil fields are in this class.

The most recent important oil find was in Libya, which is now producing about 165 million barrels of oil per year. The Sahara desert, which was opened up earlier, now produces 1 billion barrels of oil per year.

PETROLEUM REFINING

Crude oil *is a complex mixture of saturated and unsaturated hydrocarbons, most of which are in the alkane series.* From petroleum, thousands of useful products such as kerosene, gasoline, waxes, coke, and asphalt

Figure 73–2. A unicracking plant. This plant developed by Union research went on stream late in 1964. It performs chemical miracles. It can convert heavy oil entirely to gasoline, leaving no residue of fuel oil. (Courtesy, Union Oil Company of California)

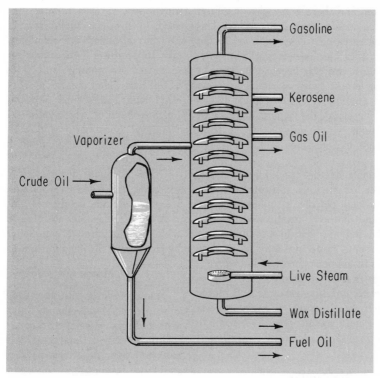

Figure 73–3. Distillation tower for the fractional distillation of petroleum. The tower shown here is known as a bubble-cap tower.

are obtained. *The* **refining** *of crude oil consists mainly of three processes, (1) distillation, (2) conversion, and (3) purification.*

Distillation

Distillation is the basic process for the separation of the component parts of crude oil. It is based on the fact that the different liquid components have different boiling points. When petroleum is heated, the lower boiling point fractions that make up gasoline come off first. As the temperature is increased, kerosene boils off. Next, the gas oil vaporizes and is condensed, and asphalt or coke residues remain. In the furnace, sufficient heat is applied to vaporize all of the volatile components at the same time. The vapors then go to the **fractionating column,** *where the various fractions are separated, as the vapor cools.*

Conversion

This refinery operation changes the molecules of the distilled fractions in such a way

as to obtain a higher yield of gasoline. **Cracking** *is an important conversion process in which larger molecules are broken up into more, smaller molecules, such as are found in gasoline.* There are many cracking processes. At one time, cracking was accomplished by the use of high temperatures and pressures alone. Today, however, catalysts are used to improve the yields and the quality of the gasoline produced.

The **octane number** *of a gasoline is a method of indicating its antiknock characteristics.* If isooctane, a saturated hydrocarbon having eight carbon atoms is taken as a standard, a 100-octane gasoline is just equal to isooctane in its antiknock characteristics.

The gasoline content of crude oil varies widely with the origin of the crude oil, but the average is about 30 per cent or less. If it were not for the development of cracking processes, which have enabled refiners to obtain an average of 44 per cent gasoline from every barrel of crude oil refined, the United States would have consumed almost twice as much crude oil, and there is no way of telling what the price would have been today. Undoubtedly, the research work which led to the cracking processes has been a most constructive conservation project, because it has not only given us almost twice as much gasoline from a given amount of crude oil, but it has also greatly increased the octane number of gasoline, without which today's higher compression automobile engines would not operate.

As by-products of the cracking processes, large amounts of various saturated or unsaturated gaseous petroleum molecules are obtained. Some of these unsaturated gaseous molecules are polymerized to produce gasoline. Other gaseous molecules may be used as raw materials in the petrochemical industry.

Alkylation *is another process used to produce high-octane aviation gasoline and motor fuel, in which small saturated hydrocarbons are combined with unsaturated hydrocarbon molecules to form molecules such as are found in gasoline.*

Purification

This operation provides additional treatments to improve the products obtained in the above processes. Gasoline is washed with chemicals and water to remove gum-forming components and other undesirable impurities. Lubricating oil must likewise be treated so as to remove waxes and unsaturated compounds. Even diesel fuel and kerosene require purification.

ADDITIVES FOR PETROLEUM PRODUCTS

Many chemical compounds are added to the various petroleum products to improve them. Well over 2 billion pounds of additives are used each year.

Gasoline Additives

Perhaps the most noticeable additives used in gasolines are dyes, which do not improve their qualities as fuels, but which serve to indicate that they contain an antiknock additive.

Modern high-compression automobile engines require high-octane fuels. As already mentioned, various refining methods may be used to produce high-octane fuels, but the fuels so obtained are relatively more expensive to produce. The octane number may be increased by adding from 1 to 3 milliliters of tetraethyl lead per gallon of gasoline. Tetraethyl lead leaves lead deposits in the combustion chamber, which cause preignition. TCP (tricresyl phosphate) and other phosphorus compounds have been added to gasoline to eliminate these lead deposits.

Other additives for gasoline include antioxidants, metal deactivators, antirust and anti-icing compounds, detergents, and lubricators.

A very desirable additive would be one which would promote complete combustion of hydrocarbons in gasoline and diesel engines.

Motor Oil Additives

Many modern oils, the 10-20-30 viscosity oils, which do not change much in viscosity with changes in temperature are obtained by use of additives. Detergents, oxidation inhibitors, antiwear additives, corrosion inhibitors, and foam inhibitors are also added to improve motor oils.

Other Petroleum Additives

Automatic transmission fluids are improved by antipressure additives, viscosity index improvers, antifoam agents, and temperature stabilizers. Aircraft, hydraulic, and turbine oils also require additives. Soaps are used in making greases, and additives impart a better gloss to paraffin wax. Even road oils and asphalt are improved with additives.

SUMMARY

Petroleum is a mixture of saturated and unsaturated hydrocarbons which probably had its origin in marine sediments of a plant and/or animal nature. It is likely that petroleum was formed in shale or limestone deposits which were subjected to high pressures and temperatures. The Colorado oil-shale deposits are typical shale deposits in which the petroleum has been trapped. In many cases, the petroleum was carried to more porous layers of sand or sandstone. If such deposits are covered with impervious rock domes, petroleum and natural gas will collect there. These domes and other pockets produced by faulting are located by various scientific methods, but drilling is the final test of the prediction. It is typical of the scientific method that many predictions do not work out.

Petroleum is refined by (1) distillation, (2) conversion, and (3) purification. Catalytic cracking processes are very important conversion methods.

Petroleum products are improved in many respects by the use of additives.

The known petroleum resources of the world should last for several generations at their present rate of consumption, but world consumption will increase as the use of automobiles and airplanes increases. Atomic energy will be used in place of petroleum and natural gas for the generation of electric power and for large industrial power needs, but it is unlikely that it will replace petroleum for motor vehicles and airplanes.

Study Questions

1. DEFINE: petroleum, "gasser," wildcatting, refining, conversion, additive, octane number, cracking, alkylation, fractionating column, purification, crude oil.
2. How do modern cracking processes differ from the early thermal cracking processes?
3. Outline the known petroleum resources of the world.
4. What has been the important contribution of cracking?
5. In addition to cracking, how is the supply of gasoline increased?
6. What kinds of additives are used for gasoline?
7. What are the functions of additives found in motor oils?
8. What were the sources of petroleum used in ancient times?
9. What were the early uses of petroleum?
10. What are the main uses of petroleum today?
11. How would you account for the tremendous growth of the petroleum industry?
12. What are the chief raw materials used in the petrochemical industry? Where are these raw materials obtained?
13. What is the probable origin of petroleum?
14. Discuss the methods of scientific petroleum prospecting.
15. How successful is scientific petroleum prospecting?
16. List the different methods of oil-well drilling.

Natural Gas

All men are by nature imbued with a desire for knowledge.

ARISTOTLE

INTRODUCTION

The natural gas industry is the sixth largest industry in the United States. There is hardly a basic industry that natural gas and petroleum do not serve either as fuels or as sources of raw materials. Lacquers, varnishes, paints, plastics, textile fibers, synthetic rubber, explosives, photographic film, printing inks, cosmetics, fertilizers, insecticides, insect repellents, perfumes, and detergents are now made from petroleum derivatives or natural gas. The oil companies are now rapidly becoming chemical companies, and they are spending large sums of money on chemical research. Since World War II, which stimulated the development of the petrochemical industry, especially in the production of synthetic rubber, most of the large chemical companies have built plants based on the use of natural gas and petroleum as raw materials. On the other hand, most of the large oil companies have greatly expanded into the field of petrochemicals. The synthetic organic chemical industry has grown at four times the rate of all American industry, and its sales have increased at five times the average sales increase.

HISTORY OF NATURAL GAS

Natural gas has been known since earliest recorded history. In some places it escaped through cracks in the rocks, and once it was accidentally ignited, it served as an "eternal" flame for ancient fire worshipers.

Natural gas was first used for commercial lighting in Fredonia, New York, about 1825. A well drilled in the Murrysville field in Pennsylvania, in 1878, came in with a roar that continued uncontrolled for several years because of the great volume and pressure of the gas. In 1883, gas from this well was piped to Pittsburgh, Pennsylvania. Seventy years later, more than 400,000 miles of pipelines were transporting natural gas to all but three states—Hawaii, Maine, and Vermont.

THE OCCURRENCE OF NATURAL GAS

Natural gas is usually found where petroleum occurs. About two-thirds of natural gas is obtained from gas wells and one-third from oil wells. Very rich sources of natural gas have been found recently in Northern Africa and the Netherlands. In 1959, an enormous supply of natural gas was discovered near Anchorage, Alaska. This natural gas contains 99.6 per cent methane, which may be liquefied and transported by tanker.

In the United States, natural gas is found chiefly in Texas, Louisiana, California, Oklahoma, West Virginia, New Mexico, Kansas, and Pennsylvania. Texas produces about one-half of the natural gas in the United States. Although California is a major producer of natural gas, it must now import natural gas from Texas and Canada to keep up with the ever-growing demand. California now uses enough natural gas to equal the energy output of twenty-six Hoover Dams.

TRANSPORTING NATURAL GAS

Pipelines with rough joints would offer too much resistance to the flow of natural gas, but the development of seamless electric-welding processes for pipes has eliminated rough joints, thus making pipelines feasible.

On its journey through the pipelines, natural gas passes through compressor stations about one hundred miles apart. The compressors are operated by internal-combustion engines that use natural gas. One of the recent oil finds was made in Alberta, Canada. Along with the oil, large amounts of natural gas are obtained. A pipeline, 2,250 miles in length, now transmits 500 million cubic feet of gas daily across Canada to Montreal. Another 650-mile, 30-inch pipeline now transmits about 400 million cubic feet per day from Alberta to the West Coast of the United States.

NATURAL GAS RESOURCES

The present reserves of natural gas would last thirty years at the present rate of consumption. However, new reserves are being discovered even faster than consumption is increasing, so it seems to be likely that natural gas resources will not play out within the next few decades. If natural gas sources begin to dwindle, the price will go up and its use as a fuel will then be replaced by coal or petroleum.

At present, less than 5 per cent of natural gas is wasted, although it was not many years ago that more gas was wasted than was used because there was no way to use it. It was burned in the form of large flares to get rid of it. Considerable amounts of gas were also burned in such a way as to produce carbon black, but this uneconomic use has been dwindling. Today, natural gas is flared only where it is unavoidable.

Natural gas is now returned to oil wells to build up the pressure, and thus make it possible to recover more oil. The gas makes some

oils less viscous, and absorbs hydrocarbons, which produce casing-head gasoline.

NATURAL GAS AS A FUEL

Natural gas is perfectly combustible, leaving no ash and no smoke or unburned residues. It is one of the safest fuels because it will explode only under limited conditions. It must be mixed with just the right proportion of air to gas, approximately $14\frac{1}{2}$ parts of air to $4\frac{1}{2}$ parts of gas. The source of ignition must be of the correct temperature, or nothing will happen. A spark or flame must be at least 1,100 to 1,200 degrees Fahrenheit in order to ignite it. A lighted cigarette will not ignite natural gas.

Natural gas is invisible and odorless. It cannot be smelled unless special ingredients are added to aid in its detection. It is non-toxic. It can do harm only when it is in such a high concentration that it replaces the oxygen needed for life.

The fuel value of natural gas probably exceeds that of the petroleum resources of the world.

Methane, the chief ingredient in natural gas, is liquefied and shipped to England and Europe, which have depended largely on manufactured gas as a fuel. Since natural gas costs about one-tenth as much as manufactured gas, and has about twice as much heating value per cubic foot, it can be shipped in the form of liquid methane and still show a profit. When liquid methane evaporates, it absorbs a great deal of heat, and, for this reason, it could serve as a refrigerant before it is used as a fuel.

In communities where manufactured gas has been used, the burners will not work with natural gas because natural gas has about twice the thermal value of manufactured gas. This problem is solved by reforming natural gas by processes that increase the hydrogen and carbon monoxide content with a resulting decrease in thermal value.

Natural gas is supplying an ever-increasing share of industrial fuel requirements. It now supplies more than 50 per cent of industrial heating requirements; petroleum supplies about 25 per cent, and coal less than 25 per cent.

HOW NATURAL GAS COMPANIES MEET PEAK DEMANDS

Natural gas is used as a fuel to operate some electric power plants. An electric utility company, rather than competing with gas companies, may join them. In some communities, both electricity and natural gas are supplied by the same company. Such a company could use excess natural gas to generate electricity during the warm season and could then change over to petroleum or other fuels during the winter in order to divert the natural gas to its customers.

Another way of balancing the demands for natural gas is to require that large consumers do the job. When the demand for natural gas is high, large consumers, which buy natural gas at low rates, would be cut off. In this case, they would have to convert to fuel-oil burners or other fuel sources which are maintained on a standby basis. Another method of balancing the demands against the supplies is to store natural gas during periods when the supply exceeds the demand, so that the pipelines can be kept in constant use. Exhausted producing fields are now being used to store natural gas under pressure. When the consumption increases, this stored reserve may then be drawn upon. Gas is not lost in this process, but it is more costly to store the gas than it originally cost to produce it. Another method for the storage of natural gas is to liquefy it and store it as a liquid in large, insulated, underground tanks.

NATURAL GAS VERSUS ELECTRICITY

Natural gas is now entering into competition with electricity in the home. Electric utility companies stress the value of all-electric homes, while gas companies stress the economy of natural gas as a fuel. Natural gas is an economical source of heat, with which electricity cannot compete unless the electric power rates are quite low. Electric utilities encourage the all-electric home by offering decreased electric rates with increased use. In some communities these lower power rates will permit competition with natural gas, but in communities having cold winters, the heating of a home with electricity can be quite expensive.

It will be recalled that heating devices consume more electricity than most other electric devices in the home. Here is where natural gas offers real competition as a rule.

The chief uses of natural gas in the home are in space heating and cooling, clothes dryers, hot-water heaters, and cooking. One of the problems of utility companies is the change in the demand from summer to winter. The demand for gas for heating increases during cold weather, so gas companies encourage the use of natural gas for refrigerating units for summer air-conditioning.

For large consumers, such as apartment houses and office buildings, an all-gas system is quite economical and feasible. Gas is burned in turbines to run electric generators. The exhaust gases are then used to produce steam to operate heating or refrigerating systems. It is interesting to speculate concerning the possible effect of fuel cells on this competition between natural gas and electricity. A fuel cell based on the use of natural gas to generate electricity might make "all-gas" homes a possibility.

LIQUID PETROLEUM GAS

Liquefied hydrocarbons, consisting of propane and butane, are sold in pressure tanks under the name of **LP** or **LPG** (Liquid Petroleum **G**as). In some sections of the country it is called "bottled gas." Liquid petroleum gas has been used in considerable amounts to operate internal-combustion engines, but its chief application has been its use as a fuel for farms and communities not reached by natural gas lines. It serves as a convenient fuel for travel trailers, in which it operates gas refrigerators, stoves, and space heaters. In many cases, it is used with the help of gas mantles to produce the lighting for trailers.

Liquid petroleum gas may vary in the relative percentage of propane and butane which it contains. Liquid propane is too volatile in the summer, and liquid butane is not volatile enough in the winter, so the composition of liquid petroleum gas is generally varied to meet seasonal requirements. Liquid petroleum hydrocarbons are nearly odorless, and their use might lead to many explosions because escaping gas might not be detected. For this reason, odorous compounds are added to LP gas. It is a common practice today to add an odor to natural gas for domestic use, for safety.

NATURAL GAS AND REFINERY GASES AS A SOURCE OF HYDROCARBONS

Natural gas is generally found along with petroleum, and it contains the more volatile hydrocarbons of the aliphatic series of hydrocarbons, found in petroleum.

The following table will serve as a review and summary of these hydrocarbons:

TABLE 74-1

THE LOWER MEMBERS OF ALIPHATIC HYDROCARBONS

Number of Carbon Atoms	The Paraffin Series (Saturated Hydrocarbons)	The Olefine Series (Unsaturated Hydrocarbons, containing double bonds)
1	Methane	—
2	Ethane	Ethylene
3	Propane	Propylene
4	Butane	Butylene
5	Heptane	Heptylene
6	Hexane	Hexylene

The names of the hydrocarbons use prefixes based on the corresponding Greek words for numbers. All of the **paraffin,** or *saturated*

Figure 74–1. Liquid-petroleum storage tanks. (Courtesy, Gulf Oil Corporation)

series of hydrocarbons, end with *ane.* The hydrocarbons containing double bonds end with *ene.* Keep in mind that, as the number of carbon atoms increases, the number of possible isomers likewise increases. Also keep in mind that the saturated hydrocarbons form derivatives by substitution, while the hydrocarbons containing a double bond form derivatives by both substitution and addition. The latter series of hydrocarbons are therefore more active.

When petroleum is cracked, large amounts of gaseous hydrocarbons of both series are obtained. The active, double-bonded hydrocarbons are not found in natural gas as a rule. Petrochemical plants are generally located near refineries where they can obtain the refinery gases.

SYNTHESIS OF RING HYDROCARBONS FROM CHAIN HYDROCARBONS

In the oil refinery, the hydroforming process consists of heating gasoline of poor quality with hydrogen in the presence of a catalyst. Ring compounds are formed in this process, and the gasoline containing ring compounds has superior antiknock properties. Natural gas is now used to produce phenol, benzene, toluene, napthalene, and other products obtained from coal tar. As a result, the organic chemical industry is no longer dependent on coal tar as a source of these compounds.

COMPOSITION OF NATURAL GAS

Natural gas is composed mostly of methane. Some natural gas may be as high as 99 per cent methane. It often contains higher members of the paraffin series, such as ethane, propane, and butane. "Wet" natural gas contains volatile gasoline compounds. These compounds must be removed before natural gas is transported. Natural gasoline is removed from "wet" gas by compression or solvent extraction. Natural gasoline, often called "casing-head" gasoline is an excellent automobile fuel, because its volatility provides the "pickup" that modern automobile drivers prize so highly.

Natural gas often contains hydrogen sulfide, sometimes as much as 20 per cent. Both sulfur and sulfuric acid are obtained from the hydrogen sulfide in natural gas.

Natural gas also contains moisture, which must likewise be removed. Carbon dioxide is also a common constituent, and may be present in amounts from 20 to 30 per cent. It must be reduced to at least 3 per cent. Some natural gas sources contain considerable amounts of helium. Helium does no harm in natural gas, but it is lost when the gas is burned. Some of the richest sources of helium are found in Kansas and the southwestern states. The federal government is now contracting for the separation and storage of helium in order to conserve this important resource. Helium is used in many ways today, and no one knows what important future uses may develop.

THE PETROCHEMICAL INDUSTRY

Petrochemistry refers to *the industry that uses petroleum and natural gas as raw materials for the production of valuable chemicals.* The growth of this industry during the past few years has been astounding. The petrochemical industry produced 60 billion pounds of products in 1960. These products accounted for a 7 billion dollar business. The petrochemical industry accounts for about 60 per cent of the value of all of the chemicals produced in the United States. All told, more than 2,500 products are obtained from petroleum and natural gas.

ROUTES TO NATURAL GAS CHEMICALS

The manufacture of chemicals from refinery gas and natural gas is too technical for discussion in this text, except in a very general way. Among the routes to natural gas chemicals the following are typical:

Halogenation

Chlorine (the most abundant halogen), for example, will replace the hydrogen atoms in methane to form such well-known compounds as chloroform and carbon tetrachloride. It will act more readily with the unsaturated

Figure 74–2. A typical chemical plant. The Commercial Solvents' nitroparaffin plant at Sterlington, Louisiana, produces 10 million pounds of nitroparaffins from natural gas annually.

Typical chemical plants consist of tanks for the storage of gases or liquids, pipes to transfer these products, and reactors, frequently in the form of towers, where the chemical transformations take place. (Courtesy, Commercial Solvents Corporation)

hydrocarbons, such as ethylene and propylene, obtained from refinery gas, to produce many products by both substitution and addition. Vinyl chloride is an important compound obtained by chlorinating ethylene. It is polymerized to produce fibers and plastic materials such as floor coverings, to such an extent that vinyl (pronounced like vine) has become a household word.

Polymerization

Ethylene, propylene, and butylene, because of their double bonds, are readily polymerized. Several billion pounds of polyethylene, for example, are made each year.

Ethylene

Ethylene is the largest volume chemical produced in the United States. About 6 billion pounds are produced annually. The chief source of ethylene is refinery gas, but it may be produced from natural gas. In the Oxo process, it is combined with carbon monoxide to produce alcohols.

One of the important intermediate compounds used in the petrochemical industry to make many other compounds is ethylene oxide. For example, ethylene oxide is used to make ethylene glycol, which is used in large quantities as an antifreeze for automobiles. Ethylene oxide is now produced at the rate of more than 1.5 billion pounds annually.

Acetylene

Acetylene, because of its great activity, is an excellent starting point for the synthesis of organic compounds. It is now being made from natural gas by a variety of processes, such as partial oxidation and thermal cracking. It can be used as the starting point for many products now using ethylene.

Propylene

Acrylonitrile is a compound used for the production of one important group of plastics and fibers. It may be prepared by the reaction of propylene with ammonia and oxygen, in the presence of a catalyst. About 2 billion pounds of detergents, plastics, resins, and solvents are produced each year from propylene.

Isopropyl alcohol, made from propylene, exceeds a billion pounds in annual production. It is a major source of acetone and other important starting compounds for organic syntheses. Polypropylene and polybutylene plastics are now offering competition to polyethylene plastics, because they are superior for some purposes. These and other plastics will be discussed in the next chapter.

SUMMARY

Composition of Natural Gas and Petroleum Gases

Natural gas is composed chiefly of methane, but higher members of the paraffin series of hydrocarbons may be present. Refinery gases also contain the paraffin hydrocarbons, but in addition, they are abundant sources of the olefine (double-bonded) series of aliphatic hydrocarbons.

Uses of Natural Gas and Petroleum Gases

Natural gas is used chiefly as a fuel, but it also serves as a raw material, along with refinery gases, for the petrochemical industry. Natural gas often contains volatile hydrocarbons which may be separated in the form of natural gasoline. Natural gas may be liquefied for storage or transportation. LP gas is composed of liquid propane or butane, which is obtained from natural gas or refinery gases.

Study Questions

1. DEFINE: LP gas, petrochemistry, paraffin series of hydrocarbons, olefine series of hydrocarbons.
2. Discuss the occurrence of natural gas.
3. Why is natural gas used in such huge quantities today?
4. In what regard has natural gas helped to solve the soot and smog nuisance of many cities?
5. Why would natural gas be wasted if it were not used as a fuel?
6. Discuss the competition between electricity and natural gas for home use.
7. What development would make it possible to have an "all-gas" home?
8. How do large apartment and office buildings manage to get along with natural gas instead of electricity?
9. Compare natural gas with electricity as to its cost in appliances which use heat?
10. How do public utility companies manage to meet the peak demands for natural gas?
11. What kinds of products are made from refinery gases and natural gas by the petrochemical industry?
12. Why should our natural gas resources be conserved as much as possible?
13. What percentage of natural gas production is associated with petroleum production?
14. Discuss the pros and cons of limiting natural gas production to that associated with the production of petroleum.
15. Why is natural gas more valuable as a raw material for the petrochemical industry than as a fuel?
16. Discuss the uses of LP gas.
17. What is the source of natural gasoline?
18. What desirable properties does natural gasoline have?

Synthetic Fibers

However significant a single experiment may seem in retrospect, no important step forward in experimental science rests solely on the record of any single investigator's observation.

J. B. CONANT

INTRODUCTION

The sale of silk decreased to one-tenth of the amount sold before rayons and the synthetic fibers came into use. An informed economist has predicted an annual sale of 4 billion pounds per year of synthetic fibers by 1975, which is likely to cut into the 5 billion pounds of cotton and the 1 billion pounds of wool sold in the early 1960's. The usual laws of economics, if given a chance, will continue to give cotton the advantage of low cost.

New synthetic fibers usually require about ten years for commercial development. The original research and process development usually takes about five years, and costs from 5 to 20 million dollars. Thousands of new fibers are possible, but only a few new fibers are likely to be made in the near future.

Some of the synthetic fibers, such as rayon and acetate, possess the advantage of a much lower price than the silk which they have largely replaced. Other synthetic fibers, such as nylon, orlon, and dacron, possess certain properties which make them superior to any natural fiber. No one fiber has all good points and no faults. So research is devoted to obtaining fibers which combine and improve the plus factors while reducing the minus ones.

METHODS OF PRODUCING FIBERS

Almost any kind of plastic material may be spun into a fiber if a process can be found to spin it. Nearly all spinning processes imitate the silkworm or the spider that extrudes solutions through minute openings. These solutions evaporate or harden on contact with the air to form fibers. The majority of fibers are thus made by forcing solutions of plastic materials through small holes in spinnerets into solutions, which will cause the plastic material to separate from its solution and form a fiber. Some plastics can be melted, and then forced through the spinnerets to form fibers as the plastic cools. In a few cases, where the plastic material cannot be melted, and in which a suitable solvent cannot be formed, an emulsion of the plastic may be extruded and then evaporated or otherwise treated to form a fiber.

The manufacture of glass fibers illustrates two methods by which fibers may be formed. Spun glass may be produced by forcing molten glass through small holes into a high-pressure steam jet. This method corresponds to the method by which fibers are made from molten plastics. Mineral wool, such as is used for insulation, may be formed by blowing a powerful stream of air into a small stream of molten slag or glass.

HOW FIBERS ARE USED

Man-made fibers may be used in one of three ways: (1) continuous filaments, (2) **tow,** *a loose rope of continuous filament,* and (3) **staple,** *which consists of fibers of short length obtained by chopping up the filaments.*

Continuous filaments, such as nylons, make good fishing lines, but their use in fabrics has been small, because their surfaces are too smooth. However, one process, known as the Taslan process, places tiny loops into a continuous filament, at irregular intervals, thus making the filament more acceptable for fabrics.

IMPROVING THE PHYSICAL CHARACTERISTICS OF FIBERS

The physical characteristics of existing fibers used for staple may sometimes be improved by special treatments similar to the Taslan process. For example, a rayon fiber with a permanent crimp is now available. This new fiber appears to be a promising substitute for wool in carpets, upholstery materials, wall coverings, and other decorative fabrics. It is mothproof and takes readily to antimildewing and fire-retardant preparations.

Crimps may be placed in Orlon fibers to improve their bulkiness for use in making lightweight sweaters. Dacron may be given a curly characteristic that makes it an excellent staple for use in making sleeping bags and pillows.

NONWOVEN FABRICS

Instead of weaving fabrics, nonwoven fabrics may be made by combining staple by heat or adhesives. Modern rubber-backed rugs and apparel interlinings are now being made in this way.

APPROACHES TO THE PRODUCTION OF NEW, IMPROVED FIBERS

The plastic materials, to be discussed in the next chapter, are prepared by *the* **polymerization** *of small molecules*, called **monomers**, *to form the larger* **polymer** *molecules*. The monomers may all be of the same kind, or they may differ from each other. In the attempt to produce fibers having the desirable characteristics of two or more different fibers various approaches are tried.

The majority of synthetic fibers are being used in the form of blends with natural fibers, or such semisynthetic fibers as the rayons. At present, the blending is done mechanically by using different fibers in the textile mills. Chemists are seeking methods of blending the best characteristics of several different fibers such as cotton, wool, and synthetic fibers into one molecular backbone by blending several different fibers into a solvent and spinning the resulting mixture.

In some cases, the *use of different kinds of monomers, which may be polymerized to form* **copolymers,** yields improved fibers. For example, Darlan, nitrile fiber, which has such desirable qualities as good shape retention and wear, is a copolymer of vinylidine dinitrile and vinyl acetate.

Another method of modifying the chemical nature of fibers is the **block** and **graft** technique. **Block polymers** *contain long chains of polymers, in which different copolymers occur alternately.* **Graft polymers** *are made by attaching segments to the main polymer backbone.* Vinyl fibers, for example, have many desirable characteristics, but their use has been retarded because of dying problems, and a tendency to build up static. These difficulties have been removed by new block and graft techniques.

Another new technique is the use of radiation to modify the properties of polymers.

WELL-KNOWN SYNTHETIC FIBERS

At least thirty synthetic fibers are on the market. Some of these fibers are very similar in nature, but are given different trade names to identify the manufacturer. The classification of some of the most common synthetic fibers is given below, together with a brief description of typical examples.

Cellulose Fibers

In 1884, Hilair Bernigaud de Chardonnet (1839–1924), produced cellulose nitrate fibers by dissolving the compound in alcohol and ether and extruding it through small holes. These fibers were then treated to remove the nitrate groups, leaving a silky thread of cellulose, the first synthetic fiber. This fiber was called "artificial silk" because of its silky appearance. However, its high price of production prevented its development.

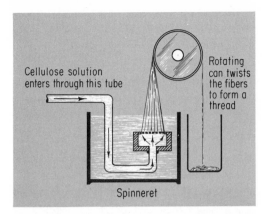

Figure 75-1. As the cellulose solution flows through the spinneret holes into dilute acid, it changes to solid threads.

This original true cellulose fiber was made by regenerating cellulose from cellulose nitrate by the use of ammonium sulfide. Today, a true cellulose fiber is made by the regeneration of cellulose acetate fibers with caustic alkali.

In the 1890's, ways were found to dissolve cellulose directly. Through the use of carbon disulfide, a viscous solution of cellulose was obtained. This solution was used to prepare viscose, which came to be known as rayon, because of its sheen, i.e., its ability to reflect light rays.

Today, all fibers made from cellulose are often classified as rayon. However, present usage limits the term, **rayon,** to *the synthetic fibers produced by the viscose process.* Different terms are used for other types of synthetic fibers made from cellulose. Thus, **acetate** is the name used to designate *fibers made from cellulose acetate.*

In 1903, a process was worked out to prepare a solution of cellulose acetate, and "acetate" synthetic "silk" fibers became available. The cuprammonium process for the manufacture of fibers from cellulose uses ammoniacal copper solution to dissolve the cellulose. This process is somewhat more costly than the viscose process. More than 80 per cent of the fibers now made from cellulose are produced by the viscose process, in which cellulose is transformed into cellulose xanthate by the action of caustic soda and carbon disulfide. The cellulose xanthate is then dissolved in caustic soda solution.

The properties of rayon depend upon the nature of the manufacturing process. Rayon, used in the cord fabric of tires, has a high strength and durability at elevated temperatures. For dress fabrics, a sheen higher than that of silk or the dullness of chalk may be achieved. Filaments finer than silk make possible very soft fabrics. Rayon, cut into small lengths, and the new irregular thick and thin yarns have created entirely new textures in fabrics. Transparent velvet, dull satins, and textiles rivaling in beauty the finest cashmere are all made from rayon.

Acrylic Fibers

Acrylic fibers are used to make fabrics which closely resemble wool, and yet they do not have some of the faults of wool. They have been used in considerable amounts for blankets and sweaters. They have a high resistance to fire, heat, and chemicals, and for that reason, they are used to make laboratory coats, aprons, and suits for people who work with acids, alkalies, and other chemicals that quickly eat holes in cotton fabrics. Acrylic

Figure 75-2. Acrilan acrylic fiber is prepared by extruding the liquid material through tiny holes in a spinneret. (Courtesy, Monsanto Company)

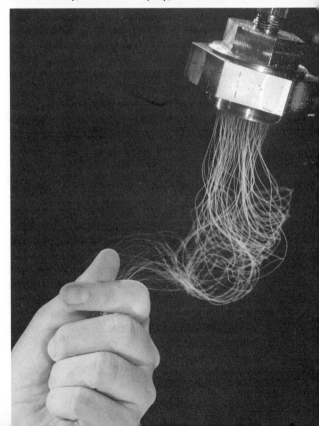

Figure 75-3. A chemical plant at Orange, Texas, for the production of nylon intermediates. (Courtesy, E. I. Du Pont de Nemours Chemical Company)

fibers are marketed under such names as Acrilan, Creslan, Dynel, Orlon, and Verel. Zefran is a nitril-acrylic co-polymer that possesses the advantages of other acrylic fibers and the dye-receptive properties of cotton and rayon.

About 50 per cent of all sweaters are now made from Orlon. Orlon keeps its shape, and is soft and warm. It resists sunlight, and is light in weight. The other acrylics have similar properties.

Polyamide Fibers (Nylons)

In 1939, the production of a new synthetic, protein-like fiber, nylon, was begun. The basic discovery of nylon was made by Wallace Hume Carothers (1896–1937) in 1930, but it required the huge E. I. Du Pont de Nemours Chemical Company nine years to perfect the process for its manufacture. Nylon has virtually replaced silk, which it resembles.

The word, nylon, is not capitalized because it represents a group of synthetic fibers rather than a single fiber. It is not a "trademarked" name. In this text, "trademarked" names are capitalized. It has been found that nylon-like fibers may be made by at least ten different chemical processes. The different nylons vary somewhat in properties, but all of them are protein-like in nature.

Nylon fibers have such great strength that they may be used to make sheer hosiery, or to reinforce automobile tires. Nylon may also be spun in the form of filaments of different diameters. Such filaments are used for fishing lines, and the bristles for brushes.

Fibers can be made from almost any protein material by breaking the protein down into its monomers, i.e., the amino acids, and then polymerizing them to form fibers. One class of protein fibers, the azlons, are made from milk protein; Lanital is an example. There are other protein fibers, such as Ardil, made from peanut protein; Vicara, made from corn protein (zein); and fibers made from soybeans, feathers, and egg albumin.

Polyesters

The outstanding resistance of these fibers to wrinkling is responsible for their wide use in wash-and-wear blends. They are light in weight, have good heat resistance, and do not build up static. Polyester fibers include Dacron, Teron, Terylene, Kodel, and Odel. Such fibers absorb little water, and as a result they are quick-drying. Furthermore, they hold a crease well.

Underwear insulated with Dacron fibers is light in weight. Dacron staple is used as a filling for pillows, and when formed into a bat, it may be quilted for sleeping bags, or it may be used for a filling for life preservers. Such fibers are non-allergenic, and cost one-sixth as much as good down, which they replace. Dacron dries quickly after washing, and resists rot and mildew.

Vinyl Polymers

Fabrics made from the vinyl polymer fibers are valued for their cashmere-like softness. Darlan and Saran fibers belong to this group.

Teflon Fibers

Teflon fibers are made from a fluorine plastic. They are the most chemically resistant fibers produced up to date. Teflon fabrics have been used to make nonlubricating bearings.

Polyolefine Fibers

Polyethylene, polybutylene, and polypropylene plastics are made in tremendous quantities. It would be expected that fibers would be made from them. Vectra is a polypropylene fiber, developed for hosiery because of its strength and resistance to snags and runs. Vectra is available in a limited number of shades because it is difficult to dye it.

Spandex, Elastic Fibers

Spandex *fibers are elastic fibers,* epecially valued for swim suits and women's founda-

tion garments. The E. I. Du Pont de Nemours Chemical Company worked on the development of Lycra for fifteen years and plowed more than $10 million into research and development before it began the production of this stretch fiber, which is in part a polyurethane. The United States Rubber Company spent about $5 million over a ten-year period in developing its spandex fiber, Vyrene. The Goodrich Chemical Company has been working on a similar fiber which it calls Estane. The Eastman Chemical Company has also been developing an elastic fiber.

Spandex fibers are replacing rubber fibers for various reasons, one of which is the relative ease with which they may be woven into fabrics.

Spandex, Lycra fibers consist of segmented polyurethane. Hard and soft segments occur at random, the soft segments providing the give, and the hard segments tying the chains together.

Textile Glass Fibers

Glass fibers can be made with fantastic tensile strength, which is the basis for their use in reinforcing plastics. Glass fabrics are coming into increased use for curtain and drapery materials because of their resistance to sunlight, mildew, moisture, and various destructive chemical compounds, so often found in the atmosphere in modern urban and manufacturing communities.

To this general class of fibers one might add asbestos fibers used to make fireproof fabrics, and fibers made from various metallic oxides, which represent a new field with many possibilities. For example, fibers of extremely high heat resistance have been made from silicon oxide (quartz) and from aluminum oxide.

Metallic Fibers

Many metallic fibers are coming into use for decorative fabrics.

MODERN TEXTILE TRENDS

Cotton and linen have been our most important textile fibers up until recently, and they are now competing successfully with man-made fibers as a result of processes that have removed some of their weaknesses. Natural fibers are more comfortable than most synthetic fibers, because they transmit moisture better. On the other hand, synthetic fibers are resistant to fire, mildew and moths, and fabrics made from synthetic fibers may be given a permanent crease or permanent pleats, not removed by washing.

There are two trends in modern textile technology: (1) blends, and (2) processing.

Textile Blends

One present trend is in the direction of engineered textiles, in which several different natural and synthetic fibers are blended, so as to minimize the weak points of each fiber. For example, nylons impart abrasion resistance, strength, durability, and elasticity, while such fibers as Acrilan, Orlon, Dacron, and Dynel provide resistance to chemicals and sunlight. Blending of rayons, wool, or cotton yarns with nylons, Orlon, or Dacron reduces shrinkage. Wool, mohair, and silk resist wrinkling when dry, but various synthetic fibers are superior in regard to wrinkling when wet. Blends thus hold their shape better under a wide range of moisture conditions.

Textile Processing

Processes have been developed to treat natural fibers, such as cotton and wool, so as to overcome some of their outstanding weaknesses. Water repellants have been found that remain effective throughout the useful life of a fabric; they resist both laundering and dry cleaning. Zelan water repellent is a good example. Water repellents render fabrics, such as hosiery, resistant to spotting by water. Hosiery may also be treated so as to reduce its tendency to snag.

Collars that retain their shape without the use of starch before ironing them are made possible by sandwiching cellulose acetate or other types of plastic materials between layers of fabric. Crease resistance is imparted to cotton, rayon, and linen by the use of urea-formaldehyde plastic materials. Satisfactory fire-retardants, such as ammonium sulfamate, are available. Textiles may be treated to prevent mildew. They may be made mothproof and shrinkproof. **"Sanforizing,"** i.e., *pre-shrinking*, is a common treatment of cotton textiles. Woolens may also be made shrink-proof by treatment with sulfuryl chloride, or other substances.

Methods have been developed to wrinkle-proof cotton. Cotton can also be treated so as to increase its ability to absorb water, a special advantage when it is used for toweling. Cotton duck for awnings and tents can be made to resist the weather for ten times its normal life by treating it with a urea-formaldehyde plastic, in combination with lead chromate.

The treatment of textiles, as outlined above, leaves much to be desired—the most serious difficulty being that most of these processes are mutually exclusive. Research must be carried out to discover materials that will provide more of the above advantages for a single fabric.

DENIER, AN EXPRESSION OF THE WEIGHT OF A FIBER

The *weight of a fiber* is expressed in **denier,** which is *the weight in grams of 9,000 meters of yarn.* For fibers of a given type, the larger the diameter of the yarn the higher the denier. The strength of a fiber would thus be likely to increase with increasing denier, but its sheerness would be obtained by decreasing the denier. The strength of a fiber or yarn is measured by determining the number of grams required to break a 40-denier yarn.

SUMMARY

The Production of Synthetic Fibers

Fibers may be obtained from almost any plastic, if they can be dissolved, melted, or emulsified, so that they can be extruded through small holes.

Fibers are used in the form of continuous filaments, tow, or staple. They may be woven, or they may be combined by heat or adhesives to form nonwoven materials.

Natural Fibers

Cotton, wool, and silk may be given special treatments, which help to improve such weaknesses as shrinking, creasing, inflammability, and poor resistance to wear or sunlight. They may also be blended with synthetic fibers to form fabrics which possess the advantages of both synthetic and natural fibers.

Synthetic Fibers

There are about thirty common synthetic fibers, which may be grouped into about eight classes, according to the types of plastic materials from which they are prepared. There is no one ideal synthetic fiber. The fibers vary as to cost and properties, and each have their special uses. Many synthetic fibers, nearly identical in composition and properties, are sold under different manufacturer's trademarked names.

Synthetic fibers may be processed in various ways so as to improve their physical properties.

Study Questions

1. DEFINE: rayon, acetate, tow, staple, monomer, polymer, copolymer, polymerization, block polymer, graft polymer, spandex fiber, denier, sanforize.
2. What are the advantages and disadvantages of each of the natural fibers?
3. What processes are now available to improve natural fibers?
4. Why is it unlikely that many new synthetic fibers will be marketed in the near future?
5. How are synthetic fibers produced?
6. In what forms are fibers used to produce textiles?
7. Give two examples of processes used to improve the physical properties of synthetic fibers.
8. What are the two trends in textile manufacturing?
9. List the two main types of fibers made from cellulose.
10. How is viscose rayon made?
11. List some of the well-known acrylic fibers.
12. What are the advantages of acrylic fibers?
13. List some of the protein materials that have been converted into fibers.
14. What are the desirable properties of the nylons?
15. Which synthetic fibers most closely resemble protein fibers?
16. What are the natural protein fibers?
17. What desirable properties do Dacron, and the other similar polyester fibers, contribute to textile mixtures?
18. What is the nature of spandex fibers? For what applications are they used?
19. List some of the inorganic fibers.
20. For what purposes are glass fibers used? What properties of glass fibers make their use in such applications desirable?

Synthetic Plastics

Here below to live is to change, and to be perfect is to have changed often.

CARDINAL NEWMAN

INTRODUCTION

A **plastic,** or **resin,** is *a material that can be molded into some desired shape.* In the broadest sense, these terms might include such materials as iron or glass; but in actual usage, they refer to such natural products as rosin, gums, and amber, and to synthetic organic molding materials.

The first synthetic plastics were devised to replace such natural materials as amber, paraffins, tar, bitumens, asphalts, rubber, rosin, glue, shellac, gelatin, waxes, and copals. Thus, celluloid was originally devised as a substitute for ivory. Synthetic plastics have opened up many new fields of usefulness in addition to those fields in which they have displaced natural products.

Plastics decrease manufacturing costs because they can be molded into shapes that would require many costly operations to obtain from metals. In 1948, the annual production of plastics was about 1 billion pounds. By 1965, the annual production had reached 9 billion pounds.

CLASSIFICATION OF PLASTICS ACCORDING TO PROPERTIES

There are three types of plastics, the thermosetting, the thermoplastic, and the elastomeric plastics. The **thermosetting plastics** are *those formed by heating, and which, once formed, cannot be reversed (softened) by heating.* **Thermoplastics** *may be softened by heating. Rubbers are typical*

elastomers, but not all plastics are elastomers. These differences in the properties of plastics are, of course, the result of differences in their structure. In thermosetting plastics, such as Bakelite, phenoxy resin, there is a strong polar attraction between the chains, but in elastomers, there is less attraction between them. The structure of thermoplastics, such as polyethylene, lies between that of the thermosetting plastics and that of the elastomers.

CLASSIFICATION OF PLASTICS ACCORDING TO THEIR METHOD OF PREPARATION

From the point of view of preparation, two types of plastics may be distinguished, namely, the polymerization, and **condensation plastics,** or **resins,** as they are often called. Polymerization plastics result from the building of large molecules by the interaction of smaller ones of the same kind or different kinds. In the latter case the product is called a copolymer. **Condensation plastics** *result from the interaction of two or more different compounds which yield new molecules of an essentially different type, usually with the loss of water.*

MADE-TO-ORDER PLASTICS

The ability to tailor-make long-chain polymers from a variety of raw materials, and to control the size of the molecules produced represents one of the technological triumphs of the twentieth century.

The strength, flexibility, toughness, solvent resistance, and heat resistance of a polymer are related in rather predictable ways to the size of the molecules, the composition of the monomers, and the degree of regularity with which they are interconnected. For example, the fluidity of a molten plastic is largely determined by the length of its chain of molecules. The molecular size determines the ease of fabrication. Some plastic molecules are in the form of chains, having as many as a thousand monomers joined to each other. Plastic molecules may have molecular weights of 5,000 to 10,000 or more.

The desired properties may be imparted to a given plastic by the proper selection of catalysts, and the careful control of the conditions under which they are polymerized. For example, in the production of Delrin, the temperature must be controlled within one degree.

THE PLASTIC FAMILIES

There are more than twenty-five families of plastics, ranging from polyethylene to nylon and Teflon. Some of these families have already been referred to because of their use in making synthetic fibers. It would serve no useful purpose to list all of the different families, their properties, the compounds from which they are made, and their chemical nature. We shall, therefore, discuss only a few of the most well-known plastics.

The Cellulose Plastics

The first synthetic plastic, celluloid, has already been referred to. Cellophane film and Tenite are examples of cellulose-based plastics, which still occupy a small niche in the plastics industry.

Bakelite, Phenolic Resinoid, the First Modern, Synthetic Plastic

In 1909, an American chemist, Leo H. Baekeland, announced a synthetic plastic, which he called Bakelite, phenolic resinoid. This synthetic resin was produced by heating phenol with formaldehyde in the presence of a catalyst. Today, phenolic resinous products

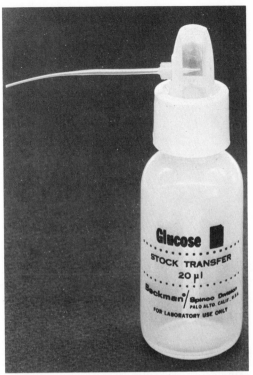

Figure 76–1.   Polyethylene molded pipettes, bottles, and laboratory apparatus are replacing glass for many purposes in scientific laboratories. (Courtesy, Union Carbide Corporation)

in a variety of forms are noted for their strength, chemical resistance, and electrical, insulating properties. They are used as adhesives in plywood and laminated materials, and in making tops for tables and counters.

Formaldehyde has also been used to make several other types of plastics. Formaldehyde is well known in zoology laboratories as the unpleasant-smelling solution used for preserving such specimens as dead cats and frogs. At one time, when it was the popular thing to fumigate houses after an infectious disease, paraldehyde candles were used. Paraldehyde is a solid polymer of formaldehyde that can be readily broken down to formaldehyde by heat. It has been recognized for a long time that formaldehyde has a great tendency to polymerize. Formaldehyde has been used with various substances to make plastics. A recent new plastic, Delrin, is made by polymerizing formaldehyde alone. Delrin was produced by the E. I. Du Pont de Nemours Chemical Company only after ten years of research and de-

Figure 76–2. Bags made from extruded polyethylene film are typical of this modern plastics age. (Courtesy, Union Carbide Corporation)

Figure 76–3. Extruded polyethylene water pipe. Pipe made from polyethylene, polypropylene and polyvinyl chloride are widely used. (Courtesy, Union Carbide Corporation)

velopment, and an expenditure exceeding the $27 million spent on the development of nylon. It consists of very dense crystals of unique strength and long wear. Delrin competes with such metals as brass, copper, aluminum, zinc, and steel, for such applications as door knobs, shower heads, and carburetor parts.

The melamine plastics are made by the reaction of melamine with formaldehyde. Their most well-known application is unbreakable dinnerware. However, they are also used as plywood adhesives, and for surface coatings for paper, textiles, and leather.

The Polyolefine Plastics

The polyolefine plastics include polyethylene, polypropylene, and polybutylene. The largest-volume plastic is polyethylene, 2 billion or more pounds of which are made annually. Polyethylene plastics are cheap, because they are made from ethylene, which is both inexpensive and abundant, as previously pointed out. These plastics may be made in the form of films, flexible materials like toothpaste tubes, or squeeze bottles used for liquid detergents, and many other products. They may also be used to make rigid, high-density plastics for bottles, toys, pipes, etc. The polyethylene plastics have become common household items, such as plastic film for drycleaning bags, refrigerator ware, chemical ware, and protective aprons. A visit to a dime store would turn up an amazing number of items made from polyethylene, especially at Christmas.

Polypropylene plastics have been found to be superior to polyethylene for pipe and pipe fixtures. Since plastic pipe is easy to assemble, will not corrode, and is less expensive than metal pipe, it is gradually replacing metals for plumbing. Polypropylene plastics can stand higher temperatures than polyethylene. Extra clear film may be made from them.

Polyesters

Dacron fibers and Mylar film are made from ethylene glycol and terephthalic acid, the result being an ester. Mylar plastic is used to make thinner, tougher photographic films. Mylar film possesses surprising physical strength and resistance to chemicals, oils, and solvents. Because of its excellent electrical insulating property, it is used in the electrical and electronics industries. Mylar shrinkable films are used to package many food articles such as cheese, meats, and poultry.

Polyurethane Plastics

One of the early plastic foams was foam rubber, but for many purposes, it has been replaced by flexible foams made from several different monomers. These new foams do not oxidize and disintegrate when used in mattresses, pillows, life preservers, and cushions as the former foam rubber did.

There are two types of urethane foams, the flexible and the rigid. The flexible polyurethane foams are cheaper than foam rubber, lighter in weight, and have greater strength. They also resist flame, sunlight, moisture, and air. These foams are the star performers for upholstery for furniture and automobile seats, and for pillows and mattresses.

A plastic made from polyurethane has been used for shoe soles which are ten times more durable than rubber soles. Polyurethane glues are very strong, and polyurethane varnish is very tough.

Corfam, poromeric material, a man-made leather, was launched in 1964 by the E. I. Du Pont de Nemours Chemical Company, after fourteen years of research and development. It is a urethane polymer reinforced with a polyester. It is now being used for the uppers for shoes, and is likely to offer competition to leather for other applications. Corfam poromeric material has the advantages of leather, but it does not have its disadvantages. It breathes like leather, allowing perspiration to evaporate through it. It is more flexible, lighter, and easier to clean than leather. It is water repellent and scuff resistant. However, other competing synthetic leather substitutes are now being developed by other companies.

Polystyrene Plastics

Polystyrene plastics are made by the polymerization of styrene, a product of the reaction of benzene with ethylene. Polystyrene is used to make rigid plastic foams, which compete with rigid polyurethane foams because of their lower cost of production. Polystyrene foams now replace foam rubber in the manu-

Figure 76–4. More than 15 thousand pairs of shoes, made from Corfam poromeric material, were given extensive field tests. (Courtesy, E. I. Du Pont de Nemours Chemical Company)

facture of floating objects, such as toys, boats, and life preservers. Rigid foams, especially those which are formed in the place where they are desired, produce very strong panels that provide excellent insulation against sound and heat. Polystyrene foam is now used for shipping containers for bottles of acids and other chemicals. As an insulating material, it possesses the advantage that $1\frac{1}{4}$ inches of polystyrene foam is equal to 3 inches of glass wool. Four cubic feet of space may be added to the average size refrigerator without increasing its outside dimensions, by use of polystyrene foam insulation.

Polystyrene solid plastic is sold under the name of Lustron or Lumitile, in the form of building tiles for decorative lighting effects. Molded articles of crystal-clear transparency are used as instrument faces, bottle caps, combs, buttons, and radiant, colored gems for costume jewelry.

The Polyvinyl Plastics

Vinyl plastics constitute the most versatile group of plastics developed to date. They are

Figure 76–5. The central control room of a Dacron polyester plant of the E. I. Du Pont de Nemours Chemical Company. One man monitors the operation of this chemical plant. This control room is typical of many highly automated chemical plants. (Courtesy, E. I. Du Pont de Nemours Chemical Company)

used for such diversified purposes as coatings for beer cans, or molding material for long playing phonograph records. Vinyl plastics are used for films, upholstery sheeting, foams for upholstery, water based paints, and floor coverings and "waxes." The chief types of vinyl plastics are polyvinyl chloride and polyvinyl acetate.

"Asphalt" floor tile were originally made from asphalt. It was found that they could be improved by adding petroleum resins, and today, most "asphalt" floor tiles are made from petroleum plastics. Vinyl asbestos tile, and vinyl coated felt, are now competing with asphalt-type floor coverings. Vinyl sheet floor coverings have become so popular that it is difficult to find the old "battleship" linoleum in stores anymore. Geon is a polyvinyl plastic that is used to make embossed floor coverings, upholstery, draperies, and raincoats.

Pipe is now being made from several different types of plastics. For example, high-density polyethylene or polypropylene pipe is used for irrigation and lawn-sprinkling systems. For such purposes they possess the advantages of low cost, ease of installation, durability, and freedom from corrosion.

Tough vinyl chloride plastic has been used for industrial piping of corrosive liquids. Vinyl plastic sewer and drainpipe have been approved by the Federal Housing Administration. National Underwriters Laboratories now approve polyvinyl chloride electrical conduits.

Vinyl chloride is used to make plastic films for rainwear, that are light in weight. All kinds of products are now protected in plastic overwraps which keep the goods in saleable condition and show them off attractively.

Vinylidene chloride, made from ethylene (obtained from natural gas) and chlorine, when copolymerized with vinyl chloride forms very interesting plastics such as Saran and Velon. These plastics are used for fishing leaders and heavy-duty upholstery materials. Saran is highly resistant to chemicals, and will not burn. It is odorless, tasteless, and nontoxic. It has extreme tensile strength and high abrasive resistance and toughness.

An outstanding use of Saran is for the manufacture of pipe and flexible tubing, which have many applications because of their resistance to chemicals. Saran pipe is tough, durable, flexible, and non-scaling. Sections can be welded together readily by heating the two ends. Saran Wrap-S is a shrinkable film that forms skintight coverings for poultry and other foods.

Polyvinylacetal resins, such as Vinylseal and Gelva, are thermoplastic, colorless, glass-clear, tasteless, odorless, low in density, and slow burning. They may be dissolved in organic solvents, such as methanol, and they may be emulsified in water. They produce durable, wear-resistant films, unaffected by oxygen or aging. These resins are used for adhesives, textile sizing and stiffening, and paints.

Polyvinyl butyral, formed from polyvinyl acetate by hydrolysis and condensation with butyraldehyde, and sold under the names

Butacite and Saflex, is used as an interlayer sandwiched in between plate glass layers to form laminated safety glass. The plastic layer stretches under a blow and holds the broken pieces together.

Polymeric Amides

Nylons are examples of polymeric amides, made from a variety of raw materials. Their use for fibers has previously been discussed. Nylon plastics are used to coat paper, to make oilproof containers, to coat leather, to make an excellent patent leather, to coat cloth, to make flexible waterproof clothing, to coat wire mesh, and to prepare a clear, strong glass. In the form of coarse monofilaments, nylon is the chief source of bristles for brushes, and of strings for tennis racquets.

Polymethyl Methacrylate

This is one of the older plastics, developed to meet the need for an organic glass. Today, we have in polymethyl methacrylate, a product clearer than optical glass, weighing half as much, which may be cut, turned, sawed, carved, drilled, polished, shaped, formed, and swaged. It is flexible, durable, and strong, and it may be given translucent, opaque, or pearl color effects. It is sold under the names of Lucite, Plexiglass, and Crystalite. This "super-glass" transmits light through its own curves, while conducting practically no heat, and thus finds applications where light is to be "piped" in medical and dental appliances. It is used in making highway reflectors, furniture, shoes, decorative panels, radiator ornaments, vanity cases, and similar products. It is thermoplastic, and it may be bent and shaped by softening it in hot oil at temperatures between 285° F and 315° F.

SOME UNUSUAL PLASTIC APPLICATIONS

Only a few of the many uses of plastics have been given in this chapter. A few unusual plastic applications are mentioned below.

Artificial teeth and tooth fillings are now made of plastics to match real teeth in appearance. Plastic skeletons are available for schools.

Plastics are now used in floor waxes, shoe polishes, and automobile waxes. Among these plastics the silicone plastics are making it possible to produce very much improved products.

The Slippery Plastics

Teflon, the fluorine plastic, is so tough and slippery that it can be used to make greaseless bearings, and cooking utensils.

Lexan is a polycarbonate, used to make housewares, toys, appliances, bowling balls, and panels for the construction industry. Lexan is a slippery plastic, and it may, therefore, be used for ballbearings, which are noiseless, and require no lubrication. An ideal use would be for children's tricycles and wagons, and for lawn mowers, whose lubrication is likely to be neglected.

SUMMARY

Classification of Plastics

Plastics may be classified as to their properties as (1) thermosetting, (2) thermoplastic, and (3) elastomeric.

Plastics may be classified as to their methods of formation, as polymerization and condensation plastics. In the formation of many plastics, both processes may take place.

Plastics may be classified as to their composition, or as to the monomers, from which they are formed. Of the twenty-five or more main families of plastics, the ones mentioned in this section were those based on cellulose, phenol-formaldehyde, other formaldehyde plastics, the polyolefines (ethylene, propylene, and butylene), polyurethane, polystyrene, vinyl (chloride and acetate), polymeric amides (the nylons), polymethyl methacrylate, fluorine (teflon), and polycarbonate.

Plastic Products

Plastics may be made in the form of filaments, films, foam, sheets, or solid molded objects.

Study Questions

1. DEFINE: condensation plastic, elastomer, resin, thermoplastic, thermosetting plastic.
2. What types of compounds are formed by polymerization?

3. List some of the plastics in which formaldehyde is used.
4. What types of compounds will polymerize?
5. Give some of the important applications of plastic foams.
6. List some of the new types of plastic paints and enamels. What advantages do they offer?
7. Classify plastics as to their general properties.
8. What are the two general methods for the preparation of plastics?
9. How are tailor-made plastics produced?
10. From what raw materials are plastics made?
11. List some of the advantages that plastics have for the fabrication of intricate devices.
12. What are some of the possible applications of the slippery plastics?
13. List some of the plastics used to make pipe.
14. What advantages do plastic pipe and plumbing fixtures offer?
15. List some of the plastics used to make plastic films.

Natural and Synthetic Rubber

That which is hidden and unknown and has not been revealed by direct methods will most likely be discovered by an accident, by the man who applies himself perseveringly to the subject and is most observing of everything related thereto.

CHARLES GOODYEAR

INTRODUCTION

Thousands of different articles made from synthetic rubber require a variety of different kinds of rubber to meet different needs. However, when one thinks of rubber he thinks of automobile tires, and rightly so, because it was the need for synthetic rubber to replace natural rubber during two World Wars that stimulated the tremendous amount of research that has now made the United States no longer dependent upon natural rubber. Furthermore, several of the synthetic rubbers now available are far superior to the natural product.

NATURAL RUBBER

Rubber is obtained by coagulating the latex emulsion obtained by tapping rubber trees. Originally the best grades of rubber were prepared *from latex obtained from wild rubber trees* (**Hevea** braziliensis) in the Amazon region of Brazil. In 1876, Sir Henry Wickham smuggled 70,000 seeds obtained from the best rubber trees along the Rio Tapajoz, which furnished the start for the cultivated rubber plantations in the East Indies. The production of plantation rubber rose from 11,000 tons in 1910 to nearly a million tons in 1940, while the production of wild rubber decreased from 54,000 tons in 1900 to about 10,000 tons in 1940.

THE DISCOVERY OF VULCANIZATION ENABLED MAN TO PUT RUBBER TO WORK

The desirable properties of natural rubber were early recognized, but products made from it had the disadvantage that they became soft and sticky when warmed, and also became very stiff at winter temperatures. In 1839, Charles Goodyear, while experimenting to find a way of hardening rubber, discovered by accident that hardness and resistance to deterioration could be imparted to rubber by *mixing sulfur with it and heating the mixture.* This process, called **vulcanization,** was but the beginning of a long series of researches, which have resulted in the improvement of natural rubber for many purposes from year to year.

The long, chainlike molecules of rubber are responsible for its extensibility, while the pronounced unsaturation of these molecules make it possible to link one molecule to another using sulfur as the bonding agent, thus producing tough, strong, and even very hard products, depending upon the amounts of sulfur used.

When the storms of Charles Goodyear's failures gave way in 1839 to the sunshine of success, he found at the end of his rainbow, not a pot of gold, but a strip of vulcanized rubber

569

that was the forerunner of today's billion-dollar rubber industry.

The discovery was one of those "accidents" that come to those who strive to observe. It happened when the difficulties of the experiment, financial worries, and even ill-health were at their worst. Ironically enough, Goodyear's success resulted from a condition previously considered a hindrance—heat.

Thoroughly familiar—to his financial loss and chagrin—with the effect of heat on rubber, Goodyear was defeated time after time in his effort to find how rubber could be made heat-resistant. That he was ultimately successful is a tribute to his perseverance, his thoroughly scientific mind, his resourcefulness, and his keen powers of observation.[1]

In 1844, Goodyear was granted a patent for his discovery, which was often and bitterly contested. He was represented in one legal battle by the eloquent Daniel Webster, who said, in the course of the trial, "This discovery will work important changes. It introduces a new material into manufacture, nothing less than elastic metal."

The rubber industry is very important today. One American manufacturer advertises over 32,000 different items made from rubber, while several hundred thousand patents dealing with rubber have been granted.

In the manufacture of commercial rubber products, in addition to the sulfur added for vulcanization, there are used reinforcing pigments, such as carbon black for black rubber, zinc oxide for white rubber, fillers, and organic compounds that will accelerate the rate of vulcanization and thus speed up production.

Many advances in vulcanization have been made since Goodyear's day. About fifty different kinds of substances are used to accelerate vulcanization, with the result that the amount of sulfur used has been decreased to about 3 per cent. Other organic compounds are added to reduce the rate of the action of light and oxygen on rubber products.

NATURAL RUBBER APPLICATIONS

Three methods of using rubber are electrodeposition, extrusion, and molding. Rubber

[1] *The Laboratory*, Fisher Scientific Company, Vol. X, No. 5.

may also be used in the form of foams and emulsions, or solutions, as in paints.

The Electrodeposition of Rubber

The particles of a rubber emulsion have a negative charge and may be attracted to a positive electrode, which may be in the form of a human hand made of metal, on which true-fitting rubber gloves are thus deposited. Or, a metal plate may be covered with a textile fabric, in which the rubber is deposited to make a waterproof material containing very little rubber.

Foams

Sponge, or foam rubber was used at one time for mattresses, upholstered furniture, and automobile seats, but it lost its popularity as the sponge rubber began to crumble and disintegrate in use. Today, sponge rubber has now been replaced by improved, plastic, elastomeric foams mentioned in the previous chapter.

Paints

Natural rubber comes out of the tree in the form of an emulsion, which is called **latex.** Some of the first water paints, which are so easy to apply, dry quickly, and are free from unpleasant solvent-forming fumes, were latex paints. Today, various synthetic rubbers are likewise used in the form of water emulsions or solvent solutions, to make both inside and outside paints. The use of such emulsions and solutions has revolutionized the paint industry.

NATURAL RUBBER COMPOUNDS

Rubber has been treated with chlorine and hydrogen chloride to obtain plastic materials with which modern synthetic plastics are competing. Rubber floor tiles and Pliofilm are typical rubber products. Pliofilm has been used for shower curtains and raincoats.

THE FIRST TWO PRACTICAL SYNTHETIC ELASTOMERS

The first two synthetic elastomers were Thiokol and neoprene, and they are still offering strong competition to the newer synthetic rubber products because of their unique properties.

Thiokol

Thiokol-B, announced in 1929, was the first synthetic rubber made in the United States. It is resistant to oils, greases, and ozone. A number of synthetic rubbers, when mixed with solid oxidizers, have been used to make solid fuels for rockets—a big business these days. Thiokol is one of the most commonly used binders, so the Thiokol Company is now one of the leading manufacturing companies engaged in the production of solid fuels for rockets.

One of the modern synthetic rubbers, somewhat similar in composition to Thiokol, is Hypalon. Hypalon is made by the reaction of chlorine and sulfur dioxide on polyethylene plastic, having an average molecular weight of about 20,000. It is highly resistant to ozone, weathering, oxidizing chemicals, and many oils and solvents. This very durable rubber is often blended with other synthetic rubbers to improve their resistance to oxidation.

Neoprene

The second, commercially introduced, synthetic rubber in the United States was neoprene, announced by the E. I. Du Pont de Nemours Chemical Company in 1931. It is made by the polymerization of chloroprene monomer. Chloroprene is made by joining two molecules of acetylene to form monovinyl-acetylene, and adding hydrogen chloride. The process seems to be simple and the product is superior, but it requires very complex manufacturing equipment. It took the E. I. Du Pont de Nemours Chemical Company nearly twenty years to develop it to the point where it became a money maker. Many markets for the raw material were promoted, so that it could be made in sufficiently large quantities to bring its price down.

Neoprene is the most versatile of man-made rubbers. It has dynamic properties closely duplicating those of natural rubber, plus the advantage that these excellent physical properties are not significantly diminished by age or continued severe operating conditions. It retains much of its flexibility at sub-zero temperatures. Neoprene does not support combustion, and it is resistant to oil and grease, sunlight, and weathering.

Neoprene is used to make such diverse products as household gloves, coal conveyor belts, industrial and garden hose, wire and cable jackets, fire-resistant foam mattresses, and numerous automotive and home appliance seals and gaskets. It is used to make long-wearing shoe soles and heels, and even fabric domes coated with neoprene for arctic living. Figures 77-1 and 77-2 show a portable warehouse which may be made from either neoprene or Hypalon.

Another chlorine-containing, synthetic elas-

Figure 77–1. A low-cost, portable warehouse being erected. A 1-horsepower blower inflates the structure and maintains slight internal supporting pressure. This warehouse was made from Hypalon. (Courtesy, E. I. Du Pont de Nemours Chemical Company)

Figure 77–2. The inside of the inflated Hypalon warehouse. Cost, only $2.24 per square foot. (Courtesy, E. I. Du Pont de Nemours Chemical Company)

tomer is Koroseal or Flamenol, a polymer of vinyl chloride, from which many modern plastics are made, as discussed in the previous section. Koroseal compositions vary from materials similar to hard rubber to stiff jellies. They are used to line metal tanks, to make gaskets, to coat papers, to insulate electrical conductors or cables, to join textile fabrics by heating with a warm iron, and to prepare acid-resistant paints, under the name of Koroplate. Koroplate is also oil-resistant, and for that reason, it is used to coat the inside of oil storage tanks. Koroseal is made in a variety of beautiful colors. Koroseal-treated cloth has been used for clothing, shower curtains, and umbrellas. Koroseal has also been used extensively for wristwatch straps, suspenders, garters, and trouser belts. A special composition containing aluminum is marketed in the form of ironing-board covers that enable the user to iron more pieces in a given time.

VITON

By incorporating fluorine into a plastic, a very superior plastic, Teflon, was obtained. Why not use fluorine instead of chlorine to make synthetic elastomers? **Viton** rubber is a fluorine-containing rubber, made of vinylidine fluoride and hexafluoropropylene by the E. I. Du Pont de Nemours Chemical Com-

pany. Viton has outstanding resistance to oils, fuels, chemicals, ozone, and temperatures up to 400° F. Viton is also well suited for use as a vacuum seal, and is widely employed in aircraft, missile, and space components. It has mechanical properties superior to other high-temperature-resistant rubbers.

BUTADIENE-STYRENE SYNTHETIC RUBBER

This rubber, developed during World War II, was known as Buna-S (Bu from butadiene, na from the sodium used as the catalyst, and S from Styrene). It was also known as GR-S (Government Rubber S).

In the preparation of synthetic substitutes for rubber, the original idea was to prepare a synthetic rubber having the composition and properties of natural rubber. An analysis of natural rubber showed that it was a polymer of a simple hydrocarbon, containing five carbon atoms and two double bonds. The first problem in imitating nature was to obtain this simple isomer, known as isoprene. It was found that isoprene could be obtained from the turpentine from pine trees, but this was too expensive a source of isoprene.

In connection with the isoprene research, it was discovered that another hydrocarbon, butadiene, having only four carbon atoms, but having two double bonds like isoprene, could be polymerized in the presence of sodium to produce a rubber-like compound. Buna rubber was developed in Germany in the late twenties from acetylene.

The improvement of natural rubber by treatment with other substances, and the discovery that Buna rubber was more resistant to organic solvents than is natural rubber, led to the idea that it might be possible to prepare new synthetic products, differing in composition from natural rubber, which would be superior to it for various purposes. It was realized that erasers and automobile tires do not need to be electrical insulators, and that hard-rubber articles need not be extensible. Natural rubber suffers from several disadvantages: it swells on contact with organic liquids, such as petroleum products (gasoline, lubricating oils, etc.); and it is not resistant to oxidation by the oxygen of the air.

The original synthetic rubber, a polymer of dimethylbutadiene, developed by Germany during World War I, was a poor substitute for natural rubber, but it has been greatly improved by building large polymers from a mixture of butadiene and other unsaturated compounds. Thus, Buna-S tires, used by the German army in 1940–1941, were made by polymerizing butadiene with styrene.

Butadiene may be obtained from butane (natural gas, or petroleum), butylene (petroleum), or ethyl alcohol, which may be obtained by the fermentation of potatoes, grains or sugars, or from petroleum.

Styrene was obtained from ethylene (petroleum) or benzene (coal tar or petroleum).

Buna-S synthetic rubber is approximately equal to natural rubber in its resistance to abrasion and heat. Buna-S was made from 75 parts of butadiene and 25 parts of styrene. Most of the synthetic tires made during the postwar years were made from butadiene and styrene, in which the styrene has been reduced to about 3 per cent.

The early types of synthetic rubber, called Buna-S and Butyl-rubber, were inferior to natural rubber for automobile tires, but the discovery of new catalysts, such as cumene hydro-peroxide, reduced the time required for polymerization, and made it possible to carry out the process at lower temperatures. The "cold rubber" so prepared resulted in the production of longer and more uniform molecules, with the result that these improved synthetic rubbers were equal to natural rubber in tire performance by 1948.

BUNA-N RUBBER

Buna-N, more commonly referred to as GR-N or Perbunan, Butaprene, Hycar, Chemigum, Amprene, or Ameripol, is another copolymer of butadiene, which is particularly desirable because of its resistance to swelling with liquid hydrocarbons. Buna-N is made by copolymerizing butadiene with acrylonitrile. Acrylonitrile may be obtained from ethylene by oxidation with oxygen (air) and reaction with hydrogen cyanide.

The sodium used as a catalyst by the Germans for the production of Buna rubber was replaced in the United States by soap, which acted as a surface catalyst, forming films that apparently oriented the rubber ingredient molecules between films of water and soap, and thus put them into a condition to combine with each other when heated under pressure.

BUTYL RUBBER

Butyl rubber has been made chiefly by copolymerizing isobutylene and isoprene, or isobutylene and butadiene. The isobutylene, obtained from cracking petroleum, constitutes about 95 to 98 per cent of butyl rubber; and butadiene or isoprene constitutes about 2 to 5 per cent. By varying the composition of the raw materials, the properties of the finished product may be controlled.

Butyl rubber is colorless, odorless, tasteless, and more stretchable than natural rubber.

Natural rubber is so unsaturated that even when it is vulcanized with sulfur there remains a degree of unsaturation that causes it to be ready to combine with oxygen of the air. Oxidation of natural rubber causes it to age or deteriorate. The Butyl rubber molecules have just enough unsaturation to allow them to combine with sulfur in vulcanization sufficient to impart strength, but to leave no unsaturation. As a result, Butyl rubber is less readily oxidized than natural rubber. It swells like natural rubber in contact with petroleum oils but, unlike natural rubber, it is little affected by vegetable and animal fats and oils.

Butyl rubber has been used for inner tubes because of its excellent impermeability to gases.

ETHYLENE-PROPYLENE RUBBER

Ethylene-Propylene Rubber (EPR), Nordel, announced by the E. I. Du Pont de Nemours Chemical Company in 1963, when vulcanized, possesses significant performance advantages over conventional, general purpose rubbers, especially its immunity to ozone. Potentially large markets for this general-purpose synthetic rubber include electric wire and cable insulation, industrial hose, garden hose, and molded and extruded goods. There are other ethylene-propylene rubbers, but Nordel owes its particular superior properties to the fact that it also contains a diene.

Nordel is a hydrocarbon-based rubber. Therefore, (in common with other general-purpose rubbers based on hydrocarbons) it is neither flame- nor oil-resistant. It has the lowest specific gravity of any elastomer (0.85), and possesses the ability to accept large amounts of fillers and oils. Nordel is well fitted for use in automatic washers, washer-dryers, and dishwashers, because it has the requisite resistance to hot water, hot air, bleach, and detergents, plus excellent flux and abrasion resistance.

POLYURETHANE RUBBER

Polyurethane rubber, similar in composition to polyurethane plastics, has high abrasion resistance and weight-bearing capacity. This rubber is made by the E. I. Du Pont de Nemours Chemical Company and is sold under their trademark, Adiprene.

SILICONE RUBBERS

Silicone rubbers have important applications where their high resistance to heat and oxidation are important. Many housewives have wished for rubber rings for their pressure cookers that would not require frequent replacement. Perhaps silicone rubber would be the answer.

SUMMARY

When polymers are stretchable or rubber-like, they are called elastomers. Natural and synthetic rubbers are elastomers.

Types of Synthetic Rubbers

1. *Hydrocarbon polymers*—Natural rubber is a polymer of isoprene. Other hydrocarbon polymers are butadiene-styrene, butyl, and ethylene-propylene rubbers. These rubbers are made from the products contained in or derived from petroleum refinery gases and natural gas, such as ethylene, propylene, and butylene. The secret of making these polymers lies in the use of special catalysts, some of which still remain secret.

2. *Halogen-containing polymers*—Neoprene is made from chloroprene. Thiokol is made from ethylene dichloride and a sulfide. Hypalon is made from polyethylene plastic by treatment with chlorine and sulfur dioxide. Koroseal is made from vinyl chloride. Viton is made from fluorine-containing monomers. Natural rubber may be treated with chlorine or hydrogen chloride to form products that belong to this class. In general, these products have high resistance to oils, greases, ozone, solvents, weathering, and sunlight.

3. *Nitrogen-containing polymers*—Buna-N rubber and polyurethane rubber contain nitrogen compounds.

Study Questions

1. DEFINE: vulcanization, Hevea rubber, latex.
2. How do you account for Goodyear's "lucky accident"?
3. What is meant by the vulcanization of rubber?
4. Describe some of the important new developments in the utilization of rubber.
5. Which type of synthetic rubber would be preferred for long-lasting garden hose? Why?
6. What are the functions and advantages of the accelerators and the antioxidants used in rubber compounding?
7. Discuss the various types of synthetic rubber as to (a) the raw materials from which they are made, (b) their properties, and (c) their uses.
8. What were the objections to the foam rubber products made from natural rubber?

9. List some of the monomers used for the production of fibers and plastics that are also used for the manufacture of synthetic rubber.

10. What are the advantages and the disadvantages of Nordel synthetic rubber?

11. What is the secret of success in polymerizing various hydrocarbons to form synthetic rubbers?

12. What were the first two kinds of synthetic rubbers in the United States?

13. In what regards is neoprene superior to natural rubber?

14. What are the outstanding properties of Viton? What is unusual about its composition?

15. What types of synthetic rubber were used for most of the automobile tires after World War II?

16. Why did the two World Wars lead to intensive research on synthetic rubber?

Spraying DDT over forests of northern Idaho to control the Douglas-fir tussock moth. (Courtesy, U.S. Department of Agriculture)

Contributions of Physical Science to Man's Physical Welfare

We cannot claim that people are happier as a result, but we have purposely post-poned the quest for happiness until we understand the human spirit, and that, we recall, is the third and last of the great mysteries of existence. Yet if we do not know the formula for happiness, we do know how to reduce human suffering. If we cannot temper the attacks of man upon man, we have reduced the attacks of Nature. If we cannot increase the richness of man's life, we have increased its length and breadth.

GERALD WENDT, *Wiley Bulletin,* November, 1938

*T*HIS UNIT takes up the contributions of physical science to agriculture in the form of fertilizers, insecticides, pesticides, and herbicides. It tells about the various substances produced by Nature that man is learning to use. Many potent drugs, including narcotics and euphoriants, are found in nature and utilized by man, although not always for the improvement of his physical welfare.

Finally, this course in Physical Science comes to a close with the study of its contributions to man's physical welfare in the form of pain killers, tranquilizers, sedatives, hypnotics, and chemotherapeutic agents, the modern weapons against disease.

And step by step, since time began,
I see the steady gain of Man.

WHITTIER

Organic Compounds Produced by Plants and Animals

In photosynthesis, we are like travelers in an unknown country around whom the early morning fog slowly begins to rise, vaguely revealing the outlines of the landscape.

E U G E N E   I .   R A B I N O W I T C H

INTRODUCTION

This chapter is intended to present an overview of photosynthesis and the products produced by plants and animals, together with methods for their utilization by man.

PHOTOSYNTHESIS

As previously mentioned, **photosynthesis** is *the process by which plants synthesize carbohydrates from water solutions drawn from the soil and from carbon dioxide obtained from the air, in which sunlight furnishes the energy, and* **chlorophyll** *is the catalyst.* After many years of intensive research, the basic processes of photosynthesis have been worked out. We know that photosynthesis is much more complicated than it was once thought to be.

The chlorophyll molecule has the shape of a tadpole. The head is polar in nature and is attracted to water. The tail, on the other hand, is nonpolar. It has been estimated that about 1 billion molecules of chlorophyll are contained in each of the chloroplasts, which are the green bodies found in cells.

In photosynthesis, oxygen is split off of water, thus leaving hydrogen to react with the carbon dioxide. Scientists have found that there are at least eleven distinct steps in which at least eight different enzymes participate.

High energy phosphorus compounds play an important part in the reactions. Three vitamins, riboflavin (B-2), vitamin K, and vitamin C, produced by the chloroplasts, catalyze the reactions. Vitamins and enzymes will be studied in Chapter 81.

PHYSIOLOGICALLY ACTIVE, NON-FOOD COMPOUNDS PRODUCED BY PLANTS AND ANIMALS

The most important plant products are foods, fibers to provide clothing, and wood to provide housing and fuel. In addition to these main products, many plants specialize in the production of such substances as the latex from which rubber is obtained, or the production of physiologically active compounds such as vitamins, alkaloids, and drugs.

Insects, snakes, lizards, etc. produce poisonous substances that enable them to combat their foes in the fight for survival. Man thus has available many physiologically active substances produced by natural processes. In order to take advantage of such substances, they must first be separated and purified, in order to control their dosage when they are used as medicines.

Some of the smallest plants are bacteria, many of which specialize in the production of particular compounds. In many cases these compounds are harmful to the body, as in the case of bacterial toxins.

THE ROLE OF ANIMALS IN THE PRODUCTION OF FOOD

Some animals, such as cows and sheep, depend upon plant foods exclusively. Carnivorous animals prey upon other animals exclusively for their foods. In the end, however, plants are the sources of all animal foods. Man can get along on plant foods alone, if they are properly selected; but for most men, animal products serve as important adjuncts to plant foods. Herbivorous animals serve as food factories to transform such plant products as grass, which man cannot utilize, into his most important protein foods, such as meat and milk.

COMPOUNDS FOUND IN FOODS PRODUCED BY PLANTS

Carbohydrates

Carbohydrates are *compounds composed of carbon, hydrogen, and oxygen, in which the ratio between the number of hydrogen atoms to the number of oxygen atoms is two to one,* the same as it is in water. **Carbohydrates** *include sugars, starches, gums, and celluloses.*

Carbohydrates having six carbon atoms per molecule include the simple sugars, called monosaccharides, such as glucose (dextrose) and fructose (levulose). Glucose is a constituent of corn syrup, and fructose is found in fruits. Carbohydrates which have twelve carbon atoms per molecule, the disaccharides, include sucrose, the common sugar obtained from sugar cane or sugar beets; lactose, the sugar found in milk; and maltose. Much larger molecules are found in starches and gums, of which there are a number of different compounds, depending upon the number of carbon atoms present. Starches are found in such cereals as corn, wheat, oats, rice, and rye, and in some vegetables such as potatoes. As certain foods such as grains develop, they form sugars at first; but as they reach maturity, the sugars are changed to starches. For example, sweet corn is not sweet when it matures. Starches seem to be the form in

which foods are stored for the use of seeds as they sprout and grow. However, many seeds such as flax seed, cotton seed, soy beans, corn, and sunflower seeds contain concentrated food reserves in the form of oils. Most nuts also contain fats and oils.

Some very large molecules of carbohydrates are lumped together under the general term of cellulose, which is found in combination with lignin in the form of wood, grass, and straw, previously discussed. Starches and the more complex sugars are broken down to the simple sugars in the digestion of foods. These simple sugars, such as glucose, furnish most of the energy of the body as they react with the oxygen carried by the blood to form carbon dioxide and water. The carbon dioxide is carried to the lungs by the blood, where it enters the inhaled air, and is exhaled. The vitamins, nicotinamide and riboflavin, play an important role in the production of water. Thiamine is necessary for the production of carbon dioxide. The vitamins seem to act as coenzymes. Both processes result in the liberation of energy. The metabolism of fats and proteins also seems to depend upon the vitamins of the B complex. Deficiencies in these vitamins may produce such symptoms as weakness, easy fatigability, constipation, loss of appetite, headache, insomnia, excessive irritability, and light-headedness, as the result of improper metabolism.

Fats and Oils

Fats and oils are compounds of carbon, hydrogen, and oxygen. Oils differ from fats in that they contain double bonds; they are unsaturated. Oils can be converted to solid fats by adding hydrogen to them in the presence of a catalyst. The double bond is removed in this way, and a saturated fat is formed.

Fats and oils are broken down into the simpler products, fatty acids, and glycerol (glycerine) in digestion. These products may be oxidized to furnish energy. If they are not all used to furnish energy, they may be recombined in the body and stored as fatty tissue, which serves as a reserve fuel, after the small amount of stored starch has been used up. Carbohydrates, and even proteins, if taken in excess of the body requirements are also stored in the body as fats. The body can reverse the process, and break the fats down into simpler substances, which may then be oxidized, but the body will not draw on this reserve fat as long as it is obtaining sufficient carbohydrates from foods. To lose weight, it is necessary to reduce the amounts of carbohydrates, fats, and oils in the food intake, below the amounts needed to furnish the energy required by the body. Exercise requires energy, so exercise not unaccompanied by a decrease in intake of energy foods will help to reduce the body weight. However, exercise seldom results in weight reduction because it simply stimulates the appetite, with the result that food intake is increased.

The use of excessive amounts of foods results in obesity. It is probable that obesity is more important than excessive use of tobacco or alcoholic liquors when it comes to shortening the life span.

Proteins

Proteins are *compounds of carbon, hydrogen, oxygen, nitrogen, and sometimes sulfur, phosphorus, or iron.*

Proteins are *long chains formed by many* **amino acids,** *which are relatively simple organic acids containing a nitrogen atom.* One end of the acid molecule has a replaceable, acid hydrogen; while the other end, containing the nitrogen, is basic in nature. The result is that amino acids may join with each other to form long chains, in which the acid end of one amino acid is joined to the basic end of the next amino acid. Proteins are formed by plants from the nitrogen compounds contained in the soil. In the process of digestion of proteins, animals break them up to form about twenty different kinds of amino acids.

The tissues of the body, such as hair, skin, nerves, eyes, muscles, and organs are protein in nature. These proteins are very large molecules built up from the approximately twenty different amino acids, to form the wide variety of highly specialized compounds. How does the human body control the kinds of proteins that are formed? Chromosomes are aggregates of huge molecules, which carry within themselves the patterns of inheritance. Within the chromosomes are groups called genes that determine the nature of the protein

molecules that will be formed. These genes are the DNA molecules, the nucleic acids, which appear to act as templates, and cause amino acids to join each other in such a way as to duplicate the template.

The proteins in foods must furnish all of the different amino acids required to build the various proteins in the body. Some plant proteins do not furnish all of the necessary amino acids required, but animal proteins are generally well-balanced sources of amino acids. Excessive amounts of proteins cannot be stored as such in the body. The body is continually renewing its tissues. Discarded proteins are broken down, and the nitrogenous part of the protein is converted into urea, and excreted in the urine. Excessive proteins are eliminated in the same way. For good health, a certain minimum amount of well-balanced proteins should be included in the diet. Large excesses should be avoided, because they simply overwork the organs involved in their elimination.

FOOD PROCESSING

Refining of Foods

Many naturally-occurring food products have been **refined,** i.e., *treated in such a way as to separate certain substances in a nearly pure form.* Very pure sucrose has been separated from sugar cane and sugar beets. Starch has been separated from corn and other grains. Glucose, a simple sugar, has been prepared from cornstarch. Various amino acids have been separated from proteins. Gelatin has been prepared from seaweeds and other sources. Pectin has been separated from fruits and vegetables, and is now used in making jellies. White flour, gluten, bran, and wheat germ have been obtained from wheat. Vegetable oils have been separated and purified.

One very common method of refining foods in the home is that of cooking them in water and discarding the water. Soluble minerals, vitamins, flavors, sugars, etc. are lost in this way. The resulting products are then made palatable by adding such products as butter, sugar, sodium glutamate, salt, and pepper. In this way an acceptable flavor may be obtained, but the valuable minerals are not replaced in this process.

Another method of refining foods in the home is to peel them and discard the peelings. For example, most of the minerals in a potato are found in the outer layer under the skin, and if the potato is peeled, a considerable portion of the minerals is lost.

Preservation of Foods

The preservation of foods by canning has become an important industry. With modern methods and machinery, canned foods seldom spoil, because they have been heated at the correct temperatures for the proper length of time.

Methods of freezing foods have been developed so as to preserve their original freshness.

Some food products, such as coffee or nuts, are vacuum packed in order to keep out oxygen, which would cause them to become rancid.

Many foods may be obtained in a dehydrated form. If water is removed from foods and they are packed so as to keep moisture out, they will keep for a long time, because the chemical changes which would result in spoilage cannot take place in the absence of water. Dehydrated foods are of special value to back-packers, because of their light weight and small bulk. For everyday use in the home, relatively few dehydrated foods are found on the supermarket shelves. Among these may be listed soup mixes, mashed potato, powdered milk, instant coffee and tea, gelatin desserts, and pudding mixes. The dehydration of eggs is a big business. Bakeries use large quantities of powdered eggs and milk. Cake mixes sold in stores usually contain powdered eggs.

Considerable research has been devoted to the preservation of foods by irradiation with rays from radioactive isotopes. Many foods have been successfully preserved in this way, but there are problems, such as the preservation of flavors, that must be solved before irradiated foods will be found in markets.

Cold storage has made it possible to store fruits and other products for use when they would not otherwise be available.

Foods have been preserved from ancient times to the present by the use of salt or vinegar. Pickles, for example, are preserved with vinegar (acetic acid), and meat and fish products have been preserved with salt. A small amount of vinegar is harmless, and, of course, extra amounts of salt can be removed by soaking in water. Meats, bacon, and fish have been preserved by smoking them. Most of the bacon of today is sugar cured, although it may be smoked or treated with liquid smoke products to impart a smoky flavor.

Almost any food can be preserved by adding chemical preservatives to kill invading microorganisms. Chemical preservatives may also destroy the digestive enzymes and the helpful bacteria in the digestive tract. Only a few chemical preservatives have been permitted to be added to foods, and the amounts used must be kept within limits in which they are relatively harmless. Benzoate of soda is such a preservative. It is used to preserve catsup and various meat products. The freshly ground, red color of hamburger can be preserved by adding benzoate of soda. One might wonder how chickens can be shipped thousands of miles, and be displayed in a meat market, in an apparently very fresh condition, and have no odor. This is made possible by treating them with an antibiotic to prevent bacterial action. Breads made in modern bakeries usually contain calcium proprionate to preserve them. Such breads can be kept for several days without becoming moldy. Dried fruits are preserved with sulfur dioxide.

CHEMICAL ADDITIVES

The Pure Food and Drug laws require that any chemical additives be listed on the package label. An examination of the labels on many food products will show that a surprising number of different chemicals are added for a variety of reasons. Perhaps the most common chemical additives are synthetic flavors and colors.

Some coal-tar dyes formerly accepted for use in foods have been found to be harmful, and research needs to be done with the fifteen dyes commonly used today to determine their possible harmful effects. There is no way in which the Pure Food laws can control the intake of such dyes. The widespread use of coal-tar dyes in ice creams and sherbets, butter, margarine, soft drinks and confections should be investigated, especially in regard to the possibility that they may cause cancer. The Food and Drug Administration has such a small budget that it is unable to carry out these and other important research programs.

Chemicals are added to foods for many purposes other than preservation. For example, there are emulsifying, stabilizing, thickening, suspending, softening, and anti-staling agents. By their use, new food products have been made possible and old products have been improved. Such products are used for ice creams, cheese spreads, salad dressings, and soups. Most of these substances are made from vegetable gums, starches, and natural fats and oils. Although they may have awesome chemical names, they are digestible. Present federal laws require that food additives be adequately tested before their use will be permitted.

THE SIGNIFICANCE OF FOOD PROCESSING

The overall results of all of the above food processing have been good. A wide variety of foods has been made readily available, and the time required for food preparation in the home has been decreased. The unintelligent use of refined foods could result in a deficiency of minerals, vitamins and roughage, all of which may be purchased in drug stores. However, it requires intelligence to know what to purchase.

MALNUTRITION

The chief causes of malnutrition are ignorance and apathy. Ignorance may be of two kinds, (1) ignorance of the importance of a good diet, and (2) lack of knowledge of how to select a diet. No two people are alike. What in one man's food is another man's poison. However, one must realize that the tissues of the body cannot be made from just any kind of food. Bones and teeth cannot be made from doughnuts, pies, and coffee; they require minerals. The hemoglobin of the blood is an iron compound. The tissues are built from the amino acids found in food proteins. For the average person without food allergies, the following rules should assure an adequate diet:

Select foods every day from each of the following groups:

1. Milk and milk products such as cheese and ice cream.

2. Meats and other sources of proteins such as eggs, fish, beans, peas, and nuts—at least two servings each day.

3. Fruits and vegetables—four or more servings each day. These servings should include one dark green and one deep yellow vegetable at least three times a week, a citrus fruit, and other vegetables such as potatoes. It is assumed that some kind of a waterless cooking method will be used so as to avoid the loss of food values which these foods contain.

4. Bread and Cereals—four or more servings each day, at least half of which should be of the whole-grain, unrefined types.

The above rules provide the basic knowledge that is needed. Apathy is an individual problem, which may be determined by one's values. If good health is a desirable outcome, then it will be reflected in a health attitude that will replace that of apathy. It is a lack of the health attitude which leads to a lack of exercise and excessive use of alcohol, and tobacco, coffee, and food. A well-balanced diet and plenty of exercise enables one to tolerate a moderate amount of such potentially harmful substances as alcohol or tobacco, but when their effects are added to the malnutrition resulting from an inadequate diet poor health is inevitable.

There is no excuse for inadequate diets. The necessary foods are readily available in adequate amounts. Even a lack of money is no excuse. It is true that the problem becomes more difficult when money is scarce; but a little money, when supplemented by considerable knowledge and ingenuity, can solve the problem.

ALCOHOL (ETHYL OR GRAIN ALCOHOL)

The preparation of alcoholic drinks by the fermentation of sugars and starches is one of the oldest methods of food processing. Alcoholic liquors are not particularly harmful when used in moderation. Small amounts of alcohol can be burned up in the body, but larger concentrations can do permanent damage. After all, alcohol is an excellent preservative and disinfectant, not a food. Alcohol furnishes a quick source of energy, but so do sugars.

Alcohol is not a narcotic, but it may lead to what amounts to addiction, in the case of alcoholics. Alcohol acts as a stimulant at first, as it speeds up the metabolism, the rate and depth of respiration, and the rate and volume of blood flow, but better stimulants are available. In the end, after its stimulating action has worn off, it acts as a sedative. Better sedatives are available. Large quantities of alcohol paralyze the nerve centers and may do permanent damage to the brain. Even moderate amounts of alcohol cause people to become unsafe drivers. Moderate amounts of alcohol deaden the inhibitions and cause people to do many things that they may later regret. Alcohol has been used for ages as a tranquilizer to enable people to forget their troubles, but better tranquilizers are now available. Since the use of alcoholic liquors often leads to alcoholism, the only sure way of not becoming an alcoholic is to avoid the use of alcoholic liquors.

An alcoholic cannot drink moderately, because alcohol has permanently anesthetized that part of the brain that tells them when to quit. Total and permanent abstinence is the only solution. Generally outside help is required to cause the alcoholic to quit.

Tranquilizers have helped alcoholics to break their habit, and they have been useful in the treatment of delirium tremens, the eventual stage of alcoholism. Two drugs have been developed to help the alcoholic, antabuse and CCC (citrated calcium carbimide). Both drugs cause such a severe reaction when alcohol is used, that the patient chooses to leave one or the other alone.

SUMMARY

Plants produce many different kinds of substances by photosynthesis. The raw materials are carbon dioxide of the air, and water solutions absorbed by the roots. The catalyst is chlorophyll, and the energy for this endothermic reaction is obtained from sunlight.

Important plant products are foods, fibers, and wood. Plant foods consist of carbohydrates (sugars, starches, and gums), fats and oils, and proteins.

Plants, animals, and insects produce many physiologically active substances, such as vitamins.

Alcoholic liquors and even foods may be used in excessive amounts.

Malnutrition is usually the result of either ignorance or apathy. Probably the chief cause of malnutrition is the lack of any desire to be healthy.

Study Questions

1. DEFINE: protein, carbohydrate, photosynthesis, chlorophyll, amino acid, food refining.
2. List the different kinds of carbohydrates found in foods.
3. How are foods refined in the home?
4. Give the rules for a balanced diet.
5. What are the advantages of refined foods?
6. What are the probable causes of malnutrition?
7. Would it be correct to say that obesity is a result of malnutrition?
8. List the various methods used to preserve foods.
9. What kinds of food additives are found in food products?
10. What do you think are the advantages of refined foods?
11. What is the possible outcome of using too much refined food?
12. List some of the dehydrated foods sold in food markets.
13. Why do dehydrated foods keep without spoiling?
14. What is a sure method of avoiding alcoholism?
15. What are the effects of alcoholic liquors on the body?
16. What are the functions of carbohydrates and fats and oils in both plants and animals?
17. What is meant by the statement that certain vegetable proteins are incomplete proteins?
18. What is wrong with the use of excessive amounts of foods, alcoholic liquors, or caffeine drinks?
19. How is it possible to ship chickens considerable distances and keep them in a meat market without any evidence of spoiling?
20. What are the functions of proteins in the body?

CHAPTER 79

The Agricultural Revolution

To science, pilot of industry, conquerer of disease, multiplier of the harvest, explorer of the universe, revealer of nature's laws, eternal guide to truth.

Inscription on the National
Academy of Sciences Building

We have a technological revolution in farming that in 20 years has transformed our agriculture more dramatically than in nearly 200 years since the War of Independence.

Ezra Taft Benson

INTRODUCTION

Agricultural technology has resulted in an ever-increasing efficiency. It has been accomplished by (1) a careful selection of crop plants, followed by constant improvements of the hardiest and most productive strains (2) hybridization, (3) eradication of pests, (4) careful preparation of the soil, and mechanization, (5) the use of fertilizers, and (6) the use of herbicides.

The United States Government Department of Agriculture has made important contributions to agricultural efficiency in the development of productive strains, hybridization, and pest control. Animal husbandry has been greatly improved likewise by the use of drugs, pesticides, animal breeding, and the development of well-balanced feeds. The contributions of biological science to agriculture have been dramatic. The contributions of physical science in pest control will be studied in the next chapter. In this chapter the part played in the development and use of fertilizers and herbicides is emphasized. Fertilizers promote the growth of crops, and herbicides prevent the growth of weeds. The use of herbicides

has played an important part in increasing farm production, in spite of a substantial reduction in the number of farmers. Chemical weeding is a great labor saver on the farm as well as for the back-yard gardener.

MINERAL REQUIREMENTS OF PLANTS

In Chapter 78, it was pointed out that the chief raw materials for plant growth are the carbon dioxide taken from the air and the water taken from the soil. If one were to plant seeds in a bed of straw, excelsior, wood shavings, sawdust, sand, or other porous material and keep this seed bed moist, the seeds would sprout and start to grow; but the young plants would soon cease to develop. It must be that plants require something else in addition to carbon dioxide and water.

Modern experiments with **hydroponics**— i.e., *soilless gardening*, in which seeds are planted in seed beds of porous materials such as those mentioned above, suspended above tanks of water containing dissolved salts into which the roots extend—have shown that there are at least eleven elements in addition to

Figure 79–1. The effect of potassium deficiency on ear formation. The ears to the right were deficient in potassium. (Courtesy, American Potash Institute, Inc.)

carbon, hydrogen and oxygen, that are essential to plant growth, namely: nitrogen, potassium, phosphorus, calcium, magnesium, sulfur, iron, manganese, boron, zinc, and copper.

DIFFERENCES IN THE COMPOSITION OF SOILS

Soils vary from rich, black loam to dry and unproductive sand; they may be acid, basic, or saline; they may contain relatively small or large amounts of organic matter (humus). The origin and nature of a given sample of soil determine the extent to which it will provide the minerals required for plant growth.

An analysis of any agricultural soil will show that it contains many times the quantity of all the minerals that plants require, with the exception of nitrogen, phosphorus, and potassium. Fortunately, most of this material is insoluble in water; otherwise, it would soon be washed out of the soil by rains and irrigation. On the other hand, this insoluble mate-

rial must dissolve before it can pass through the cell walls of plant roots by dialysis. The weathering of rocks, freezing and thawing, action of acids from decaying plants, action of carbon dioxide and other gases in the air, and many other processes are constantly changing insoluble minerals into soluble forms. Often these processes do not keep up with plant requirements, and the soil becomes depleted. At other times, soluble salts are formed more rapidly than drainage or plant growth can remove them, and they accumulate, producing "alkaline" soils. Extensive experimentation has shown that plants differ very much in their mineral requirements. Some plants will thrive only in acid soils, while others grow best in basic or saline soils. The scientific agriculturalist must first obtain analyses of the soils that he has to work with, and then either add chemicals to change the composition of the soils to satisfy the requirements of certain plants, or select plants that are adapted for growth in the soils available. Analysis is, therefore, just as important in

420 Lbs
0-20-20

420 Lbs
0-20-0

Figure 79–2. Alfalfa, like all legumes, is a greedy feeder on potassium. The plants at the left received a fertilizer with 20 percent potash, while those on the right received no potash. (Courtesy, American Potash Institute, Inc.)

agriculture as it is in industry; in each case the nature of the final products is determined by the nature of the raw materials.

THE PURPOSE OF FERTILIZERS

Analysis will show that certain soils are deficient in certain elements. In most cases, plants remove essential minerals from the soil to an extent that the soil will gradually lose its fertility unless these minerals are returned to it. A **fertilizer** is simply *a salt or mixture of salts which contains the elements that must be added to the soil to provide the proper balance of minerals for the plants which are to be grown in it.*

INCREASED PRODUCTION MADE POSSIBLE BY THE USE OF FERTILIZERS

Prior to World War II, the United States had been skimming the cream from its soil, and had depended upon large acreages and increased use of machinery to produce high yields per man. In Europe, where manpower was cheaper and land was scarcer, it had been necessary to produce larger yields per acre by the use of fertilizers. Prior to World War II, Holland used 367 pounds of fertilizer per acre, Germany 72, Japan 56, France 35, Italy 21, and the United States 8. However, during World War II, the use of fertilizers in the United States was stimulated by the need for increased production. For example, in 1930, 2 billion bushels of corn were obtained from 104 million acres, while in 1954, 3 billion bushels were obtained from only 82 million acres.

The use of fertilizers has tripled since 1940. On the average, potato yields have increased 137 per cent, cotton 81 per cent, corn 79 per cent, tobacco 73 per cent, wheat 87 per cent, and rice 52 per cent.

In 1963, only about 50 per cent of the crop lands received fertilizers, and in the South this figure was about 10 per cent. Crop lands that are fertilized could have the amounts of fertilizers used doubled, to produce still higher yields.

FERTILIZER CONSTITUENTS

In Chapter 64, the importance of sulfur and phosphorus in plant and animal nutrition was discussed. In Chapter 65, the role of nitrogen was also pointed out. Phosphorus, sulfur, and nitrogen are constituents of proteins, and as such they are essential to both plant and animal growth and nutrition. These elements are frequently deficient in soils, so they are present in most fertilizers in varying ratios, depending upon the needs of particular plants in particular soils.

Potassium does not enter into important plant or animal products, but it seems to act as a sort of helper. Thus, the amount of nitrate absorbed by a plant will depend upon the amount of potassium present in the soil.

At one time, the United States obtained most of its potassium salts from the Stassfort deposits in Germany, but these salts became unavailable during World War I, and the brines in Searles Lake in California turned out to be a good source. Later, large underground deposits were discovered in Arizona and New Mexico. Figure 79-1 shows the result of using just one fertilizer ingredient, potassium, on the yield of corn in a soil deficient in potassium.

When it is considered that 25 bushels of corn will remove 39.2 pounds of nitrogen, 13.8 pounds of phosphoric acid, and 27.6 pounds of potassium salts from the soil, it is easy to understand why soils will soon lose their fertility unless these elements are returned to them.

FURTHER POSSIBILITIES IN THE USE OF FERTILIZERS

The time may not be far off when it will be advantageous to increase forest production. If forests were fertilized, the growth of trees could be increased by 40 to 65 per cent. If the basic fertilizers were added to more than 700,000 lakes and ponds in the United States, the weight of fish produced could be increased by 400 per cent, because the fertilizers would increase the growth of plants on which the fish feed. Fertilized pasture lands could support more animals. Fertilizers are already being used to increase the growth of grasses and shrubbery to prevent erosion of embankments along freeways and highways.

THE MECHANIZATION OF AGRICULTURE

In 1940, there were 6 million farms in the United States, but twenty years later, this number had been reduced to 4.5 million. This reduced number of farms produced a 50 per cent higher yield than was produced in 1940 with a 33 per cent smaller labor force. Furthermore, 4 per cent less land was under production. About 90 per cent of the farm production is accomplished by 2 million farmers, and only about 10 per cent is accomplished by 2.6 million marginal farmers. Several factors are responsible for this great difference in the productivity among farmers. Mechanization is one very important factor, but it is not economically practical on small farms.

Owners of large farms have their own airplanes or helicopters for planting, fertilizing, spraying, and dusting. Two men can handle a 100-cow dairy equipped with milking machines and other automatic devices. One man can handle a mechanized ranch with 10,000 chickens.

Orchardists use power tools operated by compressed air to aid in pruning. Almonds and walnuts are shaken from trees by electric

Figure 79–3. Fertility tests on soybeans. The plants on the left of the man received no fertilizer, while those on the right received phosphate and potassium applied as indicated by the soil analysis. (Courtesy, U.S. Department of Agriculture)

Figure 79–4. Caterpillar-built tractors pulling rod weeders to kill weeds in this unplanted field in a western wheat field. (Courtesy, Caterpillar Tractor Company)

shakers, and are picked up from the ground by vacuum sweepers.

One man can cultivate forty to eighty acres of cotton a day with a mechanical cultivator, compared to five acres for one man and a mule.

Farmers machine-bale 90 per cent of their hay, and machine-pick 90 per cent of their corn and cotton.

Rice culture in Japan requires 900 man-hours per acre, compared with 7½ man-hours per acre in California, where airplanes do the planting.

A mechanical cotton picker does the work of forty to eighty men, but it costs about $16,000. Another machine digs potatoes as fast as eighteen men could do it. A green-bean picker does the work of fifty men.

Grain combines increased in number from about 190,000 in 1940 to about 1 million, twenty years later. Farm trucks increased from 1 million to 2.8 million, and tractors increased from 1.5 million to 4.5 million.

SCIENTIFIC FARMING

Some of the larger, more successful farms are run like factories. They have a general manager, assisted by specialists in engineering, chemistry, economics, animal husbandry, etc.

Figure 79–5. No weeds to hoe in this vineyard. These rows of grapevines were treated with "Karmex" diuron weed killer. (Courtesy, E. I. Du Pont de Nemours Chemical Company)

They are mechanized like an automobile factory. The whole production procedure is standardized to fit the machines.

The modern farmer must have a scientific training. Soils must be analyzed to determine the kinds and amounts of fertilizers to use, and the crops which will do best on the soils. Agricultural economics must be studied to determine what crops to produce. The modern farmer must be acquainted with the use of pesticides.

Scientific farmers are likely to pay more attention to providing well-balanced feeds for their animals than for their children. Basic feed rations are supplemented with proteins, vitamins, minerals, and even hormones or antibiotics. For chickens there are special formulas for starting, growing, and laying. The average egg production per hen increased from 134 to 178 between 1940 and 1952. Cobalt sulfate and carbonate, limestone, dicalcium phosphate, potassium nitrate, ferrous salts, manganous sulfate, and iodized salt are added to animal feeds.

INDUSTRIAL COMPETITION WITH AGRICULTURE

It is true that large amounts of farm products are used in industry, but, in general, industry has contributed to the problem of farm sur-

pluses. Synthetic detergents, made from petroleum or natural gas, have replaced the animal fats and vegetable oils formerly used to make soap. Synthetic fibers are replacing such agricultural products as cotton and wool.

Synthetic rubber and plastics are gradually replacing leather for many purposes. Even synthetic urea is being used as a substitute for a portion of the protein in animal feeds. Synthetic paints, varnishes, and enamels are replacing paints that formerly used such agricultural products as linseed oil.

HERBICIDES

Weeds have been defined as *plants growing where they are not wanted.* They hold up American agriculture for an estimated $3 to $5 billion a year, robbing crops of both food and water, and costing farmers much labor and money in controlling them.

Selective grass killers have become very popular among home gardeners. For example, 2-4-D is a compound that acts as a plant hormone to destroy broad-leaved weeds, but does not harm most grasses. In different forms and concentrations, it is used to kill sage brush and poison ivy, and to control wild mustard and wild onions in grain fields. Farmers in Montana have spent as much as $1.5 million a year to eliminate mustard in

Figure 79–6. Left-hand rows show typical weed control in soybeans with pre-emergence broadcast application of "Lorox" linuron weed killer. Soybeans on right were not treated. (Courtesy, E. I. Du Pont de Nemours Chemical Company)

Figure 79–7. Weeds around oil and gas pipelines and storage tanks present severe fire hazards and serious maintenance problems. Spraying with "Telvar" monuron weed killer gives control all season. (Courtesy, E. I. Du Pont de Nemours Chemical Company)

wheat fields, thus increasing the wheat production by about 15 per cent.

The application of 2-4-D is harmless to some plants, but it can kill others, such as alfalfa, beans, and soybeans. It is difficult to pinpoint the application of 2-4-D by airplanes in such a way as to avoid killing desirable plants.

A relative of 2-4-D is 2-4-5-T, which is used against brush and woody plants, such as mesquite, to clear range lands in Texas.

Several selective grass killers have been marketed for killing crab grass and quack grass.

Complete herbicides are *chemicals that will kill all vegetation.* Sodium arsenite is such a chemical that has been used to spray railroad right-of-ways, but it will also kill animals that stray onto the right-of-ways and eat the sprayed grass. CMU is a more recent complete herbicide, very slightly toxic to man and animals. It will wipe out all living plants

Figure 79–8. The use of Carbyne, a carbamate herbicide to destroy wild oats in wheat. The untreated light strip shows the growth of wild oats which cause crop losses of several hundred million dollars annually. (Courtesy, Earl V. Evans and Spencer Chemical Division, Gulf Oil Corporation)

along railroad tracks, fences, lumber yards, gasoline storage tanks, and other areas where dry grass would be a fire hazard. One railroad, for example, may spend as much as $500,000 a year to keep weeds off its right-of-way. CMU may keep down weeds for a year or two with one application.

GROWTH REGULATORS

Growth regulators are discussed in Chapter 81. They are either plant hormones or chemicals that have a similar action. Maleic Hyrazide, known as MH, slows down the growth of turf grasses, thus reducing the number of mowings required. It also prevents the growth of suckers on tomatoes, and lengthens the life of cut flowers.

SUMMARY

The Agricultural Revolution

Agriculture has increased its production dramatically in spite of a considerable reduction in the number of agricultural workers. This result has been accomplished by (1) increased mechanization, (2) increased use of fertilizers, (3) increased use of pesticides, such as weed killers and insecticides, (4) improved feeds for animals, (5) plant and animal breeding to obtain more productive strains, (6) the use of fertilizers, (7) and the use of herbicides.

Fertilizers

The important fertilizer constituents are sulfur, phosphorus, nitrogen, and potassium, which plants use in large amounts, and which must be added to the soil to assure proper nutrition.

Herbicides

There are several types of herbicides: (1) selective, (2) complete, and (3) growth regulators (plant hormones).

Study Questions

1. DEFINE: hydroponics, fertilizer, herbicide, complete herbicide, weed.
2. List some possible future large-scale uses for fertilizers.
3. What are the sources of potassium for fertilizers?
4. What has been the cause of the migration of marginal farm workers to the cities?
5. For what purposes are complete herbicides used?
6. What problems have marginal farm workers produced in cities?
7. What evidence can you suggest that plants require certain minerals for proper growth?
8. What minerals are required by plants? Which of these minerals are frequently deficient in the soil, and why? What are the sources of minerals in fertilizers?
9. Under what conditions would hydroponics be practical?
10. What processes liberate minerals in the soil?
11. Why is chemical analysis of the soil important in agriculture?
12. How can one determine what fertilizer and how much of it is required for a given soil?
13. Do plant products always contain the same amounts of minerals? Why or why not?
14. In what ways does the use of herbicides aid in agricultural production?
15. Describe some uses for herbicides which are not related to agriculture.
16. What is the nature of the agricultural revolution?

Chemical Warfare Against Nature's Pests

If human beings are to continue to exist, they must first gain mastery over insects. Life may develop into a struggle between man and insects. . . . Insects are better equipped to occupy the earth than humans, having been on the earth 50,000,000 years, while the human race is but 500,000 years old.

L. O. HOWARD

INTRODUCTION

Nearly 10,000 of the 80,000 species of insects that inhabit North America are pests, and at least 200 are important enemies of mankind. Many of these insect enemies are invaders from foreign lands. Such invaders include the Hessian fly, the codling moth, the gypsy moth, the boll weevil, the corn borer, and the Japanese beetle.

In the United States, the annual damage caused by insects is estimated to amount to more than $1 billion a year, even with the controls now used. It has been estimated that about half of the annual agricultural production would be lost without the use of insecticides. Insecticides have thus played an important part in increasing agricultural production.

INSECTS ARE MAN'S CHIEF COMPETITORS FOR FOODS

In the grim struggle between man and insects, the latter possess the advantage of small size, which enables them to live on small quantities of food and multiply enormously when plenty of food is available.

Insects also possess the advantage of rapid reproduction in large numbers. For example, a single pair of ladybird beetles (lady-bugs) could multiply to 22,000,000,000,000 beetles

in six months, if conditions were favorable. The warfare against insects is never finished, because new legions can replace their fallen brothers and sisters in a short time.

Insects Transmit Many Important Diseases

The role that mosquitoes play in spreading malaria, yellow fever, and elephantiasis is well known. Human lice and rat fleas spread typhus fever, tsetse flies disseminate sleeping sickness, and house flies carry typhoid fever and cholera germs. A long list of diseases carried by insects could be added to the few given above. Insects are also carriers of many plant diseases.

HOW INSECTICIDES KILL

Insecticides vary in their methods of attack, depending upon the particular habits of the insects involved.

Chewing insects are killed by poisons put on the foliage they ingest. Such stomach poisons as calcium arsenate, basic copper sulfate, and Paris Green were formerly used in huge amounts, but they leave poisonous residues on food products. Today they are being replaced by organic chemicals. Rotenone, extracted from Derris, has been used as a stomach poison because it is not poisonous to higher animals.

Sucking and crawling insects are killed either by contact poisons or by systemic poisons. **Systemic poisons** *are those which plants absorb, and thus poison the insects that feed on them.* Certain phosphorus compounds, taken into plants, will kill sucking insects such as aphids and mites, but they do no harm to bees or ladybirds. Contact poisons include such products as DDT, DFT, Aldrin, Chlordane, Dieldrin, Endrin, Lindane, Methoxychlor, Heptachlor, and Toxaphene. Pyrethrins, found in Pyrethrum flowers, are valuable because they give immediate results, and can be used for space spraying, without producing residues on foods that would be harmful to animals. Synthetic pyrethrins, much more powerful than the natural pyrethrins, are now used in large quantities.

Inhalation poisons are also used. Pyrethrins act as both inhalation poisons and contact poisons. Parathion, in spite of its high toxicity to humans and animals is widely used because it kills in all three ways, by inhalation, ingestion, and contact.

HOUSEHOLD "INSECT BOMBS"

Aerosol sprays are widely used to kill insects in homes. They contain a volatile, harmless, noninflammable liquid such as Freon, which will remain in the liquid state only when under pressure. Aerosol sprays usually contain pyrethrins for fast knock-downs. A chlorinated hydrocarbon, or a compound such as Lethane or Thanite, relatively harmless to humans, is included to finish off the insects; and, recently, synergists have been added to increase the effectiveness of the killing agent. Unfortunately, flys and other insects build up a resistance to these insecticides, which may be transferred through as many as thirty generations, but several substances, called **synergists,** have been found to *increase the effectiveness of the insecticides as much as 100 to 200 times.*

TERMITICIDES

Many people in the United States are making a living in the battle against termites.

Figure 80–1. Corn fields in Tripp County, South Dakota, visited by grasshopper hordes in the summer of 1940. Nothing was left to be harvested. (Courtesy, U.S. Department of Agriculture)

Figure 80–2. Power duster in operation in a cotton field. (Courtesy, U.S. Department of Agriculture)

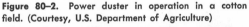

593

Nearly all homes must be inspected and treated for termites if necessary, before they can be sold. There are 2,100 species of termites in the world, 41 of which are found in the United States. Termites will eat anything made of cellulose, including clothing, furniture, books, and houses. Wood used near the ground must be treated to repel termites, and soil should be fumigated before laying concrete slabs. Termites can work their way up through cracks in concrete, or through lime mortar.

POISONED BAIT USED AGAINST FIRE ANTS

Widespread applications of heavy doses of insecticides to control serious insect infestations unfortunately kill useful as well as harmful insects. The result is that the natural enemies of some insects are destroyed, and new species of insects move in. Furthermore, insecticides also kill fish and wildlife. In some cases, insect invasions must be stopped by drastic means. For example, the fire ants, which came to us from South America, in-

Figure 80–3. The spray rig goes completely around the trees to make sure that the entire tree is wet with the insecticide solution. (Courtesy, U.S. Department of Agriculture)

Figure 80–4. Difference in yield between plots poisoned for insects and unpoisoned plots. Poisoned on the right. (Courtesy, U.S. Department of Agriculture)

vaded 20 million acres in the southern states. They killed small farm animals, and caused such painful, festering bites for humans that it was difficult to persuade laborers to work in infested fields. Large-scale applications of Heptaclor and Dieldrin caused a hue and cry against the destruction of wildlife, but the farmers' plight demanded drastic action. Finally, a better approach was tried. A mixture of peanut butter and Kepone, a slow-acting stomach poison, was placed in soda straws, which were then cut into small lengths and spread over the infested land. The ants got to this poisoned bait before animals did, and carried it to their nests where they and their families gradually succumbed to the poison.

CHEMICAL ATTRACTANTS

Chemical attractants, sometimes called chemical sirens, have odors that attract specific insects, which are then killed by various means. Research to develop chemical attractants is being carried out, but not much has been accomplished to date.

SEXUAL TRICKERY

Another approach in the war against insects, which avoids the disadvantages of the use of insecticides, is sexual trickery. This method involves the sterilization of large numbers of the male members of an insect species by atomic radiation or chemicals. The result is that subsequent matings produce no young. For example, millions of male flies that cause screwworms in cattle were sterilized with the radiation from Cobalt-60, and liberated in Florida. So successful was this technique that a serious infestation of the screwworm was wiped out. The same technique is being tried out against boll weevils, cockroaches, the Oriental fruit fly, the codling moth, and even mosquitoes. Experiments are now being tried with several chemical compounds that will sterilize houseflies.

CHEMICAL TRICKERY

Chemicals have been developed that resemble the structures of certain amino acids and vitamins required for the nutrition of moths and carpet beetles. The moths and carpet beetles eat these substances, which are as attractive to them as wool is, but they die of malnutrition because these substances have no nutritional value.

HARMFUL RESULTS OF THE USE OF INSECTICIDES

A survey of doctors' reports showed 975 cases in California in one year attributed to the use of agricultural chemicals, usually by people who were not aware of the precautions that should be followed in the use of agricultural sprays. Some of the most powerful insecticides are organic phosphorus compounds, such as parathion, related to the nerve poisons developed during World War II, and must be used with great caution. In 1954, the Miller Bill, passed by Congress, set up tolerances for pesticides that may safely appear on any food product. Tight federal controls, in some cases stricter than in the cases of pharmaceutical products, help to run up the cost of developing new insecticides. The minimum cost for the research and development of a new insecticide is usually about $1 million. On top of this, it now takes from three to five years, at an additional expenditure of up to $3 million, to run the necessary tests to check the toxicity of residues.

THE AGRICULTURAL CHEMICAL INDUSTRY

Most of the large chemical companies and several of the drug companies are engaged in the manufacture of agricultural chemicals, such as insecticides, fungicides, and herbicides. It is a big business; the number of chemicals developed for home gardens and agriculture runs into thousands, and their fanciful names run the whole gamut from Aldrin to Ziram. Some of these products are broad-spectrum products, similar to the broad-spectrum antibiotics that kill more than a hundred different kinds of disease germs. Other products are highly specific. For home gardeners, wide-range mixtures provide a sort of shotgun approach. Even then, home gardeners find it difficult to select a product from the many that are now found on the shelves in seed stores, nurseries, and even drugstores and food markets.

The proper selection and application of many agricultural products requires such specialized knowledge that modern farming is becoming more and more scientific. Government agricultural advisers solve the problem in many cases, but successful farming usually requires special training in agricultural colleges.

INSECT REPELLANTS

Insect repellants are used chiefly by humans to repel chiggers, mosquitoes, gnats, ticks and flies, which make life miserable for hunters and fishermen. Chiggers, for example, are so common that in many parts of the country a person is likely to collect a few if he sits on the grass, plays golf, or walks through the woods. Chiggers are insects nearly microscopic in size that attach themselves by their mouth parts in depressions of the skin, where they inject a fluid that breaks down the cells on which they feed. It is this fluid that causes the intense itching. Various chemicals, such as benzyl benzoate and dimethyl phthalate, have been used with fair success as insect repellants, but diethyl toluamide has

been found to be superior to them and is much more pleasant to use on the skin. It is long-lasting, not unpleasant to use, and safe.

Lawns and golf courses may be sprayed with Toxaphene or Chlordane; one application will protect against chiggers for about two months.

There are about 9,000 species of ticks and mites. Ticks and mites are not insects, but insect repellants will keep them away.

FIGHTING INSECTS WITH INSECTS

Armies of insect allies have been drafted to combat insect enemies. For example, a gnat-size wasplet has helped a great deal in abating the ravages of the codling moth. Japanese beetles have been controlled by predatory wasps brought in from Japan. Even germ warfare has been used against the Japanese beetle. A particular kind of germ that kills the Japanese beetle grubs has been used against this pest.

NEMATOCIDES

Nematodes are very small worms; so small, in fact, that they are generally too small to be seen with the naked eye. They are para-

Figure 80–5. Comparison of normal plant and plant infested with nematodes (right). (Courtesy, U.S. Department of Agriculture)

Figure 80–6. Top shows contrast between healthy corn plants and those (on left) infested with nematodes. Bottom shows contrasting root systems. (Courtesy, U.S. Department of Agriculture)

sites of man, fish, birds, animals, insects and plant life. More than one thousand species attack plants. Every plant seems to have at least one nematode bothering it. Nematodes destroy more than one-tenth of the crops that farmers grow each year. The use of nematocides has increased production as much as 25 per cent in some cases.

Soil fumigation is the most practical method of controlling nematodes. Specialized chemicals, such as DD, have been developed for soil fumigation. Soil sterilization doubled the cotton yield of the San Joaquin valley in California, and proved to be equally valuable for pineapple production in the Hawaiian Islands.

Nematodes cost the livestock industry about $500,000 a year, and various specific chemicals are now available to kill them. For example, about 5 million pounds of phenothiazine are used per year to kill intestinal organisms in farm animals.

LAMPREYCIDES

Lampreys are eel-like parasites that have nearly wiped out the fishing industry and sport fishing in the Great Lakes, where they have destroyed about 90 per cent of the Mackinaw trout. They reached the Great Lakes through the Welland Canal. The lampreys are being fought in streams where they produce their young. Electric fences have been used with some success but the process is too slow. More than 6,000 chemicals were screened to find a chemical that would kill the lampreys. One was found, at last, that is 99 per cent effective. The battle is gradually being won, but it must be continued indefinitely. Each stream is being treated every three years to kill a new crop of young larvae.

SNAIL KILLERS AND RODENTICIDES

Many home gardeners are familiar with the poisoned bran products sold to kill snails and slugs. The trouble with these products is that they do not eradicate the pests, although they do help to keep them under control.

Rats and mice are not only household pests, they also destroy large amounts of food. Furthermore, rats and ground squirrels in some parts of the country spread bubonic plague. These rodents are hosts to lice, which can spread the plague to animals and humans. Several effective rodenticides, such as Antu and Warfarin, have been developed. Antu is so poisonous that one pound could kill 300,000 rats; and it is not dangerous to other animals, in amounts that they might get.

PLANT DISEASES—FUNGICIDES, VIRICIDES, BACTERICIDES

The majority of plant diseases are caused by fungi, but some of them are caused by bacteria and viruses. Several of the pharmaceutical manufacturers have marketed special antibiotics, such as Actidione, which is used as a fungicide. The Chemical companies have contributed such products as Torsan and Semesan to destroy the fungi that attack fine grasses.

Figure 80–7. Same amount of grass seed (shown in measuring spoon) was planted in each of these flats. But seed for flat on left was treated with "Arasan" seed disinfectant, while seed for flat on right was untreated. (Courtesy, E. I. Du Pont de Nemours Chemical Company)

Agriculture spends about $1.5 billion annually for about 660 million pounds of fungicides.

There are two kinds of viruses, which have caused the Dutch Elm Disease and the Elm Scorch, that have been playing havoc with elm trees in the United States. Virus diseases in plants, as well as in animals, have been difficult to control.

Special bactericides have been developed, which act like antiseptics or disinfectants, to either kill bacteria or prevent their growth. About $17 million is spent annually for bactericides.

SUMMARY

Insects have been fought with other insects, and by chemical or sexual trickery, but most insects and other pests are fought with chemicals. The various pesticides may be classified as follows:

1. Insecticides, which may be classified according to their methods of attack as: (1) ingestion poisons for chewing and sucking insects, (2) contact poisons for sucking, crawling, and flying insects, and (3) inhalant poisons for flying insects.

2. Non-Insect pesticides, for: (1) nematodes, (2) rodents, (3) snails and slugs, (4) lampreys.

3. Plant Disease Chemicals, which include: (1) fungicides (the most common causes), (2) viricides, (3) bactericides.

Insect repellants, such as diethyl toluamide, are used against mosquitoes, flies, gnats, chiggers, ticks and mites.

Study Questions

1. DEFINE: synergist, systemic poison.
2. Why is it desirable to kill rodents?
3. Give an example of chemical trickery used against insects.
4. Give an example of the successful use of sexual trickery in fighting insects.
5. Why are lampreys such an important problem in the Great Lakes? How are they being controlled?
6. Discuss the damage done to agricultural products by nematodes.
7. For what types of insects are repellants used?
8. Discuss the chigger nuisance.
9. Discuss the war against the fire ants.
10. What is the objection to the use of arsenic and lead poisons for spraying plants?
11. What are the active ingredients in many fly sprays?
12. List two methods, other than the use of poisons, for killing insects.
13. What would be the advantages of substances which would attract or repel insects?
14. Why is rotenone such a valuable insecticide? Where is it obtained?
15. Prepare a list of diseases and their insect carriers.
16. Why is the promiscuous destruction of insects undesirable?
17. What is the principle of the aerosol bomb?
18. Why is Antu important?
19. What pests, other than insects, are controlled by chemicals?

Nature's Catalysts—
Vitamins, Enzymes, and Hormones

Whoever could make two ears of corn, or two blades of grass, to grow upon a spot of ground where only one grew before, would deserve better of mankind, and do more essential service to his country, than the whole race of politicians put together.

SWIFT

INTRODUCTION

The group of physiological catalysts consisting of vitamins, enzymes, and hormones has been the object of a tremendous amount of research during the past quarter of a century. When one realizes that these substances are present in living organisms in extremely minute quantities, one can appreciate the magnitude of the achievement which is represented by the separation, purification, analysis, and synthesis of so many of these catalysts. Little is known concerning many of these substances beyond the recognition of their existence. Few fields of research have been so fruitful in their benefits to the health of mankind, and few fields of research have been so dependent upon the methods of both the physical and biological sciences.

The main purpose of this chapter is to describe a few of the accomplishments in the field of physiological catalysts. Present progress indicates that the research in this field should give man an unbelievable control over the growth, development, and nature of living organisms.

VITAMINS

The term **vitamin** refers to *substances present in very minute concentrations in many foods, which are essential to normal nutrition.*

Early researches indicated that three fat-soluble substances and three water-soluble substances occurring in various natural foods were essential to the normal functioning of the bodily processes. These substances were given alphabetical names. The fat-soluble vitamins were A, D, and E; and the water-soluble vitamins were B, C, and G. In the early days of vitamin research, the vitamins were designated by letters of the alphabet because their chemical composition was unknown. The modern tendency is to give each vitamin a name, which is either its chemical name, or derived from it. All of the important vitamins, except vitamin D, have been synthesized. Vitamin D can be produced in certain foods by irradiation with ultraviolet light.

The vitamins do not act as building units or sources of energy because such small amounts are required. The vitamins, in this respect, are similar to catalysts. Furthermore, they seem to function as catalysts in that various chemical changes will not take place in the body unless the vitamins are present.

One of the earliest observations concerning vitamins was that beri-beri, a disease characterized by paralysis of the legs, general weakness, dropsy, and anemia, is common among people whose main article of food is polished rice. Beri-beri threatened the fighting efficiency of the Japanese army in the Russo-Japanese War in 1905. The troops were being

599

fed large quantities of polished rice. Someone remembered the work of Christian Eijkman, who, in 1897, artificially produced beri-beri in pigeons by feeding them polished rice, and then cured them by feeding them rice polishings. Shortly after the Japanese army substituted brown rice for polished rice, beri-beri disappeared. Eventually, thiamin, vitamin B_1, was found to be the active agent in brown rice that prevented beri-beri.

THE WATER-SOLUBLE VITAMINS

The B Vitamins

Many water-soluble vitamins, quite varied in structure and properties, occur together and make up the B-complex. The chief natural sources of the B vitamins are yeast, whole-grain cereals, wheat germ, legumes, greens, meat, eggs, and milk. Several of the B vitamins are known to be important in human nutrition, and their absence may result in such diseases as beri-beri, pellagra, and nervous disorders. Many other B vitamins have been synthesized, but their role in human nutrition has not been determined. The B vitamins generally found in vitamin pills are B_1 (thiamin), B_2 (riboflavin), B_6 (pyridoxine), folic acid, pantothenic acid, niacin, nicotinamide, biotin (vitamin H), and B_{12}.

Vitamin C

Vitamin C is found in citrus fruits, tomatoes, cabbages, greens, avocados, peaches, and pineapples. Its chemical name is ascorbic acid. It is synthesized at fairly low cost, and is found in most vitamin pills. It is often added to fruit drinks. Its absence will result in scurvy, and if not present in sufficient amounts, it may result in improper development of the teeth and bones, pyorrhea, and other gum disorders.

Keep in mind that the above vitamins are water soluble. They may be removed from foods by boiling them in water. They are not stored in the body.

THE FAT-SOLUBLE VITAMINS

The fat-soluble vitamins, usually found in vitamin pills, are vitamin A, vitamin D, and perhaps vitamin K. They are found in fish-liver oils, greens, yellow vegetables, eggs, wheat-germ oil, cottonseed oil, and milk fat.

Vitamin A

The absence of vitamine A in the diet may result in impaired vision, night blindness, and skin disorders.

Vitamin D

Vitamin D is important for the proper formation of teeth and bones. It may be synthesized by the body when the body is exposed to sunlight.

Vitamin E

The absence of vitamin E results in sterility in rats. Its function in the human body is uncertain.

Vitamin K

This vitamin helps to promote the clotting of blood.

Several different forms of each of the above vitamins have been discovered.

NATURAL FOODS, THE BEST SOURCE OF VITAMINS

The typical American diet, consisting of refined sugar, coffee, doughnuts, meat, mashed or fried potatoes, and white bread is deficient in vitamins. One solution, and the easiest one, is to buy vitamins at the drugstore, because this is easier than changing one's food habits. In general, however, buying vitamins at the drugstore is not recommended for the following reasons:

1. The body requires other food constituents, such as minerals and bulk, which only a well-balanced diet will provide. Buying vitamins only solves the vitamin problem, and even then it seldom provides all of the vitamins found in foods, because vitamin pills usually contain only a few vitamins.

2. Vitamins are often taken with the idea that the health will be miraculously improved. In the meantime, diagnosis and treatment of the real cause of the ailment, whatever it may be, is often delayed until it is too late.

A balanced diet does not require scientific calculation, measuring, and weighing. Neither need it cost more than an unbalanced diet. A set of rules for the selection and preparation of a balanced diet that will provide sufficient vitamins, minerals, proteins, and other essential food constituents was given on page 582. In general, meat should be supplemented by considerable amounts of milk products, eggs, vegetables, greens, fruits, and whole-grain cereals.

ENZYMES

Enzymes have been employed by man for thousands of years, in wine-making and bread-making. In the 1850's, France's wine industry was in trouble, because the aging wines went sour and became unfit to drink. Louis Pasteur was enlisted to see if he could find the trouble. He observed that the souring of the wines did not take place until after the fermentation had taken place. He suggested that the souring was caused by a type of yeast and that it could be prevented by heating the wine to kill the yeasts at the completion of the fermentation. This process, called pasteurization, was later used to kill the organisms in milk. Pasteur saved the wine industry, but he did not know how yeasts brought about fermentation.

The French physicist, René Antoine de Reaumur (1683–1757), who made a study of digestion using a hawk as his experimental animal, found that the digestive juices in the hawk's stomach would digest meat. Subsequently, other workers isolated pepsin from digestive juices and diastase from malt extract that could break down certain foods. In 1878, the German physiologist, Wilhelm Kuhne, suggested the word *enzyme* for such substances. Then, in 1897, the German chemist, Eduard Buchner (1860–1917), extracted a juice from yeast cells that would cause the same reactions that live yeast cells produced, and the term **enzyme** came to be used to refer to all such *organic catalysts*. It was not until 1930 that the American chemist, John Howard Northrop, crystalized a number of enzymes, and found that all of them were proteins. Up to 1965, more than a hundred enzymes have been isolated, and without exception, they are proteins. It seems to be likely that enzymes catalyze reactions by forming intermediate compounds.

There are at least a dozen vitamin-like substances that affect plants. The action of vitamins on plants seems to resemble their action on animals, in that they serve as coenzymes. **Coenzymes** are *substances that are essential to the action of enzymes.*

TWO MAIN CLASSES OF ENZYMES

Many enzymes catalyze the reaction of foods with oxygen; other enzymes specialize in the hydrolysis of proteins, fats, and carbohydrates. Living organisms of all kinds—ranging from bacteria, yeast, and molds to plants and animals—produce enzymes, whose main function is to catalyze the splitting of such foods as carbohydrates, fats, and proteins into smaller molecules. This is part of the process called digestion.

Enzymes are not living organisms, because they cannot reproduce themselves; but they do behave like living organisms in that they are inactivated by heat and various poisons.

The oxidative enzymes frequently make a nuisance of themselves, oxidizing vitamins and causing the spoilage of foods in storage. The hydrolytic enzymes, on the other hand,

TABLE 81-1

IMPORTANT DIGESTIVE ENZYMES

Enzymes	Source	Function
Ptyalin	Salivary glands	Changes starches to dextrins
Pepsin	Stomach glands	Splits proteins
Rennin	Stomach glands	Coagulates proteins
Amylopsin, trysin, and lipase	Pancreas	Changes carbohydrates to maltose. Splits proteins. Changes fats to fatty acids, soaps, and glycerol
Erepsin and inverting enzymes	Intestinal glands	Completes the splitting of carbohydrates and proteins

are utilized considerably in industry for the production of amino acids and other substances, produced by the hydrolysis of proteins and other types of organic compounds.

In the quick-freezing of foods, it has been found necessary to blanch the foods, i.e., heat them for a short time, in order to destroy the oxidative enzymes that would otherwise oxidize some of the vitamins in the foods, even though they are kept below the freezing point. Ascorbase is an enzyme that catalyzes the oxidation of ascorbic acid, while peroxidase catalyzes the oxidation of such fruits as peaches, bananas, and apples, causing them to turn brown in a short time after exposure to the atmosphere. Sulfur dioxide is used to inactivate these enzymes in the drying of fruits, in order to keep them from darkening in color. Pineapple juice and grapefruit juice are also effective in inactivating these oxidative enzymes.

ENZYMES USED IN INDUSTRIAL PROCESSES

All fermentations, such as are employed in the preparation of vinegar, sauerkraut, or alcoholic liquors, depend upon enzymes, which are produced by yeasts.

Papain, an enzyme obtained from papaya plants, tenderizes meat; while sausage casings are tenderized by the enzyme, bromelin, found in pineapple juice.

The sizing material (starches) used in the manufacture of textiles is removed by the use of enzymes.

Cheeses are ripened by enzymes.

HORMONES

The term *hormone* is derived from the Greek verb "to stir up or excite." The **hormones** are *substances produced chiefly by the ductless (endocrine) glands of animals*, and fed into the blood stream, which transfers them to other parts of the body, where they may produce profound changes. **Hormones,** like vitamins, are *physiological catalysts;* exceedingly small amounts either increase or decrease the rate of a given chemical reaction in the body.

The human body is a system in equilib-rium, in which various chemical reactions are balanced one against another through the catalytic action of hormones, which in turn are in equilibrium with each other. Whenever a ductless gland ceases to function normally because of disease, food deficiency, accident, or other reasons, too little or too much of one or more hormones is produced, and the resulting disturbance in this equilibrium produces profound changes in the body. The mind can affect the activity of certain ductless glands. Hormones, on the other hand, affect the mind. In dealing with human ailments the mind is an important factor. The ductless glands seem to be the seat of our emotions. Growth, reproduction, aging, anger, pleasure, bodily stature, facial configuration, sexuality, mentality, general metabolism, and even character are influenced by hormones.

The first hormone to be isolated, epinephrin (adrenaline), was obtained in 1901 from the medulla of the suprarenal gland situated above the kidney. It was synthesized in 1904. This hormone activates the nervous system and muscles, strengthens the heart beat, and increases the blood pressure. When one is angry, the various symptoms are the result of the secretion of abnormal amounts of epinephrin. Epinephrin is used as a stimulant in emergencies, and to relieve asthma.

The second hormone to be isolated, thyroxine, was obtained from the thyroid glands of cattle in 1916, and was synthesized in 1927. A deficiency of thyroxine results in cretinism in children and myxedema in adults, while an excess produces an abnormally high basal metabolic rate. In general, thyroxine helps to control growth, reproduction, and metabolism.

The parathyroid glands secrete parathormone, which regulates the concentration of calcium and phosphorus in the blood.

The cortex of the adrenal glands secretes cortin, which controls the balance between sodium and potassium in the body, and has an important function in regulating carbohydrate metabolism. A deficiency of cortin causes Addison's disease, while an excess causes children to mature precociously, and causes adult women to acquire male voices and an abnormal growth of bodily and facial hair.

The pituitary gland produces a number of

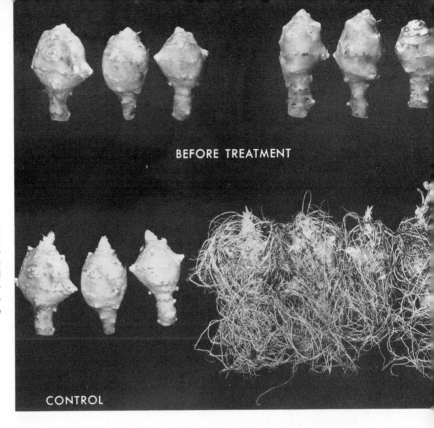

Figure 81–1. Jerusalem artichokes showing the effect of treating tubers with a growth substance known as naphthaleneacetic acid. The three tubers on the left were treated with pure water; the ones on the right were treated with 10 mg of naphthaleneacetic acid in 100 cc of water. After the water treatment, the tubers were planted in sand where they remained for 21 days, at which time they were removed and photographed. Naphthaleneacetic acid is a root-inducing and regulating substance and its effects are easily demonstrated by these results. (Courtesy, Boyce-Thompson Institute for Plant Research, Inc.)

BEFORE TREATMENT

CONTROL

hormones, one of which controls growth. Giants and dwarfs result from an excess or deficiency of this hormone. At least eight more hormones are said to be secreted by the pituitary glands. These hormones control the various sexual activities of men and women, including the ripening of germ cells, the development of mammary glands, and the secretion of milk. Several of these hormones control the functioning of the thyroid and adrenal glands and the pancreas.

Insulin was isolated in 1922 from animal pancreas. A deficiency of insulin is the cause of diabetes, which is characterized by inability to use carbohydrates.

The gonads (sex glands) secrete hormones that regulate the growth and development of sex organs and secondary sex characteristics. They also affect many of the bodily functions, either directly or indirectly, by stimulating or repressing the production of other hormones.

Both the male and female hormones are used to treat various ailments of both men and women when their sex hormone balance has been disturbed. A tremendous amount of research has been devoted to the synthesis of the sex hormones and similar substances. Some of these hormones have been used with success in oral birth-control drugs. Eventually, an outcome of this research should be low-cost oral birth-control pills, which might well prove to be a solution to the problem of the present population explosion.

A great deal of research has also been devoted to the synthesis of steroid-type hormones, such as cortisone, hydrocortisone, and ACTH, which have proven to be very powerful drugs. They have been used in the treatment of arthritis, and often have undesirable side effects. However, continued research will probably result in new, potent steroids without these defects.

PLANT HORMONES

A strict definition of the word *hormone* would not include the hormone-like substances produced by plants, which regulate their growth (i.e., their size, shape, rate of growth) and their habits. Such substances are known as plant hormones.

Colchicine, obtained from autumn crocus plants, is widely used in plant breeding experiments. Colchicine doubles the number of chromosomes in the cells, and thus produces new varieties of plants.

Many substances have been found to have hormone-like activity on plants, in stimulating flowering and growth, or in preventing or decreasing growth. 2-4-D has been widely used as a selective weed killer. 2-4-5-T reduces lemon loss in storage. Some substances inhibit the sprouting of potatoes or onions in storage. Auxin hastens the development of roots. Some substances reduce the premature dropping of tobacco leaves or apples. Other substances will produce seedless tomatoes or watermelons. Figure 81-1 shows the results of the use of a typical plant hormone.

SUMMARY

Vitamins have important effects upon many of the chemical reactions that take place in the human body. The diets of many people are deficient in vitamins. It is now possible to treat these deficiencies with vitamin pills, but a well-balanced diet is a better way to provide an adequate amount of vitamins.

Enzymes are physiological catalysts produced by all living organisms. They are responsible for the breaking down (digestion) of foods, and for the oxidation of various food constituents.

Hormones are physiological catalysts secreted by the endocrine glands of animals. Hormones control the development, growth, reproduction, appearance, and activities of animals.

Plant hormones control the growth of plants, causing them to grow roots and change their dormancy period. They may be used to kill plants or, in some cases, to produce extraordinary growth.

Study Questions

1. DEFINE: enzyme, hormone, vitamin, coenzyme.
2. What are the physiological catalysts?
3. Why is research work in the field of physiological catalysts so difficult?
4. How may the vitamins be classified?
5. What is meant by the "vitamin B complex"?
6. What is the main function of enzymes?
7. Describe some industrial applications of enzymes.
8. Are enzymes produced by plants?
9. Is an enzyme a hormone? Is a vitamin a hormone?
10. Which vitamins would be lost by boiling foods in water?
11. What are the objections to the use of vitamin pills?
12. Give the main food sources, and the results of a deficiency of vitamins A, B, C, and D.
13. Why is vitamin deficiency so widespread among the American people?
14. Why is the research work on hormones of so much value to humanity?

The Alkaloids—Narcotics and Euphoriants—Mental Drugs

We are not interested in therapy except in so far as it acts by psychologic methods, and for the moment we have no others. In the future, we shall perhaps learn to exert a direct influence by means of specific chemical substances on the quantities of energy and their distribution in the mental apparatus.

SIGMUND FREUD

INTRODUCTION

This chapter takes up the study of the alkaloids, which are plant products having many powerful effects on the body. They include the euphoriants, such as tobacco, coffee, and tea, and the whole field of **psychotropic** (*mental*) drugs. Many alkaloids have an effect on the brain. The investigation of psychotropic drugs has resulted in the discovery of many nonalkaloid compounds having a psychotropic activity. The whole field of psychotropic drugs is the topic of this chapter. Psychotropic drugs, such as tranquilizers, are among the most important contributions of modern medical research, which represents the combined efforts of chemists, biologists, and physicians.

THE ALKALOIDS

The **alkaloids** are defined as *nitrogen-containing organic bases that are synthesized by higher plants mostly, and are distinguished by the fact that they have powerful effects on the physiology of animals.* The name *alkaloid* literally means "alkali-like." However, not all alkaloids are basic in nature. For example, the alkaloid, ricinine, found in castor beans, is acid rather than basic in nature.

Alkaloids, of course, have no monopoly on nitrogen. Proteins, amino acids, and some animal hormones and vitamins also contain nitrogen.

Although all alkaloids are produced by plants, not all plants produce alkaloids. Their function in the metabolism of plants is unknown. Since earliest times, the alkaloids have served as pleasure and dream producers, medicines, and poisons.

Fungi do not produce alkaloids as a rule, and yet the ergot fungus, often found on rye, produces alkaloids. Ergotamine, an ergot alkaloid, has been found to be effective in the treatment of migraine headache.

Several hundred alkaloids are known. As a rule, several or more alkaloids are found where one occurs. Twenty-five alkaloids are found in opium, obtained from poppies. All alkaloids have a bitter taste, and, as a rule, they have profound physiological action.

Some 100,000 to 200,000 flowering plants still await investigation as possible sources of potent drugs.

The effects of the alkaloids and similar vegetable compounds on the body are many and varied. Mustard and pepper contain alkaloids that act as irritants, giving a burning sensation to the skin or mouth. Pilocarpus, ipecac, and opium contain alkaloids that promote perspiration, while atropine checks perspiration. The alkaloids of black mustard, ipecac, and apomorphine hydrochloride act

605

as emetics (i.e., they cause vomiting). The alkaloids in ergot constrict the blood vessels, and increase the blood pressure. Digitalis, obtained from purple foxglove, contains alkaloids that stimulate the heart, and are used in the treatment of some heart disorders. Aconite contains alkaloids that depress the heart action. Caffeine and atropine stimulate respiration, while codeine and morphine depress respiration. Opium, morphine, and scopolamine produce sleep. Cocaine produces delirium. Atropine and belladonna dilate the pupil of the eye, while pilocarpine contracts it. Caffeine is a cerebral stimulant and diuretic. It is often prescribed alone or in combination with other drugs such as codeine as a pain reliever, especially for headaches. Strychnine is a motor excitant. Cotarnine is a styptic (i.e., it stops bleeding). Cascara sagrada is a cathartic. Curare, the arrow poison used by the Amazon Indians, is used to relax patients who have spasms from infantile paralysis, tetanus, or shocks. It has been used to stop sieges of hiccough.

Physostigmine, employed by West African tribesmen in trials by ordeal, is used as a specific for the muscular disease, myasthenia gravis. Cocaine, obtained from the coca leaf, serves as a very useful local anesthetic, and also as a sinister narcotic if misused. Coniine, the poisonous alkaloid found in hemlock, was used in the draught that killed Socrates.

ANTI-MALARIAL DRUGS

Malaria has been wiped out in some sections of the world by eliminating the breeding places of the anopheles mosquito, but malaria still kills approximately 2,000,000 people annually. There are from 70,000,000 to 80,000,000 sufferers from malaria in India alone. For many years to come, it will be impossible to destroy the anopheles mosquito in India, China, and the tropical zones of the world. Even screening dwellings, or sleeping under nets is out of the question for many people. Malaria is caused by a microscopic, protozoan parasite, Plasmodium malariae.

Quinine, an alkaloid obtained from the bark of the cinchona tree in Java and South America has been used for centuries for the treatment of malaria. In some cases it is not effective, and a search for more effective anti-malarials was undertaken. Quinine was synthesized in 1944.

Febrifugine, obtained from a Chinese plant, Dichroa febrifuga, is one hundred times as active as quinine.

It is only in recent years that synthetic drugs, superior to quinine, have become available. Atebrin (quinacrine hydrochloride) has proven to be as effective as quinine, and it is safer to use. Unfortunately, the malaria organisms have become resistant to such synthetic anti-malarials as atebrin, and 17 of the 60 species of anopheles mosquito have grown immune to formerly successful insecticides such as DDT. New weapons are now being investigated.

COLCHICINE

Colchicine, sometimes listed as a plant hormone, is an alkaloid found in the seeds and roots of the meadow saffron. It is used to banish the pain of gout. Gout is one form of arthritis which is caused by the deposition of uric acid crystals in the joints. If one must have arthritis, he would choose gout, because something can be done about it. Colchicine banishes the pain, while benemid, a special drug for gout, gets to work on the uric acid crystals.

NARCOTICS

Marijuana, obtained from the hemp plant, Cannabis sativa, whose dried leaves are smoked in the form of cigarettes, is a very powerful narcotic. It is also known as hashish, when it is obtained from Indian hemp. It has been used in Oriental countries for many centuries. It has been employed in medicine, because of its hypnotic and antispasmodic properties.

All species of the poppy family produce alkaloids; the opium family produces twenty alkaloids. Morphine, obtained from opium, is an effective analgesic. Codeine, a derivative of morphine, is also found in opium, but it is usually prepared from morphine. Morphine is used for severe pain, while codeine is used to control coughs and mild pain. Codeine is less active and less toxic than morphine. Morphine frequently produces nausea and vomiting. Amidone, first synthesized in Germany, is two to four times more powerful than morphine for the relief of pain; like morphine and codeine it is addicting. Metapon, derived from opium, is especially valuable in the treatment of pain for cancer patients. It is addicting, but addiction builds up slower than in the case of morphine. Demerol may be used with safety in much larger doses than morphine; its most dramatic use is for patients suffering from the excruciating pain caused by gallstones or kidney stones. Like morphine, it is an addicting drug.

A great deal of research has been done on the problem of finding a pain killer with the potency of morphine, but without its side effects, and which is nonaddictive. Some new pain relievers indicate that progress is being made. For example, a cough medicine $2\frac{1}{2}$ times more effective than codeine, which has been a standard cough medicine for years, is sold under the name of Tessalon. A drug called NIH 7519, which is ten times more effective than morphine and fifty times more potent than codeine, but somewhat less addictive and safer than morphine, has been announced. Several other new synthetic pain killers have been announced. After being tried out, these new drugs may be abandoned because of undesirable side effects, which may show up.

DRUG ADDICTION, A SERIOUS SOCIAL PROBLEM

Some of the alkaloids are habit-forming, but they do not lead to addiction. The use of the principal drugs of **addiction,** opium, morphine, heroin, and cocaine *result in a physiological or a psychic dependence on the drug, to the extent that a severe physiological upset or even death may result if the drug suddenly becomes unavailable.* All of these drugs, in large doses, may act temporarily as excitants, but the ultimate action is that of a *depressant* (i.e., **narcotic**) on the nervous system. Addicts to drugs eventually become a burden on society, and often engage in crime. They will not stop at crimes of violence to obtain the drug. The chief desire of an addict is to obtain his next supply of

the drug. The addict early loses his will power to stop its use.

HABITUATION TO DRUGS

Habituation *differs from addiction, in that the drug may be discontinued without any of the ill effects of the withdrawal period, typically seen in morphine addicts.* However, it is difficult to draw a sharp line between addiction and habituation. The principal drugs of habituation are nicotine, caffeine, aspirin, acetanilide, paraldehyde, marihuana, alcohol, barbiturates, and bromides. A tobacco smoker who uses several packs of cigarettes a day may find that they are necessary to quiet his nerves, while a coffee addict may experience a headache in the absence of his usual amount of coffee. If one finds that he is gradually requiring more and more of such drugs, he is well on the way to habituation.

EUPHORIANTS, THE PLEASURE-PRODUCING ALKALOIDS

Euphoriants (i.e., *cheer-up drugs*), *which impart a sense of well-being,* are all alkaloids or similar substances, with the exception of alcohol. Among these are tobacco, coffee, tea, betel, opium, and coca.

Coffee, tea, and the cola drinks, which contain caffeine, stimulate the circulation and the mind. Caffeine is classed as an euphoriant. When used in moderation, it is relatively harmless; but since it is habit-forming, a coffee drinker must make a definite effort to keep the upper hand. Health authorities recommend that caffeine-containing drinks not be given to growing children. Overindulgence in coffee, tobacco, and tea causes the heart to race. It causes loss of weight, tremor of the fingers, nervousness, and insomnia. Caffeine raises the level of physiological activity, decreases the reaction time, and delays muscular and mental fatigue. For the average person, from one to three cups of coffee daily will be harmless; but excessive use of caffeine, like the excessive use of any such physiologically active substance, should be avoided. The tolerance for caffeine differs greatly among individuals. Tea, cola drinks, and the South American yerba mate also contain caffeine. Hundreds of millions of people experience pleasure from chewing betel nuts.

Tobacco contains nicotine and other alkaloids. Nicotine is a poison, and as such is widely used as an insecticide. Nicotine appears to serve no useful purpose in the body beyond that of euphoria.

Statistical data indicate that the use of tobacco, in the form of cigarettes, is one of the causes of cancer and heart diseases. The tar in the tobacco smoke is thought to contain the cancer-producing substances.

Smoking is one way to obtain nicotine, which is the pleasure-producing, habit-forming, and physiologically active alkaloid found in tobacco. Nicotine, rather than smoke, may account for the effect of tobacco on the nerves and the circulatory system.

The tobacco habit can be broken without a severe disturbance to the body. A drug is available that arrests the desire to smoke.

Amphetamine sulfate, first marketed in 1938, under the trade name of benzedrine, taken orally or by inhalation, in sufficient amounts, stimulates the central nervous system. Benzedrine provides a temporary lift in an emergency, but is no substitute for rest. It was used in World War II by the military services only when necessary; at times when men had not been able to get enough sleep and needed to be very alert, benzedrine was invaluable. Benzedrine may be used like caffeine to keep automobile drivers awake. Many truck drivers have taken benzedrine in order to keep awake for long hauls, but it has been found that the promiscuous use of this drug has been the direct cause of many fatal highway accidents, and that overdoses may result in death.

Synhexyl is somewhat similar to the hashish (cannabis) extracted from the hemp plant. It is not a good pain killer, but it has a cheering influence on the mind that causes the patient to be less disturbed concerning his aches and pains, real or imaginary. It is not a cure for anything, but it, like benzedrine, helps in the treatment of mentally depressed patients.

Pregnenolone, a synthetic hormone, banishes fatigue and stretches man's efficiency beyond normal limits. It is less harmful than benzedrine to the human body. It seems to be valuable in furnishing this extra energy only under conditions of stress.

PSYCHOTROPIC DRUGS

Psychotropic drugs may be classified as follows:

1. Psychoinhibitors—drugs that restrict, limit, restrain, or depress either normal or abnormal psychological functions. These drugs include:

a. Hypnotics, which induce sleep.

b. Sedatives, which reduce excitement, agitation, or overactivity,

c. Muscle relaxants,

d. Ataraxics, which reduce, restrain, or restrict hyperactivity, plus the capacity to remove, reverse, or restrict psychopathology,

2. Psychoelevators—drugs that increase, elevate, or arouse normal or abnormal psychologic functioning:

a. Psychomotor stimulants,

b. Psychostimulants,

c. Psychic energizers.

3. Psychotomimetics—drugs that cause abnormal psychologic states.

The above, technical classification may be simplified for our study as follows: (1) tranquilizers and mental depressants, (2) stimulants, and (3) hallucination producers.

The Tranquilizers and Mental Depressants

Reserpine is the active, sedative principle of the Indian plant, Rauwolfa. The natives of the Himalayan foothills have used the root of this plant for centuries to heal afflictions such as snake bite and insanity. This ancient remedy was reported in Europe in a book in 1563, but it was not until the 1930–1940 period that it was given scientific study. Reserpene was isolated from it in 1953. Fifty alkaloids have been found in the twenty-five species of the Rauwolfa plant, and the structures of forty of the alkaloids have been established.

The tranquilizing effect of reserpine was discovered, about 1954, when the drug was being investigated for use in the treatment of hypertension. At about the same time, chlorpromazine, which was being investigated for use in reducing vomiting, was found to have a tranquilizing effect. Mepromate was likewise found to be a good tranquilizer, but it was first investigated as a preservative for penicillin. These drugs were the forerunners of several other tranquilizers, which were quickly found as the various drug companies checked over the drugs already available to see whether or not they had tranquilizing properties. For example, one antihistamine was found to be a good tranquilizer. Within three years, the sale of tranquilizers reached hundreds of millions of dollars. Next to antibiotics they were among the top-selling drugs.

The introduction of reserpine opened up the whole new field of psychotropic drugs, which have been very effective in the treatment of mental ills. The old shock treatments, isolation wards, etc. have been largely eliminated. Tranquilizers have been of immense service in the treatment of severe and chronic mental disorders, and have made possible the release of many patients from mental hospitals. Furthermore, they have made the patients more comfortable and easier to live with.

Some schizophrenic patients are so much out of touch with reality that there is no use in trying to argue or reason with them. Such patients were formerly given electric shock treatments or barbiturates. Today, **tranquilizers** *calm the patients without putting them to sleep, and reduce their anxieties.* The various drugs have somewhat different effects, and the tendency is to give mixtures of several drugs, so as to combine the good effects of each drug, and minimize the side effects.

Barbiturates should be classed among the mental sedatives mentioned below. They act differently than tranquilizers, in that they depress nerve message transmission and thus eliminate anxiety. In large doses, they produce sleep and even death. Some tranquilizers enable the patient to keep awake while they calm him and remove his anxieties. Many tranquilizers, however, have strong sedative effects.

Tranquilizers have also been widely prescribed for neurotic patients, and they often help normal people meet a temporary crisis or stress, thus enabling them to treat a problem objectively.

Tranquilizers are such powerful drugs that they cannot be obtained without a doctor's prescription, and should not be used except under a doctor's supervision. Reserpine lowers the blood pressure and some people are allergic to it. Often reserpine or chlorpromazine cause tremors of the fingers, but a drug, Cogentin, has been found to counteract this effect. Many physicians question the advisability of a tranquilized population, which might decrease ambition and productivity.

Tranquilizers have been used for animals. Nervous and emotional pets are being fed tranquilizers. Animals are calmed for long sea voyages. Fighting bulls are tranquilized before transporting them. Cattle are tranquilized before shipment in trains.

Persons who take chlorpromazine should not take even a small drink of alcoholic liquor and then drive or operate complex machinery. The combination of alcohol and chlorpromazine is unsafe.

Mescaline, a powerful drug, used by the Plains Indians to achieve intoxication during religious rites, produces anxiety states in human beings. A brain hormone, serotonin, has a similar effect, except that it is 1,500 times more powerful than mescaline. It also exhibits a sedative action that may be responsible for producing mental depression. Frenquel, one of the tranquilizers, has been found to block the action of serotonin. An antihistamine pill on the market also contains anti-serotonin.

Mental Stimulants

Benzedrine, mentioned above, acts as a mental stimulant and prevents sleep.

Reserpine and chlorpromazine relieve acute and chronic psychoses, but they are disappointing in the treatment of depressive states. Isoniazide, imipramine, and niamid are antidepressants used to treat this condition, for which electric shock treatment was once prescribed.

Ritalin is another stimulating drug that is used along with tranquilizers for treating mental patients. These drugs serve as a mental awakening toward reality.

The Hallucination Drugs

The **hallucination** *drugs disturb mental activity and judgment, and tend to distort* *values.* Such drugs are mescaline, an alkaloid of peyotl, and psilocybine and psilocin found in *Psilocybe mexicana,* a mushroom found in Mexico. Cocaine, in large doses, causes such hallucinations. The opium drugs also belong to this class. The hallucination drugs seem to represent a negative influence, under which the individual loses control of himself.

SUMMARY

Alkaloids are basic nitrogen compounds of powerful physiological activity, produced by plants. Many alkaloids serve as important drugs. Some of them are narcotics, which are used to relieve pain and produce sleep. In larger doses, narcotics produce stupor, coma, convulsions, and ultimately, death. Narcotics are habit forming, and may lead to addiction.

Euphoriants, such as coffee, tea, and tobacco, contain alkaloids that are habit-forming. Once the habit has been acquired, their use results in pleasure. Unfortunately, these alkaloids, like any habit-forming drug, must be gradually increased in amount in order to achieve the desired pleasure. As a result, these increased concentrations often cause damage to the nervous system. Nicotine, the alkaloid in tobacco, for example, is a powerful poison, and like any poison the amount taken into the body must be carefully controlled.

The psychotropic drugs may be classified as mental (1) tranquilizers and depressants (psychoinhibitors), (2) stimulants (psychoelevators), and (3) hallucination producers (psychotomimetics). Caffeine, found in tea and coffee, acts as a mental stimulant. On the other hand, nicotine, found in tobacco is a mental depressant.

Study Questions

1. DEFINE: euphoriant, narcotic, alkaloid, addiction, habituation, tranquilizer, hallucination, psychotropic drug.
2. List some of the physiological effects of alkaloids.
3. List some of the alkaloids that have been used both as poisons and as medicines.
4. What is the cause of malaria? Why is it difficult to stamp out malaria in some parts of the world?
5. What remedy for gout was mentioned in this chapter?
6. What are some of the chief sources of narcotics?
7. What is a narcotic?
8. List some of the narcotics that lead to addiction?
9. Differentiate between habituation and addiction.
10. What are the most commonly used euphoriants?
11. Do the euphoriants have a psychotic activity?
12. What are the possible causes of the harmful effects of cigarette smoking?
13. Why should tranquilizers be used only under a doctor's supervision?
14. Why may the use of euphoriants often become excessive?
15. What are the three kinds of psychotropic drugs mentioned in this chapter?
16. Is the nicotine in cigarette smoke a possible cause of cancer?
17. How have tranquilizers and psychotic stimulants served in the treatment of mental diseases?
18. Why have tranquilizers been used by "normal" people?
19. Compare the action of the barbiturates with that of tranquilizers.
20. What advantages do tranquilizers have in the treatment of neurotic patients?

Relief From Pain

As nitrous oxide in its extensive operation appears capable of destroying physical pain, it may probably be used with advantage during surgical operations in which no great effusion of blood takes place.

HUMPHRY DAVY (*1800*)

INTRODUCTION

The operating room of a hundred years ago was a torture chamber, the mere contemplation of which causes our flesh to creep. Alcoholic liquors, opium, and main force were tragically inadequate. Long operations were impossible, because the average patient would die of shock after twenty minutes or more of torture. The English physician, Sir Clifford Allbutt wrote

When I was a boy . . . he was the best surgeon, both for patient and onlooker, who broke the three-minute record in an amputation or a lithotomy. . . . The obvious boon of immunity from pain, precious as it was, when we look beyond the individual, was less than the boon of time. With anesthetics ended slapdash surgery. Anesthetics gave time for the theories of Pasteur and Lister to be adopted in practice.

The use of general anesthesia has accomplished much more, however, than the relief from pain; it has made operations easier for the surgeon and safer for the patient, and has expanded the scope of possible operative procedures. Anesthesia has made possible the experimental work on animals, without which the important developments of modern medicine would not have been possible.

Oliver Wendell Holmes coined the name *anesthesia* from the Greek words meaning without perception. Holmes said that this word would be on the lips of every person of all races in time to come.

Local anesthetics and **analgesics,** i.e., *pain relievers,* have also aided in the relief of human pain. **Hypnotics** are studied in this chapter because *they produce sleep as anesthetics do,* although they do not stop pain.

Pain was doubtless the first reason for the development of the physician, and it still remains as one of the important reasons that people seek physicians' help. Much of modern medicine is still concerned with the treatment of symptoms, and of these the most compelling is pain.

The names of various compounds which are given in this chapter and the chapter that follows, are not to be memorized. They are given in order to help the reader appreciate the progress that has been made by modern Science in the field of medicine.

LAUGHING GAS, THE FIRST GENERAL ANESTHETIC

Shortly before the signing of the Declaration of Independence, Joseph Priestly (1733–1804), co-discoverer of oxygen, first prepared nitrous oxide, otherwise known as laughing gas. In 1800, Humphry Davy, only twenty years old, made the remarkable observations of the effects of nitrous oxide, which he described as follows:

I felt a sense of tangible extension highly pleasurable in every limb; my visible impressions were dazzling and apparently magnified. I heard distinctly every sound in the room and was perfectly aware of my situation. I lost all connection with external things; trains of vivid visible images rapidly passed through my mind and even connected with words in such a manner as to produce perceptions perfectly novel. I existed in a world of newly connected and newly modified ideas.

As usual, it took many years for this laboratory discovery to be applied. In 1844, Dr. D. H. Colton anesthetized an associate in a popular-science lecture. Horace Wells, a young dentist, was in the audience, and at once saw the possibilities of the use of laughing gas in dentistry. The next day Wells had a tooth pulled while anesthetized with the gas.

ETHER, THE NEXT ANESTHETIC

In 1842, Dr. Crawford W. Long introduced the use of ether in minor surgery. Several years later, in 1846, the Massachusetts General Hospital in Boston allowed the dentist, William Thomas Green Morton, to demonstrate the use of ether in surgical operations. Morton had already used it with success in extracting teeth.

Ether has been the main general anesthetic for many years, because it gives good relaxation, and the margin of safety between a useful plane of anesthesia and a dangerously deep one is reasonably wide. Ether is far from being an ideal anesthetic, however, because of the severe depression following its use, and the metabolic disturbances it produces. Like all inhalation anesthetics, ether is irritating to the respiratory tract; ether anesthesia is sometimes followed by pneumonia; and finally, ether is quite inflammable.

OTHER ADVANCES IN ANESTHESIA

A year after the discovery of ether anesthesia, James Simpson introduced the use of chloroform. The first child that he delivered via chloroform received the name Anesthesia. Critics of the use of anesthetics for childbirth quoted the biblical statement, "in sorrow thou shalt bring forth children," but Simpson answered his bitter critics with a quotation from the same Book, "the Lord God caused a deep sleep to fall upon Adam and he took one of his ribs and closed up the flesh."

Chloroform is not tolerated as well as ether as a rule. The use of chloroform as a general anesthetic in surgery is less frequent than the use of ether in the United States. Its nonflammability, however, makes it peculiarly useful in restricted fields; for example, in operations when a cautery is used.

In 1922, Dr. Arno Luckhardt found that ethylene gas was superior to ether, in that it was less irritating to the respiratory tract, and produced less post-operative nausea. The use of an ethylene-oxygen mixture has replaced ether in many hospitals. This mixture is very explosive, and many tragic accidents have resulted from ignition by static sparks.

Divinyl ether was deliberately synthesized to combine the good points of ether and ethylene, and has been used for short operative procedures.

About 1935, cyclopropane came into use for general anesthesia, because of its satisfactory relaxing ability, and its comparatively low toxicity. Dr. H. R. Griffith reported,

My conception of anesthesia with the older gases is that we administer the gas plus enough oxygen to keep the patient alive and in good condition. With cyclopropane, on the other hand, we administer oxygen with just enough of the anesthetic gas to keep the patient asleep.

Many other anesthetics have been tried out. Newspaper headlines tell about fluorinated compounds that are nonexplosive and do not have adverse side effects. Another article tells about a new fast-acting anesthetic, causing patients to lose consciousness within fifteen seconds after injection into the vein. The surgeon can begin the operation within thirty seconds. It wears off in eight minutes and leaves no bad aftereffects.

Perhaps the ideal anesthetic has already been found, but if past experience is to be the guide, it is quite likely that some of the new anesthetics will not turn out to be as satisfactory as preliminary experiments indicated.

Pentothal Sodium, a barbiturate, when administered intravenously, gives a quick anesthetic action. Avertin, an effective anesthetic discovered in 1927, is administered rectally. It is usually supplemented by the use of other anesthetics because of the danger of an overdose.

MUSCLE RELAXANTS AS AN AID IN ANESTHESIA

In 1942, two Canadian scientists introduced the use of curare for anesthesia. Instead of waiting for ten minutes or so, as in the case of ether, to relax the muscles, which in the case of ether also required deep anesthesia, the use of curare produced muscle relaxation in a very short time, under very light anesthesia. Succinylcholine, much more lethal than curare, has been used with success as a relaxant. Bobaxin, a muscular relaxant, has been used to treat neck and back aches. Meprobromate was used as a relaxant before it was known to be a tranquilizer.

LOCAL ANESTHETICS

Local anesthetics are superior to general anesthetics for many purposes because they influence only the area of the operation and do not leave such undesirable aftereffects as nausea, acidosis, and pneumonia. Local anesthetics may be injected into tissues, or they may be applied directly to surfaces such as in the eye, ear, nose, and throat.

When the Spaniards conquered Peru, they noted that the Indians reduced their sensitivity to pain by chewing the leaves of the coca plant. In 1859, the German chemist Wöhler isolated the alkaloid, cocaine, from these leaves, but it was not until 1884 that Carl Koller first used it as a local anesthetic in surgery of the eye.

Although cocaine is an excellent local anesthetic, it possesses the two disadvantages that it is quite toxic and habit-forming. Cocaine was analyzed and its structural formula determined. Soon a number of simpler substances having structural resemblances to cocaine were prepared. One of these synthetic cocaine derivatives was novocaine; it is less toxic than cocaine and it is not habit-forming. Some newer relatives of novocaine are intracaine and nupercaine, which are more

efficient and less toxic than novocaine. These local anesthetics must be injected.

There is another class of local anesthetics, the **topical anesthetics,** which are *used for direct application.* Two topical anesthetics in common use are butyn and butesin.

HYPNOTICS

Insomnia is due to overwork, worry, mental fatigue, and muscular or nervous tension. A person may get too tired to sleep, or his mind may have been so stimulated by caffeine or intense mental activity just before bedtime that it cannot be shut off. There are emergencies in which a sleeping pill is desirable, but these emergencies should be infrequent.

Hypnotics *resemble narcotics and anesthetics in that they produce sleep, but hypnotics generally do not stop pain.* When there is a need for relief from pain and also a need for sleep, either a narcotic, or a hypnotic and a non-narcotic analgesic, is prescribed.

A great variety of substances act as hypnotics. Among the simplest of these substances are the bromides of sodium and potassium. Bromides are mild sedatives, but unfortunately they often produce objectionable side reactions. When sleep is interfered with by nervous disorders unaccompanied by pain, a sleep producer (hypnotic) enables the patient to obtain the needed sleep. Hypnotics do not cure insomnia, but they do enable the patient to obtain sleep while Mother Nature or medical science is combating the causes of the insomnia. Hypnotics should never be used without a prescription by a competent physician, and they should never be allowed to take the place of needed medical treatment.

In 1869, Liebreich introduced the use of chloral (chloral hydrate), which soon came to be known as "knockout drops." Chloral is habit-forming and is injurious to the body in a number of ways. A mixture of chloral hydrate, Epsom salts, and pentobarbital sodium has given good results as a total anesthetic for large farm animals that require surgical attention. Chloral was soon superseded by urethane and sulfonal and finally by the barbiturates.

The barbiturates are the most versatile of all depressant drugs. They can produce the whole range of effects from mild sedation, to deep sleep, anesthesia, and death. They act as analgesics when taken in less than hypnotic dosages. The use of Pentabarbital-Sodium, a barbiturate, as a fast-acting anesthetic has been mentioned. Some medical authorities consider barbiturates to be equal to the modern tranquilizers in relieving anxiety.

More than 2,500 different barbiturates have been synthesized. Some valuable barbiturates are Neonal, Amytal, Phanoderm, and Nembutal (pentobarbital). Surital, a thiobarbiturate, has been found to be more potent and safer to use than other barbiturates.

People in the United States take about 3 to 4 billion doses per year, enough to supply 10 million adults with sleeping pills every night in the year.

The widespread use of the barbiturates indicates the extent of the worry and nervousness that result from the rapid tempo and intensity of life that characterize modern civilization. Barbiturates may be habit forming, and sometimes lead to addiction. There are about 50,000 addicts in the United States. Excessive usage leads to deterioration of the kidneys, liver, or heart. Patients should not hesitate to take barbiturates when and as prescribed by a physician because under these conditions barbiturates are perfectly safe. It is never safe for anyone to use barbiturates without a physician's prescription, or to continue to use them after the period prescribed.

Several more recent hypnotics have been developed. Among these are Aminosulph, Butazolidin, and Pamine. Perichlor is advertised to put patients to sleep faster, make them sleep longer, and leave them more wide-awake in the morning. If you need a sleeping pill, see your doctor. He knows which pill to prescribe for your particular need. Never buy pills peddled by radio or television.

ANALGESICS

Antipyretics are *drugs that reduce the bodily temperature,* particularly when one has a fever. All known antipyretics act to some extent as **analgesics** (i.e., *pain relievers*). Nearly all of the antipyretics are aromatic compounds. Phenacetin is an antipyretic that is often used alone or in combination with aspirin as an analgesic. For example APC (Aspirin, Phenacetin, and Caffeine) is a widely used analgesic mixture. Some of the highly advertised cold remedies are essentially equivalent to this mixture. However, phenacetin has been found to cause kidney damage, and two of the most popular cold remedies have dropped it from their formulas. Antipyretics must be given in larger doses to produce antipyretic action than are required to produce analgesic action. Undesirable effects frequently accompany the use of antipyretics; therefore they should never be used except under the guidance of a competent physician.

Acetanilide, an analgesic frequently found in "headache powders" and various proprietary analgesic remedies, has occasionally caused the development of a drug habit, and may do serious damage because of its toxicity.

It was known for many years that the juice of willow bark was useful in the treatment of colds, and eventually it was found that the active substance in willow bark was a derivative of salicylic acid. Sodium salicylate is an effective antipyretic and analgesic, used in the treatment of articular rheumatism. The desire to avoid the disagreeable taste and undesirable effects of sodium salicylate led to the introduction of such derivatives as aspirin and salol. Aspirin is noted for its analgesic properties, although it also has antipyretic and antiseptic properties. Salicylates are probably safer to use than the derivatives of acetanilide, when employed in small doses as analgesics.

More than 17 million pounds (equivalent to 24 billion tablets) of aspirin are consumed annually in the United States for relief from headaches, rheumatic pains, and neuralgia. This is enough to provide a headache-relieving dose every day of the year for every adult in the country.

Aspirin has been taken by many people to induce sleep. It can permit sleep, in case a headache or other pain prevents sleep, but it is not a hypnotic.

Aspirin is aspirin, regardless of the name

of the manufacturer or distributor. It starts to work in about ten minutes, and takes more than an hour to attain its maximum effect.

Aspirin is frequently prescribed by doctors. It is one of the few valuable drugs available without a doctor's prescription, but its indiscriminate use may result in putting off a visit to the doctor until it is too late. The American Medical Association says concerning aspirin: "Acetylsalicylic acid [aspirin] may be and has been repeatedly shown to be potentially harmful, directly or indirectly, when taken indiscriminately. . . . Indirectly, its use may mask symptoms . . . [of] any number of serious diseases too numerous for specific citation. . . ." Pains are symptoms of disease, and the great danger in the use of analgesics is that the symptoms will be treated instead of the causes, thus leaving the disease untreated.

Many young children have been poisoned by taking an overdose of aspirin, which, like other drugs, should be kept out of their reach.

Methotrimeprazine, has been found to be a nonaddictive tranquilizer, and it is reported to be as good as morphine for the relief of pain. It is reported to have such side effects as dizziness and nausea.

SYMPATHETIC NERVE DRUGS

Epinephrine (adrenaline), the first hormone to be isolated in crystalline form, was synthesized in 1904. Epinephrine is obtained from the adrenal medulla of cattle, or by synthesis. It constricts the blood vessels and therefore increases the blood pressure. It is used locally to check a hemorrhage and to relieve nasal congestion. Its duration of activity is short, and constriction of the blood vessels is often followed by undesirable dilation.

Ephedrine, found in the Chinese herb, Ma Huang, is now prepared by synthesis. It is used directly on the nasal mucosa in the treatment of sinusitis, rhinitis, hay fever, and asthma.

Benzedrine, mentioned in the previous section, when administered by inhaling, produces the same results as ephedrine.

Tuamine produces nasal shrinkage without stimulating the central nervous system.

Many other compounds have been found to have the ability to shrink the nasal membranes. A survey of the nosedrops on your druggist's shelf would indicate the variety of compounds used. They have a useful function, but if used too often, the membrane will lose its ability to function normally.

ANTIHISTAMINES

Many people suffer from definite allergic reactions to pollens, feathers, house dust, cat hairs, heat, cold, light, certain foods, and almost anything that one could name. These allergic reactions include hay fever, asthma, hives, rashes, itching, migraine (one-sided) headaches, which, while they are usually not very serious, cause a great deal of misery.

Starting about 1946, a number of drugs were discovered to be of value in eliminating these distressing symptoms for many people. These drugs are often called **antihistamines,** *because the theory is that histamine, a derivative of histidine, which is an amino acid, liberated by the body when stimulated by offending substances* such as eggs, milk, pollens, house dust, or tobacco smoke *is the cause of the allergic symptoms.* Antihistamines work differently for different people, both as to effectiveness and as to their side reactions. These side reactions include nausea, vomiting, headaches, dizziness, and drowsiness. The antihistamines do not cure allergies, but they do enable many people to live more comfortably with them. Most seasickness and motion sickness remedies are antihistamines. Among the antihistamines used for this purpose are Phenergan, Marezine, Bonamine, Benadryl, Dramamine, and Trimeton. Other antihistamines used for allergies are Forhistal and Chlortrimeton.

Migraine, one-sided, headaches are common allergic symptoms. Fortunately, such ergot drugs as dihydroergotamine, taken by injection, or Cafergot, taken orally, usually bring quick relief. Methysergide has proven to be useful for some patients.

People who are allergic to drugs, such as the nitrofurans, sulfas, or antibiotics, often find that the use of antihistamines will enable them to tolerate the drugs.

NOSTRUMS AND QUACKS

Any substance used as a remedy for disease is called a **medicine,** while *any substance used in the preparation of a medicine* is called a **drug.** Often the terms are used interchangeably.

It is common knowledge that the drug store stocks two kinds of medicines, those which may be obtained without a physician's prescription, and those which can be obtained only with a physician's prescription. The Federal Government requires that *any medicine, that might be unduly harmful if taken without the supervision of a physician, should be sold only to fill the prescription of a physician.* Such medicines are sometimes called **ethical drugs,** or prescription drugs.

Drugs that are protected by patents, trademarks, and secrecy are often called **proprietary drugs;** they are generally not admitted to the *Pharmacopoeia,* and are, therefore, not subject to legal control. A characteristic of such medicines is that they depend upon high-pressure advertising in magazines, newspapers, radio, and television to sell the product. *They are advertised and sold directly without a diagnosis or prescription by a competent physician.* Misleading and false advertising of such drugs has resulted in great harm to the American people. While it is often true that such medicines, if used intelligently, may do some good and little harm, the average person does not know enough about the human body to prescribe medicines for himself on the basis of television advertising. The danger in the indiscriminate use of proprietary remedies is that their use may delay the proper treatment of a disease by a physician until it is too late.

Such drugs, if they have a positive physiological effect, should not be used without a doctor's prescription. If they have no effect they are a waste of money.

Next to self medication, based on the advice of clever nostrum advertising, one might list the quack. The large sums of money spent on nostrums, and quack doctors indicates a widespread anti-intellectual, nonscientific attitude. The scientific attitude and method obviously needs greater emphasis in our public schools.

SUMMARY

Anesthetics

The use of general anesthetics is often preceded by a hypnotic to produce sleep, and a drug to relieve anxiety. A muscle relaxant may be used to decrease the amount of anesthetic required. Local anesthetics may be injected, as in the case of cocaine and its derivatives, or they may be used on the surface as in the case of such topical anesthetics as butesin.

Hypnotics

Hypnotics, such as the barbiturates or bromides, produce sleep but do not reduce pain.

Analgesics

Analgesics, such as aspirin and phenacetin, reduce pain and also act as antipyretics.

Antihistamines

Antihistamines eliminate allergic symptoms by counteracting the effects of histamine, which is produced in allergic reactions.

Sympathetic Nerve Drugs

These compounds, such as adrenaline, ephedrine, and benzidrine stimulate the nerves of the sympathetic nerve system. A very common application is their use in nosedrops to relieve nasal stuffiness.

The Use of Drugs

Drugs, either proprietary or ethical, should not be used without a doctor's prescription.

Study Questions

1. DEFINE: anesthetic, topical anesthetic, hypnotic, analgesic, antihistamine, proprietary drug, antipyretic, ethical drug, medicine, drug.
2. What were the contributions of general and local anesthetics to surgery?

3. How may the amount of anesthetic used for an operation be decreased?

4. What is the function of a hypnotic?

5. List two widely used hypnotics.

6. Why should barbiturates be used only with a doctor's prescription?

7. What is the objection to the use of phenacetin in cold remedies?

8. What are the objections to the use of ethylene and various other hydrocarbon gases as anesthetics?

9. What are the advantages and disadvantages in the use of ether as a general anesthetic?

10. What are the advantages and disadvantages in the use of chloroform as a general anesthetic?

11. For what type of anesthesia are cocaine and its derivatives used?

12. In what regard does the use of muscle relaxants aid in anesthesia?

13. Name two drugs that serve as both antipyretics and analgesics. In which group would quinine be placed?

14. Would one manufacturer's aspirin be better than that of another if they both meet government standards?

15. What are the possible objections to the indiscriminate use of aspirin?

16. For what types of diseases is aspirin widely used?

17. What is the objection to the excessive use of nasal decongestants?

CHAPTER 84

Modern Weapons Against Disease

It was, however, fortunate that . . . I was always on the lookout for new bacterial inhibitors, and when I noticed on a culture plate that the staphylococcal colonies in the neighborhood of a mold had faded away I was sufficiently interested in the antibacterial substance produced by the mold to pursue the subject.

SIR ALEXANDER FLEMING

INTRODUCTION

Many years ago, Locke said that "a sound mind in a sound body is a short, but full description of a happy state in this world. He that has these two, has little more to wish for; and he that wants either of them, will be but little better for anything else."

The checking of disease represents the outstanding contribution of chemistry to the welfare of humanity. **Chemotherapy,** *the selective destruction of pathogenic (disease producing) organisms within the body by chemical agents,* discussed in this chapter, represents the latest and most important contribution of chemistry to the control of disease. Chemotherapy does not include the use of drugs having physiological effects on the body. In fact, a good chemotherapeutic agent is one that will kill or prevent the growth of a given pathogenic organism with the least possible physiological effect on the body. Many substances will destroy pathogenic bacteria in test tubes, but are useless because of their toxic effects on the body.

The marked decline (about 80 to 90 per cent) in the death rate from many contagious diseases, such as whooping cough, diphtheria, measles, and scarlet fever, during the past twenty-five years, can be attributed in large part, to the so-called "miracle drugs," such as the sulfa drugs and the antibiotics discussed in this chapter. The new drugs have probably saved at least 3 million lives in the United States. Life expectancy has been raised from 60 to 70 years since World War II.

The development of new drugs has become a big business. Drug companies spend many millions of dollars in research every year. One drug company spent twenty years in an investigation of 40,000 chemicals for activity against tuberculosis without finding a single effective drug. In 1958, the drug industry investigated 114,600 substances and came up with only 40 new drugs.

The bewildering array of new "wonder drugs," with their long chemical names which are hopeless for general use, now have fanciful names, which, in many cases, required the aid of electronic "brains" to devise. It must be as difficult for the modern physician to keep up with the advances in medicine today as it is for the chemist to try to keep up with the tremendous advances in his field.

The names of some of the typical drugs, just as in the case of the plastics or synthetic rubbers, are given to indicate the progress being made in the development of drugs. They are not to be memorized. By the time this book is published, many of them will have been superseded by better drugs.

MEDICINE FIFTY YEARS AGO

The physician of 1910 was relatively helpless when it came to the treatment of diseases caused by pathogenic organisms. He had diphtheria antitoxin, smallpox vaccine, and similar antitoxins and vaccines to control rabies, anthrax, typhoid fever, scarlet fever, tetanus, cholera, bacillary dysentery, and snakebite. Most of these diseases are caused by viruses. A tremendous amount of research has been devoted to the search for drugs to combat viruses. Just enough progress has been made to justify the hope that this research will result in the next great breakthrough in chemotherapy. In the meantime, modern biologists have continued the great work started by Louis Pasteur and Edward Jenner, and have developed new vaccines for the prevention of poliomyelitis, yellow fever, and regular measles. Much biological research has been devoted to the development of vaccines for influenza, the common cold, and even cancer. Some progress has been made with influenza vaccines. The battle against virus diseases has not been won, and presents the most important challenge of today, with the exception of the battle against cancer, the causes of which are being sought.

ARSPHENAMINE, THE FIRST GREAT MILESTONE IN CHEMOTHERAPY

Paul Ehrlich (1854–1915) observed that certain dyes would stain only one kind of tissue. This observation led to the idea that specific "magic bullets" might be found to combat disease. A **specific** is *a substance that kills a given organism or microorganism but does not kill others.* Paul Ehrlich's original observation was that a bit of dye, methylene blue, injected into a rabbit's ear, spread throughout the body and wound up by staining the nerve endings blue. "The dye," he reasoned, "singles out just one tissue in the rabbit's body and has no effect on other tissues. Why not chemical agents that single out murderous microbes and have no effect on any tissues of the patient's body?"

Twenty-one years after his first observation, during which time he made many important contributions to immunology, he read about a disease in horses caused by large protozoan parasites called trypanosomes. He found that this disease would also attack mice.

After trying about 500 dyes without success, Ehrlich and Dr. Kiyoshi Shiga, the discoverer of the germ responsible for bacillary dysentery, found a dye that destroyed the trypansomes in mice, but it proved to be ineffective for rats and rabbits. Shiga and Ehrlich began a research based on the principle of changing the structure of an active drug to try to find a derivative that would be more potent or more specific, and have fewer undesirable side effects. This method has been one of the main approaches in modern research on drugs. Ehrlich read about atoxyl, an arsenical drug intended for sleeping sickness, which unfortunately was extremely poisonous. So he set his assistants to work preparing modifications of this drug. The 606th atoxyl derivative was found to cure a disease in mice, which does not attack man. So Ehrlich decided to see if this drug would have any effect on syphilis, a disease that had been a scourge of Europe for over four hundred years, ever since Columbus' men brought it to Europe from the Caribbean Indians, to whom they donated smallpox in return. This new drug proved to be a specific against syphilis, and thus became the first of the large number of chemotherapeutic agents to follow in its wake. It was called Salvarsan, or "606," although its chemical name was arsphenamine. Eventually, less toxic and more effective arsenical cures such as tryparsamide and Mapharsen were prepared.

SULFONAMIDES, THE FIRST MODERN "MIRACLE DRUGS"

A whole generation elapsed before other workers began to follow the path pioneered so well by Paul Ehrlich. It had been found that Prontosil, a red dye, and similar dyes, were effective in the treatment of streptococcic infections in mice. Jacques Trefouels (1897–) and his fellow workers found that an active fragment of Prontosil, called sulfanilamide, was responsible for its therapeutic action. Thousands of derivatives of sulfanilamide were prepared and tested in order to obtain more specific, more effective, and less toxic drugs. By 1945, 5,485 compounds allied to sulfanilamide had been prepared. New, more effective sulfonamide drugs (popularly known as "sulfa" drugs), as these derivatives of sulfanilamide are called, continued to come from the research laboratories. Among the early, powerful sulfa drugs were sulfathiazole, sulfadiazine, and sulfamerazine.

Diamox, a sulfa drug used as a diuretic and for the treatment of glaucoma, was found only after 6,063 sulfa derivatives had been prepared and investigated for their therapeutic effects.

Sulfa drugs frequently show toxic effects. They tend to deposit crystals in the kidneys, and for that reason, physicians prescribe sodium bicarbonate and large amounts of water along with sulfa drugs. Later, it was found that a mixture of two or three of the best sulfa drugs do not affect the kidneys in this way.

In 1943, 10,005,307 pounds of sulfa drugs were produced in the United States. In 1946, this production had dropped to about 5,000,000 pounds because of the competition furnished by a new type of drug, the antibiotic, discussed later in this chapter.

The research on sulfa drugs continued. One new sulfa drug, sulfaethylthiadiazole, was so soluble that it did not form crystals in the kidneys, but because of its solubility it was excreted too fast. However, it is such a good drug that one manufacturer invested $1.5 million in the development of a method of coating small granules of the drug, which could be suspended in a liquid which would release the medication evenly over a twelve-hour period. This liquid suspension is called a Sulspansion. Another modification of this idea is the modern Spansule, which consists of drug granules that have been coated with different thicknesses of a fatty substance, which release the drug over a period of twelve hours, thus providing a constant dosage in contrast to the varying dosage obtained with pills. Such Spansules have been used for a variety of different drugs.

Among the newer sulfa drugs, there are Thiabendazole, which is used to combat trichinosis and round worms in man and animals; Dapsone, which arrests or cures leprosy; phthalylsulfathiazole, used successfully in 1962 in combating travelers' diarrhea in Mexico; sulfaguanidine, and sulfasuccidine,

used for treatment of cholera and dysenteries; and nisulfazone, used for chronic ulcerative colitis.

THE PROPER USE OF SULFA DRUGS

The sulfa drugs should be used only under the supervision of a physician. Self medication with aspirin, sleeping tablets, and laxatives frequently proves to be serious; but self medication with powerful physiological agents, such as the sulfa drugs, is like playing with dynamite. The effectiveness of these drugs depends upon their concentration, method of administration, and length of time to be used. Only the physician can determine which drug is needed, what the proper dosage is, and when to stop treatment.

Sulfa drugs build up a sensitivity in some people that prevents their subsequent use. Furthermore, sulfa drugs, when taken in insufficient amounts, may produce sulfa-resistant bacteria that cannot be controlled by subsequent treatment with sulfa drugs.

The commonly used sulfa drugs do not cure virus diseases, such as colds and influenza, and they should not be taken for every disease that comes along. In general, do not use sulfa drugs unless there is good reason to believe that they will do more good than harm. It is important to keep in mind that in the use of chemotherapeutic agents there is not a large difference between the concentrations that are effective against bacteria and the concentrations that are harmful to the host.

PENICILLIN, A NEW TYPE OF DRUG

Alexander Fleming (1881–1955), in 1929, made the chance observation that a mold colony of the common bread mold, *Penicillium notatum,* was inhibiting the growth of a nearby colony of pathogenic bacteria on a test plate. He published his results, but no one was interested in them at the time. Ten years after Fleming's original discovery in 1929, Howard Walter Florey (1898–   ) and Ernst Boris Chain (1906–   ), became interested in Fleming's discovery and helped to launch a program to produce the new miracle drug, penicillin. This drug supplanted the sulfa drugs for many diseases, and became one of the most important drugs in the practice of medicine.

It was found that a small percentage of the people were allergic to penicillin, but the preparation of various forms of penicillin helped to overcome this difficulty. Eventually, again, substances were found to prevent the allergic reaction for many people. Despite its faults, penicillin proved to be one of the most important drugs ever produced.

Improved, less toxic forms of penicillin were announced from time to time. Duracillin, (penicillin-G), an injectible form, required only one dose per day. Later, an oral form of penicillin-G became available in 1948. In 1955, penicillin-V, an improved oral form was announced. This was followed by penicillin-V-cillin-K, which was absorbed twice as well. In 1959, a synthetic penicillin, called Syncillin, was announced. More than five hundred new compounds of penicillin were prepared, sixty of which underwent clinical trials, before this latest, less toxic, and more effective form of penicillin was developed. The research on penicillin is just one example of the work that is done to improve a drug, once it has been found to be effective.

Penicillin proved to be very effective in the treatment of (a) staphylococcic infections such as osteomyelitis, carbuncles, meningitis, pneumonia, burns, endocarditis, (b) clostridia infections such as gas gangrene, (c) hemolytic streptococcic infections such as mastoiditis, pneumonia, childbed fever and peritonitis, (d) sulfa-drug resistant pneumococcic pneumonia, (e) gonococcic infections, (f) anthrax, (g) sulfa-drug resistant meningococcic infections, bacterial endocarditis, and scarlet fever.

ANTIBIOTICS—THE MOLD DRUGS

The discovery of penicillin led to investigations of other molds. It was found that microbes commonly found in the soil produce substances that prevent the growth of pathogenic microbes. These *substances, produced by living organisms that have the property of inhibiting the growth of or of killing microbes,* are called **antibiotics.** They differ from ordinary antiseptics or disinfectants in that they are more selective in their action. Almost every group of living organisms has some representative capable of forming antibiotics. Algae, lichens, molds, bacteria, actinomycetes, and higher organisms, even rabbits and human beings, produce antibiotics.

Antibiotics are chemical compounds, differing greatly in their chemical composition and in their toxicity to animals. More than a hundred antibiotics had been discovered during the period 1942–1949, but nearly all of these substances, which killed pathogenic microbes in test tubes, were found to be toxic to animals.

Soon, hundreds of thousands of samples of soil were tested to discover new antibiotics.

THE AGE OF ANTIBIOTICS

The twenty-year period following the introduction of penicillin in 1942 has been called the age of antibiotics. It would be strange indeed if the first antibiotic produced and tested should be the only one or the best one for controlling infectious diseases. So spectacular was the success of penicillin that scientists undertook a systematic search for other antibiotics, with the result that more than three hundred antibiotics have followed one after another. By 1950, the chemotherapeutic revolution was in full bloom. Streptomycin came into use in 1947. It was produced by actinomycetes, which are neither molds nor bacteria. It was found to control diseases not attacked by penicillin, such as typhoid fever, paratyphoid, dysentery, undulant fever, tularemia, and, in 1948, it was the best drug available for tuberculosis. Unfortunately, it proved to be as toxic as the sulfa drugs, and bacteria soon became resistant to it.

Then came chloromycin, polymixin, and aureomycin in 1947, neomycin in 1949, and terramycin in 1950. Tests were made on 100,000 different molds before terramycin was discovered. In contrast with penicillin which combated twenty-five diseases, Terramycin was found to be effective against nearly a hundred diseases.

Every year, new and improved antibiotics have been announced.

Antibiotics have been estimated to have saved the lives of at least 1.5 million people in the United States. They have more than cut in half the death rate from pneumonia, meningococcal infections, mastoid and ear infections, scarlet fever, and many other infectious diseases.

The drug industry spends about seven cents of every sales dollar on research. Research is very expensive, and is often reflected in the price of the products.

The sale of antibiotics for human use hit about $450 million in 1965, and large amounts were being used in agriculture. For example, antibiotics are now being used to fight formerly uncontrollable plant diseases, such as fire blight of pears and apples, walnut blight, blue mold of tobacco, and bacterial blight of celery. Plant diseases cost the nation an estimated $2 billion per year.

Spontin, a new antibiotic, effective against resistant staphylococci, streptococci, and pneumonococci was announced in 1957. It is given intravenously. The drug company that made it had examined at least half a million microorganisms obtained from soil samples before finding this drug. It destroys disease-causing bacteria rather than merely halting their growth, as is true of many other antibiotics.

Declomycin, announced in 1959, required six years of research and development which cost $2.5 million.

Vancomycin, marketed under the name, Vancocin, one of the most powerful bactericidal antibiotics in medical history, was developed from a mold obtained from a soil sample from Borneo.

Kanamycin, developed in Japan in 1958, is a broad-spectrum antibiotic similar to neomycin and streptomycin. **Broad-spectrum** *means that it is effective against a wide range of bacteria.* This antibiotic is noted for its great stability.

Griseofulvin has been found to be an orally effective antibiotic in the treatment of many superficial fungus infections, such as ringworm. The antibiotic, amphotericin B, shows great promise against many serious, systemic fungus infections, such as histoplasmosis.

THE USE OF ANTIBIOTICS

Antibiotics, like the sulfa drugs, are too powerful to be used for every little fever or cold that comes along. In the first place, they are effective against only about 5 per cent of all respiratory infections. Their use may result in allergic reactions, and encourage the development of resistant bacteria. For example, the outbreak of staphylococcic infections in hospitals was the result of the resistance of these organisms caused by excessive use of antibiotics in the hospitals. Antibiotics generally kill intestinal bacteria, and upset the germ balance in the body, which can lead to the possibility of the good germs being replaced by bad ones.

Don't press your doctor to prescribe an antibiotic before he has diagnosed your illness, which he cannot do via telephone.

THE NITROFURANS

The nitrofurans, furfural derivatives, were the most revolutionary germ killers to appear since the antibiotics came into use. The nitrofurans have been found to produce undesirable side reactions for some people. Further research will doubtless lead to improved, less toxic compounds. The important thing about these drugs is that they provide evidence that there may be still more new types of chemotherapeutic agents to come.

OTHER CHEMOTHERAPEUTIC DRUGS

Glucosamine is reported to be successful in the treatment of schistosomiasis, a worm infestation spread by fresh-water snails. There are over 150,000,000 cases in the world today.

Dithiazanine is a broad-spectrum **anthelmintic,** *which works against a variety of worm infections,* such as whipworm, roundworm, pinworm, and hookworm. Another anthelmintic is Povan, which was the result of nine years of research, during which 5,000 compounds were screened for antiworm properties. When one considers that about 20 per cent of the population is infected with pinworms, such drugs are a welcome addition to the chemotherapeutic armory.

There is reason to hope for the development of antivirus drugs. Virugon, and Flumidin have been reported to be effective against colds, influenza, mumps, measles, chickenpox, and shingles. Like other new drugs, the enthusiastic claims for them may not be substantiated.

Isoniazid, salizid, and para-amino salicylic acid are providing knockout blows for tuberculosis. The battle against tuberculosis has not been won, but the weapons are at hand. An all-out war could defeat tuberculosis in twenty years.

The Atomic Energy Commission has tested about 10,000 compounds for their possible antiradiation activity with encouraging results.

The hexahydropyrimidines are broad-spectrum drugs announced in 1957. They were reported to be more potent than the sulfa drugs and the nitrofurans. One of these, Sterisil or Triosil, has antifungus activity for topical treatment.

We have used the term "announced" because subsequent clinical testing often reveals that the announcements were premature.

SUMMARY

Chemotherapy is the selective destruction of disease-producing organisms within the body by chemical agents.

Examples of early chemotherapeutic agents were quinine, used in the treatment of malaria, and mercury compounds used in the treatment of venereal diseases, but these drugs were far from satisfactory.

The first modern chemotherapeutic drug was Arsphenamine, used against syphilis.

A generation later, the sulfa drugs were developed. Next came the antibiotics, and finally, the nitrofurans.

The success scored by the sulfa drugs led the drug companies to invest large sums of money in the research that led to many new, improved sulfa drugs and antibiotics.

The antibiotics are compounds produced by microorganisms, usually molds.

The sulfa drugs and the antibiotics are very potent drugs, which may cause allergic reactions, may develop sensitivities, and may cause bacteria to become resistant to them. Their use should be limited as far as possible.

Study Questions

1. DEFINE: chemotherapy, broad spectrum, antibiotic, anthelmintic, specific.
2. In what regards are chemotherapeutic drugs different from the drugs discussed in the previous section?
3. What observations led to Paul Ehrlich's discovery of Arsphenamine?
4. What was the initial discovery that led to the sulfa drugs?
5. What chance observation of Alexander Fleming led to the discovery of antibiotics?
6. What have been the sources of antibiotics?
7. What is the nature of an antibiotic?
8. What types of organisms produce antibiotics?
9. Name an antibiotic which was not produced by molds.
10. Why was Salvarsan called "606?"
11. What was the source of syphilis in Europe?
12. What biological methods have been used in combatting virus diseases?
13. List some of the diseases that are controlled by biological methods.
14. To what extent are sulfas and antibiotics of value in treating respiratory diseases?
15. What types of diseases remain as a major challenge to chemotherapy?
16. Give an example of the use of antibiotics in agriculture.
17. Why are antibiotics usually relatively expensive?
18. How much money is spent annually for antibiotics for human use?
19. What is the world's second largest killer?

Biographical Index

Subject Index

NAMES OF PEOPLE are listed in the Biographical Index, pages 625–627. Names of individual drugs, fibers, rubbers, drugs, stars, etc., are not listed. Page references to definitions are printed in **boldface** type. The letter *t* after a page number refers to a table.